Physics

BY

ERICH HAUSMANN, E.E., Sc.D.

THOMAS POTTS PROFESSOR OF PHYSICS AND DEAN OF GRADUATE STUDY
POLYTECHNIC INSTITUTE OF BROOKLYN

AND

EDGAR P. SLACK, S.B., M.S.

ASSOCIATE PROFESSOR OF PHYSICS
POLYTECHNIC INSTITUTE OF BROOKLYN

SECOND EDITION

NEW YORK
D. VAN NOSTRAND COMPANY, Inc.
250 FOURTH AVENUE

PRINTED IN U. S. A.

PRESS OF
BRAUNWORTH & CO., INC.
BUILDERS OF BOOKS
BRIDGEPORT, CONN.

PREFACE

THIS text aims to present the essentials of Physics to college students who major particularly in science, technology, or engineering. It is intended to give a gradual and logical approach to the subject, to develop and illustrate the fundamental concepts clearly, and to afford a mastery of the basic principles of this fascinating branch of natural philosophy. To those who study Physics for its cultural value, the text should aid in developing a power of analysis that will be useful in any career.

Many years of teaching and professional experience have led the authors to devote considerable space to the subject of Mechanics, so that this initial part of the book may be found clear and understandable even by the student without previous training in Physics. The subsequent parts have been treated with more and more conciseness in keeping with the increased comprehension of the well-grounded student. This policy has been carried out also in connection with the handling of units, the inclusion of worked-out problems, and the mathematical steps in formulating the results.

The book should be found suitable for courses in which all parts of the subject are covered in one year, or for individual courses in Mechanics, Heat, Electricity and Magnetism, and Sound and Light that extend in the aggregate over longer periods. A number of the more advanced sections in the various chapters have been starred; these may be omitted in the shorter courses, but may well be used as additional assignments for the gifted student. It is expected that class work will be supplemented by demonstration lectures and laboratory experiments.

In presenting derivations of physical laws and relationships, the purpose of the proof and the course to be followed are stated before embarking upon the detailed description and mathematical processes. In working out the illustrative examples, attention is given to the units of measurement involved, and in the early part of the text the units are carried through the various steps and balanced. These details of presentation will aid the student in acquiring clarity and definiteness of thought, and should enable him to analyze and solve original problems with confidence.

The gratifying reception accorded the first edition of this book has encouraged the authors to believe that they have met, at least in part, the objectives they had sought. They have carried out the revision along the same general lines, striving for greater clarity and usefulness. To this end they have changed the sequence of chapters in Electricity and Magnetism, have merged the material on vector processes into a single chapter, have rearranged the treatment of force, have replaced some rather detailed technological applications of physical principles by more recent developments in industrial physics (such as cathode ray and iconoscope tubes, electric organs, the cyclotron and electron microscope, non-reflecting glass, and polarizing films), have included the latest evaluations of the electronic charge and of other fundamental constants, and have mentioned some of the advances along the frontiers of physical science.

Many problems have been added (there are now over 800 of them) to give the student ample experience in applying the essential ideas treated in the various chapters and thereby to broaden his scientific outlook. Problems that illustrate the material covered in starred sections are similarly marked. The earlier policy of giving at the end of the book the answers of only the odd-numbered problems has been continued.

Following suggestions received from teachers who wish occasionally to introduce statics or fluids earlier in the work in Mechanics, a few connecting links have been introduced in the new edition so that the student should not find it difficult to pursue these subjects after completing Chapter II. Further, more sections have been starred to aid those in charge of shorter courses; if all sections so marked were omitted, the book would become one of 620 rather than 729 pages.

It is believed that improvements in teachability have been gained through the closer correlation of topics, the more liberal use of italics for important words and concepts, and the introduction of words as well as symbols in the equations of the first few chapters. Small type has been used for solved problems to avoid discontinuity in treatment, and the chapter number has been added at each page opening for convenience of reference.

The authors appreciate the valuable suggestions received from teachers of Physics in their own and in other institutions of learning, as well as from teachers and research workers in several technological fields. These comments varied widely in scope from the critical review of the entire book by Professor Guy E. Grantham of Cornell University to the informal criticisms of specific topics by several users. For all of them, covering the original manuscript and the material of the present edition, the authors express their sincere thanks.

ERICH HAUSMANN

EDGAR P. SLACK

August 1, 1939

CONTENTS

MECHANICS

CONTENTS

SOUND

MECHANICS

CHAPTER I

FUNDAMENTAL QUANTITIES

1. Measurement. — Physics takes its place among the physical sciences with astronomy, chemistry, and geology, in dealing with natural phenomena concerning the behavior of inanimate objects, and some of its principles apply to living things as well. The fields of knowledge of these sciences overlap considerably and give rise to such branches as astrophysics, physical chemistry, geophysics, and biophysics. The laws and facts of Physics are concerned broadly with matter and energy, together with such related quantities as force and motion. These concepts and their interrelations are fundamental to all parts of the subject, comprising mechanics of solids and fluids, heat, electricity and magnetism, sound, and light.

A definite knowledge of natural phenomena, and of the precise relations between them, is based upon experimental information concerning the quantities involved. If this information should be indefinite or ambiguous it would be subject to different interpretations, and naturally the conclusions drawn therefrom would be open to much speculation. Clearly, the evidence obtained must be quantitative in order that it may have definite meaning. Evidence of this type is obtained by *measurement*, one of the most important elements in all scientific work.

The usual way to measure a quantity is to compare it with some other quantity of the same kind which is used as a basis of comparison. Everyone is familiar with the process of measuring the length of an object by laying a foot-rule alongside of it and expressing the result in feet and inches. A statement that a pole is 15 feet in length will give anyone having a foot-rule a correct picture of that length by laying off a distance equal to 15 one-foot distances. The length of the pole can also be expressed as 180

1

inches. This illustration shows that *the measurement of a quantity involves two things: a number and a unit.* To say that the pole measures 15 or 180 is an incomplete statement; it is necessary to say 15 feet or 180 inches. The unit shows how large a quantity is used as the basis of comparison, and the number shows how many of these units are contained in the quantity being measured.

Some statements based on physical measurements are given below to indicate the necessity for both number and unit: The rating of a certain automobile engine is 65 horsepower. The speed of a large steamship was found to be 25.3 knots. Comfortable room temperature is 68 degrees fahrenheit. Atmospheric pressure is about 14.7 pounds per square inch. The angular speed of a particular motor is 1800 revolutions per minute. The wave length of yellow light is 0.0000589 centimeter. The charge of an electron is 1.60×10^{-19} coulomb.

Physics is called an exact science because the quantities with which it is concerned are capable of accurate measurement. Accuracy in a measurement requires a knowledge of the correctness of the standard of comparison, a measuring device of adequate sensitiveness, and care on the part of the operator in manipulation and computation.

Among the quantities with which Physics deals, three are generally regarded as fundamental, namely, *length*, *mass*, and *time*. These fundamental quantities and their measurement are considered in this chapter, together with some computations involving their use.

2. Standards and Units of Length. — The units of length commonly used belong to two groups, namely *British Units* and *Metric Units*, and these are based upon definite distances on bars that are preserved as standards. The *yard* is the standard of length in the British group and is the distance at 62 degrees fahrenheit (°F.) between two fine lines engraved on gold plugs in a bronze bar kept at the Standards Office in Westminster, London. The *meter* is the standard of length in the Metric group and is the distance at 0 degree centigrade (°C.) between the centers of two lines traced on a platinum-iridium bar kept in a subterranean vault of the International Bureau of Weights and Measures at Sèvres, France. Several such standards are kept at the Bureau of Standards in Washington, D. C. Because of difficulty in marking and because of variations in length due to shrinkage and expansion since construction, the distance between marks on any one meter bar is not precisely 1 meter; the length of Meter Bar No. 27 is 1.6 ± 0.1 microns short as certified by several recent comparisons with the standard meter bar at Sèvres. Fig. 1 shows a portion of this bar.

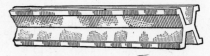

The multiples and sub-multiples of the yard and of the meter in common use are given below with their equivalents for reference purposes:

FIG. 1. Standard meter bar. The defining lines are engraved in the plane of the neutral axis

Units of Length

British Units	Metric Units
1 mile (mi.) = 1760 yards	1 kilometer (km.) = 1000 meters
1 yard (yd.) = 3 feet	1 meter = 100 centimeters
1 mile (mi.) = 5280 feet	1 centimeter (cm.) = 10 millimeters
1 foot (ft.) = 12 inches	1 meter = 1000 millimeters
1 inch (in.) = 1000 mils	1 millimeter (mm.) = 1000 microns

It is often necessary to convert expressions of length in one group to corresponding ones in the other group. The fundamental relationship between the yard and the meter, as fixed by the Act of 1866, is: 1 yard = 3600/3937 meter. In consequence, the following relations hold with sufficient exactness for most purposes:

Conversion Factors for Lengths

1 mile	=	1.6093 kilometers
1 kilometer	=	0.6214 mile
1 foot	=	30.48 centimeters
1 meter	=	3.281 feet
1 meter	=	39.37 inches
1 inch	=	2.540 centimeters

At least the last two relationships should be remembered.

In carrying out a computation involving lengths or other physical quantities, *the units should be included throughout;* they may be cancelled, multiplied or divided as though they were numbers. For example, find the number of kilometers in a mile by using the conversion factor 1 meter = 39.37 in. Since 5280 feet = 1 mile, the fraction $\dfrac{5280 \text{ feet}}{1 \text{ mile}}$ will have a value of unity, and the specified distance may be multiplied by this factor without altering its value. Three other fractions, each having a value of unity, are introduced in the same manner, and the entire solution is given by

$$1 \text{ mile} = 1 \text{ mile} \times \frac{5280 \text{ feet}}{1 \text{ mile}} \times \frac{12 \text{ inches}}{1 \text{ foot}} \times \frac{1 \text{ meter}}{39.37 \text{ inches}}$$

$$\times \frac{1 \text{ kilometer}}{1000 \text{ meters}} = \frac{5280 \times 12}{39.37 \times 1000} \text{ kilometers} = 1.609 \text{ km.}$$

This procedure may seem laborious for such a simple computation, but in the more involved calculations which will be met with further on in this subject there is a distinct advantage in carrying all units through to avoid ambiguity and error.

3. Aids in Measuring Length. — It is difficult to read with the unaided eye divisions engraved on metal scales that are smaller

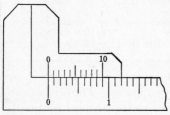

FIG. 2.   Enlargement of vernier

than 1/50 in. or $\frac{1}{2}$ mm., because the width of the engraved lines leaves too little space between those lines. An auxiliary scale or *vernier*, named after Pierre Vernier, may be added which permits measurements to be made respectively to distances as short as 1 mil or 1/50 mm.

A vernier of simple design is shown in Fig. 2, applied to a caliper. The scale of the caliper is divided into millimeters, and the vernier has 10 divisions. These 10 divisions correspond in length to 9 scale divisions and, therefore, each vernier division is 1/10 mm. shorter than a scale division. When the two jaws of the vernier caliper touch, the zero division of the vernier matches the zero division of the scale. When the jaws are separated 1/10 of a scale division, that is, 0.1 mm., the first division of the vernier will match the first scale division, because the vernier division is 1/10 mm. shorter than the other. When the jaws are separated by 7/10 scale division, the seventh vernier division will match a scale division. Thus, the reading of the vernier at coincidence gives the number of tenths of a scale division by which the jaws are separated. When the jaws are separated further than one scale division, the reading of the scale in full divisions up to the zero mark of the vernier is first taken, and to this is added the fractional part of a division as given by the vernier. This device aids the observer only in reading the fractional parts of a division; the smallest part to which it can be read by the vernier is called the *least count*. In the example chosen the least count is 0.1 mm.

The *micrometer screw* is another device that is used in many instruments for precise measurement; it consists of an accurately threaded screw with a head that is divided into an integral number of divisions on its rim. Fig. 3 shows a micrometer caliper for the measurement of objects up to one inch. The screw has 40 threads to the inch and the head has 25 divisions, consequently a move-

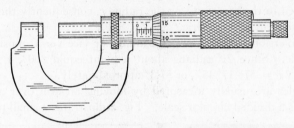

FIG. 3. Micrometer caliper; reading is 0.163 in.

ment of the screw through one division on the head changes the distance between the screw end and the fixed jaw by $\frac{1}{25}$ of $\frac{1}{40}$ in., or 0.001 in. Estimation of tenths of the head divisions enables measurements to be made to 0.0001 in. The whole number of revolutions of the screw is read on a fixed scale uncovered by the head as it moves away from the fixed jaw.

4. Angular Measure. — Where two lines lie along different directions, the angle between them is usually expressed in *degrees* (°). The total angle about a point is composed of 360°, and a right angle is equal to 90°. A degree has 60 *minutes* of arc ('), and a minute has 60 *seconds* of arc (").

Another unit for measuring angles is based upon the relative dimensions of a sector of a circle. In Fig. 4, the ratio of the arc s_1 to its radius r_1 is the same as that of any other arc s_2 to its radius r_2. This ratio of the arc length to the radius is not affected by the size of the sector but depends only upon the central angle θ (theta).

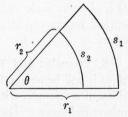

FIG. 4. Illustrating radian measure

The angle subtended at the center of a circle by an arc equal in length to the radius is called a radian. Since the circumference of a circle is 2π (that is, 2×3.1416) times its radius, the total angle around the central point is 2π radians, and a right angle is $\pi/2$ radians. In general,

$$\text{Angle in radians} = \frac{\text{arc length}}{\text{radius}}$$

or in symbols

$$\theta = \frac{s}{r} \tag{1}$$

The angle θ is a ratio of two lengths; the arc length s must be expressed in the same unit as the radius r, consequently the angle in radians will be a numeric.

Conversion from degrees to radians, or vice versa, must often be made. Since 2π radians about a point equal 360°, 1 radian $= 360/2\pi = 57°\ 17'\ 45''$, or 57.3° approximately.

Angles are usually measured by moving an arm over a plate that has a divided circular scale. Fig. 5 illustrates a small portion

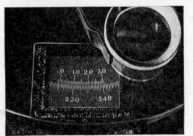 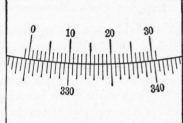

FIG. 5. Accurately divided scale with magnifier for ease in reading. The enlargement shows the reading to be 325° 18′

of a circular scale and vernier of a spectrometer that is used for optical measurements; the least count of the vernier is 1 minute of arc.

5. Triangles and Triangulation. — In many physical calculations it will be necessary to deal with lengths so located as to form sides of a triangle, with some of the sides and angles known and others unknown. The determination of the unknown elements is generally made by applying the methods of trigonometry.

The trigonometric functions most often used are the sine, cosine and tangent; their definitions are reviewed below in connection with the right-angled triangle *ABC* of Fig. 6. The sine of either acute angle is the ratio of the length of the side opposite that angle to the length of the hypotenuse. The cosine of either acute angle is the ratio of the side adjacent to that angle to the hypotenuse. The tangent of either acute angle is the ratio of the side opposite that angle to the side adjacent to that angle. These statements are symbolized as follows:

Function:	For angle A:	For angle B:	
$\sin = \dfrac{\text{opposite side}}{\text{hypotenuse}}$	$\sin A = \dfrac{a}{c}$	$\sin B = \dfrac{b}{c}$	(2)
$\cos = \dfrac{\text{adjacent side}}{\text{hypotenuse}}$	$\cos A = \dfrac{b}{c}$	$\cos B = \dfrac{a}{c}$	(3)
$\tan = \dfrac{\text{opposite side}}{\text{adjacent side}}$	$\tan A = \dfrac{a}{b}$	$\tan B = \dfrac{b}{a}$	(4)

It will be observed that $\sin A = \cos B$; that is, the sine of an angle is equal to the cosine of its complementary angle.

Experience should be acquired in handling these functions so that upon an inspection of a right-angled triangle as $p\,m\,n$ in Fig. 6, the following can be written promptly without first writing the ratios expressing the foregoing functions:

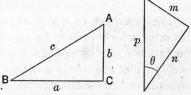

Fig. 6. Illustrating the trigonometric functions

$$m = p \sin \theta \qquad n = p \cos \theta \qquad m = n \tan \theta$$

Values of these functions for angles between 0° and 90° are tabulated in the Appendix. The values for larger angles are obtained by applying the rules at the end of the table.

The *Law of Cosines* is used in the solution of an oblique triangle when two sides and the included angle are known, and the length of the other side is required. This law states that in any triangle, the square of any side is equal to the sum of the squares of the other two sides minus twice the product of these two sides and the cosine of the angle included between them. For example, in Fig. 7,

$$c^2 = a^2 + b^2 - 2a\,b \cos \theta \tag{5}$$

where θ is the angle between sides a and b, and c is the side opposite this angle. When $\theta = 90°$, the last term disappears, and the expression reduces to the form $c^2 = a^2 + b^2$, which is the familiar Theorem of Pythagoras for a right triangle.

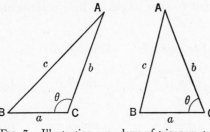

FIG. 7.   Illustrating some laws of trigonometry

The *Law of Sines* expresses the relation between the sides of a triangle and the sines of the angles opposite them. Referring again to Fig. 7, the mathematical statement of this law is given by

$$\frac{a}{\sin A} = \frac{b}{\sin B} = \frac{c}{\sin C} \qquad (6)$$

which shows that the ratio of any side of a triangle to the sine of the opposite angle is a constant. This law applies to a right-angled triangle or to an oblique triangle as in the figure.

The principles of trigonometry may be used in determining distances which cannot be measured directly. Such measurements are made by indirect methods which usually require the calculation of one side of a triangle of which the other sides or the angles have been measured. These indirect processes are spoken of as *triangulation*. The angles are frequently measured with a surveying instrument called a *transit*. This consists essentially of a telescope suitably mounted on a tripod and so arranged that its angular position can be read on two graduated circles fixed at right angles to each other. To measure either the horizontal or the vertical angle between two objects, the telescope is sighted first upon one object and then upon the other, the angle through which it is turned being read by a vernier on the corresponding graduated circle.

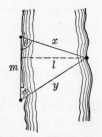

FIG. 8. Determining the width of a stream by triangulation

An example of triangulation is the measurement of the width of a river from one river bank. A known distance m is laid off with a tape along the bank parallel to the river; from its two extremities some spot on the opposite river edge is sighted, and the angles which these lines of sight make with the known length m are measured. Calling these angles θ and ϕ (phi), the information may be plotted on a diagram to scale, and the width of the river determined. Analytically the problem is solved by reference to Fig. 8 and the Law of Sines, equation (6), from which

$$\frac{y}{m} = \frac{\sin \theta}{\sin (180° - \theta - \phi)} = \frac{\sin \theta}{\sin (\theta + \phi)}$$

Upon solving this expression for y, the width l of the river is obtained at once from the relation $l = y \sin \phi$.

*6. **Latitude and Longitude.** — For purposes of navigation and cartography the surface of the earth is considered to be marked off by two sets of circles at right angles to each other, so that the location of all places can be described with reference to them. One set of circles is formed on the surface by planes passed perpendicular to the earth's axis. These are called *parallels of latitude*. The largest of these, the great circle called the *equator*, has zero lati-

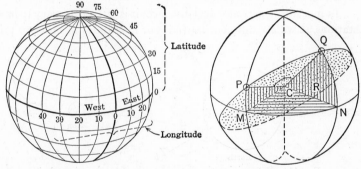

FIG. 9. Parallels of latitude and meridians FIG. 10. Determining distances
of longitude   along great circles

tude, and from it latitude is reckoned northward and southward up to the value 90° at the poles. The other set of circles is formed by planes which include the earth's axis, each plane intersecting the surface in a great circle passing through the poles. These circles are called *meridians of longitude*. The circle through Greenwich, England, is taken as the starting line and from it longitude is reckoned eastward and westward as far as 180° each way. Fig. 9 shows the marking of the globe in this manner.

Taking the average radius of the earth as 3958 miles, the length of arc for each degree of latitude is $2\pi\ 3958 \div 360 = 69.1$ mi. This is also the length of a degree of longitude at the equator, but elsewhere a degree of longitude is less, depending upon the latitude. A distance subtending one minute of latitude is called a nautical mile; its value is $69.1 \div 60 = 1.152$ (land) miles.

In long-distance flights by aircraft it is necessary to know the shortest distance between places on the surface of the earth. These distances are measured along great circles. The shortest distance between the places P and Q in Fig. 10, for example, is measured along the great circle PQR having its center at the center of the earth C. The length of arc PQ in miles is equal to 69.1 times the number of degrees in the angle PCQ, which angle lies in the plane of the great circle under consideration. The angle is determined from an expression from spherical trigonometry, namely

$$\cos PCQ = \sin p \times \sin q + \cos p \times \cos q \times \cos l$$

where p = angle PCM = latitude of P, q = angle QCN = latitude of Q, and l = angle MCN = difference in longitude between the two places P and Q. Southern latitudes are considered negative.

In measuring astronomical distances it is often necessary to have stations at widely different latitudes or longitudes in order to pro-

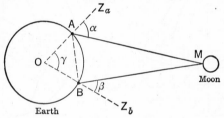

Fig. 11. Determining the distance to the moon by triangulation

vide adequate base lines for triangulation. In measuring the distance to the moon, for example, observations are taken on some point of the moon from two stations that are quite far apart. For simplicity assume these stations to be on the same meridian of longitude, as shown in Fig. 11, and the points A, B, O and M to lie in the same plane. At station A the angle of depression α (alpha) of the telescope away from the zenith Z_a is measured when the reference point on the moon is in the center of the field of view. The corresponding angle β (beta) from OZ_b is measured by a telescope at station B. Knowing the latitudes of the two stations, the angle γ (gamma) subtended by them at the center of the earth O becomes known, and the distance AB can be ascertained by the Law of Cosines applied to the isosceles triangle OAB, having the radius of the earth, namely 3958 mi., for two of its sides. Thereafter, the distances AM and BM can be determined by applying the Law of Sines to the triangle *ABM*, and finally the distance *OM* is ascertained. The distance from the earth to the moon (center to center) varies from 225,000 to 252,000 mi.

7. Area and Bulk. — The areas and volumes of regular geometric figures are often found by calculation, based upon measurements of their linear dimensions. A few formulas which are frequently used for this purpose in physical calculations are given herewith:

Areas and Volumes

Figure	Area
Triangle of altitude h and base b	$\frac{1}{2}hb$
Triangle of sides a, b, and c, and semi-perimeter $s = \frac{1}{2}(a + b + c)$	$\sqrt{s(s - a)(s - b)(s - c)}$
Trapezium of altitude h and bases b and b'	$\frac{h}{2}(b + b')$
Circle of radius r	πr^2
Sphere of radius r, surface area	$4\pi r^2$

Figure	Volume
Right cylinder of altitude h and base of area B	hB
Pyramid or cone of altitude h and base of area B	$\frac{1}{3}hB$
Sphere of radius r	$\frac{4}{3}\pi r^3$
Prismoid of altitude h, parallel bases of areas B and B', and midsection of area M	$\frac{h}{6}(B + B' + 4M)$

The prismoid is a solid bounded by any number of planes, two of which (called the bases) are parallel and contain all the vertices. The prismoidal formula can be used for the volume of a prism, cylinder, pyramid, cone, frustum of pyramid or cone, or sphere. It is useful in approximating the volumes of fills and excavations.

The units in which areas and volumes are expressed are usually the squares and cubes respectively of the regular linear dimensions; for example, square feet (abbreviated sq. ft. or ft.²), square centimeters (sq. cm. or cm.²), cubic yards (yd.³), and cubic meters. Other units met with and their equivalents appear in the following table:

Some Units of Area and Volume

Circular mil = area of circle 1 mil in diameter
  Acre = 43,560 sq. ft. = 1⁄640 square mile
  Gallon = 4 quarts (liquid measure) = 231 cu. in. = 3.785 liters
  Liter = 1000 cu. cm. = 61.02 cu. in. = 1.057 quarts (liquid measure)
  Bushel = 32 quarts (dry measure) = 2150.4 cu. in.

⋆8. The Planimeter. — For measuring small areas, such as indicator cards and map areas, an instrument called the *planimeter* is used. The usual form consists of two arms hinged together as shown in Fig. 12; the far end of one arm is provided with a stylus

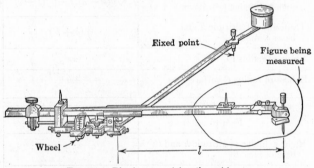

Fixed point

Figure being measured

Wheel

l

FIG. 12. Planimeter with adjustable arm

to be moved clockwise around the perimeter of the figure under measurement, while the other arm has a pin point for anchoring the instrument to some point outside of the figure. The arm with the stylus carries a graduated wheel; the axis is parallel to that arm, and the wheel rolls and slides along the paper on which the figure is drawn. It can be shown by mathematical analysis that the area of the figure is

Area = arm length × wheel radius × wheel rotation

or $$A = lr\phi \tag{7}$$

where l is the length of the arm carrying the wheel, r is the radius of the wheel, and ϕ is the angle through which the wheel turns while the stylus traces completely around the figure. The wheel is calibrated to read directly in square inches, square centimeters, or the like, and the calibration can be verified by tracing the perimeter of some geometric figure of which the area can be computed readily.

9. Mass and its Measurement. — It is assumed that all matter is composed of extremely small particles called molecules. All the molecules of a particular substance are, in general, alike and each consists of a definite structure of component parts to be discussed later; the structure of a molecule of one substance will, however, differ from that of another substance. Consequently, any particular object is composed of a definite quantity of matter determined by the number of molecules it contains and by the structure of the molecules themselves.

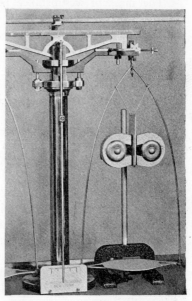

The term *mass* will be used for the present as a measure of the quantity of matter in a body; a broader definition will be given in § 37. The British and Metric standards of mass are:

The *pound of mass* is defined as the mass of a particular block of platinum known as a standard pound, which is kept at the Standards Office in Westminster, London.

Fig. 13. Portion of analytical balance with magnetic damping device. (*Courtesy of Christian Becker, Inc. and Central Scientific Company*)

The *kilogram of mass* is defined as the mass of a certain block of platinum preserved at the International Bureau of Weights and Measures and known as the standard kilogram.

Other units of mass and the relations between them appear in the following table:

Units of Mass

British Units	Metric Units
1 ton = 2000 pounds	1 kilogram (kg.) = 1000 grams
1 pound (lb.) = 16 ounces (oz.)	1 gram (gm.) = 1000 milligrams (mg.)
1 pound = 453.6 grams	1 kilogram = 2.2046 pounds

The measurement of mass is usually accomplished with an equal-arm balance, Fig. 13, the mass to be measured being placed on one of its scale-pans, and known masses on the other, the latter being varied until a balance is obtained. The operating principle is in reality the balancing of two forces, the earth's attraction for the mass on one pan being just counteracted by the earth's attraction for the known masses on the other.

The mass of a substance per unit volume is known as its *density*, a dense substance being one in which a large quantity of matter occupies a small volume. A gallon of water is found to have a mass of 8.34 lb., and since its volume is 231 cu. in. = 0.1337 cu. ft., the density of water is $\dfrac{8.34 \text{ lb.}}{0.1337 \text{ cu. ft.}}$ = 62.4 lb. per cu. ft. In metric units it is 1 gm. per cu. cm.

10. Measurement of Time. — The regularity of the earth's motion around the sun affords the basis for measurements of time. The earth revolves about the sun once a year (about $365\frac{1}{4}$ days). Its orbit or ecliptic is strictly an ellipse with the sun at one focus, but it may be considered approximately as a circle having a radius of 92,900,000 mi. The speed of the earth along this path varies slightly on account of the eccentricity of the orbit, the speed being greater where the earth is nearer the sun. The earth also rotates uniformly on its axis once a day. The axis passes through the north and south geographic poles, and is not perpendicular to the plane of the ecliptic but is inclined about 23.5° from a perpendicular position. The direction of the axis remains almost fixed in space as the earth rotates, and points almost directly toward the North Star, Polaris.

The stars are tremendously distant, the nearest star being many thousand times as far away as the sun. For this reason, the stars appear almost like fixed points in space, occupying virtually the same positions regardless of the position of the earth in its orbit. To us it appears that the earth is stationary and that the sun and stars move; and when one of the celestial bodies appears to pass through the plane of a given meridian it is said to cross the meridian.

If the instants that a given *star* crosses the meridian are recorded on two successive nights, the elapsed interval will be the time required for one complete rotation of the earth with reference to a star. This is called a *sidereal* day, and this constant interval is used in astronomical measurements. On the other hand, if the instants that the *sun* crosses the meridian are recorded on two successive days, the elapsed interval will be the time required for an apparent rotation of the earth with respect to the sun, and this is called a *solar* day. The solar days vary somewhat in length, the average throughout the year being known as the *mean solar day*. Through the course of a year, a given point on the earth in facing the sun 365 times must face a fixed point in space (i.e., a star) 366 times, and owing to this fact the mean solar day is about 366/365 of a sidereal day; that is, the mean solar day is about 4 min. longer than the sidereal day.

The mean solar day is subdivided into 24 hours, each hour being further divided into 60 minutes, and each minute into 60 seconds. Thus the mean solar day is composed of 86,400 mean solar seconds. This *mean solar second* is the unit of time which is in general use for physical and engineering work, as well as for everyday purposes.

In most clocks or watches a spring-driven gear train is allowed to run down at a slow and uniform rate under the action of an escapement, controlled either by a pendulum or a balance wheel, and the gear train turns the hands of the instrument in front of a dial or faceplate. In the synchronous electric clock, the hands are driven by a small motor which is connected to an alternating-current circuit and runs in synchronism with the generators at the power station, their speed being accurately controlled.

For the recording of official time, a *precision clock* is used, the accuracy of which is checked at regular intervals with a meridian telescope. Precision clocks are designed and constructed with the utmost care, and are kept in constant-temperature rooms to insure uniform operation. The mechanism is enclosed in a glass case from which most of the air is removed. They are the most accurate timekeepers available.

In scientific and engineering work, it is usually desired to measure the *duration of an interval of time* rather than to determine the correct time at a certain instant. For this purpose the familiar stop watch is widely used. In laboratory work, clocks are used in which each sweep of the pendulum operates an electrical contact in a sounder circuit, the audible clicks of the sounder making the intervals easy to count. Short time intervals can be measured accurately by indirect methods that make use of tuning forks, chronographs, oscillographs, and crystals exhibiting the piezoelectric effect.

*11. The Slide Rule. — An indispensable tool to the engineer, technologist, and scientist is the *slide rule*. It enables him to multiply and divide, to square and to extract the square root, to obtain logarithms of numbers and trigonometric functions of angles; all of these operations are performed simply and the result is given to an accuracy which is sufficient for most computations. The student is urged to procure a slide rule and to become proficient in its use.

In adding two distances along the same line, one places the beginning of the second distance at the end of the first and reads the mark opposite the end of the second distance. This is illustrated in Fig. 14, which represents two centimeter rules used for

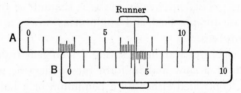

Fig. 14.   Adding lengths with sliding rules

the measurement.   The setting shows the addition of 2.7 cm. and 4.2 cm.; the index of scale B (that is, its zero mark) is set on 2.7 cm. of scale A, and the result is read off with the aid of a runner from scale A opposite 4.2 cm. on scale B, the answer being 6.9 cm.   Subtraction is obviously carried out in the reverse manner.   This simple process of sliding one rule next to another to add and subtract is the fundamental principle of the slide rule.

The student knows that numbers can be multiplied by adding their logarithms.   Therefore, if the logarithms of numbers be laid off along two rules, and one rule is moved with respect to the other to add distances as just described, then the corresponding numbers will be multiplied.   In marking the rule the numbers themselves are used rather than their logarithms; this marking is shown in Fig. 15.   The two scales A and B are identical and 2.5 inches long and represent the standard 10-inch rule to $\frac{1}{4}$ size.   To verify the marking of a full-sized scale, lay an inch-rule upon it and note that the distance from the index to a particular number on the scale is 10 times the logarithm of that number.

The setting in Fig. 15 shows the multiplication of 2.24 and 3.14. The index of scale *B* is placed opposite 2.24 on scale *A*, and the runner is placed at 3.14 on scale *B*; the answer is found on scale *A* under the runner; namely 7.03. Actually the logarithm of 2.24 (namely 0.350) is added to the logarithm of 3.14 (namely 0.497); the logarithm of the answer is therefore 0.350 + 0.497 = 0.847, and the corresponding number (or anti-logarithm) is 7.03. If the setting of the scales is such that the result falls beyond the end of the *A* scale, the *B* scale is moved the other way, using the right end-mark as the index.

The process of division is carried out in the reverse order. To divide 7.03 by 3.14, place 3.14 of the *B* scale opposite 7.03 on the *A* scale; the result will be given on the *A* scale opposite the index of the *B* scale, namely 2.24, as shown in Fig. 15.

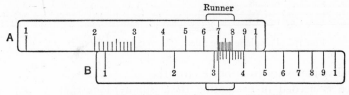

FIG. 15. Multiplying numbers with a slide rule

The numbers on the slide rule may be multiplied or divided by any power of ten; for example, mark 3 might mean 0.003 in one computation and 300 in another. Obviously, care must be exercised in locating the decimal point of the answer. The setting shown in Fig. 15 would be the same for the following multiplications:

$$22.4 \times 314 = 7030$$
$$0.224 \times 0.00314 = 0.000703$$
$$224 \times 10^3 \times 314 \times 10^6 = 703 \times 10^{11}$$

The location of the decimal point in any multiplication or division should be determined by carrying out the computation roughly, using round numbers to approximate the numbers involved. For example, in multiplying 22.4 × 314, call the first number 25 and the second 300, the product is 7500; therefore, the correct answer cannot be 703, nor 70,300, but must be 7030.

Fig. 16 depicts a slide rule of the usual variety. Scales *A* and *B* are identical and extend from 1 to 100 with 10 at the center of the scale, although only one digit is used in each number. Scales *C* and *D* are also identical and extend only from 1 to 10.

Therefore the square of any number on the D scale is directly over it on the A scale and can be read accurately by using the indicator or glass runner; thus in the setting shown the square of 2.78 is 7.73. Scale K extends from 1 to 1000; therefore the cubes of numbers on scale D are read directly from scale K.   Scale CI is the same as scale C but inverted; it enables reciprocals of numbers to be read directly and also reduces the number of settings in long computations; in the setting shown the reciprocal of 2.78 is 0.360.   On the reverse side of the slide are scales of logarithms, sines and tangents. The figure shows the actual subdivisions of the various scales. From 1 to 2 the length is much greater than from 9 to 10, and vastly greater than from 99 to 100; consequently the values of the

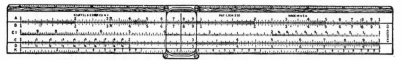

FIG. 16.   Polyphase slide rule.   (*Courtesy of Keuffel & Esser Co.*)

subdivisions vary from one end of the rule to the other.   Experience is needed in evaluating these subdivisions rapidly and in estimating tenths of them.   A book of detailed directions is supplied with each slide rule.

12. Numerical Computations. — Numerical work should be carried out to a number of places consistent with the data provided and the nature of the problem.   Results should usually be stated to three or four significant figures, and such precision can be obtained directly from a standard slide rule.   In stating problems in this text, numerical quantities are often given to only one or two digits, such as 7 ft. or 0.12 mm.   This is done to lessen mathematical work and to avoid detraction from the physical concepts involved; these figures should be regarded as precise to three or four places.

Where data are supplied to many places, as in dealing with the wave length of light, or where the effect under observation is very small, as in the expansion caused by heat, the number of figures to be kept in the computations and result should be correspondingly increased.   Care should be taken, however, not to express results to more figures than are justified by the data.   For example, in computing the area of a rectangle that is stated to be 2.26 in. long and 1.89 in. wide, it should be noted that these dimensions are expressed to the nearest 0.01 in., and are precise to about 1 part in 200, or $\frac{1}{2}$ of 1 per cent. Since the area cannot be ascertained more precisely than this, the result should be expressed as 2.26 in. × 1.89 in. = 4.27 sq. in. It is needless and incorrect to express it with more figures, as *these would imply a precision not obtainable from the data provided.*

PROBLEMS

1. The highest mountain in North America is Mount McKinley in Alaska, and its height is 20,300 feet. Express this altitude in meters.

2. The height of the Washington monument is recorded as 555 ft., $5\frac{1}{8}$ in. Express this height in meters.

3. The tallest tree in the United States is Founder's Tree, a redwood in northern California. Its height is 364 ft. and its girth is 47.1 ft. Express these dimensions in meters.

4. Using 1 meter = 39.37 in., show that 1 kilometer = 0.6214 mile by carrying all the units through the computation.

5. A railroad track curves through an angle of 20° in forming an arc 260 ft. long. What is the radius of the curve?

6. The angle subtended by the moon's diameter at a place on the surface of the earth is 31′ 5.16″. Determine the approximate diameter of the moon based on an average distance of 235,000 miles from that place on the earth's surface.

7. The No. 10 bull's-eye used in rifle practice has a diameter of 0.150 in. What angular separation from the true center line can the marksman allow and still hit this bull's-eye if he is 50 ft. away from the target?

8. It is convenient to measure astronomical distances in terms of the distance that light travels in one year; this distance, known as a light-year, is equal to 588 × 10^{10} mi. The parsec is also used in astronomical measurements; it is defined as that distance at which the radius of the earth's orbit (92.9 × 10^6 mi.) subtends an angle of one second of arc. How many light-years are in one parsec?

9. The highest and lowest points in the United States are in California within sight of each other and only 86 mi. apart. They are the crest of Mt. Whitney, 14,496 ft. above sea level, and Bad Water, the terminal pool of Amargosa River, 276 ft. below sea level. What angle does a line joining these points make with the horizontal plane?

10. Three towns, A, B, and C, are connected by straight roads. AB is 6 mi., BC is 4 mi. and AC is 5 mi. Find the angle between AB and BC.

11. A datum line 50 ft. long is measured along the bank of a stream and from its ends an intermediate point on the opposite bank is sighted. If the angles which these lines of sight make with the datum line are 60° and 75° respectively, calculate the width of the stream.

12. From a point on the level with the base of a flag pole and at a distance of 120 ft. from it, an observer sees its top at an angle of elevation of 24°. How high is the flag pole?

13. Radio signals are picked up by two shore stations A and B from a ship which desires its location by radio bearings. Station A reports an angle of 9° south of east, and station B reports an angle of 56.5° north of east. Knowing that station B is 190 miles south and 65 miles east of station A, how far is the ship away from both stations?

14. How far is the horizon from a person at sea when his eyes are 50 ft. above sea level?

*15. Calculate the great-circle distance between Lisbon, Portugal (lat. 38° 42′ North, long. 9° 5′ West) and Pernambuco, Brazil (lat. 8° 7′ South, long. 34° 49′ West).

16. A plot of ground is bounded by four straight lines having successive lengths of 400, 320, 350 and 200 ft. individually. The 400-ft. and 320-ft. sides meet in a right angle. Find the acreage of the plot.

17. Compute the diameter of a cylindrical tank 5 ft. high which is to hold 100 gal.

18. The sphere of the theme structure at the 1939 World's Fair in New York is 180 ft. in diameter. What is the area of its surface and what is its volume?

19. How many cubic inches of iron are there in a 6-ft. length of pipe which has an inside diameter of 4 in. and an outside diameter of 4.5 in.? How many gallons of water would fill this section of pipe?

20. Calculate the volumetric piston displacement in the six cylinders of an automobile engine if the cylinder bore is $3\frac{7}{16}$ in. and the stroke of the piston is $4\frac{1}{8}$ in.

21. How many gallons of water fall on an acre of ground during a 1-in. rainfall?

22. A cylindrical graduate is 8.6 cm. in diameter. What is the separation of two scale divisions which represent a volume of 1 liter between them?

23. How many gallons of water would fill a rectangular swimming pool 80 ft. long, 40 ft. wide, and having a depth of 4 ft. at one end and 10 ft. at the other?

*24. A planimeter has an arm 5.1 in. long and a wheel 0.90 in. in diameter. What area does each of the 100 divisions on the wheel indicate?

25. Each cable of the George Washington Bridge at New York City consists of 26,474 steel wires each $\frac{1}{5}$ in. in diameter. Taking the density of steel as 490 lb. per ft.³, determine the mass of the cable per foot length.

26. Howard Hughes took less than 4 days in his eastward flight around the world in 1938 yet reported that he had witnessed the sun rise on 5 mornings. Explain.

*27. Mention all the mathematical processes that are indicated by the setting of the slide rule shown on this page at the glass runner, state each numerically, and give the scales used.

CHAPTER II

VECTORS

13. Addition of Directed Quantities. — There are many quantities involved in physical measurements or calculations which can be added by simple arithmetic. Thus, a 100-gm. mass placed on a scale-pan in addition to 500 gm. already there makes a total mass of 600 gm.; again, a 4-min. interval followed without pause by one of 8 min. makes the total elapsed time 12 min. Additions can be carried out in this manner when the quantities do not involve the idea of direction.

Physical quantities that have directions can also be added; the process is more involved but not difficult. Such an addition is necessary, for example, when a man walks a certain distance in one direction, another distance in a different direction, and perhaps other distances in still different directions, and desires to know his position with respect to the starting point. A direct line joining any two points of the man's walk is called a *displacement*. His entire journey may be mapped out as a series of displacements, one after another, each represented by an arrow of appropriate length and direction. An arrow drawn from the beginning to the end of such a diagram shows the man's final position with respect to the starting point and represents the "sum" of the separate displacements, taking account of their directions; this sum is also known as the *resultant* displacement.

In solving such a problem *graphically*, the diagram is made carefully to scale, and the resultant is measured with rule and protractor to determine its length and direction. To solve the problem *analytically*, a rough diagram will suffice and from this sketch the length and direction of the resultant are calculated by mathematics. Both procedures will be illustrated by a specific problem.

Consider a pedestrian to walk 2 mi. due east and then 3 mi. in a northeast direction. How far is he from the starting point and in what direction is he from that point? To solve the problem graphically, lay off the arrows representing the displacements accurately to suitable scale and with the exact inclinations, placing the tail-end of the second arrow at the head-end of the first, thereby forming two sides of a triangle, as in

21

Fig. 17. Draw the closing side of the triangle, and measure its length carefully to the same scale. This will give the numerical value of the

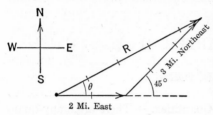

distance sought as $R = 4.6$ mi. Measure the direction that this closing side of the triangle makes with the east direction, using a protractor; this angle is marked θ in the diagram. The result shows that side R is north of east by an angle $\theta = 27°$. It will be observed that both R and θ are accurate to only two significant figures.

FIG. 17. Addition of two displacements

The accuracy of a graphical result depends not only upon care in using the correct lengths and directions, but also upon making the drawing of adequate size. If a directed quantity were represented as an arrow 6 in. long, an error of $\frac{1}{32}$ in. in its length would mean an inaccuracy of one part in 6×32 or 192, that is, an error of $\frac{1}{2}$ per cent. Graphical solutions like the foregoing can be depended upon for an accuracy of one per cent if care is exercised. Much greater accuracy may be attained by analytical solutions since these do not require the making of drawings to scale.

To solve the foregoing problem analytically, a rough sketch is made to resemble Fig. 17, and the unknown parts of the triangle are figured out by trigonometry. First, using the Law of Cosines to determine the magnitude of the resultant R,

$$R^2 = (2)^2 + (3)^2 - 2 \times 2 \times 3 \cos 135°$$
$$= 4 + 9 - 12(- \cos 45°) = 13 + 12 \times 0.707 = 21.484;$$

whence $R = 4.63$ mi. Next, applying the Law of Sines to find the direction of R,

$$\frac{\sin \theta}{\sin 135°} = \frac{3 \text{ mi.}}{4.63 \text{ mi.}}$$

whence $\sin \theta = (3/4.63) \sin 135° = 0.648 \times 0.707 = 0.458$. From trigonometric tables, the angle having this value for its sine is $\theta = 27.2°$.

It is apparent from this illustration that an analytical solution is inherently more precise than a graphical one since it does not depend upon the accuracy of a diagram, but only upon the precision of the data given and the number of places to which the computation is carried out.

14. Parallelogram Method of Combining Displacements. — In adding displacements, or other directed quantities, several methods may be used.

In the first of these, represented in Fig. 18, two displacements a and b are laid off graphically to scale in the proper directions *from a common starting point* S, so as to form two adjacent sides of a parallelogram. The parallelogram is then completed by drawing the sides a' and b' parallel to a and b respectively and intersecting at T. The diagonal R drawn from the starting point, called the *concurrent diagonal*, gives the resultant both in length and direction. This method of finding the distance and direction from the starting point S to the terminating point T is called the Parallelogram Method of adding displacements. Since lengths b and b' are equal, the resultant R is the same as though distance b' were added to distance a by the method described in the preceding section. Con-sequently the same mathematical steps used in the solution of the oblique tri-

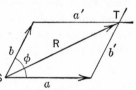

Fig. 18. Adding two displace-ments by the Parallelogram Method

angle may be used to obtain an analytical solution for the Parallelogram Method. In this case it will be convenient to use the Law of Cosines [§ 5] in a modified form. Applied to a parallelogram having adjacent sides a and b at an angle ϕ with each other, this law gives the length of the concurrent diagonal R from the expression

$$R^2 = a^2 + b^2 + 2ab \cos \phi \tag{8}$$

The Parallelogram Method may be used for the addition of any number of displacements, by first finding the resultant of two of them, then adding another displacement to this resultant in the same way, and continuing this process until all are included.

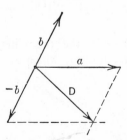

The process of addition just described applies also to the reverse operation of *subtraction* with but a slight modification. Thus, to subtract one displacement, or other directed quantity, from another, *reverse its direction and proceed as in addition.* For example, to subtract the displacement b from displacement a in Fig. 18, b is first reversed in direction giving $-b$ as in Fig. 19, and next a and $-b$ are added by the Parallelogram Method,

Fig. 19. Subtracting one displacement from another

giving the difference D, as shown. To verify this result, it is necessary merely to add D and b; their "sum" or resultant would be identical with a.

15. Polygon Method. — In adding three or more displacements, the Parallelogram Method described in §14 is somewhat unwieldy, and a more convenient procedure is the so-called Polygon Method. From a chosen starting point lay off one of the displacements to appropriate scale and in proper direction; *from its terminal* or head-end lay off another of the displacements similarly; from the terminal of the latter lay off the third distance; and so on until all are included. Lastly, draw the line that is necessary to close the figure to form a polygon; this is the resultant. This method is illustrated in Fig. 20, wherein the four displace-

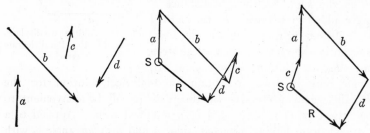

Fig. 20. The Polygon Method of adding displacements

ments *a*, *b*, *c*, and *d* shown at the left are to be added. At the center of the figure the order of addition, starting at *S*, is *a*, *b*, *c*, *d*, and at the right is *c*, *a*, *b*, *d*; the resultant *R* is, of course, the same in magnitude and direction whatever the order followed in the additive process. It is to be noted that the resultant is directed away from the starting point.

The Polygon Method is an extension of that used in the problem of §13 in which only two displacements were added; in that case the polygon had the simpler form of a triangle.

16. Resolution of Directed Quantities. — In the preceding sections, attention was focussed upon two methods by which dis-

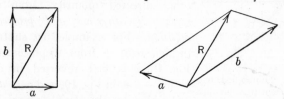

Fig. 21. Resolution of a displacement into components

placements could be added to form a resultant. Reversing the point of view, the resultant displacement may be regarded as composed of *components*. Thus, in either diagram of Fig. 21, *R* may be considered the resultant of *a* and *b*, or *a* and *b* may be considered the components of *R*. The diagram at the left illustrates the most frequent case, in which the components are at right angles to each other and hence are termed *rectangular components*. The process of breaking up a directed quantity into components is called *resolution*.

To resolve a displacement into two components a definite procedure should be followed. This is illustrated in Fig. 22, where the displacement *L* to be resolved and the two direction lines 1 and 2, along which the desired components shall lie, are shown at I. Draw the displacement *L* and the two direction lines from a common point *S* as depicted in II. From the head-end of length *L*

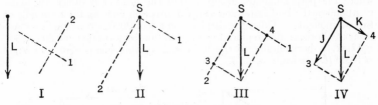

Fɪɢ. 22. The process of resolution

draw lines parallel to the two direction lines 1 and 2, meeting those lines at points 3 and 4, as in III. Finally, replace the intercepts of these direction lines by the desired components *J* and *K*, locating their head-ends at the intersecting points 3 and 4, as illustrated in IV. Naturally *J* and *K* must be measured with the same scale that is used in constructing *L*. This procedure is the same whatever the directions of the displacement to be resolved or the direction lines may be.

17. Addition by the Resolution Method. — The process of resolution just described is extremely useful when applied to the addition of displacements analytically, particularly where there are more than two such quantities to be added. Under these circumstances, each of the displacements concerned is resolved into rectangular components, usually in the horizontal and vertical directions, then the horizontal and vertical components of all displacements are added separately, and finally these results are combined at right angles to form the resultant. The diagrams need not be drawn to scale, since the lengths are determined accurately by trigonometric methods.

The following numerical example will clarify the procedure: Add the five displacements shown in Fig. 23 by the Resolution Method. Displacement *a* is 13.5 ft. vertically up, and has no horizontal component. Displacement *e* is 3.4 ft. horizontally to the right, and has no vertical component. The other three displacements must be resolved into their hori-

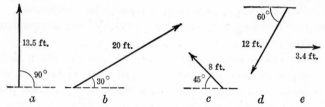

Fig. 23. Addition of displacements by the Resolution Method

zontal and vertical components. This resolution is shown in Fig. 24, where the perpendiculars dropped from the head-ends of the displacements upon the horizontal and vertical direction lines fix the terminals of the components. Thus, the displacement *b* of 20 ft. at an angle 30° up from the horizontal is replaced in the addition by a component 20 cos 30° =17.32 ft. horizontally to the right and another component 20 sin 30° =10.00 ft. vertically up.

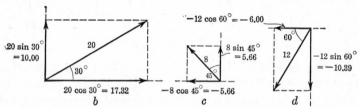

Fig. 24. Resolution into rectangular components

The addition of the components is tabulated below, distances downward and to the left being taken as negative:

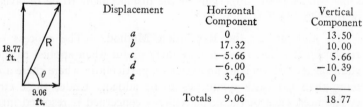

Fig. 25. Composition of rectangular components to form resultant

Displacement	Horizontal Component	Vertical Component
a	0	13.50
b	17.32	10.00
c	−5.66	5.66
d	−6.00	−10.39
e	3.40	0
Totals	9.06	18.77

Consequently the result of the addition is a displacement 9.06 ft. horizontally to the right and 18.77 ft. vertically up. The resultant *R* of these components is obtained in Fig. 25; its magnitude is given by equation (5) as $\sqrt{(18.77)^2 + (9.06)^2} = 20.84$ ft., and its direction is upward from the horizontal datum by an angle θ of which the tangent is 18.77/9.06 = 2.072, namely 64.2°.

18. Vector and Scalar Quantities. — It will be observed upon reviewing the quantities discussed so far that some have direction as well as numerical value or *magnitude*, while others are completely expressed by magnitude alone. *The term vector is applied to quantities which have both direction and magnitude.* The displacement of a box along a chute, the force used in stretching a spring, and the velocity of an airplane, are examples of vector quantities. *The term scalar refers to quantities which have magnitude only.* As illustrations of scalar quantities, the mass of a pendulum bob, the density of platinum, the horsepower of a motor, or the energy used in boiling some water, may be mentioned.

Any vector quantity may be represented by an arrow drawn in the appropriate direction and having a length which represents, to some convenient scale, the numerical value of the quantity which it represents.

19. Vector Addition Applied to Forces. — The methods described for adding displacements can be applied to the addition of all vector quantities. Vector addition is particularly important in dealing with *force*, for it happens frequently that an object is acted upon by several forces in different directions at the same time, and it becomes necessary to determine a single force that is equivalent to all of them. For this reason, the methods already described in this chapter will be further illustrated by applying them to the addition of forces.

A force is a push or a pull exerted upon an object, and is described subjectively as muscular effort. Forces produce a variety of effects. Sometimes a force is applied to set an object into motion, as in pushing a stalled automobile; sometimes it acts to retard a body already moving, as in a machine slowing down because of the backward drag of friction. Again, a force may produce distortion, as in stretching or compressing a spring. Such effects are described and analyzed in Chapter V, and from these effects, precise statements of the units of force are derived. It will suffice here in illustrating the addition of forces to use just one unit of force, the *pound*, and to define it as the pull which the earth exerts upon a 1-pound mass. This is the unit familiar alike to the engineer, physicist and layman.

If the forces acting on a body have the same or opposite directions, their resultant is found by direct addition or subtraction. Thus, if two locomotives are pulling a train up a grade and each exerts a force of 50,000 lb., the resultant of these forces is twice 50,000 lb., or 100,000 lb. acting in the same direction as the separate forces. Again, if a boy is pulling a sled over level snow with a horizontal force of 15 lb., and the snow exerts a backward force of friction of 2 lb. on it, the resultant force is 13 lb. in the direction of the boy's pull. When a number of forces act on a body in different directions, the resultant is found by vector addition as previously used in finding the resultant of several displacements.

For example, find a single force which would replace two forces *a* and *b*, both in a horizontal plane, *a* being a force of 10 lb. forward and *b* being a force of 7 lb. backward at an angle of 30° with the extension of force *a*. The separate forces are shown in part I of Fig. 26, drawn to

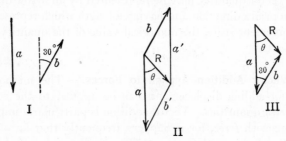

FIG. 26. Addition of two forces

scale and in proper direction. To find their resultant graphically, place them as in part II of the figure, so as to form two sides of a parallelogram; next, complete the parallelogram; and finally draw in the concurrent diagonal *R*. This diagonal represents the resultant of the two forces; upon measuring its length and direction, it is found to have a magnitude of 5.3 lb., and make an angle of $\theta = 41°$ with *a*.

The resultant force may be found analytically from a diagram of the general form shown in part III of the figure, not necessarily to scale. From such a figure, the Law of Cosines shows that

$$R^2 = a^2 + b^2 - 2ab \cos 30° = (10)^2 + (7)^2 - 2 \times 10 \times 7 \times 0.866 = 27.8,$$

whence $R = 5.27$ lb. Denoting the upper angle by θ, it follows from the Law of Sines that $\dfrac{b}{\sin \theta} = \dfrac{R}{\sin 30°}$, whence

$$\sin \theta = \frac{b \sin 30°}{R} = \frac{7 \text{ lb.} \times 0.500}{5.27 \text{ lb.}} = 0.664,$$

and $\theta = 41.3°$

The Resolution Method, applied to the addition of displacements in § 17, is equally useful in finding the resultant of several forces analytically. The procedure is, first, to resolve each of the forces into components along two lines at right angles to each other; next, to combine the components along each of these

lines into a single force by simple addition or subtraction; and
finally, from the two rectangular forces thus found, to calculate
the resultant.

To illustrate this procedure, suppose that it is desired to find the
resultant of four forces acting on a body as shown in Fig. 27, where
A = 50 lb., acting upward and to the right, at an angle of 20° with the
horizontal; B = 30 lb., acting directly upward; C = 60 lb., acting down-

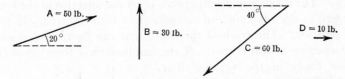

FIG. 27.   Illustrating forces to be added

ward and to the left at an angle of 40° with the horizontal; and D = 10 lb.
acting toward the right.   In resolving these forces, the horizontal and
vertical directions will be used for the components, since two of the forces
already have these directions, and so will require no resolution.   Thus A
(50 lb.) is composed of a horizontal component 50 cos 20° and a vertical
component 50 sin 20°, as shown in Fig. 28; B (30 lb.) is vertical; C (60 lb.)
consists of a horizontal component 60 cos 40° and a vertical component

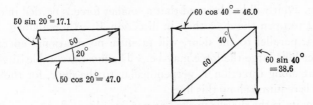

FIG. 28.   Forces resolved into rectangular components

60 sin 40° as shown; and D (10 lb.) is horizontal.   Evaluating and tabulat-
ing components:

Force	Components			
	Up	Down	Right	Left
A	17.1	0	47.0	0
B	30.0	0	0	0
C	0	38.6	0	46.0
D	0	0	10.0	0
Totals	47.1	38.6	57.0	46.0

The net vertical force is 47.1 − 38.6 or 8.5 lb. upward, and the net
horizontal force is 57.0 − 46.0 = 11.0 lb. to the right; upon combining
these at right angles, the resultant of the four forces A, B, C and D is
found to be $R = \sqrt{(8.5)^2 + (11.0)^2}$ = 13.9 lb., directed upward and
toward the right at an angle θ = tan^{-1} 8.5/11.0 = tan^{-1} 0.773 = 37.7°
with the horizontal.

20. Moment of a Force; Torque.— The rotation of a wheel or the twisting of a bolt may be described as either clockwise or counter-clockwise. This statement implies direction, but direction in quite a different sense from the previous use of the term. It will be of interest to note how a rotational or angular quantity can be represented by a vector.

A force applied to a body may produce rotation about some axis. The rotational effect depends upon the direction of the force as well as upon the place of its application with respect to the axis of rotation. The truth of this statement can be verified readily by opening a heavy door. If the hand exerts a force upon the door knob in the various directions shown from 1 to 4 in part I

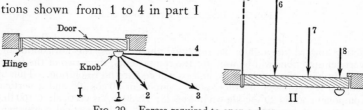

FIG. 29. Forces required to open a door

of Fig. 29, it will be observed that a smaller force is needed in direction 2 to open the door than in direction 3. A force along direction 4, parallel to the door, will produce no rotational effect, no matter how large the force may be. The most favorable direction is that along direction 1, perpendicular to the door, for the least force is required along this line.

Again, if the door is pushed at various places along its width in a direction at right angles to the door, as in part II, it will be observed that the least force is needed at position 8, along the edge furthest from the hinges, to open it; that more and more force must be exerted in approaching the hinges, positions 7 and 6; and that a force applied at the hinges, position 5, will not produce rotation, no matter how great it may be.

Experience in turning a door, together with a variety of similar experiences, shows the need of expressing definitely the effectiveness of a force in setting a body into rotation. This rotational effect is known as the *moment* of force, or *torque*, and is measured by *the product of the force and the perpendicular distance from the axis of rotation to the line of action of the force.* Or, calling this perpendicular distance the *lever arm*

$$\text{Torque} = \text{force} \times \text{lever arm}$$

Representing the force by F and the lever arm by L, the torque becomes

$$T = F \times L \qquad (9)$$

For example, in the crank shown in Fig. 30, the moment of force F tending to turn the crank clockwise about an axis O, is equal to $F \times OB$ for the position shown, where OB is the lever arm. Note that the lever arm L is not the length l of the crank, but is the perpendicular distance from the axis at O to the line of action of the force at point B. The lever arm can, of course, be expressed in terms of l by replacing L by its equal, $l \sin \theta$, thus making the torque $T = Fl \sin \theta$. Another way to obtain this result is to resolve the force F into two components, namely: $F \cos \theta$ along the crank, and $F \sin \theta$ at right angles to the crank. The latter component multiplied by the length of the crank, l, yields the correct value of the torque.

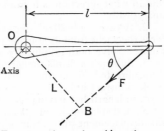

Fig. 30. A crank subjected to a torque

The units of torque depend on the units selected for the force and for the lever arm: such units as pound-inches (lb.-in.) and pound-feet (lb.-ft.) are commonly used.

Torque is represented vectorially by an arrow drawn along the axis about which it could by itself produce rotation. The

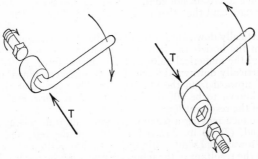

Fig. 31. Torque shown as a vector

arrow has a length which indicates the numerical value of the torque to some suitable scale, and points in the direction in which the torque would advance a bolt having the usual right-handed thread. This mode of vector representation is shown in Fig. 31.

A similar convention is used in representing other angular quantities. When so represented, they may be added by the same methods as other vector quantities. This procedure will be followed in Chapter VI in the study of the gyroscope.

PROBLEMS

1. A ship steams in still water 100 mi. due north and then 40 mi. in a direction 30° east of north. How far is the ship from its starting point, and in what direction is it from that point? Solve both graphically and analytically.

2. A yacht sails 20 mi. due east and then sails 12 mi. southwest. How far is the yacht from its starting point, and in what direction is it from that point? Solve both graphically and analytically.

3. Subtract a displacement of 4 mi. due south from a displacement of 9 mi. directed 30° north of east.

4. Subtract a displacement of 5 yd. due east from a displacement also 5 yd. in length but having a direction 30° east of north.

5. A displacement of 10 km. is directed 41° north of east. Resolve this displacement into rectangular components one of which is due north.

6. Resolve a displacement of 150 ft. along two directions which make angles of 25° and 55° with the given distance and which lie on opposite sides of it. Explain the resolution by the graphical method and ascertain the lengths of the components analytically.

7. Add the following displacements analytically: 10 ft. directed northeast, 15 ft. directed south, and 25 ft. directed 30° west of south.

8. A person walks 3 mi. northeast, then 2 mi. east, and finally 1 mi. south. Calculate the distance from the starting point to the finishing point of the walk by using the polygon and resolution methods.

9. Resolve a vertically downward force of 50 lb. into two components, one directed 30° downward from the horizontal and toward the right, and the other at right angles to this direction.

10. Resolve a 170-lb. horizontal force into two components, one vertically downward and the other at an angle of 65° upward from the horizontal.

11. A vertically downward force of 3.5 lb. is to be added to a force 50° upward from the horizontal, it being known that their resultant is horizontal. Find the numerical value of the resultant force.

12. A vertically downward force of 80 lb. when combined with a force directed 70° upward from the horizontal yields a resultant the direction of which is known to be 20° downward from the horizontal. Find the magnitude of the resultant force.

13. Three men moving a piano exert forces on it as follows: (1) 60 lb. straight ahead, (2) 80 lb. directed 10° toward the left, and (3) 50 lb. directed 20° toward the right. Find the resultant of these forces.

14. Find the resultant of the following forces by the resolution method: A, 100 lb. horizontal and toward the right; B, 40 lb. upward and toward the left, at an angle of 40° with the horizontal; C, 60 lb. downward and toward the left, at an angle of 80° with the horizontal; and D, 120 lb. vertically downward.

15. A uniform bar 12 ft. long is pivoted at its middle point. When the bar is horizontal it is found that a vertical force of 3 lb. at one end is necessary to start it moving on account of friction at the support. What

vertical force would have to be applied to the same point to start the bar moving if it is in an inclined position making an angle of 50° with the horizontal?

16. Calculate the torque exerted by a boy's foot in pushing vertically downward with a force of 30 lb. upon a pedal at the end of an 8-in. crank, (*a*) when the crank is horizontal, and (*b*) when the crank makes an angle of 40° with the horizontal.

17. What torque is exerted upon a revolving door by a force of 6 lb. applied perpendicular to the door at a point 20 in. from its axis of rotation?

18. Two shafts are coupled by means of a belt around two pulleys. The driving shaft has a 24-in. pulley and the driven shaft has a 36-in. pulley. The taut and slack sides of the belt are under tensions of 70 lb. and 10 lb. respectively. Find the torque exerted at each pulley.

CHAPTER III

UNIFORM MOTION

21. Uniform Linear Motion. — There are many examples which illustrate the motion of a body from one place to another along some sort of path. Thus, a block hoisted by a rope moves directly upward, a stone whirled around at the end of a string describes a circle, and a train traveling between two cities follows the line of track. In each of these cases the body moves along a line, and therefore its motion is said to be *linear*.

The motion of such a body may be studied by observing the body carefully for a period of time, and measuring how far it moves during every second. If the motion of the body is *uniform*, these distances will be found to be equal. For example, if a trolley car having uniform motion passes a certain point at a given instant and passes another point 30 ft. away at the end of one second, it will pass a third point 30 ft. still farther away at the end of the next second, and so on, covering the same distance (namely, 30 ft.) during each second. If shorter time intervals are chosen, the same equality of displacement will be observed. In general, a body is said to have uniform linear motion if it traverses equal distances during equal intervals of time, however brief these intervals may be.

Motion that is both linear and uniform is easy to imagine and is the simplest of all motions to study. Often motion that is linear is not uniform; for example, a falling body is known to travel faster and faster as it approaches the earth. Also, the trolley car above mentioned, after starting from rest, had to acquire the uniform motion referred to, and later will lose that uniform motion when the brakes are applied. Many other cases will doubtless suggest themselves in which uniform motion is preceded and followed by periods of non-uniform motion. Such cases of non-uniform motion are treated in later chapters; for the present, in dealing with uniform motion, it will be assumed that the body has already started from rest and reached a state of uniform motion before any consideration of its motion is begun.

The *speed* of a body having uniform linear motion is defined as *the distance which the body traverses divided by the time required to traverse this distance,* or in equation form,

$$\text{Speed} = \frac{\text{distance covered}}{\text{time needed}}$$

using symbols,

$$v = \frac{s}{t} \tag{10}$$

where v is the speed of the body, s is the space or distance traveled, and t is the time required to travel this distance, these being the symbols commonly used for these quantities.   Since s is measured along a line and is therefore linear, v is called the *linear speed.* From the fact that equal distances are covered in equal intervals of time, it is seen that the ratio of s to t in this equation remains constant; hence, if a body has uniform linear motion, it has a constant linear speed.

The unit in which linear speed is expressed depends upon the units which are used in designating distance and time.   If the distance is stated in miles and the time in hours, the speed, from equation (10), will be given in miles per hour; if instead, the distance is expressed in meters and the time in minutes, the speed will be given in meters per minute.   Any given speed may thus be stated in many different ways, depending on the units selected for distance and for time.   Although all of these may be correct, there are two particular units for linear speed which are used quite generally in scientific and technological work, namely, *feet per second* in British units, and *centimeters per second* in metric units. In expressing speeds of steamships the term *knot* is commonly used; the knot is 1 nautical mile per hour.

Suppose that a racing boat after getting under way crosses the starting line and travels with uniform motion over a 2-mi. course in exactly 4 min. Find the speed of the boat in miles per hour.   Since the boat travels 2 mi. in 4 min., that is, in $\frac{1}{15}$ hr., it would travel 30 mi. in 1 hr. if it continued at the same rate.   The speed of the boat is therefore 30 mi. per hr. The same result is found from equation (10) as follows:

$$v = \frac{s}{t} = \frac{2 \text{ mi.}}{1/15 \text{ hr.}} = 30 \frac{\text{mi.}}{\text{hr.}}$$

A speed expressed in miles per hour may be converted to feet per second by multiplying it by suitable conversion factors, each of which is equal to unity, following the method used in § 2. Thus,

$$30 \frac{\text{mi.}}{\text{hr.}} = \frac{30 \text{ mi.}}{\text{hr.}} \times \frac{5280 \text{ ft.}}{1 \text{ mi.}} \times \frac{1 \text{ hr.}}{60 \text{ min.}} \times \frac{1 \text{ min.}}{60 \text{ sec.}}$$

$$= \frac{30 \times 5280 \text{ ft.}}{3600 \text{ sec.}} = 44 \frac{\text{ft.}}{\text{sec.}}$$

It will be convenient to remember that a speed of 30 mi. per hr. is exactly equal to 44 ft. per sec. in converting from one of these units to the other.

22. Distinction Between Speed and Velocity. — In defining the speed of a body that has uniform motion as the distance which it traverses divided by the time required to traverse this distance, no reference was made to the direction in which the body moves. The *velocity* of a body is a vector quantity having the same magnitude as its *speed*, but including also the *direction* of motion. Thus, in stating the velocity of a body, both the speed and the direction of motion must be included.   If either the speed or the direction is changed, the velocity of the body will be altered. Consider, for example, a body having uniform motion along a curved path; its speed is constant for the motion is specified as uniform, but its velocity nevertheless changes at each instant because of the continual change in direction.   To be sure, the numerical value of its velocity remains unchanged, but the fact that its direction of motion keeps changing from instant to instant means that its velocity is also changing continuously. Equation (10) for the linear speed of a body also gives the numerical value of its linear velocity.

The distinction between speed and velocity applies not only to linear motion but also to angular motion, which will be discussed in the following section.

23. Uniform Angular Motion. — Consider a body spinning about a fixed axis, such as a flywheel rotating in stationary bearings, or a chuck turning in a lathe. The body as a whole, although in motion, does not move from one point to another along a line, and consequently its motion is not linear. The motion of such a rotating body can be studied most easily by referring to a radius drawn from the axis to any point on the body. As the body rotates, this radius sweeps through an angle; for instance, it sweeps through 2π radians or 360° in making one complete revolution.   For this reason, a rotating body is said to have *angular motion*.

If the rotation of a body is *uniform*, measurements will show that it sweeps through the same angle during each second (or each minute, or other convenient interval of time).   For example, if a flywheel having uniform angular motion revolves 40 times in one minute, it will revolve 40 times in the next minute, and so on.   In general, a rotating body has uniform angular motion if it sweeps through equal angles in equal intervals of time, however short. The rotation of the earth, and the motion of the hands of a clock, are familiar examples of uniform angular motion.   It is evident that a rotating body in starting from rest moves slowly at first, turning faster and faster, before it finally reaches a steady state of uniform angular motion.   Such non-uniform angular motion will be discussed in Chapter VI; for the present, consideration will be given only to bodies that have already acquired a state of uniform rotation.

The *angular speed* of a body having uniform angular motion is defined as *the angle through which the body sweeps divided by the time required to sweep through this angle*, that is

$$\text{Angular speed} = \frac{\text{angle swept through}}{\text{time needed}}$$

or
$$\omega = \frac{\theta}{t} \tag{11}$$

where ω (omega) is the angular speed, θ is the angle swept through, and t is the time required to sweep through this angle.   Since equal angles are swept through in equal intervals of time, it follows that the ratio of θ to t is a constant; hence, if a body has uniform angular motion, it has a constant angular speed.

The angular speed of a body can be expressed in several different ways.   For instance, if the angle swept through is expressed in degrees and the time in seconds, the speed, from equation (11), will be given in degrees per second; again, if the angle is expressed in revolutions and the time in minutes, the speed will be given in revolutions per minute (rev. per min.), a unit which is often used by engineers.   In scientific work it is customary to express the angle swept through in radians and the time in seconds, in which case the angular speed is given in radians per second.   Since 1 rev. = 2π radians, it follows that 1 rev. per min. = $2\pi/60$ radians per sec.

Suppose it is desired to find the time required for a wheel to make 10 complete revolutions if it is turning at a constant speed of 80 radians per sec. Transposing equation (11),

$$t = \frac{\theta}{\omega} = \frac{10 \times 2\pi \text{ radians}}{\dfrac{80 \text{ radians}}{\text{sec.}}} = 10 \times 2\pi \text{ radians} \times \frac{\text{sec.}}{80 \text{ radians}} = 0.785 \text{ sec.}$$

24. Relation Between Angular and Linear Speeds.

— When a body is rotating about a fixed axis, the different points on the body describe concentric circles about that axis. Hence, while the body as a whole has angular motion, different points on it move along lines, and so these points have linear motion. A flywheel rotating about a fixed axis O, as shown in Fig. 32, has angular motion, and the points A and B on it have linear motion. The linear speed of point A, located near the rim of the wheel, is greater than that of point B, near the axis, since A moves through a larger circle than does B for each revolution of the wheel.

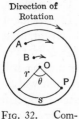

Direction of Rotation

FIG. 32. Comparing linear and angular speeds

A simple relation exists between the angular speed of a rotating body and the linear speed of any point on it. To derive this relation, first find the angular speed of a body in uniform rotation; next find the linear speed of any point on it; and then compare the two speeds. Suppose that the body in Fig. 32 turns through an angle θ radians in t sec.; its angular speed is $\omega = \dfrac{\theta}{t}$ radians per sec. In this time, any point P located at a distance r cm. from the axis travels a distance $s = \theta r$ cm., and consequently its linear speed is $v = \dfrac{s}{t} = \dfrac{\theta r}{t}$ cm. per sec. Combining these results,

$$v = \frac{\theta r}{t} = \frac{\theta}{t} \times r$$

or

$$v = \omega r \qquad (12)$$

Linear speed = angular speed × radius

In this equation, the angular speed ω must be expressed in *radians per unit time*, say radians per second, and the unit for the linear speed v will depend on that used for r. If r is expressed in centimeters, v will be given in centimeters per second, and if r is expressed in feet, v will be given in feet per second. In order to verify the correctness of these units, it will be helpful to recall that a radian is merely the ratio of two distances, an arc and a radius; and thus the term "radians" can be written as $\frac{\text{ft.}}{\text{ft.}}, \frac{\text{cm.}}{\text{cm.}}$, or the like, each ratio being merely a numerical quantity. Thus, introducing metric units in equation (12), and replacing the term "radians" by unity:

$$v = \omega r = \frac{\text{radians}}{\text{sec.}} \times \text{cm.} = \frac{1}{\text{sec.}} \times \text{cm.} = \frac{\text{cm.}}{\text{sec.}}$$

As an example, determine the maximum allowable diameter of a cast-iron flywheel which is to rotate at 90 rev. per min., if the speed of the rim is not to exceed 6000 ft. per min. Transposing equation (12),

$$r = \frac{v}{\omega} = \frac{6000 \frac{\text{ft.}}{\text{min.}}}{\frac{90 \times 2\pi \text{ radians}}{\text{min.}}} = 6000 \frac{\text{ft.}}{\text{min.}} \times \frac{\text{min.}}{90 \times 2\pi \text{ radians}} = 10.6 \text{ ft.}$$

whence the diameter = 2 × 10.6 ft. = 21.2 ft.

25. Relative Motion of Two Bodies. — It is difficult for a person to conceive of absolute motion or of absolute rest, since he can observe only relative motion; that is, the motion of bodies with respect to each other. A person seated in a train at a railroad station and looking out of the window at another train nearby, is often unable to tell whether the train in which he is seated or the other train is in motion when one of them starts; he can observe only that one of them is moving relative to the other. Again, one may say that a house is stationary, a statement which means, of course, that the house does not move with respect to the earth; nevertheless the house is in rapid motion relative to the sun, for it is carried along with the earth as it rotates on its axis and as it moves in its orbit. Moreover, the sun and the whole solar system are not at rest; measurements show that the system is moving through space at about 700 mi. per min. relative to the constellation Hercules.

In ordinary usage the term "velocity of a body" means its velocity with respect to the earth, and the expression "condition of rest" refers to a state of rest with respect to the earth.

Suppose that while a railroad train is running northward at 20 mi. per hr. a man walks through the train at 4 mi. per hr. The man has two velocities simultaneously: one due to his walking and the other due to the motion of the train. If he walks toward the front of the train, these two velocities have the same direction, and his resultant velocity with respect to the earth is 24 mi. per hr. northward. On the other hand, if he walks toward the rear of the train, the two velocities have opposite directions, and his resultant velocity with respect to the earth is only 16 mi. per hr. northward. If he walks in any other direction, the resultant velocity can also be determined, but the methods of adding vectors described in Chapter II must be applied.

Consider, for definiteness, that an object, No. 1, is moving relative to a second object (or medium), No. 2, with a velocity $v_{1 \to 2}$, while the second object is moving relative to a third object, No. 3, with a velocity $v_{2 \to 3}$. Then, the velocity of object No. 1 relative to object No. 3, $v_{1 \to 3}$, will be the vector sum of $v_{1 \to 2}$ and $v_{2 \to 3}$, or symbolically,

$$v_{1 \to 3} = v_{1 \to 2} + v_{2 \to 3} \tag{13}$$

It must be remembered that this expression is only a shorthand statement of a vectorial addition and is not intended to represent an arithmetical addition.

To illustrate, consider a traveling crane such as used in power plants and factories for moving heavy machinery from place to

Fig. 33. A traveling crane for hand operation. (*Courtesy of The Brown Hoisting Machinery Co.*)

place within a building. The crane extends across the width of the building and rolls on tracks supported along the side walls near the eaves, as shown in Fig. 33. A machine can be moved along the crane, crosswise of the building, at the same time that the crane is moving lengthwise of the building. The velocity of the machine with respect to the floor will then be the resultant or vector sum of two separate velocities, that of the machine with respect to the crane, and that of the crane with respect to the floor. Using indicative subscripts, v_{MF} will represent the velocity of the machine with respect to the floor, v_{MC} the velocity of the machine with respect to the crane, and v_{CF} the velocity of the crane with respect to the floor; then *in vector addition*,

$$v_{MF} = v_{MC} + v_{CF}$$

Attention is drawn again to the fact that vector addition takes account of the *directions* of the quantities involved; the equation just stated is true *vectorially* but not *arithmetically*. To evaluate the resultant velocity v_{MF} the separate velocities v_{MC} and v_{CF} must be shown in their proper directions, and may then be added vectorially by the procedures already described in the preceding chapter.

Numerically, suppose that the machine just mentioned is moved along the crane with a velocity $v_{MC} = 3$ ft. per sec., while at the same

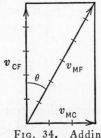

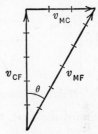

Fig. 34. Adding velocities by the Parallelogram Method

Fig. 35. Adding velocities by the Polygon Method

time the crane is moving at right angles to this direction, its velocity with respect to the floor being $v_{CF} = 5$ ft. per sec. The resultant velocity of the machine with respect to the floor, v_{MF}, is found graphically by the Parallelogram Method in Fig. 34 and by the Polygon (Triangle) Method in Fig. 35. Using a scale and a protractor, the velocity of the machine with respect to the floor is found to be 5.8 ft. per sec. at an angle $\theta = 31°$ with the side walls as shown.

Solving this problem analytically,

$$v_{MF} = \sqrt{v_{MC}{}^2 + v_{CF}{}^2} = \sqrt{3^2 + 5^2} = \sqrt{34} = 5.83 \text{ ft. per sec.}$$

and

$$\theta = \tan^{-1}\frac{3}{5} = \tan^{-1} 0.600 = 30.96°.$$

This gives the velocity of the machine with respect to the floor as 5.83 ft. per sec., in the direction shown, making an angle of 30.96° with the side walls.

*26. Motion of Craft in a Moving Medium. — The principles of relative velocity are applied wherever an object travels through a medium which is itself in motion, for example, the motion of a projectile on a windy day, the flight of an airplane in moving air currents, and the motion of a ship in flowing water. By way of illustration, three problems will be given dealing with the motion of a ship in a stream. Each problem is analyzed, but the numerical solution by the Parallelogram or Polygon Method is left to the student. The term "steered" in these problems denotes the direction in which the ship moves with respect to the water.

I. A ship is steered due west across a stream in which the current is 8 mi. per hr. south. If the ship is moving through the water at 20 mi. per hr., find its velocity with respect to the land.

The velocity of the ship with respect to the water, v_{SW}, is 20 mi.

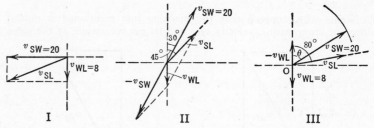

Fig. 36.   Illustrating problems in relative velocity

per hr. toward the west, and that of the water with respect to the land, v_{WL}, is 8 mi. per hr. south. The desired velocity of the ship with respect to the land, v_{SL}, is the vector sum of these two; thus, following equation (13),

$$v_{SL} = v_{SW} + v_{WL}$$

and is shown in diagram I of Fig. 36.

II. A ship moving through the water at 20 mi. per hr. is steered 30° east of north, but is carried by the current so that it actually moves in a direction 45° east of north. Find the speed of the current if its direction is toward the south.

The velocity of the ship with respect to the water, v_{SW}, is 20 mi. per hr. 30° east of north; that of the ship with respect to the land, v_{SL}, is known in direction only, being 45° east of north; and that of the water with respect to the land, v_{WL}, is also known in direction only, and is south. The relation between these velocities is represented by the vector addition $v_{SL} = v_{SW} + v_{WL}$, as before, whence $v_{WL} = v_{SL} - v_{SW}$. This vector subtraction is performed in diagram II of Fig. 36 by drawing v_{SW} and $-v_{SW}$ and showing the directions of v_{SL} and v_{WL}, and then completing a parallelogram starting at the terminal of $-v_{SW}$. The desired speed of the current can be determined by evaluating the vector v_{WL}.

III. In what direction should a ship be steered in order to reach a destination 80° east of north from the ship's position, if it steams through the water at 20 mi. per hr. while the water is flowing due south at 8 mi. per hr.?

The velocity of the ship with respect to the land, v_{SL}, is along the direction 80° east of north; that of the ship with respect to the water, v_{SW}, is 20 mi. per hr. in an unknown direction; and that of the water with respect to the land, v_{WL}, is 8 mi. per hr. south. As before, $v_{SL} = v_{SW} + v_{WL}$, from which $v_{SW} = v_{SL} - v_{WL}$. This problem is represented in diagram III of Fig. 36. First v_{WL} and $-v_{WL}$ are drawn, together with the direction line of v_{SL}. Next, since v_{SW} is known to have a magnitude of 20 mi. per hr., an arc is constructed with O as center having a radius of 20 units, to the same scale as used for v_{WL}. Starting at the terminal of $-v_{WL}$, a line should be drawn parallel to v_{SL} to intersect the arc. The intersection should then be connected to O and the angle θ measured. This angle shows the direction, reckoned from north, in which the ship should be steered.

27. Instantaneous and Average Speeds in Non-Uniform Motion. — The speeds of moving bodies often change from moment to moment. Thus, a motor bus is repeatedly started from rest, speeded up, slowed down, and stopped. Its speed along a highway may be 30 miles an hour at one moment and 50 at another. While these instantaneous speeds, as indicated by the speedometer, are of importance in driving, the average speed over a given period or distance is of importance in maintaining schedules.

The *instantaneous speed* of a body is the distance covered by it during a brief time interval divided by that interval, imagining this interval of time to be infinitesimally small. In short

$$\text{Instantaneous speed} = \frac{\text{infinitesimal distance covered}}{\text{infinitesimal time needed}}$$

Using v to represent instantaneous speed, and ds and dt to represent the extremely short distance and time intervals respectively,

$$v = \frac{ds}{dt} \tag{14}$$

The *average speed* of a body over a definite path or run is the total distance covered divided by the time required to traverse that distance, or

$$\text{Average speed} = \frac{\text{total distance covered}}{\text{total time needed}}$$

Symbolically

$$v_{av} = \frac{s}{t} \tag{15}$$

where v_{av} represents the average speed of a body which travels a distance s during a time interval t.

In the special case where a body moves uniformly, it has the same instantaneous speed at every instant, and its average speed is the same as its constant speed.

The same principles apply in the case of rotation. When a body is rotating, whether uniformly or not, its *average angular speed* ω_{av} over a given period can be found by dividing the total angle θ through which it sweeps by the total time t required to sweep through this angle. In symbols,

$$\omega_{av} = \frac{\theta}{t} \tag{16}$$

By taking shorter and shorter time intervals, a limit is approached in which the *instantaneous angular speed* ω of a rotating body is defined as the ratio of an infinitesimal angle $d\theta$ swept through to the infinitesimal time dt required to sweep through this angle. That is,

$$\omega = \frac{d\theta}{dt} \tag{17}$$

In the special case where a body is rotating uniformly, its instantaneous angular speed stays constant at the average value.

PROBLEMS

1. A world's record for the 100-yd. breast-stroke swim was established in 1931 by Walter Spence, whose time for this event was 1 min. $7\frac{1}{5}$ sec. Assuming the swimmer's motion to have been uniform, calculate his speed over this distance in feet per second and in miles per hour.

2. How long does it take light, traveling at 3×10^{10} cm. per sec., to reach us from the sun, which is 150×10^9 meters away?

3. Calculate the linear speed of the earth in its orbit around the sun, assuming its motion to be uniform; and also the linear speed of a point at the equator due to the rotation of the earth on its axis. The average

radius of the earth is 3958 mi. and the average radius of its orbit is 92,900,-000 mi.

4 Find the cruising radius of a motor boat from the following data: fuel-tank capacity, 75 gal.; fuel consumption, 7 gal. per hr.; speed, 20 mi. per hr.

5. How much longer would it take to travel a distance of 10 mi. at a speed of 40 mi. per hr. than it would at a speed of 60 mi. per hr.?

6. What is the speed in radians per second (a) of a carousel which is observed to make 1 rev. in 7 sec.? (b) of a motor operating at 1800 rev. per min.?

7. The enormous speed of 52,000 radians per sec. was reported in a recent experiment. Find the time required for a rotor revolving at this speed to sweep through a million revolutions.

8. At what time between 12 and 1 o'clock will the two hands of a watch be 1 radian apart?

9. An outboard motor is started by pulling on a rope wound upon a drum 10 in. in diameter. With what speed must the rope be pulled in order to give the drum a speed of 400 rev. per min.?

10. An automobile having wheels 28.7 in. in diameter travels along a straight road at 45 mi. per hr. (a) Compute the angular speed of the wheels in revolutions per minute. (b) Compute also the linear speed of a point on the rim with respect to the axle.

11. A belt is used to drive a pulley 8 in. in diameter from another 10 in. in diameter which revolves 168 times a minute If the belt does not slip on either pulley, find (a) the linear speed of the belt, and (b) the speed of the 8-in. pulley in revolutions per minute.

12. A drum 160 mm. in diameter rotates upon a stationary axle. How many revolutions should it make per minute in order to have a rim speed of 50 mm. per sec.?

13. To measure the speed of a bullet, two carboard disks mounted on a long axle are rotated at a constant speed and the bullet is fired through them parallel to the axle. In a given test, the disks were 36 in. apart and were driven at 1800 rev. per min., and the holes left by the bullet were displaced 18°. Find the speed of the bullet.

14. A mandrel $\frac{3}{4}$ in. in diameter is being turned in a lathe by means of a cutting tool, while revolving at a speed of 200 rev. per min. What is the linear speed of cutting?

15. An automobile going 50 mi. per hr. overtakes and passes another that is going 40 mi. per hr. Compute the distance needed in passing if each car is 12 ft. long. Assume that one car is passing the other so long as any point on it is opposite any point on the other.

16. A body has three component velocities: 5 mi. per hr. toward the east, 12 mi. per hr. toward the south, and 8 mi. per hr. toward the northwest. Find the resultant velocity of the body by the resolution method.

17. A piece of pipe rolls crosswise in a freight car with a speed of 10 ft. per sec., while the car is traveling forward with a speed of 30 mi. per hr. Find the speed of the pipe with respect to the ground.

*18. An airplane has an air speed of 100 mi. per hr. In what direction should the pilot steer the plane in order to reach a point 17° south of east from his present position if the wind is blowing toward the southwest with a speed of 50 mi. per hr.? How long will it take him to reach his destination if it is 500 mi. away?

*19. The current in a river 1 mi. wide flows due east at 3 mi. per hr. A boat leaves the south bank and crosses this river diagonally to a point on the opposite shore $\frac{1}{2}$ mi. downstream from the starting point. If the trip requires 12 min., find how fast the boat moves through the water and in what direction it is steered.

20. Captain George E. T. Eyston established an automobile speed record in September, 1938 at the Bonneville Salt Flats, Utah, by traveling a measured mile northward in 10.10 sec. and southward in 10.04 sec. Determine the average speed in miles per hour and in kilometers per hour.

21. The S. S. Queen Mary established record Atlantic crossings in August, 1938, by covering the distance between Ambrose Lightship in New York Harbor and Bishops Rock, England, westward in 3 days, 21 hours and 48 minutes, and eastward in 3 days, 20 hours and 42 minutes. Determine the average speeds on those two crossings, in which the distances covered were respectively 2907 and 2938 nautical miles.

22. A record flight around the world was made by Howard Hughes and four companions in 1938, covering a distance of 14,824 mi. around the northern hemisphere. He left Brooklyn, N. Y., on Sunday, July 10 at 7:20 P.M., and returned the following Thursday at 2:37 P.M. His time on the ground at six intermediate points totaled 20 hr. and 3 min. Find the average speed of the airplane in flight.

23. Record time was established for the marathon in the 1936 Olympic Games at Berlin by Kitei Son, a 21-year old Japanese. He covered the course of 26 mi., 385 yd. in 2 hr., 29 min., 19.2 sec. What was his average speed during the run?

24. If a person travels one-half the distance to his destination at an average speed of 24 mi. per hr., at what speed must he travel the remaining distance to average 32 mi. per hr. for the whole trip?

*25. A "drifting bottle" was dropped into the Pacific Ocean southwest of Mexico at latitude 14° 19′ North, longitude 106° 25′ West on Jan. 19, 1935, and was found at an island near Taiwan (Formosa) at latitude 22° 00′ North, longitude 121° 30′ East on Jan. 14, 1937. Assuming the drift to be along a great circle, compute the average daily travel of the bottle.

26. If the wheels of an automobile have an over-all diameter of 33 in., how many revolutions do they make while the car advances 1 mi.? Find the average angular speed of the wheels if the car travels 1 mi. in 90 sec.

CHAPTER IV

UNIFORMLY ACCELERATED MOTION

28. Acceleration and Its Units. — Every automobilist speaks of pick-up as one of the requisites of a good motor car. By this he means the rapidity with which the car gains velocity. If the car starting from rest acquires a velocity along a straight highway of 4 ft. per sec. by the end of one second, gains an additional velocity of 4 ft. per sec. during the next second, and so on, the car is said to have a pick-up, or an *acceleration*, of 4 ft. per sec. in each second. By the end of three seconds the car will have a velocity of 12 ft. per sec., and so on, as long as it can maintain the same acceleration. During this period of increasing velocity every conceivable value

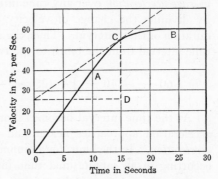

Fig. 37. Acceleration of an automobile

of velocity, from zero up to the maximum reached by the car, is passed through at some instant. The instantaneous velocity values would fall along a curve such as in Fig. 37. The curve is straight from O to A, showing that during the first ten seconds the car gains velocity at a uniform rate; that is, the acceleration is constant. The curve slopes off beyond A, showing that the acceleration is reduced, and becomes horizontal at B, the acceleration then being zero.

The acceleration of a body is defined as the change of its velocity during any interval of time divided by the duration of that interval. Observe that the definition is not based on the distance traversed but on change of velocity. It may be stated in the form of an equation by supposing the motion of a body to be observed for some stated time interval. Taking v_0 as its initial velocity at the beginning of this period and v_f as its final velocity at the end of that

47

period, then the change in velocity is $v_f - v_o$; if this change occurs in a time interval t, the acceleration of the body is

$$a = \frac{v_f - v_o}{t} \qquad (18)$$

or
$$\text{Acceleration} = \frac{\text{final velocity} - \text{original velocity}}{\text{time interval}}$$

Referring again to the performance represented in Fig. 37, the velocity of the car under consideration increases from 40 to 60 ft. per sec. during the time interval from 10 to 25 sec. after starting, but during this period the velocity does not increase uniformly, and therefore the acceleration varies from instant to instant. The *average acceleration* over any time interval can be found, however, by dividing the change of velocity during that interval by the duration of that interval. Thus, the average acceleration over the time interval from the tenth to the twenty-fifth second is

$$\left(60 \frac{\text{ft.}}{\text{sec.}} - 40 \frac{\text{ft.}}{\text{sec.}} \right) \div (25 \text{ sec.} - 10 \text{ sec.}) = 1.33 \frac{\text{ft.}}{\text{sec.}^2}.$$

As the time interval becomes shorter and shorter, the average acceleration approaches nearer and nearer to the *instantaneous acceleration*. In the limit, for an infinitesimal change of velocity dv occurring in an infinitesimal time interval dt, the instantaneous acceleration a is expressed as

$$a = \frac{dv}{dt}$$

Defined tersely, *acceleration is the time rate of change of velocity*. Its value at any particular instant is represented graphically by the slope of the velocity-time curve at the corresponding point. Thus, in Fig. 37, to find the instantaneous acceleration 15 sec. after starting the car, draw a tangent to the curve at point C where it crosses the 15-second ordinate and determine the slope of the tangent. Since $CD = 55 \frac{\text{ft.}}{\text{sec.}} - 26 \frac{\text{ft.}}{\text{sec.}} = 29 \frac{\text{ft.}}{\text{sec.}}$, the slope becomes $29 \frac{\text{ft.}}{\text{sec.}} \div 15 \text{ sec.} = 1.93 \frac{\text{ft.}}{\text{sec.}^2}$ and this value is the instantaneous acceleration at that particular moment.

When the acceleration is constant, its successive instantaneous values are all alike and the same as the average acceleration. In this chapter attention is directed only to motion in which the acceleration is constant.

From the form in which acceleration is expressed, it is clear that any velocity unit divided by any time unit would therefore be an acceleration unit.   The most usual acceleration units are:

feet per second per second,   written $\dfrac{\text{ft.}}{\text{sec.}^2}$

centimeters per second per second,   written $\dfrac{\text{cm.}}{\text{sec.}^2}$

and some other acceleration units used in scientific and engineering work are:

miles per hour per second,   written $\dfrac{\text{mi.}}{\text{hr.} \times \text{sec.}}$

kilometers per hour per second, written $\dfrac{\text{km.}}{\text{hr.} \times \text{sec.}}$

To say that a body has an acceleration of one mile per hour per second means that during every second the velocity of the body increases by one mile per hour.   An acceleration of 10 cm. per sec. per sec. means that during each second the velocity of the body concerned increases by 10 cm. per sec.

29. Equations of Uniformly Accelerated Motion. — The relations which exist between the initial velocity, final velocity, distance covered, acceleration, and the time, in uniformly accelerated motion, may be expressed mathematically by three equations.

I. One of these equations follows from the definition of acceleration, as given in § 28, namely:

$$a = \frac{v_f - v_o}{t} \qquad (18)$$

This may be solved for the final velocity, yielding

$$v_f = v_o + a\,t \qquad (19)$$

wherein v_o = initial velocity, that is, the velocity of the body at
        the moment the consideration of its motion begins,

    v_f = final velocity, that is, the velocity of the body at
        the moment the consideration of its motion ends,

    t = time interval between the two moments mentioned,

and a = acceleration, assumed constant.

The following problems will serve as illustrations:

The speedometer on an automobile was observed to read 25 mi. per hr. at a certain instant, and 8 sec. later was observed to read 49 mi. per hr. Find the acceleration (assumed constant) of the car during this interval. By equation (18), the acceleration is

$$a = \frac{49\,\frac{mi.}{hr.} - 25\,\frac{mi.}{hr.}}{8\,sec.} = \frac{24\,\frac{mi.}{hr.}}{8\,sec.} = 3 \text{ mi. per hr. per sec.}$$

A train which is accelerating at 5 km. per hr. per sec. will acquire what velocity in 8 sec., starting from rest? By equation (19), taking $v_o = 0$, the speed is

$$v_f = 0 + 5\,\frac{km.}{hr. \times sec.} \times 8 \text{ sec.} = 40 \text{ km. per hr.}$$

II. The second equation of accelerated motion expresses the distance traveled by a body having constant acceleration. It is necessary first to ascertain the average velocity of the moving body during the interval desired. This average velocity during the time interval t is the average of the velocities at the beginning and end of the interval, these being v_o and v_f respectively; therefore the average velocity is $v_{av} = \dfrac{v_o + v_f}{2}$. The distance s traversed during the interval is the product of the average velocity and the duration of the interval as mentioned in § 27, namely

$$s = v_{av}\,t = \frac{v_o + v_f}{2}\,t \tag{20}$$

Replacing the value of v_f from equation (19), the distance traversed becomes

$$s = \frac{v_o + (v_o + a\,t)}{2} \times t$$

or

$$s = v_o t + \tfrac{1}{2}a t^2 \tag{21}$$

This equation shows that when a body starts from rest ($v_o = 0$) the distance covered by it in accelerated motion is proportional to the square of the elapsed time. Thus, if the acceleration is 2 ft. per sec. per sec., the distances in feet covered will be given by $s = \tfrac{1}{2} \times 2\,\dfrac{ft.}{sec.^2}\,(t\ sec.)^2 = t^2$; these distances for $t = 1, \dots 5$ sec. are marked off to scale in Fig. 38 and show how much further the object moves each second.

Suppose it is desired to know how far an accelerated object moves during the fifth second after it begins to move, taking its acceleration as 2 ft. per sec. per sec. Since the object has no initial velocity, the distances traversed in 5 and in 4 sec. are respectively

$$s = \frac{1}{2}\left(2\,\frac{\text{ft.}}{\text{sec.}^2}\right)(5\text{ sec.})^2 = 25\text{ ft.}, \quad s = \frac{1}{2}\left(2\,\frac{\text{ft.}}{\text{sec.}^2}\right)(4\text{ sec.})^2 = 16\text{ ft.};$$

consequently, the distance traversed during the fifth second is $25 - 16 = 9$ ft. (Fig. 38).

The foregoing equation for the distance traversed assumes that the motion of the body continues in one direction. When such is not the case as, for example, when a body is projected upward and falls back part way along its path during the interval t, the

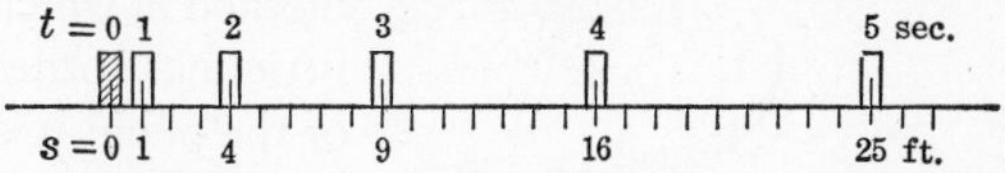

FIG. 38.   Displacements of an object moving with constant acceleration

distance s should be interpreted as the displacement of the body; that is, the distance between its initial and final positions, without regard to the distance actually traversed in moving from one position to the other.

III. The third equation of uniformly accelerated motion is derived from the other two by eliminating the time interval t. This is accomplished by multiplying equations (18) and (20) member by member, as follows:

$$a\,s = \frac{v_f - v_o}{t} \times \frac{v_o + v_f}{2}\,t = \tfrac{1}{2}(v_f - v_o)(v_f + v_o)$$

from which

$$v_f^2 = v_o^2 + 2\,a\,s \tag{22}$$

As an example, the velocity of an automobile as it passes a given point is observed to be 20 mi. per hr., and its velocity as it passes a point 200 ft. further along is 50 mi. per hr. What is the average acceleration of the car? The speeds expressed in miles per hour must first be reduced to feet per second; 20 mi./hr. = 29.3 ft./sec. = v_o, and 50 mi./hr. = 73.3 ft./sec. = v_f. Applying equation (22):

$$a = \frac{v_f^2 - v_o^2}{2s} = \frac{\left(73.3\,\frac{\text{ft.}}{\text{sec.}}\right)^2 - \left(29.3\,\frac{\text{ft.}}{\text{sec.}}\right)^2}{2 \times 200\text{ ft.}} = 11.3\,\frac{\text{ft.}}{\text{sec.}^2}.$$

Collecting the foregoing results for easy reference, the three equations of uniformly accelerated linear motion are:

$$v_f = v_o + a\,t \tag{19}$$

$$s = v_o t + \tfrac{1}{2}\,a\,t^2 \tag{21}$$

$$v_f^2 = v_o^2 + 2\,a\,s \tag{22}$$

These equations should be memorized and experience should be acquired in applying them to the solution of practical problems. Care should be exercised that the units employed are consistent. It will be noted that the first of these equations has no distance term, the second has no final velocity, and the third has no time; therefore the choice of which equation to use in a particular example is apparent.

In catapulting an airplane from a ship, a high acceleration rate must be resorted to in order to gain a sufficient velocity in the necessarily limited runway. Fig. 39 illustrates one method in which relatively little mass other than that of the plane itself need be accelerated. The cradle supporting the airplane is fastened to one end of a cable which passes around two drums, the axis of drum A being fixed and that of drum B being coupled to a piston. When compressed air is admitted suddenly to the cylinder, drum B is forced away from A, and the airplane is accelerated by the cradle.

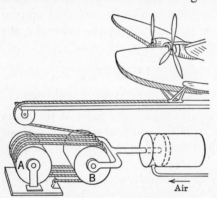

FIG. 39. A method of catapulting an airplane

30. Acceleration Due to Gravity. — Bodies fall to the ground because the earth exerts a pull upon them. This pull, called the force of gravity, causes a body to accelerate while falling. Moreover, all bodies fall with the same acceleration, regardless of their masses, as was first shown experimentally at the Leaning Tower of Pisa by Galileo Galilei (1564–1642), the Italian philosopher and astronomer.

The force of gravity exerted upon a body, and consequently the acceleration due to the earth's attraction, depends upon the distance of the body from the center of the earth, and decreases as this distance increases. The acceleration of a falling body if measured at points above the earth's surface would be found to diminish as the elevation becomes greater. All over the surface of the earth this acceleration is nearly the same. It is slightly greater at the poles than at the equator because the earth is flattened at the poles, its polar radius being 13 miles shorter than its equatorial radius. The rotation of the earth also makes the acceleration of a falling body less at the equator than at the poles because of centrifugal force, § 47. Actual values of the acceleration due to gravity at a few places are given below:

Acceleration due to Gravity at Some Places

	$\frac{\text{ft.}}{\text{sec.}^2}$	$\frac{\text{cm.}}{\text{sec.}^2}$		$\frac{\text{ft.}}{\text{sec.}^2}$	$\frac{\text{cm.}}{\text{sec.}^2}$
Equator at sea level..	32.086	977.99	New York City, N. Y.	32.160	980.23
Paris, France........	32.184	980.96	Rome, Italy.........	32.163	980.32
Berlin, Germany.....	32.193	981.26	San Francisco, Cal...	32.150	979.94
North Pole..........	32.258	983.21	London, England....	32.191	981.19
New Orleans, La.....	32.129	979.31	Madison, Wis........	32.164	980.35

The symbol generally used for the acceleration imparted by the earth is *g* and its numerical value in integral numbers is seen to be

$$g = 32 \text{ ft. per sec. per sec.}$$

or

$$g = 980 \text{ cm. per sec. per sec.}$$

These values may be used in problems unless other values or particular places are specified.

31. Falling Bodies. — The laws of falling bodies may be expressed by the same equations as used for uniformly accelerated motion, except that the acceleration due to gravity *g* is used instead of any acceleration *a*. The equations therefore read:

$$v_f = v_o + g\,t \tag{23}$$

$$s = v_o t + \tfrac{1}{2} g\, t^2 \tag{24}$$

$$v_f{}^2 = v_o{}^2 + 2\,g\,s \tag{25}$$

where v_o is the velocity at the moment consideration of the motion begins, *t* is the time interval, v_f is the velocity at the end of the interval, and *s* is the distance between the initial and final positions of the body in motion. Some direction may arbitrarily be taken as positive, and the opposite direction as negative; + and − signs will be given accordingly to displacement, velocity, and acceleration.

Two problems will illustrate the laws of falling bodies; in both air friction will be neglected, and the downward direction will be regarded as positive.

I. Suppose a ball to be thrown vertically downward with a velocity of 12.4 meters per sec. from a cliff 110 meters high. With what velocity will it strike? and how long will it take to reach the ground? In this problem the initial velocity $v_o = 1240$ cm./sec., and the displacement $s = 11,000$ cm. Applying equation (25) to find the velocity at impact,

$$v_f{}^2 = v_o{}^2 + 2\,g\,s = \left(1240\,\frac{\text{cm.}}{\text{sec.}}\right)^2 + 2\left(980\,\frac{\text{cm.}}{\text{sec.}^2}\right) \times 11,000 \text{ cm.}$$

$$= (1,537,600 + 21,560,000)\,\frac{\text{cm.}^2}{\text{sec.}^2},$$

whence

$$v_f = 4806 \text{ cm. per sec.}$$

Then using equation (23), solve for the time of flight as

$$t = \frac{v_f - v_o}{g} = \frac{4806\,\dfrac{\text{cm.}}{\text{sec.}} - 1240\,\dfrac{\text{cm.}}{\text{sec.}}}{980\,\dfrac{\text{cm.}}{\text{sec.}^2}} = 3.64 \text{ sec.}$$

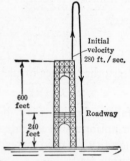

Initial velocity 280 ft./sec.

600 feet

Roadway

240 feet

FIG. 40. Illustrating problem on the flight of a bullet

Consequently the ball will strike the ground in 3.64 sec. with a velocity of 48.06 meters per sec.

II. Imagine a bullet to be fired vertically upward with a velocity of 280 ft. per sec. from the top of a tower of the George Washington Bridge at New York City which is 600 ft. above the water, as indicated in Fig. 40.

(a) How high does the bullet travel?

(b) With what velocity does the bullet pass the roadway of the bridge on its downward descent, the roadway at that part of the bridge being 240 ft. above the water?

(c) What is the velocity of the bullet on reaching the water?

In order to find how far up the bullet will travel, place the final velocity $v_f = 0$ in equation (25), place $v_o = -280$ ft./sec., and solve for s. Thus

$$s = \frac{v_f{}^2 - v_o{}^2}{2g} = \frac{0 - \left(-280\,\dfrac{\text{ft.}}{\text{sec.}}\right)^2}{2 \times 32\,\dfrac{\text{ft.}}{\text{sec.}^2}} = -1225 \text{ ft.}$$

Hence the bullet will travel up 1225 ft. beyond the top of the tower and reach an elevation of 1825 ft. above the water. In descending, the bullet will cover a distance of $1825 - 240 = 1585$ ft. to reach the level of the roadway, and its velocity at that place is obtained from equation (25) by placing the initial velocity $v_o = 0$ and solving for v_f. Thus

$$v_f{}^2 = 0 + 2 \times 32\,\frac{\text{ft.}}{\text{sec.}^2} \times 1585 \text{ ft.} = 101,440\,\frac{\text{ft.}^2}{\text{sec.}^2},$$

from which the velocity of the bullet as it passes the roadway is $v_f = 319$ ft.

per sec. The same equation is used to obtain the velocity with which the bullet strikes the water, but this time $s = 1825$ ft. Thus

$$v_f^2 = 0 + 2 \times 32 \, \frac{\text{ft.}}{\text{sec.}^2} \times 1825 \text{ ft.}$$

from which $v_f = 342$ ft. per sec. It will be noted that the other two equations of falling bodies were not used because they involve the time of flight, and this factor was not called for in the problem.

The acceleration due to gravity is so great that difficulty is experienced in measuring its value directly. However, mechanical means may be employed to lessen the effect of gravity on a particular body by partially counterbalancing it, thereby making it possible to measure the resulting acceleration more accurately. The Atwood's machine makes use of this principle by using two equal masses connected by a tape, Fig. 41, and hung over a large pulley; then putting a rider upon one of them to set the tape in motion. It also has a timing device that consists of a reed vibrating at a known rate and carrying an inked brush; this brush traces a wavy timing curve on the tape. From measurements on the curve, the experimenter can find the distances traversed by the moving system during known intervals of time, and in this way can verify the laws of accelerated motion, and measure the acceleration due to gravity.

32. Combination of Uniform and Accelerated Motions.—An experiment commonly used in the lecture room makes use of two metal balls supported at the same level near the ceiling, one having a compressed spring behind it, and the other having a trap door

Fig. 41. Atwood's machine
(*Courtesy of G. Cussons, Ltd.*)

beneath it.   By closing an electric circuit controlling both spring and door, both are released simultaneously; the spring strikes one ball horizontally and the door opens to allow the other ball to fall freely.   It is found that the two balls strike the floor at the same instant, showing that the horizontal motion imparted to the one ball by the spring did not affect its motion in the vertical direction.

The ball which is projected horizontally follows a curved path, moving both horizontally and vertically at the same time.   *The horizontal motion* of the ball is *uniform*, there being nothing either to speed it up or slow it down along this direction, and is entirely unaffected by the fact that it is falling at the same time.   *The vertical motion is accelerated*, like that of any falling body, and is neither helped nor hindered by the fact that the ball is moving horizontally while falling.   Consequently, the motion of such an object will be studied by regarding it as made up of two parts, one horizontal and the other vertical, and by recognizing the fact that these motions occur *independently* of each other.

To illustrate numerically, suppose that a ball is thrown horizontally from the top of a high building with a velocity of 50 ft. per sec.   The horizontal motion will be uniform and will be determined by equation (10), namely $s = vt$; that is, the distance covered will be equal to the product of the constant velocity and the time of flight.   The vertical motion will be accelerated and will be determined by equations (23) to (25).   During the first second of its flight it will move forward horizontally $50 \times 1 = 50$ ft., and it will fall $\frac{1}{2}g(1)^2 = 16$ ft.   During a 2-second period after projection the ball will travel 100 ft. horizontally and will fall a total of $\frac{1}{2}g(2)^2 = 64$ ft.   The uniform motion horizontally and the accelerated motion vertically result in the following displacements of the ball during the first few seconds:

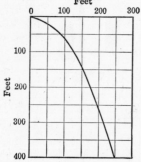

FIG. 42.   Combining accelerated and uniform motions at right angles

Total time in seconds	Horizontal travel in feet	Vertical drop in feet
1	50	16
2	100	64
3	150	144
4	200	256
5	250	400

These values are coordinated in Fig. 42, and the resulting parabola shows the trajectory of the ball.   If the building were just 400 ft. high, the ball would strike the ground at a point 250 ft. from the building.   In the foregoing illustration, air friction was ignored, as heretofore.   The actual distance traversed by the ball, that is, the length of the curve in Fig. 42, has not been determined and is of little interest.

33. Motion of Projectiles. — The composition of two motions, one uniform and the other accelerated, is of constant occurrence in the study of ballistics to determine the range of projectiles and to trace their paths. Two illustrations will explain the procedure; air friction is neglected.

I. A gun fires a projectile at a speed v in a direction θ degrees upward from the horizontal. How far from the gun will the projectile strike the ground? In this problem the first step is to resolve the projection velocity into a vertical and a horizontal component. The time of flight is determined by the vertical component of the projection velocity and the acceleration due to gravity, and can be found by application of the expressions for accelerated motion, § 31. Having found this time interval, the horizontal range of the projectile is ascertained from the horizontal component of the projection velocity by the equation for uniform motion.

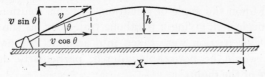

FIG. 43.   Trajectory of a projectile

The vertical component of the projection velocity is $v \sin \theta$ and its horizontal component is $v \cos \theta$, as shown in Fig. 43. If t is the time of flight, as yet unknown, the horizontal distance traversed will be the range $X = v t \cos \theta$. To find the time of flight, use equation (23) selecting some direction, say upward, as positive. First, find the time t_1 in which the projectile reaches the top point of its flight, where its vertical velocity is zero, from the expression $v \sin \theta = g t_1$. During this period t_1 the projectile rises to a height given by equation (24) as $h = (v \sin \theta)t_1 - \frac{1}{2} g t_1^2$, which can be written $h = g t_1^2 - \frac{1}{2} g t_1^2$, or

$$h = \tfrac{1}{2} g t_1^2$$

The time t_2 required for the projectile to return to ground is found from

$$-h = -\tfrac{1}{2} g t_2^2$$

and since h in the last two equations represents the same height, it follows that $t_1 = t_2$, or the time of flight to reach the maximum elevation is the same as the time to drop from that level to the datum plane. The total time of flight is therefore $t = 2t_1$. Combining this result with the first two equations of this derivation, gives the range of the gun as

$$X = vt\cos\theta = 2v t_1 \cos\theta = 2v\left(\frac{v\sin\theta}{g}\right)\cos\theta$$

or

$$X = \frac{v^2}{g}\sin 2\theta$$

Further, by eliminating t_1 from the equations $v\sin\theta = g t_1$ and $h = \frac{1}{2}g t_1^2$, the maximum elevation of the projectile is found to be

$$h = \frac{v^2}{2g}\sin^2\theta$$

It is interesting to note from the foregoing that both the range and the maximum elevation depend upon the square of the projection speed and upon the angle of elevation. In this solution, air friction was neglected, giving a parabolic trajectory, as shown in the figure. If air friction were taken into account, the path of the projectile would be noticeably altered, particularly during the latter part of the flight.

II. Consider a bombing airplane flying with constant velocity v at an elevation s toward its objective O which is being sighted by

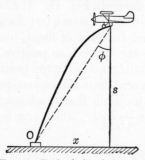

the observer in the plane. At what angle of sight ϕ with respect to the vertical should the observer release a bomb so that it will strike the objective? At the instant the bomb is released it has the same forward velocity as the airplane, and as a result the bomb travels horizontally with constant velocity independently of its accelerated motion toward the earth. In consequence, the bomb will not strike a point on the ground which

Fig. 44. Path of a bomb dropped from an airplane

was directly below the airplane at the moment of release, but will strike beyond that point in the direction of flight by an amount which depends upon the velocity and height of the airplane. This distance subtends an angle ϕ at the observer's position, and is the angle of sight to be solved for. Let t be the time of flight reckoned from the release of the bomb and x the horizontal distance between the plane and the objective O, as represented in Fig. 44. Then the following relations hold:

$$x = s \tan \phi; \quad s = \tfrac{1}{2} g t^2; \quad \text{and} \quad x = v t$$

It is necessary to eliminate herefrom both x and t, for the angle of sight ϕ should depend only on the elevation of the airplane s and its velocity v. Consequently the angle is such that

$$\tan \phi = v \sqrt{\frac{2}{g s}}$$

The substitution of numerical values in this equation will result in data from which curves may be plotted showing the proper angle of sight for any definite altitude and speed.

34. Angular Acceleration. — When a wheel is set into rotation from standstill, it gains angular velocity and ultimately assumes some desired speed. If this final speed is acquired in a short time the wheel is said to have a high *angular acceleration*, and if it takes the wheel a longer time to reach the same final speed the wheel is said to have a lower angular acceleration. The unit commonly used for angular velocity was stated in § 23 as the radian per second.

In general, if the angular velocity of a rotating body changes from ω_o to ω_f in a time interval t, then its angular acceleration is

$$\alpha = \frac{\omega_f - \omega_o}{t} \tag{26}$$

where ω_o is spoken of as the initial angular velocity and ω_f as the final angular velocity. Summarizing, *the angular acceleration of a body is defined as its time rate of change of angular velocity.*

This equation corresponds to equation (18) for linear acceleration, namely $a = \dfrac{v_f - v_o}{t}$, and it will be observed that it has the same form exactly. In consequence, the equations for uniformly accelerated angular motion may be written by analogy with those of § 29 as follows:

$$\omega_f = \omega_o + \alpha t \tag{27}$$

$$\theta = \omega_o t + \tfrac{1}{2} \alpha t^2 \tag{28}$$

$$\omega_f{}^2 = \omega_o{}^2 + 2 \alpha \theta \tag{29}$$

Herein θ is the angular displacement in the time t, α is the angular acceleration, ω_o is the initial angular velocity, and ω_f is the final angular velocity. In applying these equations it is usual to convert revolutions to radians before substituting numerical values.

As an illustration, consider the flywheel of a metal punchpress to have slowed down from 80 rev. per min. to 50 rev. per min. during the 0.7 sec. that it took to punch the metal. What is the angular acceleration (in this case an angular retardation)? Herein

$$\omega_f - \omega_o = (50 - 80)\frac{\text{rev.}}{\text{min.}} \times \frac{2\pi \text{ radians}}{1 \text{ rev.}} \times \frac{1 \text{ min.}}{60 \text{ sec.}} = -\pi\frac{\text{radians}}{\text{sec.}}$$

whence the angular acceleration of the flywheel is given by equation (26) as

$$\alpha = \frac{-\pi\dfrac{\text{radians}}{\text{sec.}}}{0.7 \text{ sec.}} = -4.5 \text{ radians per sec. per sec.}$$

To find the angle turned through by the wheel during the punching operation, apply equation (28), using $\omega_o = (80 \times 2\pi)/60 = 8.37$ radians per sec., $\alpha = -4.5$ radians per sec. per sec., and $t = 0.7$ sec. Then

$$\theta = 8.37\frac{\text{radians}}{\text{sec.}} \times 0.7 \text{ sec.} - \frac{1}{2}(4.5)\frac{\text{radians}}{\text{sec.}^2} \times (0.7 \text{ sec.})^2 = 4.76 \text{ radians.}$$

This corresponds to 272° or about three-fourths of a revolution.

35. Relation Between Angular and Linear Accelerations.— When a rotating body moves with an angular acceleration, any point upon it has a corresponding linear acceleration along a circular path. Expressing the angular acceleration of the body as $\alpha = \dfrac{\omega_f - \omega_o}{t}$ and the linear acceleration of the point as $a = \dfrac{v_f - v_o}{t}$, in accordance with equations (26) and (18), the relation between these quantities can be found by applying the expression $v = \omega r$ as given in equation (12), in which r is the distance from the axis of rotation to the point in question. Substituting,

$$a = \frac{\omega_f r - \omega_o r}{t} = r\left(\frac{\omega_f - \omega_o}{t}\right)$$

or

$$a = r\alpha \tag{30}$$

which states that *the linear acceleration of any point on a rotating body along its circular path is equal to the product of the radius extending to that point and the angular acceleration of the rotating body.*

A comparison of equations (1), (12), and (30), that associate linear and angular quantities, shows that in each case the linear quantity (displacement, velocity, or acceleration) is equal to the radius multiplied by the corresponding angular quantity.

PROBLEMS

1. Express an acceleration of 3 mi. per hr. per sec. in feet per second per second, and in centimeters per second per second.

2. Compute the acceleration of an automobile which acquires a speed of 40 mi. per hr. in 20 sec., starting from rest.

3. An airplane touches the ground at a speed of 56 mi. per hr. and comes to standstill in traveling a distance of 350 ft. What is the average acceleration during this period?

4. The speedometer of an automobile was observed to read 30 mi. per hr. just before the brakes were applied, and the car was brought to rest in 2.8 sec. What was the acceleration? How far did the car go in coming to rest?

5. An automobile traveling at 25 mi. per hr. is stopped in 38.6 ft. when the brakes are applied. In what distance would it stop in slowing down at the same rate from a speed of 50 mi. per hr.?

6. An automobile with good brakes can decelerate at 20 ft. per sec. per sec., but before the driver can apply the brakes he must think of stopping and then move his foot over on the brake pedal. The time which elapses from the instant the driver sees danger until he applies the brakes is called his reaction time, and is $\frac{3}{4}$ sec. for a fairly alert driver under ordinary circumstances. Under these conditions how far will a car go in coming to rest after the driver sees danger, if it is moving initially at 40 mi. per hr.?

7. An airplane is catapulted from a stationary ship to a speed of 90 mi. per hr. from standstill in 1.8 sec. Compute its acceleration.

8. An elevator accelerates upward from rest at 3 ft. per sec. per sec. until it reaches its maximum speed of 700 ft. per min., and then it is brought to a stop with an acceleration (retardation) of 5 ft. per sec. per sec. How far did the elevator rise during this run? How long did this run take?

9. A trolley car starting from rest accelerates at 2 mi. per hr. per sec. for 15 sec., then it coasts for an equal period losing velocity on account of friction at the rate of $\frac{1}{3}$ mi. per hr. per sec., and finally the brakes are applied to bring the car to rest in 5 sec. How far did the car travel during the 35-sec. run?

10. A ball is thrown vertically upward with a speed of 40 ft. per sec. To what maximum height will it rise?

11. In 1886, Steve Brodie dropped from Brooklyn Bridge to the water 160 ft. below. Compute his time of descent and his velocity upon striking.

12. An object is thrown vertically upward with a velocity of 120 ft. per sec. In what direction will it be moving and how far will it be from the starting point at the end of 6.5 sec.?

13. Derive an expression for the distance traveled by a freely falling body during any one second, calling it the nth second.

14. A motion picture of a freely falling ball was taken at the rate of 20 exposures (so-called frames) per second. One of the frames on the film shows the ball as it passes an upper reference point, and the 17th frame beyond shows the ball as it passes the lower reference point, which is 50 ft. below the other one. From what distance above the upper point did the ball start to fall?

15. A book on philosophy (1827) depicts an experiment of finding the depth of a well by dropping a pebble into it. How long after the pebble is dropped will it be heard striking the water if the well is 44 ft. deep? Take the velocity of sound as 1100 ft. per sec.

5/10

16. A cannon ball is fired horizontally with a muzzle velocity of 360 meters per sec. The cannon is located at an elevation of 10 meters above a level terrain. Where will the ball strike the ground?

17. A batted baseball is caught by a player 5 sec. after it was hit. How high did it rise in its flight? Assume the ball to be struck and caught in the same horizontal plane.

18. A bomb is dropped from a dirigible traveling at 70 mi. per hr. at an elevation of 8000 ft. Plot the trajectory of its flight.

19. If a projectile is fired with a velocity of 1000 ft. per sec. at an angle of 30° upward from a level plain, how far from the gun will it strike the ground?

20. A projectile is fired from a gun at a speed of 1800 ft. per sec. to hit a target at the same elevation as the gun 9500 ft. away. In what direction with respect to the horizontal should the gun be aimed?

21. A golf ball is projected with a velocity of 200 ft. per sec. at an angle of 40° upward from a level plain. Find (a) the position and (b) the velocity of the ball at an instant 3 sec. after it is struck.

22. With what speed must a ball be thrown in a direction 45° upward from level ground in order to be caught at a point on the ground 60 ft. away?

23. Derive equations (27) to (29) by using the definition of angular acceleration and following the procedure of § 29.

24. A motor turning at 1200 rev. per min. comes to rest in 30 sec. Find its average angular acceleration (retardation) and the number of revolutions which it makes while stopping.

25. A motor having a 6-in. pulley drives a 12-in. pulley by means of a leather belt. If the motor is brought from rest to a speed of 1800 rev. per min. in 45 sec., compute the acceleration of the 12-in. pulley, assuming that the belt does not slip.

26. The motor of a steel rolling mill reverses from a speed of 90 rev. per min. to an equal speed in the opposite direction in 4 sec. What is the angular acceleration during this interval? How many turns did the motor make during the reversal?

CHAPTER V

FORCE

FUNDAMENTAL PRINCIPLES

36. Effect of Force on Motion. — In the preceding chapter, accelerated motion was studied without any mention of how the acceleration was brought about; the present chapter deals with the agency which produces it. Acceleration is always produced by a *force*. Whenever a body is accelerating, a force must be acting upon it to cause the acceleration. Thus, if a body at rest is to be set into motion, it must be accelerated, and a force must be exerted on it. Again, if a body is in motion, a force must be applied to it in order to speed it up, slow it down, change its direction, or bring it to rest; any change in the velocity of a body means an acceleration, and this acceleration can be produced only by a force acting on the body.

A force has already been described as a push or a pull acting upon a body. A man pushing a lawn mower exerts a force on the lawn mower, a locomotive pulling a train exerts a force on the train, and a book resting on a table exerts a force on the table. In each of these cases it is necessary that the two bodies touch each other; for example, the man must be in contact with the lawn mower in order to exert a force on it. Moreover, as the lawn mower moves, the man must move along also and stay in contact with it if he is to continue to exert a force on it. When a person throws a ball, he exerts a force on it only so long as it stays in contact with his hand. There is, however, an exception continually met with in Mechanics to the principle that one body cannot exert a force on another body unless the two are in contact. This exception is gravitation, by means of which a body, say the earth, exerts a force of attraction on other bodies, whether they are in contact with it or not. This gravitational action was mentioned in Chapter IV, and will be considered more fully later [§ 39].

If a body is accelerating a force must be acting upon it, but it does not necessarily follow that if a force is exerted on a body the body will accelerate. For example, a man may exert a force on a crate, while at the same time friction or some other agent exerts an equal force on it in the opposite direction, in which case the two forces balance each other, and the crate will not accelerate. If, however, all of the forces acting on a body are taken into account, and if these do not balance, then the *unbalanced force* will always cause acceleration. Whenever a body is accelerating, there must be an unbalanced force acting upon it; also, whenever an unbalanced force acts on a body, the body accelerates.

37. Generalizations on Motion; Newton's Laws. — The relation of force to motion has been set forth by Sir Isaac Newton (1642–1727), one of the most profound scientists of all time, who interpreted and correlated many diverse observations in Mechanics and combined the results into three fundamental laws, known as Newton's Laws of Motion. It is impossible to estimate how much these laws have simplified the science of Mechanics, or to state how complex and difficult this subject might be without them. In the following paragraphs, each of these laws is stated in terms of quantities already defined, and is supplemented by a brief discussion.

FIRST LAW. *A body at rest remains at rest, and a body in motion continues to move at constant speed along a straight line, unless the body is acted upon in either case by an unbalanced force.*

The first part of this law is evident from everyday experience; for instance, a book placed on a table remains at rest. In explanation, one might be inclined to say that the book stays at rest simply because no force is being exerted upon it. Further thought shows that this reasoning is not true, since the force of gravity is known to pull it downward and it can be inferred that the table pushes it upward. The fact is that these two forces are equal and opposite, one balancing the other, and the unbalanced or resultant force acting on the book is zero. The book therefore stays at rest because there is no unbalanced force acting on it.

The second part of the law is more difficult to visualize; it states virtually that if a body is set into motion and left to itself, it will keep on moving without any further force being exerted on it. This statement is correct; the body would continue to move without any reduction of velocity if no force acted on it to bring it to rest. However, experience shows that a retarding force is always present on account of friction. A block of wood thrown along a rough road slides a short distance only, because the friction is large; along a floor it would slide further, the friction being smaller; and along a sheet of ice it would slide much further, since in this case the friction is still smaller. From examples like these, it is reasoned that if friction could be eliminated entirely, which cannot be done in practice, a body once set into motion on a level surface would continue to move indefinitely with undiminished velocity. Thus, uniform motion is a natural condition, and maintains itself without the action of any unbalanced force.

Suppose that a horse is drawing a log of wood along the ground at constant speed, and that it is desired to find what forward force he must be exerting on the log if the ground is exerting a backward frictional force of 80 lb. on it. The speed being constant, the unbalanced force acting on the log must be zero, and since the ground exerts a backward force of 80 lb. on the log, the horse must be exerting a forward force of 80 lb. on it. Incidentally, the horse must have exerted more than 80 lb. of force on the log in starting it moving from rest, but upon reaching the observed speed the force must have been reduced to 80 lb., otherwise the log would continue to accelerate, instead of moving at constant speed as stated.

It is interesting to note that whether a body is at rest or moving with constant speed along a straight line, its acceleration in either case is zero. Hence this law means that a body will not have an acceleration unless an unbalanced force acts upon it.

SECOND LAW.—*An unbalanced force acting on a body causes the body to accelerate in the direction of the force, and the acceleration is directly proportional to the unbalanced force and inversely proportional to the mass of the body.*

Expressed mathematically, the law states that

$$a \propto \frac{F}{m}$$

where a is the acceleration of a body of mass m when acted upon by an unbalanced force F. Introducing k as a constant of proportionality,

$$k\,a = \frac{F}{m}$$

To illustrate the meaning of this law, suppose for example, that two identical boxes are being drawn across the floor, and that more force is applied to the first than to the second; it is common experience that the first will have the greater acceleration. Again, suppose that a full box and an empty box are being drawn across the floor, with exactly the same force acting on each; experience shows that the empty one will have the greater acceleration. In general, the greater the unbalanced force and the less the mass, the greater will be the acceleration.

If in the foregoing illustrations a box has been started in motion across the floor, and the applied force is then reduced until it is exactly equal to the backward force of friction which the floor exerts on the box, the box has one force pulling it forward and an equal force pulling it back, and therefore the unbalanced force acting upon it is zero. Hence, the acceleration of the box must be zero; that is, the box will neither speed up nor slow down, and so it will continue to slide with constant speed, as expressed in the First Law.

The opposition which a body offers to any change of motion, whereby an unbalanced force is needed to give it linear acceleration, is known as *inertia*. This property is common to all matter and leads to a broader conception of mass than is given by the definition in § 9. Mass may be considered as *that property of an object by virtue of which it possesses inertia.*

If a body is given linear acceleration without rotation, the unbalanced force producing this acceleration passes through a point called the *center of mass* of the body. For uniform geometrical objects the center of mass coincides with the geometrical center; thus, for a sphere the center of mass is at the center, and for a parallelopiped it is at the intersection of the diagonals. Throughout the present chapter on linear motion, the forces acting upon a body will be assumed to pass through its center of mass.

THIRD LAW.—*For every action, there is an equal and opposite reaction.*

In stating this law, the term "action" means the force which one body exerts on a second body, and "reaction" means the force which the second body exerts on the first. A useful way to express this law is as follows: If body *A* exerts a force on body *B*, then body *B* must exert an equal and opposite force on body *A*.

Some illustrations will clarify the meaning of the law. If a book presses downward on a table with a force of 2 lb., then the table presses upward on the book with a force of 2 lb. Again, if a man pulls on a rope with a force of 50 lb., the rope pulls in the opposite direction on the man with a force of 50 lb. Note that the ability to exert a force depends not only on the agent which is exerting the force, but also on the agent which is supplying the reaction. A truck striking a tree can exert only as much force on the tree as the tree is able to exert against the truck. A golf ball when struck by a club is momentarily distorted, as shown in Fig. 45, and a restoring force is set up in it which reacts upon the club; this impedes the forward motion of the club while the ball is set into flight.

Note that two bodies are involved in each of these transactions, and that the action and reaction are never exerted on the same body. Thus *action and reaction, although equal and opposite, can never balance each other*, since in order for two equal and opposite forces to balance each other, they must be exerted on the same body.

FIG. 45. Distortion of golf ball at impact; the photograph was taken in 1/50,000 second. (*Courtesy of A. G. Spalding & Bros.*)

38. Absolute Units of Force. — Of the three laws of motion discussed in the preceding section, only the Second Law deals quantitatively with the relation between force, mass, and acceleration. To make use of this law in numerical calculations, it is necessary to establish units of force, such as the pound mentioned previously, which will be consistent with the units already adopted for mass and acceleration. Several force units are in common use, each of them being such as to give a particular acceleration to a particular mass, in accordance with the Second Law. The mathematical statement of the law can be written

$$F = k\,m\,a$$

in which a is the acceleration produced in a mass m by an unbalanced force F, and k is a proportionality constant the value of which depends upon the units used in the expression.

Fundamentally, a unit of force is one of such magnitude as to impart unit acceleration to a unit of mass, and such a unit is styled an absolute unit since it does not involve an arbitrary constant. It can be defined, therefore, from the foregoing equation by making k equal to unity and writing

$$F = m\,a \tag{31}$$

so that F will be unity when m and a are units of mass and acceleration respectively.

In British units, the unit mass is 1 lb. and the unit acceleration is $1\dfrac{ft.}{sec.^2}$, and hence the absolute unit of force is 1 lb. $\times\ 1\dfrac{ft.}{sec.^2}$ $=1\dfrac{lb\text{-}ft.}{sec.^2}$. This term "pound foot per second per second" is so long and awkward that it is given a simpler name, the *poundal*. *The poundal is that unbalanced force which acting on a mass of 1 lb. gives it an acceleration of* $1\dfrac{ft.}{sec.^2}$. The term "poundal" can always be replaced by its equivalent, $\dfrac{lb\text{-}ft.}{sec.^2}$.

Similarly, in metric units, the unit mass is 1 gm. and the unit acceleration is $1\dfrac{cm.}{sec.^2}$, and hence the absolute unit of force is $1\dfrac{gm\text{-}cm.}{sec.^2}$, which is called the *dyne*. *The dyne is that unbalanced force which acting on a mass of 1 gm. gives it an acceleration of* $1\dfrac{cm.}{sec.^2}$. The term "dyne" can always be replaced by its equivalent, $\dfrac{gm\text{-}cm.}{sec.^2}$.

To conform to these definitions, the following groups of units will be found consistent in the expression $F = ma$. If the mass m is expressed in pounds and the acceleration a is expressed in feet per second per second, then the unbalanced force F must be expressed in poundals; similarly, if m is expressed in grams and a is expressed in centimeters per second per second, then F must be expressed in dynes. To illustrate the use of these units, two elementary problems will be considered.

I. Suppose that a 10-lb. mass resting on a smooth horizontal surface is acted upon by a horizontal force of 15 poundals, and that the resulting acceleration of this body is to be found. Since the surface is smooth, there is no backward force of friction, and hence the applied force of 15 poundals acts as an unbalanced force on the body. Using equation (31) and remembering that the term "poundals" can be replaced by its equivalent, $\dfrac{lb\text{-}ft.}{sec.^2}$,

$$a = \frac{F}{m} = \frac{15\ poundals}{10\ lb.} = \frac{15\ \dfrac{lb\text{-}ft.}{sec.^2}}{10\ lb.} = 1.5\ \frac{ft.}{sec.^2}.$$

II. Find what horizontal force must be applied to a 10-gm. mass resting on a smooth horizontal plane in order to give it an acceleration of $50\ \frac{\text{cm.}}{\text{sec.}^2}$. From equation (31),

$$F = m\,a = 10\ \text{gm.} \times 50\ \frac{\text{cm.}}{\text{sec.}^2} = 500\ \frac{\text{gm-cm.}}{\text{sec.}^2} = 500\ \text{dynes.}$$

*39. Law of Universal Gravitation. — Newton's investigations in Mechanics were not limited to the facts now incorporated in his three laws of motion, but extended to the general subject of gravitation. He showed that *every body in the universe attracts every other body*, and was also able to show how this attraction is affected by the masses of the bodies and their distance apart. The Law of Universal Gravitation states that *each particle of matter attracts every other particle with a force which is directly proportional to the product of their masses and inversely proportional to the square of the distance between them.* Expressed mathematically,

$$P = G\,\frac{m_1 m_2}{d^2} \tag{32}$$

where m_1 and m_2 are the masses of two particles separated by a distance d, P is the force with which either of these particles attracts the other (in short, the attractive force between the particles), and G is known as the *gravitational constant*. Note that G does not represent the acceleration due to gravity, which is symbolized by g. When P is expressed in dynes, m_1 and m_2 in grams, and d in centimeters, G has the value $6.66 \times 10^{-8}\ \frac{\text{cm.}^3}{\text{gm-sec.}^2}$; thus, two particles each having a mass of 1 gm. when 1 cm. apart attract each other with a force of 6.66×10^{-8} dyne.

The gravitational constant may be measured by means of two metal spheres mounted on a slender rod which is suspended horizontally by a thin wire, with the spheres close to a pair of massive lead globes. Upon moving the globes slightly, the spheres are seen to follow them. The attractive force can be calculated from the amount of twist in the suspension wire, and the masses and distances can be measured directly; these factors determine the value of the gravitational constant.

40. Pull of Gravity; Weight. — The most familiar illustration of universal gravitation is the force of attraction which the earth exerts upon objects near it, by virtue of which a body accelerates downward when it is released and allowed to fall freely. If the body is constrained so that it cannot fall when released, the earth exerts the same force on it, but in this case the pull of the earth is balanced by some equal and opposite force exerted by the restraining agent. Thus, a box resting on a table is pulled downward by the earth, but is pushed upward by the table, and so it stays at rest. If the table were incapable of pushing upward on the box as much as the earth pulls downward on it; that is, if it were not strong enough to support the box; there would then be an unbalanced force acting upon the box which would make it accelerate downward, and the table, being in the way of its motion, would collapse; a result that might be expected in the case of a very heavy box on a frail table. The force of attraction which the earth exerts on a body, that is, the pull of gravity on it, is called the *weight* of the body, and shows how heavy the body is. The weight of a body is therefore a force, and is treated in exactly the same way as any other force. Its direction is toward the center of the earth.

It was shown in § 30 that the acceleration due to gravity varies slightly from point to point on or near the earth's surface; thus if a body were dropped at the pole it would have a slightly greater acceleration than if it were dropped at the equator. The increased acceleration of the body dropped at the pole must be caused by an increased force of gravity acting on it there; in other words, the body must weigh slightly more at the pole than at the equator. This result follows at once from the Law of Universal Gravitation. Since the earth is flattened at the poles, a body located there is nearer the center of the earth than if it were at the equator, thus reducing the distance d in equation (32), and consequently increasing the attraction P.

It is a matter of everyday experience that bodies having different masses also have different weights. A full barrel not only has a larger mass than an empty one, but it also has the larger weight. This result is also to be expected from the Law of Universal Gravitation. In equation (32), if m_1 represents the mass of the earth and m_2 the mass of any other object, then, for any particular value of d, it follows that $P \propto m_2$. Hence, at any given location, the weights of bodies are directly proportional to their masses.

Weight or force is often measured with a spring balance. The body to be weighed is suspended by a spring; as it settles downward the spring stretches and exerts an increasing upward force upon it, and a balance is reached when the restoring force due to the extension of the spring equals the downward pull of gravity. Such a device is calibrated by hanging bodies of known weight on it and marking the corresponding extensions of the spring on a scale. The scale may then be used to furnish a direct reading of any desired weight or force within its range.

41. Gravitational Units of Force. — The underlying principles by which force and acceleration are related are not affected by the units used in applying such relations. Nevertheless, it will be of value to introduce the gravitational units of force by a restatement of these principles, with particular reference to the subject of weight, discussed in the preceding section.

Newton's Second Law of Motion states that the acceleration of a body is directly proportional to the unbalanced force producing it. Thus, if an unbalanced force F acting upon a body gives it an acceleration a, any other unbalanced force F_1 acting upon the same body would impart a different acceleration a_1 such that

$$\frac{F}{F_1} = \frac{a}{a_1}$$

Suppose that the body were released so as to fall freely; the unbalanced force acting upon it would be its weight W, and the acceleration would be that due to gravity, or g; whence, replacing F_1 by W and a_1 by g,

$$\frac{F}{W} = \frac{a}{g} \tag{33}$$

In this expression, a is the acceleration produced by an unbalanced force F acting upon a body of weight W, and g is the acceleration due to gravity.

The form of this equation shows that if the accelerations a and g are expressed in the same units of acceleration, then the forces F and W are to be expressed in the same units of force. In British units, the accelerations are commonly stated in feet per second per second, and the forces in pounds. In metric units, the accelerations are usually stated in centimeters per second per second, and the forces in grams. The pound of force and the gram of force are the so-called gravitational force units.

The *pound of force is the force exerted by the earth on a 1-lb. mass;* that is, it is the weight of a pound of mass. Inasmuch as the weight of a body varies slightly at different places, it is necessary for exactness to specify the location where this weight is measured.

The pound of force is exactly defined as the weight of a pound of mass at 45 deg. latitude and at sea level. For most practical engineering work, slight variations in weight due to differences in location can be neglected and, consequently, for ordinary purposes the pound of force is defined simply as the weight of a pound of mass. For example, a cubic foot of water has a mass of approximately 62.4 lb.; also it is attracted to the earth with a force of approximately 62.4 lb.; that is, it weighs approximately 62.4 lb.

The *gram of force is the force exerted by the earth on a 1-gm. mass;* that is, it is the weight of a gram of mass. Thus, a cubic centimeter of water at 4° C. has a mass of 1 gm. and also has a weight of 1 gm. of force.

To establish the relation between the pound of force and the poundal, suppose a body of 1-lb. mass to be released and to fall freely. The unbalanced force acting upon the body is 1 lb. of force and its acceleration is $32 \dfrac{\text{ft.}}{\text{sec.}^2}$. Hence, a pound of unbalanced force acting upon a mass of 1 lb. gives it an acceleration of $32 \dfrac{\text{ft.}}{\text{sec.}^2}$. Since this acceleration is 32 times as great as that produced in the same body by an unbalanced force of 1 poundal, it follows that *1 lb. of force = 32 poundals.* The ratio $\dfrac{32 \text{ poundals}}{1 \text{ lb.}}$ may be used as a factor to convert pounds of force to poundals.

Similarly, a gram of unbalanced force acting upon a mass of 1 gm. gives it an acceleration of $980 \dfrac{\text{cm.}}{\text{sec.}^2}$; consequently *1 gm. of force = 980 dynes.* The ratio $\dfrac{980 \text{ dynes}}{1 \text{ gm.}}$ may be used as a factor to convert grams of force to dynes.

To illustrate the use of gravitational units, two elementary problems will be considered.

I. Find the acceleration which a horizontal force of 25 lb. will produce in a 100-lb. body resting on a horizontal plane, which exerts a backward

FIG. 46. Calculating the acceleration produced by a force

force of 10 lb. on the body on account of friction. This example is illustrated in Fig. 46, and the solution is visualized by constructing a simple diagram as in part II of the figure. Here the body being studied is indicated at O and the two forces which act upon it are represented by lines drawn to scale, pointing in the appropriate directions. Out of the 25-lb. force applied to the body, 10 lb. is balanced by friction because of the rough surface, and so the resultant or unbalanced force acting on the body is 15 lb. Transposing equation (33), the acceleration is found to be

$$a = \frac{F \times g}{W} = \frac{15\,\text{lb.} \times 32\,\frac{\text{ft.}}{\text{sec.}^2}}{100\,\text{lb.}} = 4.8\,\frac{\text{ft.}}{\text{sec.}^2}.$$

II. How much force must be applied horizontally to a 1-kg. body resting on a smooth horizontal plane, in order to give the body an acceleration of $70\,\frac{\text{cm.}}{\text{sec.}^2}$? Using equation (33) in this problem also,

$$F = \frac{W \times a}{g} = \frac{1000\,\text{gm.}}{980\,\frac{\text{cm.}}{\text{sec.}^2}} \times 70\,\frac{\text{cm.}}{\text{sec.}^2} = 71.4\,\text{gm.}$$

This shows the amount of unbalanced force which must act on the body, and since the plane is smooth, and thus does not exert any backward force on the body, this result also shows how much force must be applied.

42. Comparison of Force Units. — Either the absolute or the gravitational units described in this chapter may be used in calculations, as the following examples will show.

I. Suppose it is desired to find the acceleration produced in a 20-lb. body by an unbalanced force of 5 lb.

In absolute units, 20 lb. is taken as the mass m of the body, and the unbalanced force is $F = 5\,\text{lb.} \times \frac{32\,\text{poundals}}{1\,\text{lb.}} = 160$ poundals; therefore, from equation (31), the acceleration is

$$a = \frac{F}{m} = \frac{160\,\text{poundals}}{20\,\text{lb.}} = \frac{160\,\frac{\text{lb.-ft.}}{\text{sec.}^2}}{20\,\text{lb.}} = 8\,\frac{\text{ft.}}{\text{sec}^2}.$$

Solving the same problem in gravitational units, 20 lb. is taken as the weight W of the body, and since the unbalanced force $F = 5$ lb., the acceleration is found from equation (33) to be

$$a = \frac{F \times g}{W} = \frac{5\,\text{lb.} \times 32\,\frac{\text{ft.}}{\text{sec.}^2}}{20\,\text{lb.}} = 8\,\frac{\text{ft.}}{\text{sec.}^2},\ \text{as before.}$$

II. It is desired to find the acceleration produced in a 1000-gm. body by an unbalanced force of 200 gm.

In absolute units, 1000 gm. is taken as the mass m of the body, and the unbalanced force is $F = 200\,\text{gm.} \times \frac{980\,\text{dynes}}{1\,\text{gm.}} = 196{,}000$ dynes; therefore, from equation (31), the acceleration is

$$a = \frac{F}{m} = \frac{196{,}000\,\text{dynes}}{1000\,\text{gm.}} = \frac{196{,}000\,\frac{\text{gm.-cm.}}{\text{sec.}^2}}{1000\,\text{gm.}} = 196\,\frac{\text{cm.}}{\text{sec.}^2}.$$

Solving the same problem in gravitational units, 1000 gm. is taken as the weight W of the body, and since the unbalanced force F is 200 gm., the acceleration is found from equation (33) to be

$$a = \frac{F \times g}{W} = \frac{200 \text{ gm.} \times 980 \frac{\text{cm.}}{\text{sec.}^2}}{1000 \text{ gm.}} = 196 \frac{\text{cm.}}{\text{sec.}^2}, \text{ as before.}$$

The Usual Units of Force.—Although the foregoing examples show that either the absolute or the gravitational units may be used in calculations, those most frequently used will be employed hereafter in this text, as follows:

In British units, the gravitational units are used, and the acceleration is found from equation (33), $\frac{F}{W} = \frac{a}{g}$, in which both force and weight are in pounds. These are the units used for engineering work in this country.

In metric units, the absolute units are used, and the acceleration is found from equation (31), $F = ma$, in which the force is in dynes and the mass is in grams. These are the units generally used for scientific purposes.

43. Procedure in Problem Work. — In applying the foregoing principles to the solution of practical problems, experience has shown that much difficulty can be avoided by following a definite procedure, at least until a thorough familiarity with the subject has been attained. In any problem involving force and acceleration, the following steps are suggested:

1. Select some one body for consideration, usually the body which is being accelerated.

2. Construct a force diagram, entirely separate from any "space" diagram or picture that may be used to show the conditions of the problem. On this force diagram, let a point represent the body which has been selected, and represent *all* of the forces acting *on* this body by suitable vectors. Be careful that no forces are omitted, and also that only forces acting on the body are used (not forces which the body may be exerting on other things). If any forces are unknown, represent them also by vectors, but mark them as unknown quantities.

3. From the force diagram, find the resultant or unbalanced force acting on the body. When some of the forces are unknown, the expression for the unbalanced force will involve these unknown quantities.

4. Next, find the unknown acceleration or force, by using either equation (31) or equation (33).

5. Finally, use the equations of accelerated motion to find the distance, velocity, or other quantity required in the particular problem being solved.

To illustrate the procedure, find the upward force that must be applied to the cable of a 5-ton elevator in order that the car may have an upward acceleration of $4 \frac{\text{ft.}}{\text{sec.}^2}$ assuming no friction.

The elevator, shown in part I of Fig. 47, is acted upon by two forces: the downward pull of gravity, W, and the unknown upward pull of the cable, P. In part II of the figure, the elevator is indicated at O, and the forces W and P are represented by vectors pointing in the appropriate directions. Since the elevator is to accelerate upward, the upward force P must be greater than the downward force W; and the difference between them, $P - W$, must be the unbalanced force F acting upward on the elevator. From equation (33),

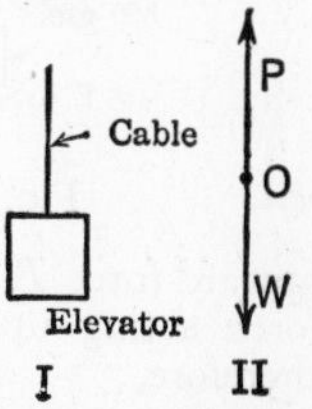

FIG. 47. Finding tension in elevator cable

$$F = \frac{W}{g} \times a$$

where $W = 5 \times 2000 = 10{,}000$ lb., and $g = 32$ ft./sec.^{2} Then taking a as 4 ft./sec.^{2}

$$P - 10{,}000 \text{ lb.} = \frac{10{,}000 \text{ lb.}}{32 \frac{\text{ft.}}{\text{sec.}^2}} \times 4 \frac{\text{ft.}}{\text{sec.}^2} = 1250 \text{ lb.}$$

hence the upward force on the elevator is $P = 10{,}000 + 1250 = 11{,}250$ lb.

Two other illustrations with their analyses follow:

I. A cord passes over a pulley and supports a 500-gm. body at one end and a 400-gm. body at the other end, as in the Atwood's machine, § 31. Find the tension in the cord, assuming that friction is absent, and neglecting the masses of the cord and pulley.

The conditions of the problem are represented in part I of Fig. 48. The 500-gm. mass is acted upon by two forces: the downward pull of gravity, which equals 500 gm. $\times \frac{980 \text{ dynes}}{1 \text{ gm.}} = 490{,}000$ dynes, and the unknown tension T in the cord pulling upward, as shown at O in part II of the figure. Since this mass accelerates downward, the downward force must be greater than the upward force, and the difference between them, namely 490,000 dynes − T, is the unbalanced force acting on the 500-gm. mass. Applying the expression $F = ma$ to this body,

$$490,000 \text{ dynes} − T = 500 \text{ gm.} \times a.$$

This equation cannot be solved by itself since it contains two unknown quantities, T and a.

Next, considering the 400-gm. body, it is found to be acted on by a downward force of 400 gm. $\times \dfrac{980 \text{ dynes}}{1 \text{ gm.}} = 392,000$ dynes, and by an

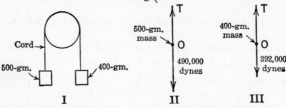

FIG. 48. Motion of two masses hanging from a pulley

upward force T, as indicated in part III of the figure. The excess upward force acting upon this body is consequently $T − 392,000$ dynes, and therefore,

$$T − 392,000 \text{ dynes} = 400 \text{ gm.} \times a.$$

This provides another equation relating the tension in the cord and the acceleration of the moving system.

Solving the two equations simultaneously, the tension T in the cord becomes 435,600 dynes, and the acceleration a of the moving system is found to be 108.9 cm./sec.[2]

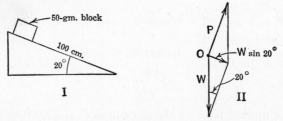

FIG. 49. Block sliding down smooth plane

II. A 50-gm. block starts from rest and slides along a smooth plane inclined 20° with the horizontal. Find its speed after sliding a distance of 100 cm.

A diagram of block and plane is shown in part I of Fig. 49. The block is chosen as the body for consideration, and is represented at O in the force diagram, shown as part II of the figure. Two forces only act on the block: the downward pull of gravity, W, and the outward push of the plane, P. Since the plane is smooth, it can exert no frictional drag on the block along the direction of the plane; the force P is thus known to be at right angles to the plane, but its magnitude is unknown. The direction of the resultant of the two forces W and P is known to be downward along the incline, this being the direction in which the block accelerates. Hence, starting at the lower end of W, construct a parallelogram having W and P for its adjacent sides. The angle indicated in part II of the figure is 20°, its sides being mutually perpendicular to the incline and the base in part I, and the resultant of W and P, which is represented by the concurrent diagonal of the parallelogram, is consequently $W \sin 20°$. This is the unbalanced force F acting on the block.

Since

$$W = 50 \text{ gm.} \times \frac{980 \text{ dynes}}{1 \text{ gm.}} = 49,000 \text{ dynes,}$$

and $F = W \sin 20° = 49,000 \times 0.342 = 16,750$ dynes; it follows from equation (31) that the acceleration is

$$a = \frac{F}{m} = \frac{16,750 \text{ dynes}}{50 \text{ gm.}} = \frac{16,750 \frac{\text{gm-cm.}}{\text{sec.}^2}}{50 \text{ gm.}} = 335 \frac{\text{cm.}}{\text{sec.}^2}.$$

The speed is obtained from equation (22), $v_f{}^2 = v_o{}^2 + 2\,a\,s$, giving

$$v_f{}^2 = 0 + 2 \times 335 \frac{\text{cm.}}{\text{sec.}^2} \times 100 \text{ cm.} = 67,000 \frac{\text{cm}^2}{\text{sec.}^2};$$

from which the speed v_f is found to be 258 cm./sec.

FRICTION

44. Sliding and Rolling Friction. — The surface of any solid if sufficiently magnified would be found rugged and uneven, and these irregularities cause it to oppose the sliding of another surface over it. This opposition is called *sliding friction*. A smooth (that is, frictionless) surface represents an ideal or limiting case which is never attained in practice. It must not be inferred that friction has no useful aspects; indeed, a person could not walk nor a wheel roll on the ground without friction.

It is found by experiment that the amount of friction depends upon the materials which are in contact, the condition of the sliding surfaces, and the force with which they are pressed together. Experiment also shows that the friction is virtually independent of the speed of sliding over a wide range of speeds, and that for any two given bodies, friction depends little, if any, upon the area of the sliding surfaces. As an illustration of the last-mentioned item, a block of iron sliding along a wood plank will encounter practically the same friction when sliding on edge as when sliding on its face. The explanation probably lies in the fact that although there is less surface in contact when the block is on edge, nevertheless, the whole weight of the block being concentrated on this smaller surface, the block and plank are brought into more intimate contact. The amount of friction when a body is starting from rest is somewhat greater than while it is sliding, but for simplicity this effect will be neglected. The foregoing statements are true only approximately, even for dry surfaces.

When a body slides over another body, a force acts upon it which opposes its motion. This force, which is opposite in direction to the motion, is called the *force of friction*. Being a force, it is expressed in the same units, and has the same properties, as any force. Much can be learned about the force of friction by merely sliding a book around to different positions on a table top. It will be noted that the force of friction always acts in the plane of sliding; and that its direction is always opposite to that of the motion. No matter which way the book is moved, the force of friction always acts on it in the opposite direction.

Suppose now that a person exerts a horizontal force of $\frac{1}{4}$ lb. toward the right on the book, but that on account of friction the book does not move. In this case, since the book stays at rest, the unbalanced force acting on it must be zero, and since the experimenter is then exerting a force on it of $\frac{1}{4}$ lb. toward the right, the surface of the table must be exerting a force of friction on it of $\frac{1}{4}$ lb. toward the left. A word of caution might be added at this point. It should not be thought that since the book stays at rest, the force of friction must be greater than $\frac{1}{4}$ lb. at this time, for if the force of friction could be greater than the applied force it would make the book move backward, and this result is absurd.

Next, suppose that the experimenter increases his force on the book from $\frac{1}{4}$ lb. to $\frac{1}{2}$ lb. and that still the book does not move; the force of friction must also have increased to $\frac{1}{2}$ lb. Imagine finally that by increasing the force little by little the book is set into motion, and that a horizontal force of 1 lb. is then found just sufficient to keep it moving with constant speed. For constant speed, the unbalanced force acting on a body is zero, and hence friction is now exerting a force of 1 lb. on the book. It is evident that in this case the force of sliding friction is as great as possible for these particular bodies, but is insufficient to hold the book at rest.

To illustrate the importance of friction, suppose that a man wishes to move a heavy packing case along the floor, the maximum force of friction between the case and the floor being 100 lb. If the man pushes horizontally with a force of 100 lb. on the case he will merely balance friction; he must push harder than this to start it from rest. Thus, if he were to push horizontally with a force of 125 lb., the result would be the same as if he had exerted only 25 lb. with friction absent.

The packing case could have been moved much more easily by rolling it along on two pieces of pipe, replacing the sliding friction by rolling friction, which has a much lower value. Thus, the maximum force of friction might be reduced to perhaps 30 lb., including the effects at both top and bottom of the rollers. Under these circumstances a horizontal push of 30 lb. would balance friction, and any harder push would start the case moving. Rolling friction is the opposition which occurs when one body rolls upon another, and is probably due to slight deformations of the bodies at the point of contact; it is treated in the same way as sliding friction.

45. Coefficient of Friction. — The maximum force of friction which one body is capable of exerting upon another is directly proportional to the normal or perpendicular force with which their surfaces are pressed together. Thus, if f is the maximum force of friction between two bodies which are pressed together with a force N perpendicular to their contacting surfaces, then $f \propto N$, or

$$f = \mu N$$

where the proportionality factor μ (mu) is a quantity which is called the *coefficient of friction* between the surfaces. Transposing, this expression becomes

$$\mu = \frac{f}{N} \tag{34}$$

from which the coefficient of friction is defined as *the ratio of the maximum force of friction between two bodies to the normal force pressing the surfaces together*. It is evident from equation (34), that since f and N are both forces, they may be expressed in any desired force unit, so long as the same unit is used for both, and that μ is a pure numeric, having no unit. Since the frictional force f is always in the plane of sliding, and the normal force N pressing the two surfaces into contact is perpendicular to this plane, it follows that f and N are always at right angles to each other.

The coefficient of sliding friction may be taken as a constant for any two surfaces, depending only on the materials involved and the condition of the surfaces in contact. Some representative values for dry surfaces appear in the accompanying table.

Coefficients of Sliding Friction

Wood on wood..........................	0.25 to 0.5
Metals on wood.......................	0.2 to 0.6
Metals on metals.....................	0.15 to 0.2
Leather on oak.......................	0.27 to 0.38
Leather on metals....................	0.56

For surfaces which are carefully machined and thoroughly lubricated, the coefficient of sliding friction is much smaller, 0.005 being a representative value.

As a typical problem involving sliding friction, consider a sled being drawn on level snow by a constant force of 10 lb. applied at an angle 25° upward from the horizontal. If the sled with its load weighs 60 lb. and if the coefficient of friction between the sled and the snow is 0.05, find the time required to travel 100 ft., starting from rest.

Following the procedure suggested in § 43, the sled, shown in part I of Fig. 50, is chosen as the body to be considered, and is represented at O

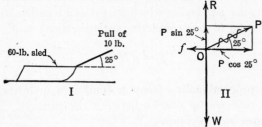

Fig. 50. Sled drawn along horizontal surface

in the force diagram forming part II of the figure. The forces acting on the sled are as follows: the downward pull of gravity, W (60 lb.); the pull P (10 lb.) applied in the direction shown; the upward reaction of the snow, R (unknown); and the backward force of friction, f (also unknown). The pull P is resolved into a horizontal component $P \cos 25° = 10 \times 0.906 = 9.06$ lb., which shows how much of the pull is effective in drawing the sled horizontally, and a vertical component $P \sin 25° = 10 \times 0.422 = 4.22$ lb., which shows how much the sled is being pulled up, reducing its pressure on the snow. The pull P may now be disregarded and may be crossed out, since it is replaced by its components. The net force which the sled exerts downward on the snow is $60 - 4.22 = 55.78$ lb., and hence the upward thrust R of the snow on the sled is also 55.78 lb., this being the normal force between the sliding surfaces. From equation (34), $f = \mu N = 0.05 \times 55.78 = 2.79$ lb. It is noted that the upward forces 55.78 lb. and 4.22 lb. exactly balance the downward force of 60 lb., and thus the unbalanced force acting on the sled is toward the right and amounts to $9.06 - 2.79$ or 6.27 lb. The acceleration of the sled, from equation (33), is consequently

$$a = \frac{F \times g}{W} = \frac{6.27 \text{ lb.} \times 32 \frac{\text{ft.}}{\text{sec.}^2}}{60 \text{ lb.}} = 3.35 \frac{\text{ft.}}{\text{sec.}^2}.$$

Substituting this acceleration value in equation (21)
$$s = v_0 t + \tfrac{1}{2}a t^2 = 0 + \tfrac{1}{2}a t^2$$
the time to travel 100 ft. is found to be
$$t = \sqrt{\frac{2s}{a}} = \sqrt{\frac{2 \times 100 \text{ ft.}}{3.35 \frac{\text{ft.}}{\text{sec.}^2}}} = \sqrt{59.8 \text{ sec.}^2} = 7.73 \text{ sec.}$$

The coefficients of rolling friction are much smaller than for sliding friction; some typical values appear in the accompanying table:

Coefficients of Rolling Friction

Cast-iron wheels on rails............	0.004
Ball bearings in rolling contact......	0.001 to 0.003
Roller bearings in rolling contact....	0.002 to 0.007

It is because rolling friction is so small compared with sliding friction that wheels are used instead of runners on wagons, that gear teeth are designed so as to roll together when meshed, and that for many purposes ball bearings are preferred to those of the sliding, or sleeve, type. In the sleeve bearing the shaft slides, while in the ball bearing it rolls, and although the balls slide somewhat upon each other, the force of friction is much reduced.

In addition to sliding and rolling friction, retardation is also offered to the motion of an object by the air, and this is of particular importance in the propulsion of ships, automobiles, trains, and aircraft. This retardation increases with velocity, and at relatively low speeds is often regarded as being proportional to the velocity. Taking v as the velocity of an object, the retarding force would be expressed as $f \propto v$ or $f = R v$, where R is the proportionality factor which may be termed mechanical resistance. If this frictional force is included in equation (31) for accelerated motion, the total force required to produce an acceleration $a = \dfrac{dv}{dt}$ [§ 28] in a mass m is

$$P = m a + R v = m \frac{dv}{dt} + R v$$

In starting, $v = 0$ and the entire unbalanced force produces acceleration; when the body has accelerated to the maximum speed permitted by the frictional drag, $v = $ constant, $\dfrac{dv}{dt} = 0$, and the entire force is exerted in maintaining the speed acquired against the mechanical resistance. The foregoing equation is useful in studying motion at relatively low speeds; the behavior at high speeds is complicated by the fact that air resistance is then more nearly proportional to the square of the speed.

For further treatment of static, sliding, and rolling friction, and of air resistance, the student is referred to advanced texts.

CIRCULAR MOTION

46. Force Involved in Circular Motion. — In accordance with Newton's First Law of Motion, a moving body left to itself will travel in a straight line; a body will not move around a curve unless a lateral force is exerted upon it. When a locomotive encounters a curve, its forward motion causes the flanges on the wheels to press outwardly against the edge of the outer rail, and consequently the rail presses inwardly against the flanges; the locomotive, under the action of this inward force, undergoes a change of direction and continues to follow the track.

There are many other examples that show the existence of this lateral force which is necessary for motion along a curve. If a stone is whirled around at the end of a cord, it pulls outwardly on the cord, whereupon the cord becomes taut and pulls inwardly upon the stone. In the same way, the earth, in moving along its orbit, is always being drawn inward by the gravitational attraction of the sun. A little thought will show why an automobile sometimes skids when the driver tries to make a sharp turn on a slippery street.

The motion of a body traveling around a circular curve with constant speed is of special interest, for *in such circular motion the moving object acts upon the restraining agent with a constant force directed radially outward from the center; this outward push or pull is called the centrifugal force.* Since for any action there is always an equal and opposite reaction, *the restraining agent exerts an equal inward force upon the moving object, and this is called the centripetal force.* In all motion on curves, the centrifugal and centripetal forces are equal and opposite, and both are exerted in the plane of rotation. *Although equal, these forces cannot balance each other, because they are not exerted upon the same object.*

An unbalanced force always produces acceleration, and thus the centripetal force acting upon a body in circular motion continually accelerates it toward the center of the circle; in fact, it is this inward motion combined with the forward motion that makes the body move in a circle.

47. Centripetal and Centrifugal Force. — In studying the factors upon which centripetal force depends, use will be made of the fact that when a body traverses a circular path with constant speed its velocity changes continually, the change taking place in direction but not in magnitude.

Suppose that a body moves with constant speed v around a circle of radius r as indicated in part I of Fig. 51, and that in a

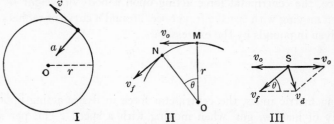

Fig. 51. Pertaining to centripetal acceleration

time interval t it moves a distance $MN = vt$ as shown in part II. Its velocities at M and at N may be represented by vectors v_o and v_f, tangent to the circle at these points respectively and each having the same magnitude as v. These velocities differ in direction, and thus some additional velocity must have been given to the body in moving from M to N, in order to change its velocity from v_o to v_f. To find this additional velocity, draw v_o and v_f from a common point S as in part III of the figure, and subtract v_o from v_f. This result is accomplished by reversing the direction of v_o and proceeding as in addition [§ 14]; the desired change in velocity is found to be v_d, and the acceleration is therefore $a = \dfrac{v_d}{t}.$ The two angles marked θ are equal, and as the time interval is taken shorter and shorter, the sector in part II becomes more and more nearly similar to the isosceles triangle in part III. Hence, in the limit,

$$\frac{v_d}{v_f} = \frac{MN}{OM} \quad \text{or} \quad \frac{at}{v_f} = \frac{vt}{r}$$

Numerically $v_f = v$, and hence the magnitude of the acceleration a is obtained from this equation as

$$a = \frac{v^2}{r} \tag{35}$$

It is evident that acceleration is a vector quantity. In the present instance its direction may be found by observing that the shorter the time interval taken, the more nearly does v_d become perpendicular to v_o and v_f; in the limit it is perpendicular to both of these vectors. Therefore, *the centripetal acceleration is directed toward the center of the circle.*

The force which must be exerted upon the body to produce the acceleration is given in British units by equation (33), $F = \dfrac{W}{g} \times a$; hence, the centripetal force acting upon a body of weight W lb. when moving with speed v ft. per sec. around a curve of radius r ft. is given in pounds by the expression

$$F = \frac{W}{g} \times \frac{v^2}{r} \tag{36}$$

Using metric units, the centripetal force in dynes acting upon a body of mass m gm. when moving with a speed v cm. per sec. around a curve of radius r cm. is found from equation (31), $F = m\,a$, to be

$$F = m\,\frac{v^2}{r} \tag{37}$$

It is interesting to note that the centripetal force acting on a body moving in a circular path varies directly as the square of the speed, and inversely as the radius of the circle. In traveling around a given curve with doubled speed, for example, four times as much centripetal force is brought into play; again, when the same speed is maintained around a curve of half the radius, the centripetal force is doubled.

As an illustrative problem, calculate the centrifugal force exerted by a 30-ton railway car traveling at 75 ft. per sec. around a curve of 1000-ft. radius. Applying equation (36), the centrifugal force is found to be

$$F = \frac{60,000 \text{ lb.}}{32 \ \frac{\text{ft.}}{\text{sec.}}} \times \frac{(75)^2 \ \frac{\text{ft.}^2}{\text{sec.}^2}}{1000 \ \text{ft.}} = 10,500 \text{ lb}_t$$

Again, suppose it is desired to find the centripetal force exerted on a 200-gm. stone whirled in a vertical circle at the end of a string 50 cm. long, at the rate of 3 rev. per sec. In this example,

$$v = \frac{s}{t} = \frac{3 \times 2\pi\,50 \text{ cm.}}{1 \text{ sec.}} = 300\pi \ \frac{\text{cm.}}{\text{sec.}}$$

The centripetal force, by equation (37), is therefore

$$F = 200 \text{ gm.} \times \frac{(300\pi)^2 \frac{\text{cm.}^2}{\text{sec.}^2}}{50 \text{ cm.}} = 3{,}552{,}000 \text{ dynes.}$$

The rotation of the earth causes a reduction in the force with which a body is pulled toward the earth by gravitation. The error due to this cause is greatest at the equator, where it amounts to about 7 lb. per ton, and is zero at the poles. This situation is somewhat like that of a passenger in an elevator which is accelerating downward: the floor of the car tends to fall away from him and so he presses against it with less force than if the elevator were stationary.

48. Banking of Curves. — When an automobile rounds a curve at constant speed, it is accelerating toward the center of the curve, and thus the resultant force acting upon it must also have this

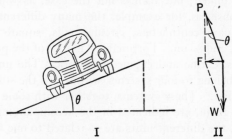

Fig. 52. Car rounding a banked curve

direction. If the highway is level, the only way to get such a force is by means of road friction. In such a case, the central force is likely to be small and uncertain, and the curve must be rounded slowly to avoid skidding. To overcome this difficulty, it is usual to bank curves, by sloping the roadbed upward from the inner to the outer edge; when the angle of banking is correct, a car can round the curve safely at a higher speed without depending upon friction. In Fig. 52, part I represents a car rounding a curve banked at an angle θ, the roadbed being shown in cross-section. Two forces act upon the car: the pull of gravity W downward, and the push P exerted by the road. The latter force is regarded as acting perpendicularly to the roadway in order not to count upon friction. The forces W and P are shown in part II of the figure acting in appropriate directions. These forces must be so proportioned that their resultant, F, is horizontal, this being the centripetal force needed for circular motion around a horizontal curve. Since the two angles marked θ are equal, it follows that

$$\tan \theta = \frac{F}{W} = \frac{\dfrac{Wv^2}{gr}}{W} = \frac{v^2}{gr} \tag{38}$$

and hence the banking angle is $\theta = \tan^{-1} \dfrac{v^2}{gr}$, where v is the speed of the car, g is the acceleration of gravity, and r is the radius of the curve.

UNITS AND DIMENSIONS

*49. Survey of Physical Units. — One of the most difficult matters encountered in beginning the study of Physics, but nevertheless one of the most important, is the subject of units. If there were a single unit for each kind of quantity, the work would be much simplified; but such is not the case, as will be evident when one considers, for example, the many different units used for area: square centimeters, circular mils, square feet, acres, square miles, and so on. Fortunately, not all of the possible units are used in scientific and engineering work. The units that are used widely belong to four systems, with which the student should become familiar. These systems, together with some of the units employed in them, are indicated in the accompanying table. In each system, the different units are so related to one another that

Systems of Units

	Absolute units			Gravitational units		
Quantity	British (f.p.s.)	Metric (c.g.s.)		Quantity	British	Metric
Fundamental				*Fundamental*		
Length.....	ft.	cm.		Length	ft.	cm.
Mass......	lb.	gm.		Force......	lb.	gm.
Time......	sec.	sec.		Time......	sec.	sec.
Derived				*Derived*		
Area.......	ft.^{2}	cm.^{2}		Area.......	ft.^{2}	cm.^{2}
Volume....	ft.^{3}	cm.^{3}		Volume....	ft.^{3}	cm.^{3}
Speed......	ft./sec.	cm./sec.		Speed......	ft./sec.	cm./sec.
Acceleration	ft./sec.^{2}	cm./sec.^{2}		Acceleration	ft./sec.^{2}	cm./sec.^{2}
Force......	poundal	dyne		Mass......	No names assigned	
Energy.....	ft-poundal	erg		Energy.....	ft-lb.	cm-gm.
Power......	ft-poundal/sec.	erg/sec.		Power......	ft-lb./sec.	cm-gm./sec.
(etc.)				(etc.)		

any true equation will hold in any system of units, provided the quantities which appear in it are all expressed in the units of a single system.

Absolute Systems.—The *British absolute system* is based on three fundamental units: the foot as the unit of length, the pound as the unit of mass, and the second as the unit of time; for which reason this system is known as the *foot-pound-second* or *f.p.s.* system. The remaining units in this system, including those for all other mechanical quantities, are derived from the three fundamental units. Thus, instead of arbitrarily choosing the square yard or the acre as the unit of area, recognition is given to the fact that area is fundamentally the square of a length, and since the foot has already been selected as the unit of length, the unit of area becomes the square foot. Similarly unit volume is the cubic foot; unit speed ($v = s/t$) is the foot per second; unit acceleration $[a = (v_f - v_o)/t]$ is the foot per second per second; unit force ($F = ma$) is the pound foot per second per second or poundal, and so on. Note that in solving any equation using this system of units, mass must always be expressed in pounds, acceleration in feet per second per second, and force in poundals. For instance, if a force were given as 10 lb., it would be necessary to convert it to 320 poundals before using it in connection with this system of units.

In a similar manner the *metric absolute system* is based on three fundamental units of length, mass and time, these units being the centimeter, gram, and second respectively; whence this system is called the *centimeter-gram-second* or *c.g.s.* system. For scientific purposes, this system is used more than any other. The remaining units are derived from the fundamental units in the same way as previously described; thus, unit area is the square centimeter, unit volume is the cubic centimeter, unit force is the gram centimeter per second per second or dyne, and so on. In solving an equation using this system of units, mass must always be expressed in grams, acceleration in centimeters per second per second, and force in dynes.

Gravitational Systems.—An examination of the foregoing table shows that the gravitational systems of units differ from the absolute systems in that they employ force as a fundamental quantity instead of mass. They are called gravitational systems because in each of them the unit of force is defined as the attraction of gravity upon a certain mass.

The *British gravitational system* is based on the following fundamental units: the foot as the unit of length, the pound as the unit of force, and the second as the unit of time; and the remaining units are derived from these as already explained. This is the system commonly used in engineering work. The unit of mass in this system is not often used, and no name has been generally adopted for it. Actually, this unit of mass is a mass of 32 lb. (strictly speaking, g lb.), and is sometimes called a "slug" or a "g-pound," but this usage is not general.

Finally, there is the *metric gravitational system*, which is based on the centimeter, gram, and second, as the units of length, force, and time respectively, the remaining units being derived from these, as indicated in the table.

*50. Dimensional Analysis. — The relations among physical quantities can be analyzed apart from the units in which these quantities may be expressed, by a method known as dimensional analysis. This method will be illustrated by reference to the absolute system.

The entities length, mass, and time, are recognized as fundamental concepts, and are represented dimensionally as: length = $[L]$, mass = $[M]$, and time = $[T]$. Since area is essentially the product of two lengths its dimensions are $[L^2]$; similarly, those of volume are $[L^3]$. The dimensions of speed ($v = s/t$) are $[LT^{-1}]$; those of acceleration are similarly $[LT^{-2}]$; and those of force ($F = ma$) are $[LMT^{-2}]$. In this manner, *all mechanical quantities can be expressed in terms of the three fundamental quantities.*

One purpose for which dimensional analysis is useful is in verifying equations for correctness; an equation must have the same dimensions on both sides and thus reduce dimensionally to an identity if it is correct and complete. Thus, an assumed equation $F = \dfrac{Wv^2}{2g}$ under analysis would be written dimensionally as

$$[LMT^{-2}] = \frac{[LMT^{-2}][LT^{-1}]^2}{[LT^{-2}]}$$

the coefficient 2 being omitted because it has no dimensions. The dimensional equation reduces to $[LMT^{-2}] = [L^2MT^{-2}]$, and since this form is not an identity, the assumed equation is incorrect. The equation $F = \dfrac{Wv^2}{gr}$ similarly analyzed would be found correct dimensionally.

PROBLEMS

1. Find the acceleration which will be produced in a 100-lb. body when acted upon by an unbalanced force of 256 poundals.

2. With what steady horizontal force must a man pull a 1-ton boat toward a dock in order to move it through the water 15 ft. in 5 sec., starting from rest, if friction is neglected?

3. In towing a 5-ton truck along a level road, what horizontal force must be exerted to give it an acceleration of 2 ft./sec.^{2}, if friction exerts a backward drag of 8000 poundals upon it?

4. A horizontal force of 5 million dynes is applied continuously to a 20-kg. body, causing it to slide along a horizontal surface. If the body starts from rest and acquires a speed of 600 cm./sec. in sliding 20 meters, find the backward force of friction acting upon it.

*5. Compute the mass of the earth, knowing that at its surface, 6370 km. from the center, it attracts a mass of 1 gm. with a force of 980 dynes.

6. What horizontal force must a locomotive exert on a train weighing 300 tons in order to increase its speed from 10 mi. per hr. to 30 mi. per hr. in 12 sec. along a level track, if the backward force of friction amounts to 8 lb. per ton of weight?

7. A 1.2-kg. metal plate is released and slides vertically downward in grooves which exert an opposing frictional drag of 100 gm. upon it. Find (a) the acceleration of the plate, and (b) the distance that it will fall during the third second after starting from rest.

8. A horizontal force of 10 lb. is applied steadily to a 75-lb. box resting on a level floor. How far will the box slide in 5 sec., neglecting friction?

9. In structural design a usual allowance for steel in tension is 16,000 lb. per sq. in. Express this value in kilograms per square centimeter.

10. The monthly summary of the New York Meteorological Observatory shows that for April, 1939, the air pollution averaged 0.70 ton per cubic mile. Convert this value to milligrams per cubic meter.

11. What steady horizontal pull must be exerted upon a 1000-lb. automobile trailer in order to give it a speed of 15 mi. per hr. in traveling 60 ft., assuming that friction exerts a retarding force of 20 lb. upon it?

12. The heaviest steel rail in regular use by American railroads weighs 152 lb. per yd. Determine the cross-section of this rail, taking 1 cu. ft. of steel to weigh 487 lb.

13. A 90-lb. sled is acted upon by four forces as follows: gravity pulls it downward with a force of 90 lb., the snow pushes it upward with a force of 90 lb., a boy pulls it to the left with a force of 15 lb., and friction exerts a force on it to the right of 9 lb. Find the acceleration of the sled, both in magnitude and direction.

14. A cable exerts an upward pull of $5\frac{1}{2}$ tons on a 5-ton elevator. Find the resulting acceleration of the elevator, if friction is neglected, and how far it will travel in 3 sec., starting from rest.

15. A 600-lb. elevator contains 5 people averaging 145 lb. each. Find the tension in the cable when the elevator ascends with a uniform acceleration of 3.5 ft. per sec. per sec. Find also the tension when the elevator descends with the same acceleration.

16. If an elevator has an upward acceleration of 3 ft./sec.^{2}, find how much force a 150-lb. passenger will exert upon the floor of the car.

17. An elevator which, with its load, weighs 8 tons, is descending with a speed of 900 ft. per min. If the load on the cables must not exceed 14 tons, find the shortest distance in which the elevator should be stopped.

18. A 10-kg. block slides from rest down a smooth plane 200 cm. long inclined 35° with the horizontal. Find the time required to reach the bottom.

19. A block of mass m on a smooth plane inclined at an angle θ with the horizontal is subjected to a steady push P directed upward along the incline. Find the value of P in order that the block, starting from rest, may move up the incline a distance s in time t.

20. A 10-lb. weight and a 6-lb. weight are fastened to opposite ends of a string, and the string is placed over a frictionless pulley. Compute the acceleration of the system.

21. A 5-kg. block is placed on a level table and a string is fastened to it which passes horizontally to a pulley at the edge of the table and thence extends downward to a 1-kg. block suspended from its other end. Find the acceleration of the 5-kg. block if friction is ignored.

22. In a test on an Atwood's machine, § 31, the tape supported a 300-gm. body at one end and a 310-gm. body at the other. When released from rest, the moving system was found to move 72.4 cm. in 3.0 sec. Calculate the acceleration due to gravity at the place where the test was conducted. Also find the tension in the tape.

23. A 30-ton trolley car is moving up a 3% grade, that is, one which rises 3 ft. in a horizontal distance of 100 ft. Find (a) what force must be exerted on it to keep it moving at any constant speed, neglecting friction, and (b) how much more force is needed to give it an acceleration of 1 mi. per hr. per sec.

24. A steady horizontal push of 40 lb. is exerted upon a 120-lb. box, causing it to slide along a level floor. If the coefficient of friction between the box and the floor is 0.25, find the acceleration of the box.

25. A package thrown along a bench with an initial speed of 20 ft./sec. slides to rest in 25 ft. Find the coefficient of friction between the package and the bench.

26. An automobile is going 45 mi. per hr. on a level pavement. If the brakes are applied suddenly, locking the wheels, in what distance will the automobile come to rest? Assume a coefficient of friction of 0.625 between the tires and the pavement.

27. If a block is placed on an inclined plane and the angle which the plane makes with the horizontal is varied, a limiting value will be found, called the limiting angle of repose, at which the block if at rest will remain at rest but if started will slide down the plane with constant speed. Show that the coefficient of friction between block and plane is equal to the tangent of the limiting angle of repose.

28. A box sliding at 25 ft. per sec. encounters a plane inclined 15° upward from the horizontal. How far will it slide up the incline before stopping if the coefficient of friction between the sliding surfaces is 0.35?

29. Find the time required for a 20-kg. box, starting from rest, to slide down a straight chute 1000 cm. long, one end of which is raised 600 cm. above the other, (a) if the chute is smooth, (b) if the chute is rough, the coefficient of friction between box and chute being 0.25.

30. A 500-lb. cake of ice is being drawn up an incline 60 ft. long, which makes an angle of 30° with the horizontal. When 10 ft. from the top the cake slips. Find its speed at the foot of the incline, if the coefficient of friction between the sliding surfaces is 0.1.

31. In moving a 400-lb. motor upstairs, a plank is placed over the steps, making an angle of 40° with the floor, and the motor is drawn up this incline by pulling on a rope in the direction of motion. Assuming the coefficient of friction between motor and plank to be 0.4, what pull must

be exerted on the rope in order that the motor, when once started from rest, may continue to move with constant speed?

32. A horse draws a 400-lb. wagon along a level road at constant speed, by means of traces which make an angle of 10° upward from the horizontal. How hard must he pull if the coefficient of friction is taken as 0.1?

33. A 25-lb. window sash has two ropes at the sides, each rope passing upward over a pulley and each supporting a 12½-lb. counterweight. The counterweights are free to move, the pulleys may be considered frictionless, and the window sash merely rests against the frame. The coefficient of friction between sash and frame is 0.3. In raising the sash with a pole, a central force is exerted upon it in an upward direction at an angle of 15° with the vertical. How much force must be applied in this manner to raise the sash 3 ft. in 2 sec., starting from rest?

34. Calculate the centrifugal force exerted by a 4000-lb. automobile while rounding a curve of 500-ft. radius at 40 mi. per hr.

35. A 500-gm. stone is whirled around in a vertical circle at the end of a string 50 cm. long which has a breaking strength of 10 kg. What is the maximum speed in revolutions per minute, in order that the centrifugal force shall not exceed the breaking strength of the string?

36. A balancing weight of 15 lb. is bolted to an arm of a flywheel at a point 18 in. from the center of the shaft. If the wheel rotates at 360 rev. per min., what force must the bolt which supports the weight be capable of withstanding because of rotation?

37. In the ultra-centrifuge a small quantity of liquid is rotated very rapidly to separate tiny particles suspended in it. If the particles move in a circular path of 7-in. diameter, at what speed must the centrifuge be driven in order to exert a radial force 300,000 times as great as the force of gravity?

38. What is the highest speed at which a 5000-lb. automobile could travel around a curve of 100-ft. radius, if the roadway were level and if the coefficient of friction between the tires and the roadway were 0.25?

39. A ball attached to a cord 20 cm. long travels in a horizontal circle, the cord describing the surface of a cone. Find the speed in revolutions per minute at which the string will stand out at an angle of 30° with the vertical.

*40. The centripetal force on the earth, by which it is constrained to follow its orbit, is provided by the gravitational attraction of the sun [§ 39]. Compute the mass of the sun, taking the earth's orbit as a circle 92,900,000 mi. in radius.

41. Compute the angle of banking of a curve 500 ft. in radius in order that traffic moving at 50 mi. per hr. may round the curve without depending upon friction.

42. If the rails of a railroad track are 4 ft. 8½ in. apart, calculate how much the outer rail must be elevated above the inner one at a curve of 660-ft. radius, in order that a locomotive may press normally against both rails in rounding the curve at 30 mi. per hr.

*43. Refer to equations (19), (21), and (22), and show that in each equation all terms have the same dimensions. Also determine the dimensions of mechanical resistance as expressed in the last equation of § 45.

CHAPTER VI

ROTATIONAL MOTION

51. Relation Between Torque and Angular Acceleration. — The action of a force in producing acceleration was considered in the preceding chapter, and it was found that the acceleration imparted to a body was directly proportional to the unbalanced force acting upon it, and inversely proportional to the mass of the body. This statement, which is Newton's Second Law of Motion, is expressed mathematically by

$$a = \frac{F}{m}$$

where a is the acceleration of the body, F is the unbalanced force upon it, and m is its mass. It was understood throughout the chapter that the force remained unchanged in direction and, in consequence, the acceleration was linear and produced motion in the same direction as the force.

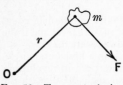

FIG. 53. Torque producing angular acceleration

Now suppose that the force does not act steadily in one direction; specifically, imagine the force F to act on a small mass m attached to some form of crank, Fig. 53, that is pivoted at O, the force being so directed that it always acts at right angles to the crank. Then, of course, the mass will move in a circular path with increasing speed and its linear acceleration will be $a = \frac{F}{m}$. In the meantime the crank of length r will have an increasing angular velocity, its rate of increase or angular acceleration being

$$\alpha = \frac{a}{r}$$

according to § 35. The force acting on the mass produces an amount of torque about the axis O given by

$$T = Fr$$

92

as in § 20.   Merging the three foregoing equations, the torque may be expressed as

$$T = Fr = ma \times r = mr^2\alpha$$

where the product mr^2 is a constant for the particular combination of mass m and crank length r.   Choosing the single letter I for this constant, the angular acceleration of the crank becomes

$$\alpha = \frac{T}{I} \qquad (39)$$

an expression similar in form to that expressing Newton's Law for linear acceleration at the beginning of this section.   The constant I is called the *moment of inertia* of the rotating system; it depends not alone upon the mass m, but also upon its distance r from the center of rotation.

*52. Laws of Angular Motion. — The analogy between the expressions for the linear and angular accelerations in a rotating system, outlined in the preceding section, indicates that the motion of rotating bodies follows laws that are similar to the Laws of Newton for linear motion.   Expressing them in similar fashion, the laws of angular motion are:

First Law.—A body in rotation will continue to turn about a fixed axis with undiminished angular speed unless acted upon by some unbalanced torque.   An example of this law is the rotation of the earth on its axis, making one revolution during each sidereal day.   The attractive force between the sun and the earth acts centrally on the earth and therefore does not affect its angular speed.

Second Law.—A body that is subjected to an unbalanced torque will be accelerated angularly, and the acceleration produced will be proportional to and in the same direction as the torque, and further, the acceleration will be inversely proportional to the moment of inertia of the body about its axis of rotation.   The numerical examples in §§ 53 and 58 illustrate this law.

Third Law.—When a body exerts a torque upon another body, the second exerts an equal torque upon the first in the opposite direction and about the same axis of rotation.   In cranking an automobile, a man exerts a certain torque upon the crank, and the crank exerts an equal and opposite torque upon him.

53. Units for Moment of Inertia. — It has been pointed out in § 51 that a particle of mass m located at a distance r from an axis

of rotation has a moment of inertia with respect to that axis of $I = m\,r^2$. This expression will later be applied to a rigid body comprising many particles located at different distances from the axis, but it will suffice now to point out the fact that the moment of inertia of a rigid body depends not only upon the entire mass of that body but also upon the distribution of the many tiny masses

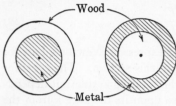

of which it is composed. For example, the two wheels in Fig. 54 are solid disks composed in part of metal and in part of wood. Both wheels have the same radius, and are so designed as to have the same mass. The wheel with the heavy rim is found to require a larger torque than

Fig. 54. Wheels of same size having different moments of inertia

the other to start it spinning, and hence it has the larger moment of inertia. The constant I for a body with reference to a particular axis is independent of the speed of the body and of the forces acting upon it.

Moment of inertia is generally expressed in units of the absolute systems [§ 49]. These units may be found by transposing equation (39) to read

$$I = \frac{T}{\alpha}$$

and substituting appropriate units for the torque T and the angular acceleration α. If T is in dyne-centimeters and α is in radians per second per second, the unit for moment of inertia will be

$$I = \frac{\text{dyne-cm.}}{\dfrac{\text{radians}}{\text{sec.}^2}} = \frac{\dfrac{\text{gm.} \times \text{cm.}}{\text{sec.}^2} \times \text{cm.}}{\dfrac{\text{radians}}{\text{sec.}^2}} = \text{gm-cm.}^2$$

The corresponding unit for moment of inertia in the British system is the pound-foot.² To obtain this unit it is necessary to modify the equation above to read

$$I = \frac{T'g}{\alpha} \tag{40}$$

where T' is the torque in pound-feet and g is the acceleration of gravity in feet per second per second.   Then

$$I = \frac{\text{lb-ft.} \times \dfrac{\text{ft.}}{\text{sec.}^2}}{\dfrac{\text{radians}}{\text{sec.}^2}} = \text{lb-ft.}^2$$

The same result could have been obtained if the torque in the

equation $I = \dfrac{T}{\alpha}$ had been expressed in poundal-ft.   The above-

mentioned units in which I is expressed are those generally used;
in both cases the unit is a mass unit multiplied by the square of a
length unit, or dimensionally $[ML^2]$ (see § 50).   Two examples will
illustrate the application of equations (39) and (40) to problems
involving rotation.

I. A water turbine having a moment of inertia of 250 kg-meters²
comes to rest from a speed of 180 rev. per min. in 26 min. after the gate-
valve is closed.   What is the frictional torque?

To avoid confusion, it is desirable to convert the data to the c.g.s.
system of units, so that moment of inertia will be expressed in gram-
centimeters² and angular acceleration in radians per second per second.
Thus

$$I = 250 \times 1000 \times (100)^2 = 25 \times 10^8 \text{ gm-cm.}^2,$$

and

$$\alpha = \frac{0 - 180 \times 2\pi}{60 \times 26 \times 60} = -\ 0.0121 \text{ radians per sec.}^2$$

Transposing equation (39) and substituting,

$$T = I\alpha = 25 \times 10^8 \text{ gm-cm.}^2 \times \left(-\ 0.0121\ \frac{\text{radians}}{\text{sec.}^2}\right)$$

$$= -\ 303 \times 10^5\ \frac{\text{gm-cm.}^2}{\text{sec.}^2} = -\ 303 \times 10^5 \text{ dyne-cm.}$$

Since a force of 1 gm. = 980 dynes, the frictional torque that brings the
turbine to rest is 30,900 gm-cm. = 0.309 kg-meter.

II. A motor armature is brought from rest to its normal speed of
1200 rev. per min. in 3 sec.   The torque exerted between the current
flowing in the armature conductors and the magnetism of the field structure is 53 lb-ft., and the frictional drag is 3 lb-ft.   Determine the moment
of inertia of the armature.

It took 3 sec. to acquire the normal speed of 1200 rev. per min., or
20 rev. per sec., or 40π radians per sec.; therefore the angular acceleration
is $\dfrac{40\pi}{3} = 41.9$ radians per sec.² The unbalanced torque is $53 - 3 = 50$ lb-ft.

Applying equation (40), the moment of inertia of the armature is

$$I = \frac{T'g}{\alpha} = \frac{50 \text{ lb-ft.} \times 32\dfrac{\text{ft.}}{\text{sec.}^2}}{41.9\dfrac{\text{radians}}{\text{sec.}^2}} = 38.2 \text{ lb-ft.}^2$$

54. Moments of Inertia of Rigid Bodies. — In order to ascertain how the distribution of mass about the axis of a rotating body influences its moment of inertia, consider a rigid body divided into a number of particles and subject to a torque which produces rotation. Imagine the force which develops this torque to be separated into a number of individual forces which act severally on the particles. Investigate the torque on each particle and the acceleration which it produces, and then

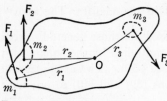

FIG. 55. Determining the moment of inertia of a body

collect the results to find the effect upon the entire body.

A body is shown in Fig. 55 pivoted at O, and several of its particles are indicated by dotted lines. The masses of these particles are marked m_1, m_2, m_3, $\cdots$, their radial distances from the axis are designated as r_1, r_2, r_3, $\cdots$ respectively, and the forces acting perpendicularly to these distances are denoted by the vectors F_1, F_2, F_3, $\cdots$ respectively. The torque produced by force F_1 acting on particle m_1 is given in § 51 as

$$T_1 = F_1 r_1 = m_1 a_1 r_1 = m_1 r_1^2 \alpha$$

where α, the angular acceleration of the rigid body, is the same for all of its particles, so that there is no need of subscripting it. Similarly, for the other particles, the torques are

$$T_2 = m_2 r_2^2 \alpha \qquad T_3 = m_3 r_3^2 \alpha$$

Designating the total unbalanced torque on the body, namely $T_1 + T_2 + T_3 + \cdots$, merely by T, it follows that

$$T = m_1 r_1^2 \alpha + m_2 r_2^2 \alpha + m_3 r_3^2 \alpha + \cdots$$
$$= [m_1 r_1^2 + m_2 r_2^2 + m_3 r_3^2 + \cdots] \alpha = \Sigma m r^2 \times \alpha$$

where the bracketed expression containing a number of terms of the same type is replaced by the symbolic form $\Sigma m r^2$. The letter Σ (sigma) is used to represent "sum," consequently $\Sigma m r^2$ means the sum of a number of terms, each of which is a mass multiplied by the square of its distance from the axis of rotation. Comparing this result with equation (39), from which the torque is

$$T = I\alpha$$

it is clear that $\Sigma m r^2$ is the quantity previously called the moment of inertia. The derivation also proves that angular acceleration α is proportional to the unbalanced torque T which produces it.

The moment of inertia of a body is equal to the mass of one particle multiplied by the square of its distance from the axis of rotation, plus the mass of another particle multiplied by the square of its distance from the axis, plus $\cdots$ *and so on, until all the particles of the body have been included,* or in symbols

$$I = \Sigma m r^2 \tag{41}$$

This equation explains why the unit of moment of inertia is a mass unit multiplied by the square of a length unit, such as lb-ft.^{2} and kg-meters^2, as used in the problems of § 53.

★55. Computing the Moment of Inertia of a Stick. — The moment of inertia of a single particle of mass m located at a distance r from the axis of rotation is merely $m r^2$, since there is but one particle and no need for summation. In a thin ring the mass is distributed all around the axis but the various particles have the same distance from the axis of rotation, making r constant; thus, the moment of inertia becomes $r^2 \Sigma m = M r^2$, where M is the total mass of the ring. While these values follow directly from the definition of moment of inertia, the application of the expression $I = \Sigma m r^2$ to most geometric shapes requires the methods of calculus, because the correct result is obtained only when the body is considered to be made up of a vast number of particles. An approximation to the value of the moment of inertia of a body may be made, however, by considering the body subdivided into relatively few particles. The method of procedure will be illustrated by determining the moment of inertia of a slim stick about a transverse axis through one end.

As a first approximation consider the entire uniform stick of length l to be just one particle of mass M, as shown in part I of Fig. 56. Then the equation for the moment of inertia reduces to $I = m r^2$, where m is equal to the entire mass M of the stick, and r is the distance $\dfrac{l}{2}$ from the axis of rotation to the center of mass C, which is at the center of the stick since it is uniform in cross-section. The moment of inertia of the stick on this assumption is, therefore,

$$I = M \left(\frac{l}{2}\right)^2 = \frac{1}{4} M l^2 = 0.250 \, M l^2$$

As a second approximation, consider the stick to be divided into two particles of equal mass and centered at C_1 and C_2, as shown in part II of the same figure. In this case $m_1 = m_2 = \dfrac{M}{2}$, $r_1 = \dfrac{l}{4}$, and $r_2 = \dfrac{3}{4}l$. Consequently, the moment of inertia of the stick on this assumption is

$$I = m_1 r_1{}^2 + m_2 r_2{}^2 = \frac{M}{2}\left(\frac{l}{4}\right)^2 + \frac{M}{2}\left(\frac{3l}{4}\right)^2 = \frac{10}{32}M l^2 = 0.313\,M l^2$$

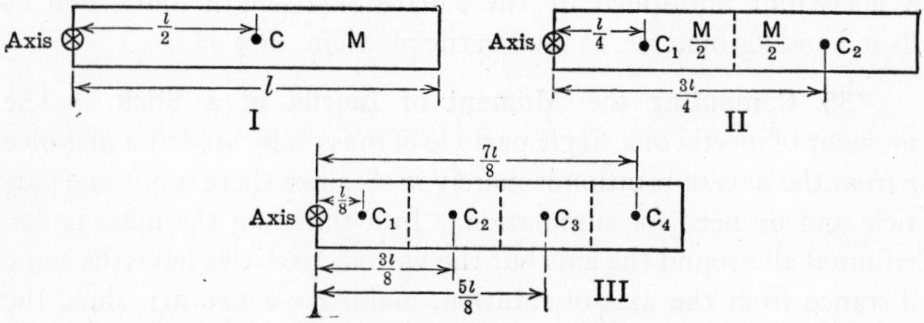

Fig. 56. How moments of inertia are calculated

As a third approximation, assume the stick to be divided further, this time into four equal particles having their centers of mass located at C_1 to C_4 in part III of Fig. 56. Here

$$m_1 = m_2 = m_3 = m_4 = \frac{M}{4}, \quad r_1 = \frac{l}{8}, \quad \cdots r_4 = \frac{7l}{8},$$

and the moment of inertia becomes

$$I = \frac{M}{4}\left(\frac{l}{8}\right)^2 + \frac{M}{4}\left(\frac{3l}{8}\right)^2 + \frac{M}{4}\left(\frac{5l}{8}\right)^2 + \frac{M}{4}\left(\frac{7l}{8}\right)^2$$

$$= \frac{21}{64}\,M l^2 = 0.328\,M l^2.$$

Continuing this process of subdivision into smaller and smaller particles until the stick is divided into an infinitely large number of particles, the ultimate result for its moment of inertia as determined by calculus is

$$I = \tfrac{1}{3}M l^2 = 0.333\,M l^2.$$

In the third approximation in which the stick was divided into quarters, the result was less than 2 per cent below the correct value.

56. Moments of Inertia of Some Shapes. — While the values of the moments of inertia of various geometric shapes will not be derived in this text, the results are easy to understand and to apply; accordingly some useful ones are given in the accompanying table for reference.

Moments of Inertia

Shape	I
Slim rod of mass M and length l, about a transverse axis through one end....................................	$\frac{1}{3}Ml^2$
Same, but transverse axis is through center................	$\frac{1}{12}Ml^2$
Hollow cylinder (thin wall) of mass M, radius r, and of any axial length, about its own axis........................	Mr^2
Solid cylinder or disk of mass M, radius r, and of any axial length, about its own axis............................	$\frac{1}{2}Mr^2$
Solid disk of mass M and radius r about any diameter......	$\frac{1}{4}Mr^2$
Rectangular bar of mass M, length l, and width b, about an axis through its center and at right angles to dimensions b and l...	$\frac{M}{12}(b^2+l^2)$
Solid sphere of mass M and radius r about any diameter. . . .	$\frac{2}{5}Mr^2$

It is often necessary to determine the moment of inertia of a body about an axis that is parallel to another axis about which the moment of inertia of the body is known. Analysis shows that if the moment of inertia of a body of mass M about an axis through its center of mass [§ 37] is I_G, then the moment of inertia about a parallel axis distant a from the first axis is

$$I = I_G + Ma^2 \tag{42}$$

For example, when a solid cylinder rolls on a flat surface it may be necessary to know the moment of inertia of the cylinder about its line of contact with the surface. The moment of inertia about its own axis is $I_G = \frac{1}{2}Mr^2$, and when the axis is shifted parallel to itself a distance r to the line of contact with the surface on which it rolls, the moment of inertia of the cylinder will be $I = \frac{1}{2}Mr^2 + Mr^2 = \frac{3}{2}Mr^2$.

57. Radius of Gyration. — The moment of inertia of a meter stick about an axis through one end perpendicular to the stick can be calculated from the first equation in the table of the preceding section, namely $I = \frac{1}{3}Ml^2$, by taking $l = 100$ cm. Now imagine its entire mass to be concentrated into a single particle that is so located with reference to the axis of rotation that it will have the same moment of inertia as the meter stick itself (Fig. 57). For a single particle the moment of inertia is Mr^2, and consequently to have a moment of inertia of $\frac{1}{3}Ml^2$ the particle must be located at a distance r from the axis such that

$$Mr^2 = \tfrac{1}{3}M l^2$$

from which

$$r = \frac{l}{\sqrt{3}} = \frac{100 \text{ cm.}}{1.732} = 57.7 \text{ cm.}$$

This distance is called the radius of gyration of the meter stick; it is marked off at the bottom of the figure.

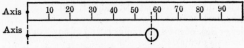

Fig. 57.   Radius of gyration of a meter stick

The radius of gyration of a body is defined as the distance from its axis of rotation to a point at which the entire mass of the body may be considered concentrated without altering the moment of inertia. Calling the mass of the body M and the moment of inertia I, as before, the radius of gyration K will be $K = \sqrt{I/M}$, or the moment of inertia of any body will be

$$I = MK^2 \tag{43}$$

Manufacturers of rotating machinery, such as turbines and generators, indicate the radii of gyration of the rotating elements so that the users may readily compute the moments of inertia of these odd-shaped elements.

58. Typical Problems on Rotation. — Two problems will illustrate the action of torque on rotating bodies of given form.

I. A steel wheel of a gyro-stabilizer is a solid disk 12.5 ft. in diameter and 7.5 in. thick, and a motor brings it up to its operating speed of 600 rev. per min. in 1.5 hr. What torque does the motor exert? In this problem it is necessary to compute the moment of inertia of the wheel knowing that steel weighs 490 lb. per ft.³, and then to determine the angular acceleration during the starting period. From these data the required torque of the motor can be calculated by using equation (39).

The mass of the disk is

$$\pi\left(\frac{12.5}{2} \text{ ft.}\right)^2 \times \frac{7.5}{12} \text{ ft.} \times 490 \frac{\text{lb.}}{\text{ft.}^3} = 37{,}600 \text{ lb.,}$$

and the moment of inertia about its axis is

$$I = \tfrac{1}{2}Mr^2 = \tfrac{1}{2}(37{,}600 \text{ lb.}) \times \left(\frac{12.5}{2} \text{ ft.}\right)^2 = 734{,}000 \text{ lb-ft.}^2$$

The angular velocity of the wheel at full speed is $\dfrac{600}{60} 2\pi = 20\pi$ radians per second, and its angular acceleration during the 1.5-hr. starting period is $\dfrac{20\pi}{3600 \times 1.5} = 0.0116$ radians per sec. per sec. Therefore, the motor must exert a torque of

$$T' = \frac{I\alpha}{g} = \frac{734,000 \text{ lb.-ft.}^2 \times 0.0116 \dfrac{\text{radians}}{\text{sec.}^2}}{32 \dfrac{\text{ft.}}{\text{sec.}^2}} = 266 \text{ lb.-ft.,}$$

by applying equation (40).

II. A wheel and axle has a total weight of 4 kg. and is rotated by a 200-gm. weight fastened to a cord that is wrapped around the 6-cm. axle, as shown in Fig. 58. The weight is observed to fall a distance of 3 meters, starting from rest, in 5.2 sec. Find the radius of gyration of the wheel. In solving this problem, the first step is to determine the linear acceleration of the descending weight and then the tension in the cord. From these data the torque applied to the wheel and axle and its angular acceleration are computed. Finally, the moment of inertia and the radius of gyration of the wheel and axle are obtained.

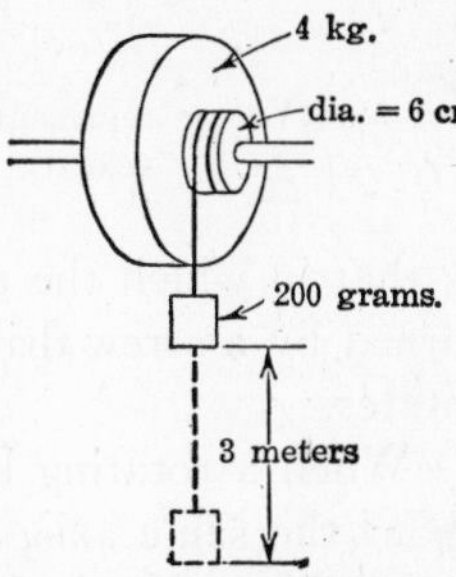

Since the weight starts from rest and covers a distance of 3 meters with uniformly accelerated motion in 5.2 sec., its linear acceleration is

FIG. 58. Radius of gyration of a wheel and axle

$$a = \frac{2s}{t^2} = \frac{2 \times 300 \text{ cm.}}{(5.2 \text{ sec.})^2} = 22.2 \frac{\text{cm.}}{\text{sec.}^2},$$

and the angular acceleration of the wheel having an axle of 3 cm. radius is

$$\alpha = \frac{a}{r} = \frac{22.2 \dfrac{\text{cm.}}{\text{sec.}^2}}{3 \text{ cm.}} = 7.4 \text{ radians/sec.}^2$$

The tension in the cord is ascertained by investigating the forces acting upon the 200-gm. mass. A force of gravity of 200 gm. or $200 \times 980 = 196,000$ dynes acts downward upon this body and the unknown tension P in the cord pulls upward upon it. The unbalanced force of $(196,000$ dynes $- P)$ produces the acceleration of $22.2 \dfrac{\text{cm.}}{\text{sec.}^2}$ in the 200-gm. body. Applying equation (31),

$$196,000 \text{ dynes} - P = 200 \text{ gm.} \times 22.2 \frac{\text{cm.}}{\text{sec.}^2} = 4440 \text{ dynes}$$

from which the tension is found to be $P = 191,560$ dynes, and thus the torque exerted by the cord is $3 \times 191,560 = 574,680$ dyne-cm. This is the unbalanced torque acting on the apparatus, assuming friction as absent, and therefore the moment of inertia of the wheel and axle must be

$$I = \frac{T}{\alpha} = \frac{574,680 \text{ dyne-cm.}}{7.4 \dfrac{\text{radians}}{\text{sec.}^2}} = 77,700 \text{ gm.-cm.}^2,$$

consequently its radius of gyration will be

$$K = \sqrt{\frac{I}{M}} = \sqrt{\frac{77,700 \text{ gm-cm.}^2}{4000 \text{ gm.}}} = 4.4 \text{ cm.}$$

*59. Motion of Precession. — Any angular quantity can be represented vectorially by a line which is directed along the axis of the rotating body, as explained for torque in § 20. Thus, the

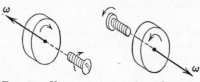

angular velocity of a wheel is represented by an axial line having a length which indicates the numerical value of that velocity according to some suitable scale, as shown by ω in Fig. 59. The direction of this vector is chosen

Fig. 59.   Vector representation of angular velocity

as that in which the usual right-handed screw will advance when turned by a screw driver in the same direction in which the body rotates.

When a rotating body is given an additional angular velocity about the same axis, the resulting velocity will be their algebraic sum.   Thus, if a body rotating at 20 radians per sec. in a clockwise direction were given an additional angular velocity of 3 radians per sec. in a counter-clockwise direction, then its resulting velocity would be 17 radians per sec. clockwise about that axis.   When the added velocity is about a different axis from that of the original rotation, there results an angular motion about a third axis, and this motion is called *precession*.

To explain this type of motion, consider a wheel to be mounted loosely between collars on an axle A, as shown in Fig. 60, and to be set in rotation by some agency not illustrated.   The shaft does not rotate with the wheel and one end of it is set horizontally upon a pivot on the vertical support C, the other end of the shaft being free.   If the wheel were not revolving, the free end of the shaft would drop and the whole system would fall off the vertical support.   But with the wheel revolving, the tendency for the free end of the shaft to drop causes the wheel and shaft to describe horizontal circles about the pivot; that is, the wheel precesses in the horizontal plane.

The angular velocity of the wheel spinning in the direction a about axis A is represented by the vector A' parallel to shaft A in the perspective diagram at the right.   The pull of the earth upon the wheel produces a torque which tends to turn the entire moving system about the axis B in the direction shown by arrow b. This torque sets up an angular acceleration and gives the body an additional angular velocity about axis B which is represented in the vector diagram as B'. If this velocity B' is added to the spin velocity A', both being in the same horizontal plane, the resultant will be R. Accordingly the shaft will shift its position to point in the direction R, turning about the vertical axis C as shown by arrow c. This motion of precession occurs, therefore, about an axis that is perpendicular to both of the other axes A and B. This

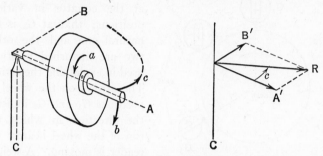

Fig. 60. Precession of a revolving wheel about one end of its axle

motion continues, for as soon as the wheel reaches position R, it is subject to another torque due to the tendency of the free end of the shaft to drop, the corresponding change in angular velocity is at right angles to R, and a new resultant is formed, to which position the shaft progresses; and so on. As described, the shaft would seem to shift in discrete steps, but the process is one of infinitesimally small angular shifts, thus producing a uniform velocity of precession.

It can be shown that the angular velocity of precession Ω (omega) of a wheel is equal to the torque T which tends to change the direction of its axis, divided by the product of the angular velocity ω of the wheel and its moment of inertia I, that is

$$\Omega = \frac{T}{\omega I} \qquad (44)$$

*60. The Gyroscope. — A gyroscope is a wheel and axle supported in gimbal rings so that it can be set in rotation with its axis in any desired direction. When revolving, the wheel maintains its axis in the initial direction in accordance with the first law of angular motion, even though the gyroscope as a whole is moved from one position to another, because the force exerted on the gyroscope is not transmitted through the gimbal rings to produce a torque on the wheel.

The action of the gyroscope as a compass is an application of the addition of two angular velocities in different directions. In

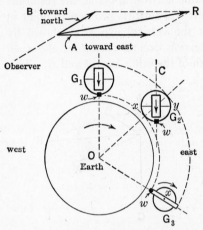

Fig. 61, the earth is viewed from a point in space beyond the south pole, and is seen to revolve in a clockwise direction. The gyroscope is shown at the equator in various positions; that at G_3 is the natural one and the other two are disturbed positions used in explaining the action. The arrows on the wheel in positions G_1 and G_2 indicate the direction in which the rim of the wheel nearest the reader is moving. A weight

Fig. 61. The use of a gyroscope as a compass (The observer is looking northward toward the earth)

is placed on the inner gimbal ring and is shown at w; this, of course, will always seek the position nearest the center of the earth because of the earth's attraction for it, no matter where the gyroscope is situated.

Suppose the gyroscope is placed at position G_1 with its axis directed arbitrarily from east to west. The angular velocity of the rotating wheel is represented by a vector directed axially toward the east; it is shown as A in the vector diagram. As the earth revolves and carries the gyroscope to position G_2, its axis will continue to point eastward, thereby bringing the weight w out of line with the earth's radius. The earth's attraction for this weight sets up a torque which tends to produce clockwise rotation of the gyroscope about an axis perpendicular to the page. The additional angular velocity produced by this torque is represented by a vector directed into the paper; it is shown in perspective as B in the vector diagram. Adding these velocities yields the resultant R as the direction toward which the axis of the wheel turns. Consequently the shaft-end y will move northward (into the paper) and the shaft-end x will move southward (out of the paper); this precessional motion occurs about the axis C. As the gyroscope is carried further by the earth the precession continues until the shaft of the gyroscope becomes parallel to the axis *O* of the earth, with the shaft-end *x* pointing toward the reader as at G_3. When the gyroscope reaches this position the earth's pull on weight *w* will exert no further torque action and the gimbal ring will remain in a plane with the earth's axis (as at G_3).

Thus, the gyroscope wheel will seek a position so that its axis will point north and south, and thereafter maintain that position. This directive action of the earth upon the gyroscope enables this instrument to be used as a compass.   Such a compass indicates the

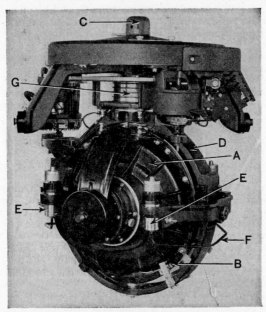

FIG. 62.   Gyro-compass.   (*Courtesy of Sperry Gyroscope Company, Inc.*)

true geographic north-south direction, whereas the magnetic compass points to the magnetic poles of the earth, and is subject to local magnetic variations and to the effects of magnetic materials on vessels.   Fig. 62 shows the assembly of a Sperry gyro-compass. The wheel is the rotating element of an induction motor [§ 296] which revolves upon a horizontal shaft inside a casing *A*, the casing being supported on horizontal bearings within a vertical ring *B*. This ring, in turn, is suspended by a wire from the top point *C* of an outer element *D*, torsion in the wire being prevented by making the outer element follow all movements of the spinning wheel about the vertical axis. The mass upon which the earth exerts its directive influence is composed of two pairs of mercury reservoirs *E E*, each pair being connected by a small tube *F*. Current is supplied to the stator of the motor through the collector rings *G* to drive the rotor at approximately 6000 rev. per min.

PROBLEMS

1. A pulley 10 in. in diameter is brought from rest to a speed of 1200 rev. per min. in 30 sec. Compute the average linear acceleration of a point on its rim during this interval.

2. An unbalanced torque of 65,000 gm-cm. acts upon a circular drum having a mass of 20 kg. and a moment of inertia of 4 kg-meters.² What is the result?

3. A string is fastened to a solid cylinder and is wrapped around the central portion of the cylindrical surface. When the end of the string is held and the cylinder is released, the cylinder descends and unwinds the string. With what acceleration does the cylinder fall?

4. A cylinder having a diameter of 22 cm. and a mass of 20 kg. is rotated in stationary bearings by a steady pull of 100 gm. applied to a cord wound tightly around its rim. How many revolutions will the cylinder make in 4 sec., starting from rest?

5. Find the moment of inertia of a bowling ball, 9 in. in diameter and weighing 16 lb.: (*a*) about an axis through its center, and (*b*) about an axis tangent to the ball.

6. A pendulum consists of a disk and a slim rod in the same plane, the rim of the disk being attached to one end of the rod. The disk has a mass of 4 lb. and a diameter of 6 in.; the rod has a mass of 0.5 lb. and a length of 30 in. Find the moment of inertia of the pendulum about an axis at the free end of the rod and perpendicular to the plane of the disk.

7. A flywheel has a hub 1 ft. in diameter and 1 ft. long, from which extend six rectangular-sectioned spokes each 2 ft. long and 4 in. wide and having an axial length of 3 in.; these spokes join to the rim of the wheel which is 6 in. thick and 1 ft. in axial length. Taking the density of the material as 490 lb. per cu. ft., determine the moment of inertia of the flywheel about its axis.

8. A cylindrical grindstone 20 in. in diameter weighs 52 lb.; it is turned by a handle fastened to a crank at a distance of 8 in. from the center of the grindstone. What steady force applied perpendicularly to the crank will bring the stone to a speed of 150 rev. per min. in 10 sec., ignoring friction?

9. Find the radius of gyration of a meter stick arranged to rotate about a transverse axis through its midpoint.

10. An airplane propeller weighs 58 lb. and has a radius of gyration of 2 ft. Compute its moment of inertia.

11. Determine the radius of gyration of the drum mentioned in Problem 2.

12. An 80-lb. wheel 18 in. in diameter, which is turning at 90 rev. per min. in stationary bearings, is brought to rest by pressing a brake shoe radially against it with a force of 20 lb. If the radius of gyration of the wheel is 6 in., and if the coefficient of friction between the shoe and the rim has the steady value of 0.20, how many revolutions will the wheel make in coming to rest?

13. The armature of a certain motor has a mass of 90 lb. and a radius of gyration of 4 in. How much torque must be applied to this armature in order to give it a speed of 1140 rev. per min. in 20 sec. starting from rest, if friction meanwhile exerts a retarding torque of 2 lb-ft. upon it?

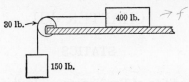

14. A 400-lb. weight slides along a horizontal surface under the pull of a rope to which a 150-lb. weight is fastened, the rope passing over a pulley as shown in the accompanying sketch. The pulley has a mass of 30 lb., a radius at the groove of 6 in., and a radius of gyration of 5 in. The coefficient of friction between the sliding surfaces is 0.2. Find the acceleration of the moving system.

*15. A wheel, mounted on an axle as shown in Fig. 60, has a weight of 6 kg. and its center of mass is 10 cm. from the pivot on the vertical support. The wheel is a solid disk 15 cm. in diameter and revolves at a speed of 720 rev. per min. Determine the velocity of precession in a horizontal plane, neglecting the weight of the axle.

CHAPTER VII

STATICS

61. First Condition of Equilibrium. — In this chapter, a study will be made of bodies which are at rest, and of the requirements which must be fulfilled in order to maintain them in this condition. An object which continues in a state of rest is said to be in static *equilibrium*. A stone lying on the ground and a picture hanging by a cord are at rest, and a body which continues at rest is always in equilibrium.

If an unbalanced force were to act upon a stationary object, it is known that the object would be set into motion. The type of motion which would be produced is called *translation*, and is

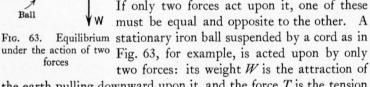

described as such motion of an object that a line connecting any two of its particles remains fixed in direction.

When a body is in equilibrium, there can be no unbalanced force acting upon it, otherwise it would be given motion of translation. If only two forces act upon it, one of these must be equal and opposite to the other. A stationary iron ball suspended by a cord as in Fig. 63, for example, is acted upon by only two forces: its weight W is the attraction of the earth pulling downward upon it, and the force T is the tension in the cord pulling upward upon it. Since the ball is in equilibrium, the tension in the cord is equal to the weight of the ball and the forces T and W shown at O are equal.

Fig. 63. Equilibrium under the action of two forces

When a body is in equilibrium under the action of three forces, it follows that the resultant of any two must be equal and opposite to the third force. Using this principle, the forces necessary to support a body in equilibrium can be found. Suppose, for example, that a ball of weight W is supported by two cords as shown in Fig. 64, part I; the cords A and B make angles of θ and ϕ respectively with the ceiling, and are knotted at O to the vertical cord C. The tension in cord C is equal to the weight of the ball, as in the previous example, and the tensions in cords A and B are to be determined.

Each cord exerts a force on the knot O, and since the knot is at rest, it is in equilibrium under the action of three forces. The forces acting upon it are represented in part II of the figure as follows: the weight of the ball, W, acts directly downward; the tension in cord A (unknown) acts along the direction of A; and the tension in cord B (also unknown) acts along the direction of B. Since the forces must be balanced, the tensions in A and B, if known, would form a resultant W' equal and opposite to W; hence W' may be drawn and the parallelogram constructed, giving T_A as the tension in cord A and T_B as the tension in cord B. The values of T_A and T_B may be found graphically by constructing a diagram as in part II of the figure accurately to scale and measuring the corresponding lengths, or they may be found analytically by means of the Law of Sines. It should not be thought that the shorter cord has the smaller tension; as it hangs more nearly vertical it naturally supports the greater part of the load.

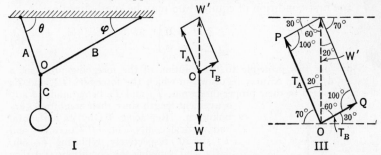

Fig. 64. Equilibrium under the action of three forces

To illustrate the analytical solution, suppose that in the foregoing example, the weight of the ball is $W = 10$ lb., and that the angles which the cords make with the ceiling are $\theta = 70°$ and $\phi = 30°$. To assist in calculating the angles, the parallelogram of part II, Fig. 64, is redrawn in part III. The angles at P and Q are seen to be 100° each. Applying the Law of Sines, and noting that W and W' are numerically equal,

$$\frac{T_A}{W} = \frac{\sin 60°}{\sin 100°} \; ; \quad \frac{T_A}{10 \text{ lb.}} = \frac{\sin 60°}{\cos 10°} \; ,$$

whence the tension in cord A is

$$T_A = \frac{10 \text{ lb.} \times \sin 60°}{\cos 10°} = 8.79 \text{ lb.},$$

and similarly the tension in cord B is $T_B = 3.47$ lb. Thus, in supporting the 10-lb. weight the cords A and B are subjected to tensions of 8.79 lb. and 3.47 lb. respectively.

Generalizing from these illustrations, *the first condition of equilibrium requires that the vector sum of all the forces acting on a body along any direction must equal zero.* This condition must be satisfied to prevent motion of translation.

Resolution into Components.—The study of a body in equilibrium may be simplified by resolving all of the forces which act upon the body into components, and considering the components rather than the forces themselves. The forces may be resolved along any directions desired, but are usually resolved along the horizontal and vertical axes. When a body is in equilibrium, it must be in equilibrium along the horizontal direction, which means that the horizontal components of the forces must balance. Calling components to the right positive and those to the left negative, the algebraic sum of all the horizontal components must be zero. Similarly, the body must be in equilibrium along the vertical direction, which means that the sum of all the vertical components must be zero. Representing the sum of the horizontal components by ΣH, and the sum of the vertical components by ΣV, the first condition of equilibrium may be symbolized as:

$$\left.\begin{array}{r}\Sigma H = 0 \\ \Sigma V = 0\end{array}\right\} \qquad (45)$$

Applying this principle to the solution of the foregoing problem, a diagram as in Fig. 65 may be drawn in which the forces W, T_A, and T_B are represented in their proper directions, T_A and T_B being made of any convenient length since their magnitudes are unknown. Replacing T_A by its horizontal and vertical components of $T_A \cos 70°$ and $T_A \sin 70°$ respectively, replacing T_B similarly, and applying the conditions stated in equations (45),

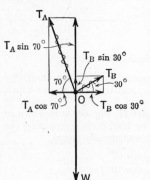

$$\Sigma H = T_B \cos 30° - T_A \cos 70° = 0$$

$$\Sigma V = T_A \sin 70° + T_B \sin 30° - W = 0$$

whence

$$0.866\, T_B = 0.342\, T_A$$

and

$$0.940\, T_A + 0.500\, T_B = 10.$$

FIG. 65. Use of components in study of equilibrium

Upon solving these equations simultaneously, the tension in cord A is found to be $T_A = 8.79$ lb. while that in cord B is $T_B = 3.47$ lb., these results agreeing with those previously found.

The foregoing principles may be extended to cases where a body is in equilibrium under the action of any number of forces, without change in method. The forces referred to throughout this chapter are assumed in each instance to act in a single plane.

62. Second Condition of Equilibrium. — When forces acting upon a body satisfy the first condition of equilibrium, the body will not be given translatory motion, but this fact does not necessarily mean that the body will remain at rest. The forces may act in such a manner as to produce *rotation*, the various particles of the body moving in circles about a fixed axis perpendicular to the plane of the forces. Fig. 66 represents a body acted upon by two equal and opposite forces F_1 and F_2, from which it is evident that $\Sigma H = 0$ and $\Sigma V = 0$, as

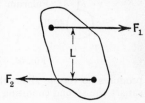

FIG. 66.   Couple acting upon a body

specified in equations (45), and yet this body is not in equilibrium, for there is an unbalanced torque acting upon it which tends to produce rotation. Two equal and opposite forces not acting along the same line constitute a *couple*, and exert a torque which is equal to the product of one of the forces and the perpendicular distance L between their lines of action. To overcome the tendency to rotate, another couple having an equal and opposite torque must be applied to the body. Hence, to provide against rotation, *the second condition of equilibrium requires that the torques acting upon a body shall be balanced, the clockwise torques being equal to the counter-clockwise torques.* Calling clockwise torques positive and counter-clockwise torques negative, the second condition of equilibrium requires that the sum of all the torques, ΣT, acting upon a body shall be zero, thus:

$$\Sigma T = 0 \qquad\qquad (46)$$

When the forces which maintain equilibrium do not all pass through a common point, both conditions must be satisfied.

As a typical problem illustrating the two conditions of equilibrium, find the point at which a 12-ft. bar should be pivoted in order to remain at rest while supporting a load of 40 lb. at one end and a load of 8 lb. at the other end, if the weight of the bar itself is negligible. The bar is shown at AB in part I of Fig. 67, with the fulcrum C located a distance x ft. from the point where the 40-lb. load is applied. The forces acting on the bar are shown in part II of the figure. Since there are downward forces of 40 lb. at A and 8 lb. at B, the fulcrum must exert an upward force of 48 lb. at C to satisfy the first condition of equilibrium. Then, applying equation (46), the moments of all the forces will be ascertained about the fulcrum, and their algebraic sum will be placed equal to zero.

Thus, the 8-lb. force produces a torque of 8 lb. $\times$ (12 − x) ft. and the 40-lb. force produces a torque of −40 lb. $\times$ x ft. The 48-lb. force

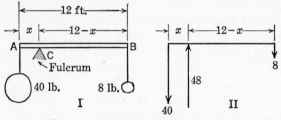

FIG. 67. Locating the fulcrum of a bar

produces no torque about this axis, its lever arm being zero. Hence, to satisfy the second condition of equilibrium

$$8 \text{ lb.} \times (12 - x) \text{ ft.} - 40 \text{ lb.} \times x \text{ ft.} = 0,$$

from which $x = 2$ ft. This is the distance from the 40-lb. load at which the fulcrum should be located to have the bar remain in balance.

Although it was natural to choose the fulcrum as the axis about which torques were taken in the foregoing problem, any other point might have been selected equally well, provided the same point were used throughout the calculation. The correctness of this statement may be verified by solving the problem again, taking torques about some other point.

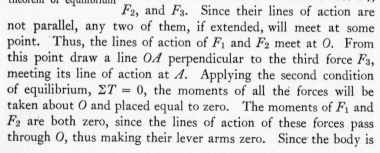

FIG. 68. Illustrating a theorem of equilibrium

A theorem of great value, based upon the second condition of equilibrium, states that *if three non-parallel forces acting upon a body produce equilibrium, their lines of action must pass through a common point.* This theorem will be demonstrated by taking moments of forces about the intersection of two of the lines of action and showing that the lever arm of the remaining force must be zero. Suppose a body, as in Fig. 68, to be in equilibrium under the action of three forces F_1, F_2, and F_3. Since their lines of action are not parallel, any two of them, if extended, will meet at some point. Thus, the lines of action of F_1 and F_2 meet at O. From this point draw a line OA perpendicular to the third force F_3, meeting its line of action at A. Applying the second condition of equilibrium, $\Sigma T = 0$, the moments of all the forces will be taken about O and placed equal to zero. The moments of F_1 and F_2 are both zero, since the lines of action of these forces pass through O, thus making their lever arms zero. Since the body is in equilibrium, the moment of the remaining force F_3 about O must be zero; and since the force F_3 is not zero, its lever arm OA must be zero; that is, the line of action of F_3 must pass through O. Hence the lines of action of three forces in equilibrium pass through a common point.

63. Resultant of Parallel Forces. — It was pointed out in § 61 that when a body is in equilibrium under the action of three forces, the resultant of any two of these forces is equal and opposite to the third force. This principle may be used in finding the resultant of two parallel forces. Suppose the body represented in Fig. 69 to be in equilibrium under the action of the three parallel forces F_1, F_2, and F_3. From the first condition of equilibrium, $F_3 = F_1 + F_2$; and from the second condition of equilibrium, taking moments about O, $F_1 \times a - F_2 \times b = 0$, whence $a:b = F_2:F_1$. But the resultant R of the forces F_1 and F_2 is equal and opposite to F_3. Therefore, the resultant of two parallel forces has the same direction as the forces and is equal to their sum, and its line of action divides the distance between them into two parts which are inversely proportional to the respective forces.

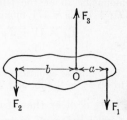

FIG. 69. Equilibrium under the action of parallel forces

Extending this principle, the resultant of any number of parallel forces can be found by first finding a force which included with the forces given will produce equilibrium; such a force is called the *equilibrant* of the given forces, and *the resultant is equal and opposite to the equilibrant and acts along the same line.*

Under certain conditions a body which is acted upon by several parallel forces is held in equilibrium by two or more forces instead of by a single equilibrant. These forces may be found by applying the conditions of equilibrium, as previously.

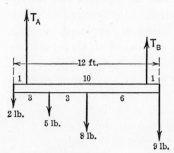

FIG. 70. Weighted rod supported by two cords

As an illustration, consider a rod 12 ft. long supported by two cords, and carrying four loads aggregating 24 lb. The location of these loads is shown in Fig. 70 where the distances are indicated in feet. Find the tension T_A and T_B in the cords, assuming the weight of the rod to be negligible. In solving problems of this type, the units are usually omitted for simplicity; this practice is not likely to cause confusion. Applying the first condition of equilibrium,

$$\Sigma V = T_A + T_B - 2 - 5 - 8 - 9 = 0;$$

whence $T_A + T_B = 24$. Applying the second condition of equilibrium, taking moments about the left end of the rod,

$$\Sigma T = 5 \times 3 + 8 \times 6 + 9 \times 12 - T_A \times 1 - T_B \times 11 = 0,$$

or $T_A + 11 T_B = 171$. Solving these equations simultaneously, the tensions in the cords are found to be $T_A = 9.3$ lb. and $T_B = 14.7$ lb.

It is interesting to note that this problem might have been solved by two applications of the condition $\Sigma T = 0$. Having previously taken moments about the left end of the rod, resulting in the expression: $T_A + 11\,T_B = 171$, moments are next taken about the right end of the rod:

$$T_A \times 11 + T_B \times 1 - 2 \times 12 - 5 \times 9 - 8 \times 6 = 0,$$

or

$$11 T_A + T_B = 117.$$

Solving these equations simultaneously, the tensions in the cords are found to be $T_A = 9.3$ lb. and $T_B = 14.7$ lb., as before.

It is clear that if the rod of the foregoing problem were supported by props instead of by cords, and if these were located at the same places as the cords, the props would divide the total load between them in the same way, the props being under compression and each exerting an upward force on the rod. The upward forces exerted by the props are usually termed the *reactions* of the support on the rod.

64. Center of Gravity. — The attraction which the earth exerts upon a body extends to each particle of matter which the body contains, and thus the weight of a body may be regarded as a system of parallel forces acting upon the individual particles which make up the body. When these parallel forces are replaced by their resultant, this single force is exactly equivalent to them, and its point of application is called the *center of gravity* of the body. Thus the weight of a body, although actually a system of parallel forces acting upon all parts of the body, can be correctly represented by a single force acting downward at the center of gravity. This point coincides with the center of mass described in § 37, and its location is independent of the position of the body.

For bodies of simple shapes, the center of gravity can be located by inspection, being at the geometric center of the body, assuming the material to be uniform in density throughout; thus the center of gravity of a rod, tube, or bar, whether of circular or rectangular cross-section, is located on the axis and midway between the ends, for a sphere it is at the center, and for a cone it is on the axis at a point one-fourth of the way from the base to the vertex.

For a homogeneous body in the form of a sheet, the center of gravity is the same as the center of area of the sheet. For a sheet of circular shape, the center of area is located at the center of the circle; for a rectangle it is at the intersection of the two diagonals, and for a triangle it is one-third of the distance from the middle point of any side to the opposite vertex.

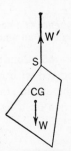

For a body of irregular shape, the center of gravity may be determined experimentally by suspending the body successively from two different points. In each test the body will come to rest with its center of gravity directly beneath the point of suspension; the intersection of the two lines is the center of gravity. In Fig. 71 a model, representing the cross-section of a retaining wall, is under test in this manner. The model is shown displaced from its position of rest and the forces

Fig. 71. Experiment to locate center of gravity

W and W' constitute a counter-clockwise couple which will rotate the model until its center of gravity CG is directly below the point of suspension S.

As an illustrative problem, consider the forces on a truck having a 150-inch wheel base. The empty truck weighs 2600 lb. and its center of gravity is 90 in. in front of the rear axle. The truck carries a load of 3200 lb. which is placed centrally with its center of gravity 30 in. in front of the rear axle. What force does each tire exert upon the ground?

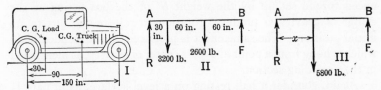

Fig. 72. Finding pressure of wheels on ground

The conditions of the problem are indicated in part I of Fig. 72. The truck is represented by the line AB in part II of the figure, and the weights of truck and load are shown, each acting downward at its own center of gravity. The upward thrust of the ground on the two rear tires is represented as a single force R; and a similar thrust at the front tires is represented likewise as F. From the first condition of equilibrium, $R + F - 3200 - 2600 = 0$, whence $R = 5800$ lb. $- F$. Next, applying the second condition of equilibrium, moments being taken about A: $3200 \times 30 + 2600 \times 90 - F \times 150 = 0$, whence $F = 2200$ lb., and therefore, $R = 5800$ lb. $- F = 3600$ lb. But the pressure of the tires on the ground is equal to the reaction of the ground on the tires, and thus each front tire presses against the ground with a force of $F \div 2 = 1100$ lb., and each rear tire presses against the ground with a force of $R \div 2 = 1800$ lb.

It is of interest in this problem to find the center of gravity of the loaded truck. This can be done by considering the combined weight of 5800 lb. to act downward at a single point distant x from the rear axle, as shown in part III. Taking moments about A:

$$5800 \times x - 2200 \times 150 = 0,$$

whence the center of gravity of the loaded truck is in front of the rear axle by an amount $x = 57$ in.

65. Conditions of Stability. — The way in which a body is supported with respect to its center of gravity has a great effect upon the static stability of equilibrium of the body. If a cubical box rests on a level floor as shown in part I of Fig. 73, it is in *stable*

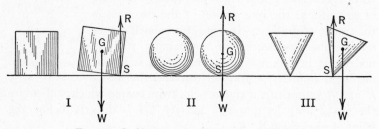

FIG. 73. Stable, neutral, and unstable equilibrium

equilibrium because if one edge is raised a little and then released, the box falls back again to its original position. The tilting of the box shifts the reaction R of the floor to the edge S, and the unbalanced torque set up by the weight W of the box acting at the center of gravity G produces rotation to restore the box to its initial position. The same effect is produced in a suspended body which is hung from a point above its center of gravity, as mentioned in the preceding section.

Again, consider a ball resting on a level surface, as in part II of the figure. No matter how the ball is moved, it shows no tendency either to return to its former position or to fall over the other way. Its weight W and the reaction R of the surface lie along a single line and therefore do not produce a couple; in consequence the ball is said to be in *neutral equilibrium*. So also is a cylinder lying on its side.

Sometimes an electrical galvanometer which is specially susceptible to jarring is supported in neutral equilibrium by attaching the instrument to a massive frame which in turn is suspended by long springs. Careful adjustment is made to bring the center of gravity of the entire system into coincidence with the point of suspension of the moving system of the instrument. A recent development in automotive engineering applies the idea of neutral equilibrium to the engine of the automobile. This part is supported in such a manner that the plane of support includes the center of gravity of the engine, thus reducing vibration resulting from road shocks, and improving riding comfort.

The third part of Fig. 73 illustrates a condition of *unstable equilibrium*. Here a cone (not revolving) is shown while momentarily balanced upon the vertex. It is evident that upon a slight displacement of the cone its weight W will produce a torque about the vertex S which increases the displacement, and the cone will fall over.

*66. The Balance. — The equal-arm analytical balance offers an interesting study in equilibrium. In this instrument, which is shown pictorially in Fig. 13 and diagrammatically in Fig. 74, a long slender beam AB of length $2l$ supports a scale-pan at each end

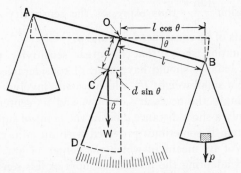

Fig. 74. The equal-arm balance

and is pivoted at its midpoint O. At this point it carries a downwardly projecting pointer OD, the lower end of which plays across a scale. The moving system has a weight W, and being symmetrical, its center of gravity is located at some point C along the pointer, a distance d below the pivot O. This distance is of importance in the operation of the balance and is exaggerated in the figure for clearness. The broken lines represent the beam and pointer when not deflected, and the solid lines show the result of adding a very small weight p to one of the scale-pans. This action sets up a deflecting torque about O equal to $p \times l \cos \theta$, which becomes smaller and smaller as θ increases. At the same time, the center of gravity is displaced, thus producing an opposing torque about the same axis equal to $Wd \sin \theta$ which becomes larger and larger as θ increases. The balance will evidently come to rest at some angle θ such that

$$pl \cos \theta = Wd \sin \theta$$

A sensitive balance is one which sweeps through a large angle when a very small weight is added to one scale-pan, the sensitivity of a balance usually being expressed as the amount of deflection in scale divisions produced by a weight of one milligram. Physically, however, the sensitivity of a balance is defined from the equation of balance that appears above. While the ratio of the deflection θ to the load p cannot be found directly from this equation, the ratio of $\tan \theta$ to p is seen to be

$$\frac{\tan \theta}{p} = \frac{\sin \theta}{p \cos \theta} = \frac{l}{Wd}$$

The expression $\dfrac{\tan \theta}{p}$ thus expresses the sensitivity of the balance in terms of its constants l, W, and d.

This equation shows that for great sensitivity the moving system of a balance should have arms of considerable length l, it should have a small weight W, which usually involves a truss-like design to obtain the necessary rigidity, and its center of gravity should be only a short distance d below the point of support. The moving system is sometimes provided with an adjustable weight near the pivot by means of which the center of gravity may be shifted, thus adapting the balance to more or less sensitive measurements.

67. Application of the Principles of Equilibrium. — In applying the conditions of equilibrium to the solution of statical problems it is expedient to follow a definite procedure in order to avoid confusion and error. The procedure recommended is as follows:

1. Make a sketch of the device or structure; mark upon it all the known data; and assign symbols to the desired quantities.

2. Consider some member or point of the body and make a force diagram showing all the forces acting upon the portion considered.

3. Apply the conditions of equilibrium to this portion, by writing the equations expressing $\Sigma H = 0$, $\Sigma V = 0$, and $\Sigma T = 0$.

4. Solve these equations for the quantities desired.

5. Follow the same procedure for the other points or members involved in the problem.

Several examples will illustrate the procedure.

I. A telephone pole at a turn in the line is anchored by a guy-wire and strut as shown in Part I of Fig. 75, the pull on the pole being 1800 lb. Determine the tension in the guy and the compressive force in the strut.

The point selected for consideration is the upper end of the strut, point A, since all the forces concerned act at that point. In the force

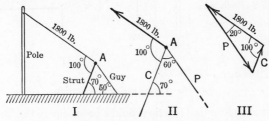

Fig. 75. Forces involved in guying a telephone pole

diagram, part II of the figure, the force of 1800 lb. is shown acting at point A, but the compressive force C in the strut and the pull P in the guy are indicated in direction only because their magnitudes are still unknown. In the polygon (triangle) of forces in part III, the 1800-lb. force is laid off by a line drawn to scale and the direction lines of P and C are drawn from its ends; the location of their intersection determines the magnitudes of the forces. The strut is in compression and therefore its force line C will be toward the point A; the other two forces are tensile forces and are shown directed away from point A. By scaling the polygon, the tension of the guy is determined as 2000 lb., and the compression of the strut as 700 lb.

In the analytical solution, the desired forces are computed by the Law of Sines; thus the accurate solution of the problem gives

$$\frac{P}{1800} = \frac{\sin 100°}{\sin 60°} = \frac{0.985}{0.866}, \text{ whence } P = 2050 \text{ lb.}$$

and

$$\frac{C}{1800} = \frac{\sin 20°}{\sin 60°} = \frac{0.342}{0.866}, \text{ whence } C = 711 \text{ lb.}$$

The conditions $\Sigma H = 0$ and $\Sigma V = 0$ may also be applied to this problem, and the following simultaneous equations result when the forces involved have been resolved into horizontal and vertical components:

$$\Sigma H = -1800 \cos 30° + C \cos 70° + P \cos 50° = 0,$$
$$\Sigma V = 1800 \sin 30° + C \sin 70° - P \sin 50° = 0,$$

which give the same answers as before, but require somewhat more computation.

II. A derrick consists of a uniform boom 24 ft. long weighing 700 lb., and a vertical mast to which the boom is hinged. A load of 5000 lb. is being supported by a cable which is fastened to the outer end of the boom. The directions of boom and cable are shown in part I of Fig. 76. Compute the tension in the cable which extends between the boom and the mast, and also the horizontal and vertical thrusts on the hinge-pin.

Selecting the boom as the body to be considered, a force diagram is made as shown in part II, wherein the tension in the rope is called P, and

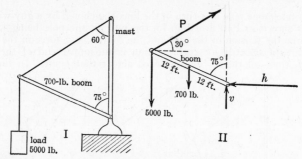

FIG. 76. Forces acting in a derrick

the horizontal and vertical reactions on the boom due to the thrust of the hinge-pin are marked h and v respectively. The weight of the boom is considered as a single force acting at its center of gravity. Applying the conditions of equilibrium with respect to translation, yields

$$\Sigma H = P \cos 30° - h = 0,$$
$$\Sigma V = P \sin 30° - 5000 - 700 + v = 0,$$

and taking moments about the hinge-pin, thereby eliminating both h and v, the torque equation in pound-feet becomes

$$\Sigma T = P\ 24 \sin 45° - 5000 \times 24 \sin 75° - 700 \times 12 \sin 75° = 0.$$

Simplifying these equations, gives

$$h = P \cos 30° = 0.866P,$$
$$v = 5700 - P \sin 30° = 5700 - 0.500P,$$
$$P \sin 45° = 5350 \sin 75°,$$

whence $P = 7310$, $h = 6330$, and $v = 2045$. That is, the tension in the cable is 7310 lb., and the horizontal and vertical thrusts on the hinge-pin are respectively 6330 and 2045 lb. Letting C represent the resultant of these thrusts, the force acting on the lower end of the boom becomes

$$C = \sqrt{(6330)^2 + (2045)^2} = 6660 \text{ lb.}$$

and its direction with respect to the vertical is given by

$$\tan \phi = \frac{h}{v} = \frac{6330}{2045} = 3.10, \quad \text{or} \quad \phi = 72°.$$

Note that this force is not directed along the boom.

III. A uniform ladder, 18 ft. long and weighing 90 lb., leans against a smooth vertical wall at an angle of 70° with the ground. With what forces does the ladder press against the wall and ground?

The ladder is shown in position in part I of Fig. 77, and the forces acting upon it are represented in part II. Herein h is the reaction by the wall upon the ladder and balances its push against the wall; it is perpendicular to the wall because that surface was assumed frictionless. Force v is the vertical reaction of the ground on the ladder and f is the frictional force of the ground and acts in opposition to the direction in which the ladder tends to slide. Applying the conditions of equilibrium to find these three forces,

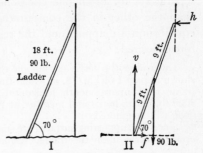

$$\Sigma H = f - h = 0,$$
$$\Sigma V = v - 90 = 0,$$

Fig. 77. Forces on a ladder leaning against a smooth wall

ΣT (about foot of ladder) $= 90 \times 9 \cos 70° - h\, 18 \sin 70° = 0$, whence $f = h = \dfrac{90 \times 9}{18} \cot 70° = 16.4$ lb. and $v = 90$ lb. Thus, the ladder pushes against the wall with a normal force of 16.4 lb., and pushes against the ground with a force having a horizontal component of 16.4 lb. and a vertical component of 90 lb.

Next, assume that a 150-lb. man is standing two-thirds the way up on this ladder. The equations of equilibrium are then

$$\Sigma H = f - h = 0$$
$$\Sigma V = v - 90 - 150 = 0$$

$\Sigma T = 90 \times 9 \cos 70° + 150 \times 12 \cos 70° - h\, 18 \sin 70° = 0$; whence $f = h = 52.9$ lb. and $v = 240$ lb.

In the first case the frictional force is $\dfrac{16.4}{90} = 0.182$ of the normal force v at the base of the ladder, while in the latter case the frictional force is $\dfrac{52.9}{240} = 0.22$ of that normal force. If the coefficient of friction between ladder and ground were just 0.22, the ladder would commence to slide when the man reached the position two-thirds of the way up.

*68. Elementary Structures. — The principles of equilibrium find a wide application in the design of structures of all kinds. When the forces have been determined in the various portions of a proposed structure, the designer will know how large to make the various sections in order to give the structure sufficient strength. The calculation of the forces acting in the members of an A-frame will serve as an elementary example.

The first step is to find the reactions of the supports upon the frame, as though the structure were a simple beam. Next, each member of the frame is considered by itself and all forces acting upon each are indicated; instead of showing any inclined forces, the horizontal and vertical components of each will be indicated separately, for often one component may be determined earlier than the other in the computation. Finally, the conditions of equilibrium are applied and the resulting equations solved for the forces desired.

Determine the forces acting on the three members of the A-frame shown in part I of Fig. 78, in which the lengths are marked in feet. The frame rests upon smooth horizontal surfaces and supports a load of 3000 lb. on its horizontal member at point F. The weight of the frame itself will be ignored.

Since the supporting surfaces are smooth, they can exert only vertically upward forces upon the frame. Calling these reactions A and B, it is

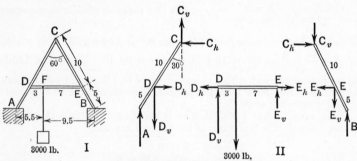

FIG. 78.   Forces in an A-frame

clear that $A + B = 3000$ lb. from the first condition of equilibrium. The individual values are found from the second condition by taking moments about the two supports:

About A
$$3000 \times 5.5 - 15B = 0, \quad \text{whence } B = 1100 \text{ lb.}$$
About B
$$15A - 3000 \times 9.5 = 0, \quad \text{whence } A = 1900 \text{ lb.}$$

The sum of these, 3000 lb., agrees with the result from the first condition of equilibrium.

Part II of the figure shows the three members considered separately, with force lines at each joint in the structure to indicate the horizontal and vertical components, these being differentiated by the subscripts h and v respectively. The conditions of equilibrium must be applied first to the tie-member DE, for there are as yet too many unknown forces on the inclined members. Applying moments:

About D
$$3000 \times 3 - 10E_v = 0, \quad \text{whence } E_v = 900 \text{ lb.}$$
About E
$$10 D_v - 3000 \times 7 = 0, \quad \text{whence } D_v = 2100 \text{ lb.}$$

$$\overline{\text{Sum} \quad = 3000 \text{ lb.}}$$

These reactions are directed perpendicularly upward on member DE at its ends, and hence this member must exert corresponding downward forces on the inclined members, as shown. The horizontal components on DE cannot be determined from the forces on this member alone.

Considering the left-hand member AC, it is apparent that there must be a push against it at the top by the right-hand member BC. Its magnitude and direction are unknown, but it will consist of two components C_h and C_v as represented, the vertical component being taken upward because D_v was found to be greater than the reaction A. Applying $\Sigma H = 0$ and $\Sigma V = 0$, and taking $\Sigma T = 0$ about C, there result

$$\Sigma H = D_h - C_h = 0$$
$$\Sigma V = A - D_v + C_v = 1900 - 2100 + C_v = 0$$
$$\Sigma T = A\ 15 \sin 30° - D_v\ 10 \sin 30° - D_h\ 10 \cos 30° = 0$$
$$= 1900 \times 7.5 - 2100 \times 5 - D_h \times 8.66 = 0$$

From these equations, the forces on member AC are

$C_v = 200$ lb. upward
$C_h = 433$ lb. to the left
$D_h = 433$ lb. to the right (because C_h is to the left as above explained).

The horizontal forces on the tie-member DE are therefore

$D_h = 433$ lb. to the left   and $E_h = 433$ lb. to the right.

It is apparent from the foregoing that the forces on the remaining member BC are as follows:
$E_h = 433$ lb. to the left
$C_h = 433$ lb. to the right
$C_v = 1100 - 900 = 200$ lb. downward.

Thus, all of the force actions on the A-frame have been determined by computing their components; if the forces themselves are desired they may be calculated in the usual way.

PROBLEMS

1. Two ropes 6 ft. and 8 ft. long respectively, which are attached to the ceiling at two points 10 ft. apart, are tied together at their lower ends, and jointly support a 60-lb. load. Calculate (a) the tension in the 6-ft. rope, and (b) the tension in the 8-ft. rope.

2. A weight of 100 lb. is hung at the middle point of a horizontal wire 12 ft. long, whereupon the wire stretches and the middle point sags 6 in. Find the tension in the wire.

3. An arc lamp weighing 50 lb. is supported 16 ft. above the ground by two wires which extend to the tops of two poles spaced 21 ft. apart and each 20 ft. high. If the lamp is 7 ft. from one pole and 14 ft. from the other, find the tension in each of the supporting wires.

4. A picture weighing 12 lb. is supported by a wire passing over a smooth hook. The wire is 6 ft. long and is fastened to the picture at two points 3 ft. apart. Compute the tension in the wire.

5. A 100-gm. ball is supported by a thread. How much force must be exerted upon this ball in a horizontal direction in order to hold it at rest with the supporting thread at an angle of 30° with the vertical?

6. A pole 35 ft. high at the end of a line has 16 parallel electric wires terminating at its upper end. The wires sag 5° from the horizontal at the point of attachment, and are subjected to an average tension of 24 lb. At the opposite side, a guy wire extending from the top of the pole is anchored

to the ground at a point 28 ft. from its base.   What tension is necessary in the guy to offset the horizontal pull of the electric wires?

7. A meter stick is loaded with four weights, a 500-gm. weight at the 20-cm. mark, a 1000-gm. weight at the 30-cm. mark, a 750-gm. weight at the 60-cm. mark, and a 900-gm. weight at the 90-cm. mark.   At what mark should the stick be supported in order to balance, if its own weight is negligible?

8. If a threaded pipe coupling is not loosened by a 50-lb. force applied perpendicularly to a Stillson wrench at a point 12 in. from the pipe center, find what torque the pipe meanwhile exerts upon the coupling.

9. A 100-lb. load is hung on a uniform bar which has a length of 12 ft. and a weight of 50 lb.   The loaded bar is carried by a man at one end and a boy at the other end.   Where should the 100-lb. load be applied in order for the man to lift twice as much as the boy?

10. A uniform bar 12 ft. long supports two loads, 100 lb. applied at a point 2 ft. from the left end, and 150 lb. applied at a point 1 ft. from the right end.   If the bar balances at a point midway between these loads, calculate its weight.   *450 lb*

11. A broom balances at a point 37 in. from its upper end, and when an 8-oz. weight is attached to that end, the point of balance is shifted 6.5 in. Find the weight of the broom.

12. A 4000-lb. truck with 150-in. wheelbase has its center of gravity 90 in. in front of the rear axle.   If a load of 1600 lb. is placed centrally on the truck at a distance of 40 in. from the rear axle, find the force with which each tire will press upon the ground.   *2126 - 3774*

13. When the front wheels of an automobile are run on a platform scale, the scale balances at 1890 lb., and when the rear wheels are run on the scale, it balances at 1530 lb.   The automobile has a 131-in. wheelbase; locate its center of gravity with respect to the rear axle.

14. A yard stick which weighs 12 oz. is loaded with three weights, a 32-oz. weight at the 2-in. mark, a 24-oz. weight at the 20-in. mark, and a 16-oz. weight at the 32-in. mark.   At what mark should the stick be supported in order to balance?

15. A truck having a wheelbase of 148 in. weighs 6200 lb. without load, its center of gravity being 82 in. in front of the rear axle.   Where should a 5-ton load be centered in order that the pressure on the rear tires shall be twice as great as that on the front tires?

16. Using the principle employed at the end of §64, assume that a homogeneous cone-shaped pole which tapers uniformly to a point 28 ft. above the base is sawed in two at the middle, and locate the center of gravity of the lower portion.

17. A traveling crane, consisting essentially of a horizontal beam mounted on wheels at the ends, has a length of 26 ft. and a weight of 3 tons; the center of gravity of the crane with its hoisting machinery is located 9 ft. from the left end.   When lifting a 5-ton load at a point 11 ft. from this end, find how much force is exerted at the two ends by the wheels upon the supporting rails.

18. A rectangular frame ABCD which measures 15 in. by 12 in. hangs with the 15-in. sides AB and CD horizontal and the other sides AD and BC vertical.   The frame weighs 2 lb. and is subject to four forces, namely: 5 lb. acting vertically up and 4 lb. acting to the left, both at the upper-left corner A; 3 lb. acting vertically up at the upper-right corner B; and 6 lb. acting horizontally to the left at the lower-left corner D.   What additional force must be exerted and at what point along the side CD should it be applied for the frame to be in equilibrium in the position described?

19. Prove that the correct weight of a body may be determined with a balance that has unequal arms, by first weighing the body in the left scale-pan, then weighing it in the right scale-pan, and taking the square root of the product of the results of these weighings as the correct weight. Neglect the weights of the balance arms.

20. A uniform ladder 12 ft. long and weighing 20 lb. is placed upon the ground with its upper end resting against a smooth vertical show window. If the ladder makes an angle of 80° with the ground, find what force it will exert on the window when a 140-lb. man has climbed up the ladder a distance of 8 ft.

21. A 100-lb. sign is supported on an 8-ft. bar fastened to a wall as shown in the accompanying sketch, in which the distances are indicated

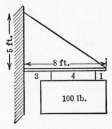

in feet. Find the tension in the guy and the thrust exerted by the bar against the wall. Neglect the weight of the bar.

*22. A ladder having the shape of the A-frame shown in Fig. 78 has two members 18 ft. long and a tie-rod 6 ft. long connecting the members at points 12 ft. from the hinged apex. Neglecting the weight of the ladder, and assuming the ladder to rest on a smooth surface, ascertain the tension in the tie-rod when a load of 200 lb. is placed at the apex of the ladder.

23. A derrick consists of an upright mast, a boom pivoted to the mast near its base, and a tie-rod joining the outer end of the boom with the top of the mast. The boom is a uniform bar 12 ft. long and weighing 300 lb., and makes an angle of 60° with the mast. The tie-rod makes an angle of 45° with the mast. When a load of 1 ton is applied to the boom 3 ft. from its outer end, compute the tension in the tie-rod and the thrust of the boom against the mast.

24. A crane has a boom 20 ft. long which is socketed to the bottom of a vertical mast 30 ft. high. A load of 3000 lb. is supported by the boom at a point 5 ft. from its outer end. What is the tension in the cable joining the outer end of the boom with the top of the mast when that cable is 25 ft. long? Neglect the weight of the boom.

*25. Find the reactions A, B, and C on a roof truss supporting the wind

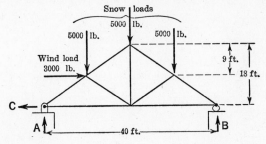

STATICS

and snow loads shown in the accompanying diagram. The truss is fixed
at the left support and is free to roll at the right support.

*26. A parallel-chord bridge truss having a span of 36 ft. is composed of
members in triangular units and the members are hinged at the joints, as
shown in the accompanying sketch. A single load of 1000 lb. is placed at
point E, this number being selected for simplicity, although such trusses

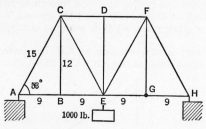

usually support loads hundreds of times greater. The dimensions shown
are in feet, and the weight of the truss itself is disregarded. Calculate
the forces in AB, AC, BC, and CD. *Hint.* Consider the equilibrium of
joints A, B, and C separately.

CHAPTER VIII

MECHANICAL ENERGY

WORK AND ENERGY

69. Work. — In popular language, the term "work" is applied to any form of labor, physical or mental, for producing any kind of result. In science and engineering, on the other hand, "work" has a definite technical meaning, which involves two physical concepts that have been developed in previous chapters. A few illustrations will make the meaning clear.

Suppose that a man moves a piano from one place to another meanwhile exerting a steady push on the instrument, or that he pulls an oar toward him in rowing, or that he lifts a weight from the floor to the top of a table. In each of these instances, two things should be noted: first, that the man exerts a *force*, and second, that he exerts it through a *distance* in the direction of that force. Under these conditions, the man is said to do *work*, the amount of work depending on the two factors: the force which he exerts, and the distance along the direction of the force through which he exerts it. The amount of work done is measured by the product of these two quantities, thus,

$$E = Fs \tag{47}$$

where E is the amount of work which an agent does on a body in exerting a push or pull F on it through a distance s, provided F and s have the same direction. Referring again to the man moving the piano, if he exerts a horizontal force of 50 lb. continuously through a horizontal distance of 10 ft., he does 50 lb. $\times$ 10 ft. = 500 ft-lb. of work. The symbol E is used to represent work (rather than the initial letter of work), in order that W may continue to represent weight, as previously, without confusion. The product of force and distance was encountered in § 20, but these quantities were at right angles to each other to produce torque, instead of being in the same direction, as at present, to produce work.

127

Note that inanimate objects also can exert forces, and that any agent which exerts a force through a distance does work; hence a general statement may be made as follows: *Any agent does work on a body when it exerts a force on the body through a distance along the direction of the force.* A tugboat which exerts a steady force of 600 lb. on a barge in towing it a distance of one mile does 600 lb. × 5280 ft. = 3,168,000 ft-lb. of work.

It frequently happens when work is being done, that the force exerted on the body is not in the same direction as the distance through which this force is exerted; that is, F is not in the same direction as s. In such cases the term F in equation (47) should be interpreted as that component of the force which is along the direction of s. Consider, for example, a boy pushing a sled a

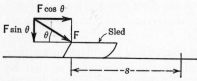

FIG. 79. Work being done in sliding sled

distance s along a level surface, with a force F which makes an angle θ with the horizontal plane, as shown in Fig. 79. Here F may be resolved into two components, $F \cos \theta$ along the direction of s, and $F \sin \theta$ at right angles to this direction. Only the first of these components is effective in doing work on the sled, while the other component increases the pressure of the sled against the snow-covered ground and thereby adds to the backward drag of friction. The amount of work which the boy does on the sled is therefore

$$E = Fs \cos \theta \qquad (48)$$

Giving a general interpretation to this equation, E is the amount of work done on a body by an agent which exerts a force F on it through a distance s, the directions of F and s making an angle θ with each other. It might be remarked that F is the force applied by the agent which is doing the work, and is not, in general, the unbalanced force acting on the body.

As an illustrative problem, calculate the work done by a horse in plowing a furrow 200 yd. long, if he exerts a steady force of 150 lb. on the plow at an angle of 15° with the ground. From equation (48), the work done is $E = Fs \cos \theta = 150$ lb. × 200 yd. × cos 15° = 150 lb. × 600 ft. × 0.966 = 86,940 ft-lb.

Since work is essentially the product of a force and a length, the unit for work is the product of a force unit and a length unit. In the c.g.s. system of units, the unit of work is called the erg. One *erg* of work is done on a body when a force of 1 dyne is exerted upon it through a distance of 1 cm. Lifting a half-dollar through a height of 1 meter requires the expenditure of 1,196,000 ergs of work. Because this unit is so small, a multiple of it called the *joule* is frequently used; 1 joule = 10^7 ergs. This unit is named after the British experimenter, James P. Joule (1818–1889). In ordinary engineering work, where the British gravitational system of units is used, the unit of work is the *foot-pound*, being the amount of work done on a body when a force of 1 lb. is exerted on the body through a distance of 1 ft.

The amount of work done upon a rotating body may also be calculated from the foregoing equations, but usually it can be found more directly when expressed in terms of the angular quan-

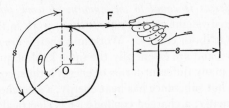

FIG. 80. Work being done upon a rotating body

tities, torque and angle. The desired expression is found by supposing that a drum of radius r has a cord fastened to the rim, as represented in Fig. 80, and that the cord is pulled with a force F for a distance s along its length, so that an amount of work $E = Fs$ is done upon the drum. The torque T resulting from the force F is $T = Fr$, whence $F = T \div r$. The angle through which the drum turns is found by observing that as the cord is pulled, every point on the rim of the drum travels through an arc of length s, and therefore the drum rotates through an angle θ such that $s = r\theta$. Substituting these values for F and s in the expression for work, $E = Fs = \dfrac{T}{r} \times r\theta$, whence

$$E = T\theta \qquad (49)$$

where E is the amount of work done upon a rotating body by an agent which exerts a torque T upon the body through an angle θ.

Sometimes bodies move in opposition to the efforts exerted upon them, for instance: a heavy weight may slide down a steep incline in spite of a man's attempt to pull it upward, a rotating wheel will continue to turn in a certain direction even after a brake is applied to exert a torque upon it in the opposite direction, and a clock spring having been wound will drive the clock oppositely in unwinding.   In such cases *the body does work instead of having work done upon it;* equations (47 to 49) may be used as before, but they will determine the amount of work done *by* the body rather than the amount of work done *upon* it.

70. Energy. — If an agent is able to do work, it is said to possess *energy*.   For example, a man or a horse can do work and so he possesses energy; steam possesses energy since it is able to push the piston within the cylinder of a steam engine; the mainspring of a watch possesses energy when wound, since it is able to drive the hands of the instrument.   *The amount of energy which an agent possesses is equal to the amount of work that it can do.* Thus, if a raised weight can do 1000 ft-lb. of work in falling, it has initially 1000 ft-lb. of energy.   Work and energy are expressed in the same units, and are essentially the same kind of quantity.

There are many different forms of energy; thus, coal has chemical energy, a hot substance has heat energy, a stretched spring has mechanical energy, a charged condenser has electrical energy, and so on.

In the study of Mechanics, mechanical energy is naturally the type which is of special interest.   A body may possess mechanical energy from either or both of two causes.   First, whenever a body is in motion it will be able to exert a force and do work in coming to rest; a moving body always possesses energy by virtue of its motion; this is called *kinetic* energy.   A moving hammer possesses kinetic energy, and this enables it to do work in driving a nail.   Second, a body which has been moved to a new position is sometimes able to do work because of this fact; such a body possesses energy by virtue of its position, and is said to have *potential* energy.   A body is not necessarily given potential energy by displacing it, but only when it is able to do more work in its new position than it was originally.   A weight which has been raised or a spring which has been wound is thereby given potential energy, but if a weight is merely moved along a level floor from one position to another, its potential energy is not changed.

71. Conservation and Transformation of Energy. — Since the amount of energy which a body possesses is equal to the amount of work it can perform, it seems reasonable that after a body has done some work, it will then be able to do less work than it could originally, and therefore its supply of energy should be reduced. Such is found to be the case, and it can be said in general that whenever a body does a certain amount of work, its supply of energy becomes reduced by exactly that amount. The question naturally arises as to what becomes of the energy which has left the body. In answer to this question, experience shows that when a body does work, it must do this work on some other body or bodies, and that while the body which does the work gives up energy, the bodies on which the work is done gain energy, the amount given up by the first body in doing the work being equal to that gained by the other bodies on which the work is done. When a man does 20 ft-lb. of work in throwing a ball, he gives up to 20 ft-lb. of energy, and the ball gains 20 ft-lb. of energy, since 20 ft-lb. of work are done upon it. The energy which is given up by a body is imparted to others without loss, and thus within any imaginary boundary through which no energy is lost or gained, the total amount of energy remains unchanged. This case illustrates a general law known as the *law of Conservation of Energy*. This law states that *energy can neither be created nor destroyed*, and that therefore *the total amount of energy in the universe remains constant*.

Consider a body which is raised to the top of an inclined plane and is then allowed to slide down. A certain amount of work is done on the body in raising it, thus increasing its potential energy. As the body slides down the incline, it gives up potential energy and gains kinetic energy; and if no energy is given up on account of friction, the increase of kinetic energy will equal the reduction of potential energy. If, however, part of the potential energy possessed by the body must be used in opposing friction on the way down, then the kinetic energy of the body at the bottom will be less than before by this amount. This example shows that while energy can be transformed from one kind to another, it is not destroyed in the process. When energy is used in opposing friction, it is said to be wasted, that is, rendered unavailable for useful purposes; but it is not destroyed, since it appears as heat, which is recognized as a form of energy. When mechanical work is done on a body, it can be entirely accounted for by one or more of the following effects: (1) *increase in the kinetic energy of the body*, (2) *increase in its potential energy*, or (3) *production of heat in opposing friction*.

Although energy cannot be destroyed, it is sometimes wasted, as just pointed out. When a train is driven at constant speed along a level track neither its kinetic energy nor its potential energy is increasing, and thus all of the energy in the fuel burned is wasted in opposing friction. With the exhaustion of natural fuels, the provision of energy in sufficient quantities to meet the future demands of mankind will be an engineering problem of utmost importance.

72. Kinetic Energy. — *Kinetic energy is the kind of energy that a body has by virtue of its motion.* It will be possible to derive an expression for kinetic energy by remembering that the only effects of doing mechanical work on a body are to increase either its kinetic energy or its potential energy or to produce heat in opposing friction. The expression will be found by calculating the amount of work done upon a body during motion of translation under such conditions that there is no change in its potential energy and that no energy is wasted in opposing friction; under these conditions the work done will appear entirely in the form of kinetic energy.

Suppose that a block of weight W is at rest on a smooth horizontal plane and that a steady horizontal force F is exerted on it through a distance s, in which case an amount of work Fs is performed on the block. There being no friction, F acts as an unbalanced force causing the block to accelerate uniformly, in accordance with equation (33), $F = \dfrac{W}{g} \times a$. From the laws of uniformly accelerated motion [§ 29], the distance traversed by a body having the acceleration a and acquiring a velocity v starting from rest is found to be $s = \dfrac{v^2}{2a}$. The energy acquired by the block is obtained by substituting for F and s the values just found; thus it becomes

$$KE = Fs = \left(\frac{W}{g} \times a\right)\left(\frac{v^2}{2a}\right), \text{ or}$$

$$KE = \frac{Wv^2}{2g} \qquad (50)$$

This expression involves the weight of the body W and the acceleration of gravity g; it is therefore adapted to the gravitational systems of units. If the weight is expressed in pounds, and the velocity in feet per second, and if the value 32 ft./sec.[2] is used for g, it can easily be shown that the kinetic energy will be in foot-pounds.

Similarly, in absolute units, $KE = Fs = (m \times a)\left(\dfrac{v^2}{2a}\right)$, giving the kinetic energy of a body as

$$KE = \frac{m\,v^2}{2} \qquad (51)$$

It can be shown that with m in grams and v in centimeters per second, the kinetic energy is expressed in ergs.

To find the kinetic energy of a rotating body, suppose that a symmetrical body is free to turn about its center in frictionless bearings, and that a force F is applied to a pin A at the end of a radius r, F being at right angles to the radius, as shown in Fig. 81. The force produces a torque $T = Fr$, causing the body to sweep through an angle θ, starting from rest. The work done on the body, from equation (49), is $T\theta$. The body will accelerate in accordance with equation (39), $\alpha = \dfrac{T}{I}$, and in sweeping through the angle θ will acquire a velocity ω, such that $\theta = \dfrac{\omega^2}{2\alpha}$. But the kinetic energy of the body equals the work performed upon it, hence, in absolute units, $KE = T\theta = I\alpha \times \dfrac{\omega^2}{2\alpha}$, or

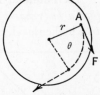

Fig. 81. Calculating kinetic energy of rotation

$$KE = \frac{I\omega^2}{2} \qquad (52)$$

This expression gives the kinetic energy of a rotating body having a moment of inertia I and an angular velocity ω. The student should have no difficulty in showing that in metric units, with I expressed in gram-centimeters^2 and ω in radians per second, KE will be in cm-dynes or ergs. In British units, α is obtained from equation (40), and it becomes necessary to divide equation (52) by g in order to have I expressed in pound-feet^2, ω in radians per second, and KE in foot-pounds.

A body that is undergoing both translation and rotation at the same time possesses an amount of energy $\dfrac{m\,v^2}{2}$ on account of its translation, and an amount $\dfrac{I\omega^2}{2}$ on account of its rotation. The total kinetic energy of such a body is, therefore,

$$KE = \frac{m\,v^2}{2} + \frac{I\omega^2}{2} \tag{53}$$

To obtain KE in foot-pounds from this equation, the numerical value obtained must be divided by g.

73. Potential Energy. — *Potential energy is the kind of energy that a body has by virtue of its position.* When a body is raised to a higher level, it is able to do a certain amount of work in falling

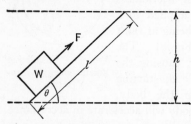

back again, and hence it was given this amount of potential energy in raising it. Although elevating a body is not the only way to give it potential energy, it is perhaps the most usual way. If the body is raised in such a manner that its kinetic energy is not increased, and without waste of energy on account of

FIG. 82. Calculating potential energy due to elevation

friction, the work done in raising it will all be expended in giving the body potential energy.

Suppose that a body of weight W is raised from one level to another at constant speed along a smooth plane, as represented in Fig. 82, the second level being a vertical distance h above the first. The plane has a length l and makes an angle θ with the horizontal. The force F necessary to move the weight along the plane with constant speed is $W \sin \theta$, and since this force is exerted through a distance l, the work done on the body, and hence the

potential energy given to the body, is $PE = W \sin \theta \times l = W\dfrac{h}{l} \times l$.

Consequently, in gravitational units,

$$PE = Wh \tag{54}$$

which shows that the amount of potential energy given to a body by raising it from one level to another depends only on the weight of the body and the vertical distance h between the two levels. Since the result is independent of the value of θ, the path of the body may be inclined at any angle, it may have different inclinations at different points, or it may be a curved surface. The potential energy of the body is not affected by the path over which it is moved in reaching a fixed elevation. In absolute units, the potentital energy due to elevation is found to be

$$PE = mgh \qquad (55)$$

The appropriate units may be found as explained previously for other equations.

It should be noted that potential energy is a relative term; a book raised a certain distance above a table has a certain potential energy with respect to the table, but has more potential energy with respect to the floor, since it is located further above the floor. Its potential energy with respect to the surface of the earth is again different, and so on.

74. Energy Wasted in Opposing Friction. — *Whenever one body moves upon another, some energy is used in opposing the friction present.* The amount of energy expended in this manner can be found by supposing work to be done upon a body under such conditions that neither the kinetic energy nor the potential energy of the body is increased, since the work done will then be used entirely in opposing friction. Suppose, then, that a body, having been started from rest, is moved at constant speed along a rough horizontal surface; to give it this motion a force must be exerted upon it equal and opposite to the maximum force of friction f, and the work done in exerting this force through a distance s is equal to the product fs. Hence, the energy used in opposing friction is

$$FE = fs \qquad (56)$$

The method of calculating f was discussed in § 45.

The energy used in opposing friction is converted into heat and is usually wasted. Frequently the heating is so slight as to escape notice, but sometimes it is quite evident, such as the heating produced in an automobile brake, in an overheated bearing, or in striking a match.

75. Application of Energy Principles. — The principles of work and energy provide a method of procedure by means of which many problems may be solved with great simplicity. To illustrate how these principles are applied, three typical problems will be considered.

I. It is required to find the time needed for a solid cylinder, starting from rest, to roll without sliding down a plane 200 cm. long, one end

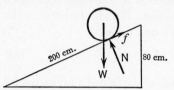

of which is raised 80 cm. higher than the other. The conditions of the problem are represented in Fig. 83.

Neglecting any waste of energy due to rolling friction, the cylinder will possess the same amount of energy when it reaches the bottom of the plane as it had at the top. At the

FIG. 83. Cylinder rolling down plane top, this is entirely in the form of potential energy, but as the cylinder rolls down, its potential energy becomes transformed into kinetic energy, partly of translation and partly of rotation. By equating the energies at the top and bottom of the incline, the velocity of the cylinder upon reaching the bottom can be found, and the desired time follows at once from the laws of uniformly accelerated motion.

The reduction in potential energy from top to bottom of the plane, from equation (55), is mgh; and the kinetic energy acquired upon reaching the bottom, from equation (53), is $\dfrac{mv^2}{2} + \dfrac{I\omega^2}{2}$. Equating these expressions, there results

$$mgh = \frac{mv^2}{2} + \frac{I\omega^2}{2}$$

where m is the mass of the cylinder, I is its moment of inertia about its own axis, v and ω are its linear and angular velocities respectively upon reaching the bottom of the incline, h is the elevation of the upper end of the plane, and g is the acceleration of gravity. Since the moment of inertia of the cylinder about its own axis is $I = \dfrac{mr^2}{2}$ [§ 56] and its angular velocity is $\omega = \dfrac{v}{r}$, the last term can be replaced by $\dfrac{I\omega^2}{2} = \dfrac{1}{2}\left(\dfrac{mr^2}{2}\right)\left(\dfrac{v}{r}\right)^2 = \dfrac{mv^2}{4}$; whence $mgh = \dfrac{mv^2}{2} + \dfrac{mv^2}{4} = \dfrac{3mv^2}{4}$; and

$$v = \sqrt{\frac{4gh}{3}} = \sqrt{\frac{4 \times 980 \frac{\text{cm.}}{\text{sec.}^2} \times 80 \text{ cm.}}{3}} = 324 \frac{\text{cm.}}{\text{sec.}}$$

Hence from equation (20), the time of descent is

$$t = \frac{2s}{v} = \frac{400 \text{ cm.}}{324 \frac{\text{cm.}}{\text{sec.}}} = 1.24 \text{ sec.}$$

This result may be verified by applying the dynamical methods of Chapter VI, using the forces represented by vectors W, N, and f in the figure.

II. A 2-ton weight in a pile driver is raised 12 ft. above the top of a pile and then released. What average force does it exert against the pile upon falling if it drives the pile 1 ft. into the ground?

In this case, the potential energy given up by the weight is expended in work done upon the pile; by equating these two quantities, the desired force can be found. Since the weight finally comes to rest 13 ft. below its initial position, its potential energy is reduced by an amount $Wh =$ 4000 lb. $\times$ 13 ft. = 52,000 ft-lb. The work done on the pile is $E = F \times s$ $= F \times 1$ ft., where F is the average force exerted upon it. Therefore $F \times 1$ ft. = 52,000 ft-lb., or $F = 52,000$ lb.

III. A box is placed at the top of a chute 50 ft. long, the first 20 ft. of the chute being inclined downward at an angle of 30 deg. with the horizontal, as shown in Fig. 84. If the coefficient of friction between the box and the chute is 0.2, find the velocity of the box as it leaves the chute at C.

In this problem, the potential energy which the box gives up as it moves from A is partly used in overcoming friction from A to B and from B to C, and the remainder appears in the form of kinetic energy at C. By writing the foregoing sentence in the form of an equation, the desired velocity can be found. The potential energy given up is mgh, where m is the mass of the box and h is its elevation. The energy used in opposing friction = (force of friction) $\times$ (distance) = (coefficient of friction) $\times$ (normal force between surfaces) $\times$ (distance). The box leaves the chute at C with a kinetic energy of $\frac{1}{2}mv^2$, where v is the terminating velocity. The energy equation becomes:

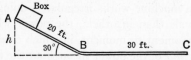

FIG. 84. Box sliding down chute

$$mgh = \mu(mg \cos 30°)\,(20 \text{ ft.}) + \mu(mg)\,(30 \text{ ft.}) + \frac{mv^2}{2}.$$

Cancelling the common factor m and solving for v, the result is that the box leaves the end of the chute with a velocity of 5.9 ft./sec.

POWER

76. Rate of Doing Work. — Practically in all cases where work is done, the amount of work is not the only item of importance, but the time during which that work is done is of equal consequence. Suppose, for example, that a motor-driven hoist is to be selected for raising a certain load. If the load has to be raised quickly, a more powerful hoist and a larger driving motor must be provided than if more time is allowed. Usually the size of machinery is determined, not by the total amount of work to be done, but by the rate at which it must be done; that is, the amount of work required per unit of time. *The time rate of doing work is called power.*

When 1 joule of work is performed per second, the power is called 1 *watt*. When 1 ft-lb. of work is done per second, the power is 1 *ft-lb. per sec.* If a machine working steadily performs 150,000 ft-lb. of work in 10 min., it does work at the rate of 15,000 ft-lb. every minute, and its power output is therefore 15,000 ft-lb. per min. or 250 ft-lb. per sec. Generalizing, the power P delivered by any agent which performs an amount of work E in a time interval t is given by the relation

$$P = \frac{E}{t} \qquad (57)$$

If a machine operates steadily, performing the same amount of work every second, the power which it delivers is constant. But if a machine works irregularly, doing more work during some intervals than in others, the power which it delivers fluctuates from moment to moment, in which case equation (57) gives the *average value* of the power throughout the time interval considered.

Since power is the time rate of doing work, the unit for power in any system of units is found by dividing the work unit in that system by the time unit. Thus, in the c.g.s. system, power is expressed in ergs per second, and in the British gravitational system, power is expressed in foot-pounds per second. In addition to the units which occur in the standard systems of units, there are other practical units for power which are much used in engineering work. *The horsepower (hp.) is the power delivered by an agent while doing work at the rate of 550 ft-lb. per sec. or 33,000 ft-lb. per min.* The watt and the kilowatt (kw.) are power units used in rating electrical machines. The relations between some power units are given below:

Units of Power

$$1 \text{ watt} = 10^7 \frac{\text{ergs}}{\text{sec.}} = 1 \frac{\text{joule}}{\text{sec.}}$$

$$1 \text{ hp.} = 550 \frac{\text{ft-lb.}}{\text{sec.}} = 33{,}000 \frac{\text{ft-lb.}}{\text{min.}}$$

$$1 \text{ hp.} = 746 \text{ watts}$$

$$1 \text{ kw.} = 1000 \text{ watts} = 1.34 \text{ hp.}$$

$$1 \text{ ft-lb. per sec.} = 1.356 \text{ watts}$$

The use of power units will be illustrated by considering some practical examples.

I. A horse exerts a horizontal pull of 100 lb. on a load; how fast must he walk in order to develop exactly 1 hp.? Here the horse is to do 550 ft-lb. of work each second, meantime exerting a force of 100 lb. and hence, from equation (47), he must travel each second a distance

$$s = \frac{E}{F} = \frac{550 \text{ ft-lb.}}{100 \text{ lb.}} = 5.5 \text{ ft.}$$

II. Calculate the power wasted in friction in a sleeve bearing supporting a 2-in. shaft which turns at 480 rev. per min., if the shaft presses against the bearing with a force of 1 ton, and the coefficient of friction between the sliding surfaces is 0.005. The force of friction, from equation (34), is 0.005×2000 lb. $= 10$ lb. This force is tangent to the shaft at its rim, and is thus exerted through a distance $\frac{2\pi}{12}$ ft. in each revolution. Hence the work done in opposing friction during one minute, from equation (56), is

$$FE = fs = 10 \text{ lb.} \times \frac{2\pi}{12} \frac{\text{ft.}}{\text{rev.}} \times 480 \text{ rev.} = 2510 \text{ ft-lb.}$$

which is equivalent to $\frac{2510}{33,000} = 0.076$ hp.

The relation between work and power is emphasized by transposing equation (57) to read: $E = Pt$. In this form, the expression shows that if an agent delivers an amount of power P continuously for a period of time t, the agent does an amount of work E which is equal to the product of P and t. This conception of work as the product of power and time values leads to some energy units which are widely used in engineering practice. The *horse-power-hour* (hp-hr.) is thus a unit of work, being the amount of work performed when power is expended at the rate of one horsepower over a period of one hour. Similarly, the *kilowatt-hour* (kw-hr.), the unit upon which the cost of electrical energy is based, is the amount of work performed when power is used at the rate of one kilowatt over a period of one hour. If an engine delivers 60 hp. steadily for 5 hr., it does $60 \times 5 = 300$ hp-hr. of work, and if a motor requires 12 kw. steadily for 4 hr., it requires $12 \times 4 = 48$ kw-hr. of electrical energy.

*77. Measurement of Mechanical Power. — The mechanical output of a rotating machine can be measured by equipping the machine with a special form of brake which absorbs the output of the machine in friction and converts it into heat, and which at the same time measures the amount of power delivered.

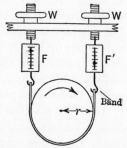

FIG. 85. Measuring power output with a band brake

A simple style of brake used for small machines consists of a band of asbestos fabric which passes around the rotating pulley of the machine and is supported at the ends, as shown in Fig. 85. Two hand-wheels WW serve to tighten or loosen the band, thus regulating the output of the machine, and two spring balances show how much force is being exerted on the ends of the band. When arranged as in the figure, the band is dragged around in a clockwise direction by friction at the rim of the rotating pulley and remains slightly displaced. The band is in equilibrium under the action of three torques, as follows: one due to the drag of friction f at the rim of the pulley tending to twist the band clockwise, one due to the force F' which is counter-clockwise, opposing the drag of friction, and one due to the force F, which is clockwise. For equilibrium, the clockwise torques must balance the counterclockwise torques, thus

$$fr + Fr = F'r, \qquad \text{whence} \qquad f = F' - F.$$

The force of friction acting on the band is, therefore, equal to the difference between the spring-balance readings. But the machine in opposing friction does an amount of work $f \times (2\pi r)$ during each revolution, or $f \times (2\pi rn)$ in one minute, where n is the number of revolutions which it makes per minute. Expressing forces in pounds and the radius in feet, the power output of the machine in foot-pounds per minute is $(2\pi rn) \times f$ or $2\pi rn (F' - F)$; or

$$\text{Output} = 2\pi rn (F' - F)\frac{\text{ft.-lb.}}{\text{min.}} \times \frac{1 \text{ hp.}}{33,000\frac{\text{ft.-lb.}}{\text{min.}}} = \frac{2\pi rn(F' - F)}{33,000} \text{ hp.}$$

MACHINES

78. Simple Machines. — It is a matter of common experience that a stone firmly embedded in the ground can usually be dislodged easily with a crowbar, and that a heavy automobile can be raised with ease by means of a jack. The crowbar or jack serves as an intermediate device upon which work may be done, and which in turn will do work upon some other object. A device which accomplishes this result is technically called a *machine*. The complex machines used in industry are found upon analysis to be made up largely of certain elements which may be considered simple machines in themselves. These simple machines are generally considered as comprising the lever, the wheel and axle, the pulley, the inclined plane, the screw, and the wedge.

Usually a machine is used in order to lessen the force required in doing a certain piece of work. Thus, if a 500-lb. weight is to be lifted, a machine may be used to exert this amount of upward force upon it while the person operating the machine exerts a smaller force, say only 50 lb. It is thus possible, and indeed usual, to obtain a larger force from a machine than that which is exerted upon it. Note that *this statement applies to force and not to energy;* for according to the law of conservation of energy *more work cannot be obtained from a machine than the energy that is supplied to it.* It is evident, since work = force × distance, that when a machine exerts a larger force than does the operator, it must exert the larger force through a correspondingly shorter distance.

79. Efficiency. — On account of the waste due to friction in all moving machinery, the energy given out by a machine is less than that supplied to it. More definitely, the principle of conservation of energy shows that

$$\text{energy input} = \text{energy output} + \text{energy wasted},$$

assuming that no energy is stored up in the machine. This statement is true over any period of time, and hence applies to unit time; and since work or energy per unit time is power, it can also be said that

$$\text{power input} = \text{power output} + \text{power wasted}.$$

The efficiency of a machine is defined as the ratio of its output to its input, both output and input being expressed in the same units of energy or power. This ratio is always less than unity, and is usually multiplied by 100 and expressed in per cent. Thus,

$$\left.\begin{array}{l} \text{Per cent efficiency} = \dfrac{\text{energy output}}{\text{energy input}} \times 100 \\[3mm] \text{Per cent efficiency} = \dfrac{\text{power output}}{\text{power input}} \times 100 \end{array}\right\} \quad (58)$$

or

A machine has a high efficiency if a large part of the power supplied to it is given out by the machine to its load and only a small part wasted. The efficiency may be as high as 98% for a large electrical generator and will be below 50% for a screw jack.

Suppose it is desired to calculate the power supplied to a 10-hp. motor which is delivering its full rated output at an efficiency of 85%. Transposing equation (58),

$$\text{Power input} = \frac{\text{power output} \times 100}{\text{per cent efficiency}} = \frac{10 \text{ hp.} \times 100}{85} = 11.75 \text{ hp.}$$

Machines are rated in terms of their *output;* thus, a 10-hp. motor, such as that referred to in the foregoing problem, is one which is capable of *delivering* 10 hp. without exceeding its design limitations.

80. Mechanical Advantage. — The utility of a machine, as pointed out in § 78, is chiefly its capacity for enabling a person to lift a load or to do some similar mechanical work by the application of a comparatively small force. The ratio of the force W exerted by a machine on a load to the force F exerted by an operator on the machine, is called the *mechanical advantage* of the machine. If a machine is available which has a mechanical advantage of 20, the force which must be exerted upon it in raising a load weighing 1 ton is 2000 lb. ÷ 20 = 100 lb.

If it is assumed that the machine operates without friction, the ratio $\dfrac{W}{F}$ is called the *theoretical mechanical advantage* (TA) of that machine. Hence, neglecting friction,

$$TA = \frac{W}{F} \tag{59}$$

Under this assumption the energy output would equal the energy input, an ideal condition which cannot be attained in practice. Suppose the machine to exert the force W through a distance h while the operator exerts his force F through a distance s. Equating the energy output and the energy input, $Wh = Fs$, whence $\dfrac{W}{F} = \dfrac{s}{h}$. Therefore the theoretical mechanical advantage can also be expressed in terms of these distances, as follows:

$$TA = \frac{s}{h} \tag{60}$$

If, on the other hand, friction is considered in calculating the mechanical advantage of a machine, or if the mechanical advantage is found by actual test, in which case friction would be present and produce a loss, the result is called the *actual mechanical advantage*, and is expressed by the actual force ratio $\dfrac{W}{F}$.

81. Mechanical Advantage of Machines. — The actual mechanical advantage of a machine, such as the simple machines listed in § 78, cannot be calculated with great exactness, since such a calculation would involve a knowledge of the frictional forces and these are uncertain because the coefficient of friction is not very definite [§ 45].

The theoretical mechanical advantage, on the other hand, can be calculated without difficulty, since friction is assumed to be absent. The general equations (59) and (60) will be applied in determining the theoretical mechanical advantage of the various simple machines mentioned. In finding these expressions, the procedure followed in each case will be to assume that the machine exerts a force W through a distance h while the operator exerts a force F through a distance s; the ratio $\dfrac{W}{F}$ or $\dfrac{s}{h}$ is then expressed in terms of the dimensions of the machine.

I. In the *lever*, one class of which is shown in Fig. 86, a bar of length AB is arranged with a fulcrum at X, dividing its length into two parts, l_1 and l_2, as shown. In order for the machine to raise a load W through a height h, the operator exerts a force F downward through a distance s. The triangles AXC and BXD

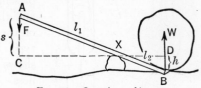

Fig. 86. One class of lever

are similar, and their corresponding sides are proportional; hence $\dfrac{s}{h} = \dfrac{l_1}{l_2}$, and the theoretical mechanical advantage of the lever shown is

$$TA = \frac{l_1}{l_2}$$

Other arrangements of the lever are frequently used, the fulcrum being differently located with respect to the forces F and W, but the theoretical mechanical advantage is found in the same way.

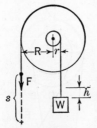

Fig. 87. Wheel and axle

II. The *wheel and axle*, shown in Fig. 87, is a modified form of lever, consisting of a wheel of radius R fastened to an axle of radius r. A rope attached to the axle extends to the load W, and another rope attached to the wheel enables the operator to exert a force upon the machine. In order to raise the load through a height h, the operator exerts his force F through a distance s. During this process, the wheel and axle turn through an angle θ such that $\theta = \dfrac{h}{r}$ and also $\theta = \dfrac{s}{R}$. Hence $\dfrac{s}{h} = \dfrac{R}{r}$, and the theoretical mechanical advantage of the wheel and axle is

$$TA = \frac{R}{r}$$

III. The *pulley* is used in a variety of ways. A single pulley merely produces a change in the direction of the force, and the mechanical advantage is unity. By using a combination of pulleys, a considerable mechanical advantage may be secured. In a typ-

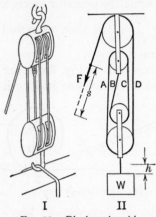

ical pulley system, shown in Fig. 88, each block consists of two pulleys or sheaves encased in a frame or shell. The upper block is fixed and the lower one is attached to the load and moves with it, a rope fastened at one end passing around the several pulleys and thence to the operator. Part I of the figure represents a common type of construction, and part II shows the pulleys separated for clearness. It will be clear that in order to raise the load through a height h, each of the four ropes A, B, C, and D must be shortened by this amount,

I   II

FIG. 88.   Block and tackle

hence the operator must exert his force F through a distance and $s = 4h$, making $\dfrac{s}{h} = 4$. Therefore, the theoretical mechanical

advantage of the arrangement shown is 4, corresponding to the four ropes used to support W. For any pulley system arranged in the same general manner as that shown, the theoretical mechanical advantage is equal to the number of parallel ropes supporting the load.

IV. The *differential pulley* is an interesting modification of the simple pulley, in which an endless chain passes over toothed pulleys as represented in Fig. 89. At the top are two pulleys having nearly equal radii R and r and which are rigidly fastened together, turning in a block suspended from above. At the bottom a pulley of any convenient size turns in another block which is attached to the load and moves with it. In raising the weight, the operator exerts a downward force on the chain at D, the portions A

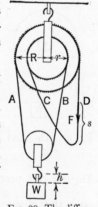

FIG. 89. The differential pulley

and B of the chain supporting the load, while the portion C remains slack. Suppose that in raising the load through a height *h* the operator exerts his force through a distance *s*. During this process the top pulleys rotate clockwise through an angle θ such that $\theta = \dfrac{s}{R}$. This rotation shortens the chain at *A* by an amount θR and lengthens the chain at *B* by an amount θr. As a result the loop *AB* is shortened a net amount $\theta R - \theta r = \theta(R - r)$, and the load is raised one-half of this distance, or $h = \frac{1}{2}\theta(R - r)$. But $s = \theta R$, and hence $\dfrac{s}{h} = \dfrac{\theta R}{\frac{1}{2}\theta(R - r)} = \dfrac{2R}{R - r}$; therefore the theoretical mechanical advantage of the differential pulley is

$$TA = \frac{2R}{R - r}$$

V. An *inclined plane*, Fig. 90, may also be used to reduce the force needed in raising an object. To push the object up a smooth plane inclined at an angle θ with the horizontal requires a force $F = W \sin \theta$ along the plane, and in order to raise the object through a vertical height *h*, this force must be exerted through a distance

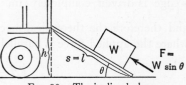

FIG. 90. The inclined plane

$s = l$. The ratio of *W* to *F* or the ratio of *s* to *h* is equal to $\dfrac{1}{\sin \theta}$ or $\dfrac{l}{h}$, and therefore the theoretical mechanical advantage of an inclined plane, where the force is exerted along the direction of the incline, is

$$TA = \frac{l}{h}$$

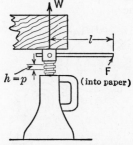

FIG. 91. A screw jack

VI. The *screw* may be looked upon as an inclined plane wrapped around a cylinder. In a common form of screw jack, an upright screw threads into a stationary base and supports a load at the top, the screw being turned by means of a horizontal bar, as shown in Fig. 91. In order to raise the load *W* a distance *h* equal to the pitch *p* of the screw, the operator exerts a force *F* at the end of the bar through a circle of length $s = 2\pi l$, where *l* is the length of the bar. Hence $\dfrac{s}{h} = \dfrac{2\pi l}{p}$, and therefore the theoretical mechanical advantage of the screw jack is

$$TA = \frac{2\pi l}{p}$$

VII. The *wedge*, Fig. 92, consists of a block having a base of

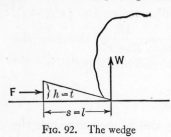

length l and a thickness which varies from t at one end to zero at the other. When placed under a load, it is caused to exert an upward force W through a distance h by driving it with a force F through a larger distance s. If the force F is parallel to the base, the ratio of s to h is easily found, for if the

FIG. 92. The wedge

wedge is driven completely in, $s = l$ and $h = t$. Thus $\dfrac{s}{h} = \dfrac{l}{t}$, and therefore the theoretical mechanical advantage of the wedge, where the applied force is parallel to the base, is

$$TA = \frac{l}{t}$$

VIII. *Gear wheels* are used in rotating machinery not only to transmit motion from one point to another, but also for the mechanical advantage which they offer. Since the same time interval is used by the operator in exerting his force F through the distance s as is occupied by the machine in exerting the force W through the distance h, the theoretical mechanical advantage of a machine may be expressed equally well by the ratio

$$TA = \frac{\text{speed of operator}}{\text{speed of machine}}$$

Applying this expression to angular motion, if one shaft drives another by means of gear wheels, as in Fig. 93, the angular speeds of these shafts are inversely proportional to the numbers of teeth on their respective gear wheels, and therefore, if the driving gear has n teeth and the driven gear has n' teeth, the theoretical mechanical advantage of a

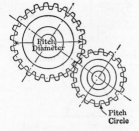

FIG. 93. Gear wheels

pair of gear wheels is

$$TA = \frac{n'}{n}$$

If n' is larger than n, the driven gear having the larger number of teeth, the driven shaft turns slower than the driving shaft, and exerts a larger torque through a smaller angle. The same results may also be obtained where one shaft is driven from another by means of a chain or a belt.

Illustration. A single illustration will serve to coordinate the ideas of efficiency and mechanical advantage of a machine.

Suppose that an operator exerts a force of 40 lb. in raising a load weighing 360 lb. with a wheel and axle having radii of 12 in. and 1 in. respectively. The actual mechanical advantage of the machine is $\frac{W}{F} = \frac{360 \text{ lb.}}{40 \text{ lb.}}$ = 9, and the theoretical mechanical advantage is $\frac{R}{r} = \frac{12 \text{ in.}}{1 \text{ in.}} = 12$. Since in raising the load 1 ft. the operator exerts his force through a distance of 12 ft., the energy output is 360 lb. $\times$ 1 ft. = 360 ft-lb., and the energy input is 40 lb. $\times$ 12 ft. = 480 ft-lb. The efficiency is therefore $\frac{360 \text{ ft-lb.}}{480 \text{ ft-lb.}} \times 100 = 75\%$.

Incidentally, it may be stated that the efficiency of a machine is always equal to the ratio of the actual mechanical advantage to the theoretical mechanical advantage. This statement may be verified without difficulty from the results calculated in the foregoing illustration.

PROBLEMS

1. How much work is done in lifting an 80-lb. anchor upward through a distance of 5 fathoms (1 fathom = 6 ft.)?

2. How much work is done on a 4-ton elevator in accelerating it upward at 3 ft. per sec. per sec. for a period of 5 sec., starting from rest?

3. A horizontal push is exerted on a 100-lb. box through a distance of 30 ft., causing the box to slide along a level floor at constant speed. If the coefficient of friction between the box and the floor is 0.3, calculate the amount of work done.

4. A pull of 5 lb. is exerted upon a sled, drawing the sled 100 ft. along a level surface. If the direction of pull makes an angle of 20° upward from the horizontal, how much work is done?

5. How much work must be done in pushing a 75-lb. sled 200 ft. along a level surface at constant speed, if the push is applied in a downward direction at an angle of 45° with the horizontal, assuming the coefficient of friction between the sled and the surface to be 0.05?

6. A 600-lb. flywheel has a radius of gyration of $1\frac{1}{2}$ ft. What torque is needed to bring the wheel from rest to a speed of 120 rev. per min. in 30 sec., and how much work is done in this interval?

W = 3330   T = 17L.7 *UH.*

7. From what height must a 100-lb. weight fall in order to have the same amount of kinetic energy as a 2-ton truck traveling at 25 mi. per hr.?

8. Each propeller of the S.S. Normandie has a mass of 19 tons and a radius of gyration of 7 ft. With four such propellers revolving at 200 rev. per min. the speed of the ship is 29 knots. Determine the moment of inertia of each propeller, and compute how much energy of rotation the four propellers have at the speed stated.

9. A grindstone 24 in. in diameter is driven at a constant speed of 80 rev. per min., and an axe is pressed perpendicularly against it with a force of 20 lb. for a period of 5 min. Taking the coefficient of sliding friction between the axe and the stone as 0.3, find how much energy was used in grinding the axe.

10. A 50-gm. pendulum bob on a 100-cm. cord sweeps through an angle of 60° as it vibrates to and fro. (a) How much is the potential energy of the bob increased as it moves from its midposition to the end of *1 ʟʙ 9ᵐ* its travel? (b) With what velocity does it sweep through its midposition?

11. The stabilizer plant of the S.S. Conte di Savoia consists of three gyro-stabilizing units which may be used together or separately. Each unit has a rotor 13.0 ft. in diameter with a normal speed of 800 rev. per min. The weight of each rotor is 246,000 lb. and its moment of inertia is 4,700,000 lb-ft.² Determine the radius of gyration of the rotor and its kinetic energy at the speed stated.

12. A wheel of a trolley car has an overall diameter of 24 in., a radius of gyration of 9 in., and a mass of 260 lb. Calculate its kinetic energy when the trolley car has a speed of 20 mi. per hr.   *1965 FT. LBS.*

13. There are 2240 steps in the Empire State Building in New York City from the pavement to the 103d floor, with 18 steps for each 10-ft. rise. In 1937, A. W. Aldrich, whose weight is 120 lb., climbed these steps in 36 min., 22 sec. What average horsepower did he develop during the climb?

14. An automobile weighing 3000 lb. driven at 40 mi. per hr. is brought to rest by the brakes in 100 ft. Find (a) the time required in stopping, and (b) the number of horsepower expended in the brakes.

15. Calculate the horsepower developed in a steam engine in which the steam exerts a force of 11,000 lb. on a piston and moves it forward and backward 90 times a minute through a distance of 14 in. each way.

16. A 500-ton locomotive of recent design develops 5000 hp. while hauling a 1000-ton train at a constant speed of 110 mi. per hr. along a level track. Under these conditions, compute (a) the kinetic energy of the locomotive together with the train, and (b) the retarding force due to friction which acts upon them.

17. Owing to the small amount of friction in the bearings of the new 200-in. telescope, only 0.00000625 hp. is required to turn it at the rate of 1 rev. per day. Compute the value of the retarding torque due to friction.

18. How heavy a load can a 15-hp. hoist lift at a steady speed of 240 ft. per min. without exceeding its rated output?

19. What horsepower is being transmitted by a steel shaft which turns at 1080 rev. per min. while exerting a torque of 15,000 lb-in.?

20. A 10-hp. motor operates at rated load for 8 hr. a day. Its efficiency is 87%. How much does it cost to operate it daily if electrical energy costs 5 cents per kw-hr.?

21. A motor drives a hoist which in turn lifts a ½-ton load 100 ft. in 18 sec. If the hoist has an efficiency of 40% and the motor an efficiency of 80%, find how many watts are supplied (a) to the load, (b) to the hoist, and (c) to the motor.

22. What horsepower must be developed by the engine of an automobile running at 30 mi. per hr. while exerting a tractive pull of 400 lb., if 20 per cent of the power developed is wasted?

23. A screw jack has a screw of $\frac{1}{4}$-in. pitch which is turned by a bar 2 ft. long. What load could be lifted by a 20-lb. push at the end of the bar if friction were neglected?

24. A force of 3 lb. is required to raise a weight of 16 lb. by means of a pulley system. If the weight is raised 1 ft. while the applied force is exerted through a distance of 8 ft., find (*a*) the theoretical mechanical advantage, (*b*) the actual mechanical advantage, and (*c*) the efficiency of the pulley system.

25. An escalator carries persons from one floor to another 18 ft. higher, and the steps move with a speed of 80 ft. per min. along the incline. The steps are 8 in. high and measure 16 in. from edge to edge along the direction of motion. Taking the overall efficiency to be 60 per cent, what size motor is needed to take care of a load of 125 lb. per step?

26. The two upper pulleys of a differential pulley hoist have diameters of $11\frac{1}{2}$ in. and 12 in. respectively. Upon testing this machine it is found necessary to apply a force of 54 lb. in raising a $\frac{1}{2}$-ton load. Calculate the theoretical mechanical advantage, the actual mechanical advantage, and the efficiency of this machine.

CHAPTER IX

HARMONIC MOTION

82. Harmonic Motion Defined. — In addition to uniform motion and uniformly accelerated motion considered previously, there is another type of importance which is of common occurrence. It is a vibratory motion, in which the moving object sweeps back and forth repeatedly over the same path. Such motion may be illustrated by the oscillation of a weight hanging from the end of a coiled spring, the swinging of the bob of a long pendulum, or the vibration of the prongs of a tuning fork.

To investigate the characteristics of this type of motion, suppose that a weight fastened to a coiled spring is pulled down and released, so that it vibrates up and down about its original position as a central point. In pulling the weight down, if only a small force is applied, the spring stretches only slightly, and if more force is applied, it stretches more; provided that the force is not too large, the stretching force and the extension of the spring vary in direct proportion. This behavior is, indeed, characteristic of elastic substances, and the properties of these will be studied in the following chapter.

Whenever a force is applied to stretch the spring, there is set up within it an equal force in the opposite direction, in accordance with Newton's Third Law of Motion. It is this restoring force which causes the spring to pull the weight up when it is released. Since acceleration is proportional to the force which causes it, the acceleration of the weight is proportional to the restoring force and thus varies directly as the displacement of the weight from its central position of equilibrium. It may also be observed that when the displacement is downward, the restoring force and acceleration are directed upward, and vice versa. Summarizing, it is found that in this vibratory motion, *the acceleration of the vibrating body and the restoring force acting upon it are proportional to its displacement from the midpoint of its path, and are directed toward that point.* This type of motion is known as simple harmonic motion, or, more briefly, *harmonic motion.*

150

83. Relation Between Circular and Harmonic Motion. — The study of harmonic motion is much simplified by the discovery of a relation that it bears to motion in a circle. If a body describing uniform circular motion is viewed in the plane of the circle, it will be observed to vibrate to and fro along a line equal in length to the diameter of the circle, and this particular form of vibratory motion is found to be harmonic motion. In brief, the projection of uniform circular motion upon a diameter of the circle is harmonic motion. This kind of motion can be produced mechanically by a disk and a bar coupled by a pin-and-slot arrangement as shown in Fig. 94. The projecting pin near the rim of the disk engages the slot in the bar, the bar itself being supported in stationary guides to constrain its motion to the vertical direction. When the disk is driven at constant speed, the pin moves uniformly in a circle, but the bar receives only the vertical projection of this motion, and consequently slides up and down across the diameter of the circle with harmonic motion.

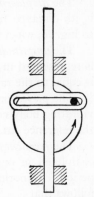

Fig. 94. Illustrating harmonic motion

84. Amplitude, Frequency, and Related Terms. — Usually when a body describes harmonic motion, there is no associated body which actually travels with circular motion as just described. It is then convenient to construct an artificial *reference circle*, and to imagine a body moving uniformly around it, as in Fig. 95. Here, if a body vibrates up and down harmonically along CD, its motion can always be considered as the projection of the motion of another body that is assumed to revolve uniformly around a reference circle of diameter $C'D'$. Thus, when the revolving body is at M', the vibrating body is at the midpoint M of its path; as the revolving body moves to P', the vibrating body moves to P; when the revolving body reaches D', the vibrating body arrives at D, and so on. In this way the angle θ at the center O increases, sweeping out 2π radians in each revolution.

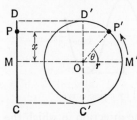

Fig. 95. The relation between harmonic and circular motion

When the body in harmonic motion moves from M to D, then from D to C, and finally from C back to M, it has completed one *vibration*. More briefly, a vibration is a complete to-and-fro movement of the body over its entire path. It corresponds to a complete revolution of the body in the reference circle.

The *displacement* of a body in harmonic motion at any instant is its distance from the midposition at that instant. Referring to Fig. 95, when the body is at P its displacement is $x = MP$.

The *amplitude* of a vibration is the maximum displacement, and is represented in the figure by either MC or MD. The amplitude is equal to the radius r of the reference circle.

The *period* or *periodic time* is the time interval during which a vibrating body completes one vibration. In this time the body in the reference circle makes one revolution.

The *frequency* of vibratory motion is the number of vibrations completed in one second, and is therefore the reciprocal of the period. Denoting the frequency by n and the period by T, it follows that

$$n = \frac{1}{T}$$

The *equilibrium position* of a body in harmonic motion is the midpoint of its path. In the figure, the equilibrium position is at point M.

85. Sinusoidal Representation. — A body having harmonic motion continually traces the same path over and over, and this

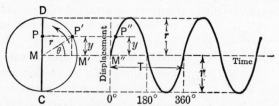

FIG. 96. Vibratory motion represented by a sine curve

fact makes it difficult to indicate clearly the direction in which the body is moving at a particular instant. To overcome this difficulty, the path of the vibration may be spread out laterally to form a curve such as shown in Fig. 96. This curve combines the harmonic motion up and down with uniform linear motion sideways, the two motions being at right angles. Such a curve can be traced on a strip of paper by a body vibrating on the path CD if the paper

is moved uniformly in a transverse direction. The starting point
M'' of the curve represents the vibrating body at an instant when
it is at point M and moving upward, the corresponding body in the
reference circle being at M'. As this body rotates through the
angle θ to the position P', the curve advances to P'', which therefore represents the vibrating body when at the point P. In a
similar manner, the entire vibration may be mapped out, and
the position and direction of the vibrating body may be identified
at any instant by a corresponding point on the curve.

The amplitude of the vibration is represented on the curve by
the distance r between the extreme points and the axis; and the
displacement at a particular instant, which is variously referred to
as x or y, is indicated by the distance marked y in the figure. The
angle θ through which P' has rotated from its assumed datum position M' is called the *phase angle*. At the instant represented by
P, P', and P'' in the figure, the phase of the vibration is 30° or
$\frac{1}{12}$ period. Phase angles may also be indicated on the curve as
shown, since in one period T the curve advances a complete cycle,
while the phase angle increases from 0° to 360°. The displacement of the particle can be expressed in terms of the angular
position, for the ratio of y to r is equal to sin θ. If t is the time
reckoned from the instant when $\theta = 0$, the angular velocity of the
radius r can be expressed as $\omega = \theta/t$, whence $\theta = \omega t$, and the displacement becomes

$$y = r \sin \theta = r \sin \omega t$$

This equation indicates why the curve is called a sine **curve**.

86. Velocity in Harmonic Motion. — In the foregoing sine
curve representing the motion of a vibrating body, the slope at
any point shows how rapidly
the displacement is changing
at the corresponding instant,
and thus the slope of the
curve at that point is an
indication of the instan-
taneous velocity. The slope
varies from zero at the extreme points to a maximum
where the curve crosses the

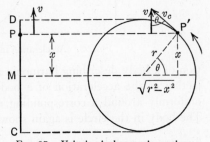

Fig. 97.   Velocity in harmonic motion

axis, consequently the velocity of the vibrating body shows these
same variations.

In Fig. 97 a body having harmonic motion along CD is represented as the projection of a second body moving uniformly around a reference circle of radius $r = CD/2$. At a particular instant when the body in the circle is at point P', its velocity is represented by a vector v_c (the subscript referring to the *circle* as path); this vector is tangent to the circle at P' and represents a constant speed of $2\pi r n$, where n is the frequency. At the instant mentioned, the body having harmonic motion is at P, the projection of P' on the path CD; its velocity is represented by v, the projection of v_c on that path. The angle between v_c and v is equal to the phase angle θ at the center, and hence $v = v_c \cos \theta$. But $v_c = 2\pi r n$ and $\cos \theta = \dfrac{\sqrt{r^2 - x^2}}{r}$, hence the instantaneous velocity of the body in harmonic motion when it is passing a point distant x from the equilibrium position is

$$v = 2\pi n \sqrt{r^2 - x^2} \tag{61}$$

The velocity has a maximum value of $v = 2\pi r n$ when the body is at the equilibrium position M for which $x = 0$, and is zero when the body is at the end points C and D for which $x = r$.

87. Acceleration and Restoring Force in Harmonic Motion. — Following the procedure used in the foregoing section, the accelera-

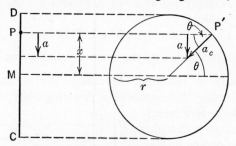

Fig. 98.   Acceleration in harmonic motion

tion of a body describing harmonic motion is regarded as the projection of the acceleration of a body which is assumed to travel uniformly around a corresponding reference circle, as in Fig. 98. The body in the circle is again shown at P', its acceleration being directed toward the center and having the value $a_c = \dfrac{v_c^2}{r}$ exactly as in equation (35) except that the subscript is used here to designate the path as circular. At the same instant, the body describing harmonic motion is at P, and its acceleration is represented by a, the projection of a_c along the path CD, thus $a = - a_c \sin \theta$. But $v_c = 2\pi r n$ and $\sin \theta = x/r$, whence

$$a = - 4\pi^2 n^2 x \qquad (62)$$

The negative sign is introduced to show that the acceleration is opposite in direction to the displacement.

The acceleration is zero at the instant the vibrating body sweeps through the equilibrium position M for which $x = 0$, and has its maximum value at the end positions C and D, being then equal to the acceleration of the body in the reference circle, $4\pi^2 n^2 r$.

In deriving the expressions for velocity and acceleration in harmonic motion, a vertical vibration was used for illustration. However, the final equations involve only the frequency, displacement, and amplitude, and hence apply to vibrations along any direction.

Since a body describing harmonic motion is continually being accelerated toward its midposition, and since an unbalanced force is necessary to produce acceleration, it follows that such a body must be acted upon continually by an unbalanced restoring force. This force may be calculated in gravitational units from equation (33), thus:

$$F = \frac{W}{g} \times a = \frac{W}{g} \times (-4\pi^2 n^2 x)$$

from which the ratio of the force to the displacement is found to be

$$\frac{F}{x} = - 4\pi^2 n^2 \frac{W}{g} \qquad (63)$$

W being the weight of the vibrating body and g the acceleration of gravity. Similarly, in absolute units, $F = ma = m \times (-4\pi^2 n^2 x)$, whence

$$\frac{F}{x} = - 4\pi^2 n^2 m \qquad (64)$$

where m represents the mass of the vibrating body.

Characteristics of Harmonic Motion.—Since $4\pi^2$ in the foregoing equations is a numerical constant, and n, W, g, and m are fixed for any one vibrating body under particular conditions, the expressions for acceleration and force may be written: $a \propto - x$ and $F \propto - x$, which show that both acceleration and force are proportional to the displacement of the body. These facts conform to the definition in § 82, and show that the projection of uniform circular motion upon a diameter of the circle is harmonic motion.

88. Illustrative Problem. — The foregoing principles may be illustrated by the behavior of a block attached to a flexible spring. The spring is elastic (see Chapter X) and sets up a restoring force when distorted, which force is proportional to the amount of distortion. When the block is released, it will vibrate with harmonic motion, and the foregoing expressions may be applied.

Suppose that a 15-lb. block, which originally hangs at the bottom of a long helical spring, is pulled down 1 ft., a force of 5 lb. being needed to hold it at this point, and then released. Calculate the frequency of vibration, and also the velocity and acceleration of the block at an instant when it is 3 in. above its original position.

The block upon release sweeps upward through its original position and vibrates above and below it with an amplitude $r = 1$ ft. which will remain the same if friction is ignored. Since a force of 5 lb. is needed to produce a displacement of 1 ft., the restoring force F is also equal to 5 lb. when $x = 1$ ft. Also, the weight of the vibrating body is 15 lb., neglecting the weight of the spring. Therefore, rearranging equation (63), the frequency is found to be

$$n = \frac{1}{2\pi} \sqrt{\frac{F}{x} \times \frac{g}{W}} = \frac{1}{2\pi} \sqrt{\frac{5 \text{ lb.}}{1 \text{ ft.}} \times \frac{32 \frac{\text{ft.}}{\text{sec.}^2}}{15 \text{ lb.}}} = 0.52 \text{ per sec.}$$

At an instant when the block is 3 in. above the equilibrium position, $x = 3$ in. $= \frac{1}{4}$ ft., and the velocity, from equation (61), is

$$v = 2\pi n \sqrt{r^2 - x^2} = 2\pi \times \frac{0.52}{\text{sec.}} \sqrt{(1 \text{ ft.})^2 - (\tfrac{1}{4} \text{ ft.})^2} = 3.16 \frac{\text{ft.}}{\text{sec.}}.$$

Similarly, the acceleration of the block at this instant is found from equation (62) as follows:

$$a = -4\pi^2 n^2 x = -4\pi^2 \left(\frac{0.52}{\text{sec.}}\right)^2 (\tfrac{1}{4} \text{ ft.}) = -2.67 \frac{\text{ft.}}{\text{sec.}^2}.$$

89. The Simple Pendulum. — The *simple pendulum* consists of a concentrated mass at the end of a cord of negligible weight. It is closely approximated by a small metal bob carried by a thin thread. The time of vibration of such a pendulum can be found by considering the pendulum bob as slightly displaced and studying the forces acting upon it; such analysis will show that the unbalanced force is proportional to the displacement. It then follows that the vibration of the bob is harmonic, and the equations of harmonic motion can be applied to determine the period.

Consider a pendulum bob B suspended from S by a thin cord of length l which has been displaced slightly to one side, as in Fig. 99. Two forces act upon the bob: the attraction of gravity, W, vertically downward, and the pull P in the cord acting toward S. The resultant or unbalanced force F acting on the bob is found by completing a parallelogram as in the figure, from which it is seen that the angles marked β are equal. The force F acts at right angles to the cord, since this is the direction in which the bob will accelerate when released, and thus $F = W \sin \beta = \dfrac{Wx}{l}$. The displacement of the bob, AB, may be considered equal to x if β is small; and under this condition the restoring force F is directly proportional to the displacement; the motion of the bob is harmonic; and the equations for harmonic motion apply. The restoring force corresponding to the displacement x is found from equation (63), to

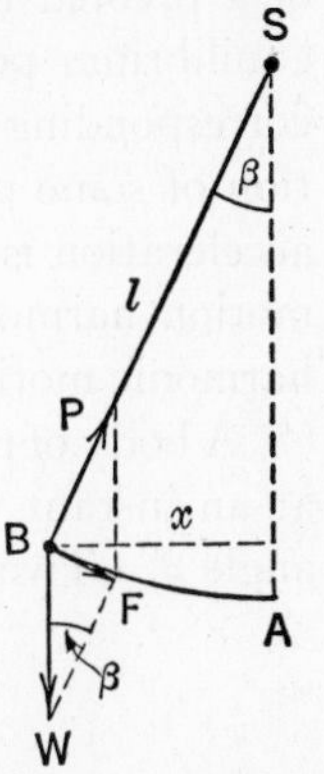

Fig. 99. Finding the period of a simple pendulum

be numerically $F = 4\pi^2 n^2 \dfrac{W}{g} x$. Equating the two values of F,

$$\frac{Wx}{l} = 4\pi^2 n^2 \frac{W}{g} x$$

from which $n = \dfrac{1}{2\pi} \sqrt{\dfrac{g}{l}}$, and hence the period $T = \dfrac{1}{n}$ is given by the expression

$$T = 2\pi \sqrt{\frac{l}{g}} \tag{65}$$

The time of vibration of a pendulum is seen to be determined by its length l, and by the acceleration of gravity g at the point where the pendulum is located. By using a pendulum of known length and measuring its period of vibration, the value of g can be determined with accuracy. Equation (65) applies only to small values of the displacement angle β, which, however, need not be constant. If the vibration of a pendulum is allowed to die away, the amplitude becomes smaller and smaller but the period remains practically unchanged. It is this property which makes the pendulum of value in controlling the escapements of timekeepers.

90. The Physical Pendulum. — Any body which vibrates in the manner of a pendulum but whose mass is distributed and not concentrated as in the simple pendulum is called a *physical* or *compound pendulum*. A rod suspended at one end, or a hoop hung on a nail, would vibrate as a physical pendulum if displaced and released.

To find the period of a physical pendulum, consider the motion of a pivoted body at an instant when slightly displaced from its equilibrium position; the restoring torque set up will produce a corresponding angular acceleration, from which the linear acceleration of some point can be determined. It will be found that this acceleration is proportional to the displacement, which makes the motion harmonic, and the period can be found from the laws of harmonic motion as in the simple pendulum.

A body of mass M vibrating about an axis S is shown in Fig. 100 at an instant when displaced from its equilibrium position by an angle β. Two forces act upon the body. One of these is the

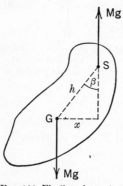

attraction of gravity downward at the center of gravity G, and may be expressed in absolute units as Mg (for example, if the mass of the pendulum is $M = 1000$ gm., its weight is $1000 \times 980 = 980,000$ dynes). The other force is an equal upward force exerted by the support at S. These forces are separated by a perpendicular distance x, and so produce a restoring couple of moment Mgx. The angular acceleration which this moment or torque produces is $\alpha = Mgx/I$, where I is the moment of inertia of the body about a transverse axis at the point of suspension.

FIG. 100. Finding the period of a physical pendulum

The linear acceleration of the point G follows from equation (30):

$a = \alpha h = \dfrac{Mgx}{I} \times h$, where h is the distance between the center of

suspension S and the center of gravity G. If the displacement angle β is small, x may be taken as the displacement of G, and under this condition the acceleration of this point is proportional to its displacement. Thus G may be considered as having harmonic motion, and its acceleration is given numerically by equation (62) as $a = 4\pi^2 n^2 x$. The entire body describes harmonic motion, since every other point which has a different acceleration has a proportionately different displacement. Equating the foregoing values for acceleration,

$$\frac{Mgx}{I} \times h = 4\pi^2 n^2 x$$

Hence, $n = \dfrac{1}{2\pi}\sqrt{\dfrac{Mgh}{I}}$, and the period is

$$T = 2\pi\sqrt{\dfrac{I}{Mgh}} \qquad (66)$$

where, as before, I is the moment of inertia of the pendulum about a transverse axis at the point of suspension and h is the distance between the axis of suspension and the center of gravity.

Suppose it is desired to find the time of vibration of a meter stick pivoted at one end, as pictured in Fig. 101. The moment of inertia of the stick about the axis of suspension is given in § 56 as $I = \frac{1}{3}Ml^2$, and the distance between the center of suspension S and the center of gravity G is $h = l/2$; whence the period is

$$T = 2\pi\sqrt{\dfrac{Ml^2/3}{Mgl/2}} = 2\pi\sqrt{\dfrac{2l}{3g}} = 2\pi\sqrt{\dfrac{2 \times 100 \text{ cm.}}{3 \times 980 \text{ cm./sec.}^2}} = 1.64 \text{ sec.}$$

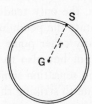

FIG. 101. A vibrating stick   FIG. 102. A vibrating hoop

As another example, find the time of vibration of a hoop 1 ft. in diameter about an axis S at its circumference, as shown in Fig. 102. The moment of inertia of the hoop about a transverse axis at G is $I_G = Mr^2$, and hence about a parallel axis at S its moment of inertia is

$$I = I_G + Mr^2 = Mr^2 + Mr^2 = 2Mr^2$$

The distance between S and G in this case is r; therefore the period is

$$T = 2\pi\sqrt{\dfrac{2Mr^2}{Mgr}} = 2\pi\sqrt{\dfrac{2r}{g}} = 2\pi\sqrt{\dfrac{2 \times \frac{1}{2} \text{ ft.}}{32 \text{ ft./sec.}^2}} = 1.11 \text{ sec.}$$

*91. Centers of Oscillation and Percussion. — The *center of oscillation* of a physical pendulum is that point at which the concentration of the whole mass of the pendulum would cause no change in its moment of inertia. When considered in this way the physical pendulum reduces to a simple pendulum having the same period. The period is $2\pi\sqrt{\dfrac{l}{g}}$ for a simple pendulum and $2\pi\sqrt{\dfrac{I}{Mgh}}$ for a physical pendulum; if these are equated it follows that the length of the equivalent simple pendulum is

$$l = \dfrac{I}{Mh} \qquad (67)$$

The center of oscillation of a physical pendulum is therefore separated from the axis of suspension by the distance $\dfrac{I}{Mh}$, and this expression also shows the length of a simple pendulum which will have the same period as the physical pendulum. In this expression the symbols have the same meaning as previously.

The center of oscillation may be interchanged with the center of suspension without affecting the period. To prove this statement, it is merely necessary to compute the equivalent length of a physical pendulum when suspended (1) at its axis of suspension, and (2) at its center of oscillation, and to show that the two values found are equal.

The center of oscillation is also called the *center of percussion*, since it is a point at which the pendulum can be struck without jar on the axis, the only tendency produced by a blow at this point being to rotate the pendulum about its axis of suspension. When struck at any other point there is not only a tendency to rotate the pendulum but also to give the axis a motion of translation. The stinging sensation sometimes experienced in batting a ball is probably due to striking the ball with the bat at some point other than the center of percussion.

*92. The Torsion Pendulum. — When a weight attached to a vertical wire as shown in Fig. 103 is twisted and released, it will act

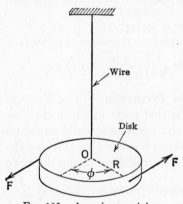

as a *torsion pendulum*, describing a series of angular vibrations similar to the linear vibrations met with previously in harmonic motion. The twisting of the wire sets up a restoring torque in it which is proportional to the angular displacement, just as in linear harmonic motion a restoring force is set up which is proportional to the linear displacement. The two types of motion are closely analogous, and angular harmonic motion can be studied

Fig. 103.   A torsion pendulum

most simply by comparing it directly with linear harmonic motion. In the figure the forces $F\,F$ acting at the distance R from the center O produce a torque $2RF$.

Starting with equation (64), $\dfrac{F}{x} = -4\pi^2 n^2 m$, which is one of the characteristic expressions for linear harmonic motion, and replacing each linear quantity by the corresponding angular quantity, there results as the corresponding expression for angular harmonic motion:

$$\frac{T'}{\phi} = -4\pi^2 n^2 I \tag{68}$$

wherein T' represents the restoring torque, this symbol being used to avoid confusion with the period T; ϕ is the corresponding angular displacement, n is the frequency, and I is the moment of inertia of the vibrating body about the axis of rotation. The ratio of the torque T' to the corresponding twist ϕ is a constant determined by the stiffness of the suspension wire. Replacing this ratio by τ (tau), neglecting the negative sign, which indicates direction only, and rearranging the expression, the frequency of angular vibration is found to be $n = \dfrac{1}{2\pi}\sqrt{\dfrac{\tau}{I}}$, and the period $T = \dfrac{1}{n}$ is consequently

$$T = 2\pi\sqrt{\frac{I}{\tau}} \tag{69}$$

an expression which is analogous to equation (65) for the period of linear vibration.

The balance wheel of a watch operates as a torsion pendulum, and this type of pendulum is also used in some styles of clocks for controlling the escapement. The torsion principle may also be used to determine the moment of inertia of a body; the body is supported as a torsion pendulum and measurements are made of its period and of the angle of twist produced by a measured torque. From the data thus obtained and the use of equation (69), the moment of inertia of the suspended body can be determined.

PROBLEMS

1. The bob of a pendulum makes 75 complete vibrations in 31.2 sec. Determine the frequency and period of the vibration.

2. A particle moves with harmonic motion in a vertical line between two points 20 cm. apart. How far does it move during the first $\frac{1}{8}$ period after passing through the top point of its path?

3. A ball travels once each second with constant speed around a horizontal circle 12 in. in diameter, its shadow moving with harmonic motion on a wall behind it. Find the velocity and the acceleration of the shadow (*a*) at the midpoint of its travel, (*b*) at one end point, and (*c*) at a point half way between the midpoint and the end point.

4. Harmonic motion is described by a body, the period being 3.6 sec. and the amplitude 10 in. What is the least distance that the body moves in 1 sec.? What is the greatest distance covered in 1 sec.?

5. A mass of 7.5 gm. is executing harmonic motion along a vertical line 20 cm. long, with a frequency of 2 vibrations per sec. Calculate the position and acceleration of the mass and the restoring force acting upon it at an instant 0.6 sec. after it has left the highest point in its path.

6. A spring scale used for weighing ice has scale divisions $\frac{1}{8}$ in. long, each representing 1 lb. A 50-lb. cake of ice hung from this spring scale is set vibrating up and down. How many vibrations will it make per second?

7. The crosshead of a certain engine weighs 400 lb. and travels back and forth between two points 18 in. apart, moving from one point to the other and back 120 times each minute. Considering the motion to be harmonic, at what points in its stroke is the cross-head subjected to the greatest force, and what is the value of this force?

8. A hack-saw blade suspended vertically in a vise supports a 2-lb. weight at its lower end. A horizontal force is exerted upon the weight, displacing it laterally 1 in., the applied force being then 10 oz. If the weight is released and allowed to vibrate horizontally, calculate the frequency and period of its vibration.

9. A 500-gm. weight attached to a spring extends it 10 cm. A weight of 100 gm. is then added, following which the system is set into vibration of 4-cm. amplitude. Calculate the frequency of vibration; also the velocity and acceleration of the weight and the restoring force acting upon it at an instant one-eighth of a period after passing through the mid-position.

10. Find approximately the time of vibration of a child's swing, if the vertical ropes supporting the seat are each 15 ft. long.

11. A seconds pendulum is one which beats seconds, its period being 2 sec. (a) Find the length of a simple seconds pendulum. (b) Find the period of a simple pendulum having one-fourth of this length.

12. Determine the acceleration of gravity at a place where a simple pendulum exactly 1 meter long makes 200 complete vibrations in 401.2 sec.

13. A hole is bored transversely through a meter stick at the 20-cm. mark and the stick is set into vibration about this point upon a horizontal nail. Find the period of vibration.

14. Find the length of a simple pendulum which will be equivalent to a physical pendulum composed of a disk 6 in. in diameter vibrating about an axis at its rim.

15. Find the length of a simple pendulum which will have the same period of vibration as that of a meter stick pivoted at one end.

*16. A bar supported horizontally by a wire at its center is twisted through an angle of 14° by a torque of 6.4×10^6 dyne-cm., and upon release vibrates 3 times a second as a torsion pendulum. Find the moment of inertia of the bar.

*17. A method for comparing masses without recourse to gravity uses a torsion pendulum with a vertical wire attached at its lower end to the middle of a slender horizontal rod of negligible mass. With a pair of 5-lb. masses attached to the ends of the rod, the pendulum vibrates 20 times per min. When these masses are replaced by a different pair, the pendulum vibrates 50 times per min. What masses were used for the second pair?

CHAPTER X

ELASTICITY AND IMPACT

MODULI OF ELASTICITY

93. Elastic Bodies. — Perhaps everyone has observed the bending of a piece of wood and its return to the original shape upon removal of the bending force, as well as the twisting of a wire or rod of metal and its return to the original shape upon removal of the twisting force. These effects are evidences of the *elasticity* of matter, and the substances are said to be *elastic bodies*. More strictly, an elastic body is one which changes its size or shape upon the application of a distorting force, provided it returns to its original condition upon the removal of that force. If the distorting force is very large, the *elastic limit* of the material may be exceeded, resulting in a permanent distortion of the body under observation, and it may be large enough to reach the *breaking strength* of the material, causing the body to break. This chapter deals with perfectly elastic bodies that are subjected to forces which do not exceed the elastic limits of the materials employed.

In the foregoing chapters, it was assumed that bodies were rigid, and that under the action of applied forces the body would move as a whole, perhaps with translation, or rotation, or vibration, or combinations of these types of motion. Consideration is given here to the action of forces in distorting a body, the particles of the body moving relatively to each other through rather narrow ranges, and it is understood that the forces are applied in such a manner that the body in its entirety will not move.

94. Stress and Strain; Hooke's Law. — When a load is applied to an elastic body, the body becomes distorted; that is, some portion of the body is displaced with respect to some other portion which has not been disturbed. As a result of this displacement, a force action is developed between the molecules of the body which resists the change that the applied load has brought about, and tends to restore the body to its original condition. The aggregate of these molecular forces will just balance the applied

163

load when the body has reached a stable condition (namely rest) under the action of these forces. The larger the load, the larger will be the deformation necessary to establish molecular restoring forces that will balance the increased load. The fact that the deformation of a body is proportional to the restoring force was

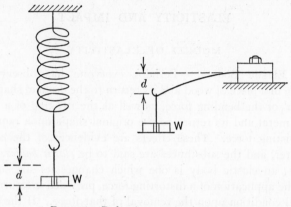

FIG. 104. Deforming a spring by loading

discovered by Robert Hooke (1635–1703), English experimental physicist. Hooke's Law states that the force developed within a body to withstand an outside load is proportional to the deformation of the body under that load, provided the elastic limit of the material is not exceeded.

The correctness of this law can be verified by applying weights to a helical spring or a flat spring in the manner indicated in Fig. 104. If different weights W_1, W_2, W_3, etc., are placed in turn upon either spring, it will be found that the steady deflections produced by them, respectively d_1, d_2, d_3, etc., are proportional to the applied weights. This means that if the deflections are plotted against weights placed upon the spring, the points will fall along a straight line as shown in Fig. 105.

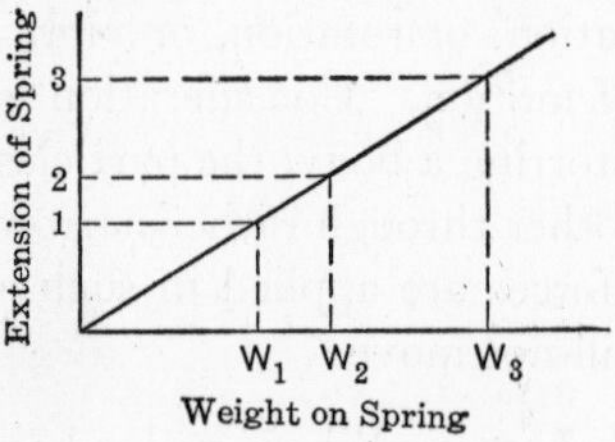

FIG. 105. The dependence of stretch upon applied load

It is customary to express the restoring force set up in an elastic body that is subject to deformation as the force per unit area over which the force acts, and the term *stress* is used for this purpose.

Thus, *stress is the restoring force per unit area* and its interpretation depends upon the particular manner in which the load is applied to the body. Engineers commonly refer to this quantity as the *unit stress*.

The deformation of an elastic body is expressed by the change produced by the applied force in terms of some original dimension of the body, and the term *strain* is used as the measure of deformation. Thus, if a sheet of rubber 10 in. square is stretched to 11 in. in both directions, the strain would appropriately be reckoned as the ratio of change in area to original area, or $\dfrac{121 - 100}{100} = 0.21$.

Using the terms stress and strain respectively as the measures of restoring force and deformation, Hooke's Law states that *the stress set up within an elastic body is proportional to the strain to which the body is subjected by the applied load;* that is

$$\text{stress} \propto \text{strain},$$

or

$$\text{stress} = k \times \text{strain},$$

$$\therefore k = \frac{\text{stress}}{\text{strain}},$$

where k is a constant for the material of the elastic body. This constant is known as the *modulus of elasticity* of the material, and its numerical value depends upon the units selected for the stress and the strain.

An elastic body may be loaded in three different ways: in one the load tends to change the length of the body, in another to change its shape, and in the third to change its volume. Naturally, different procedures are necessary to evaluate the stress and the strain for these cases, but Hooke's Law applies equally to all three.

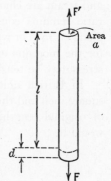

Fig. 106. Measuring stress and strain in a wire or rod

95. Elasticity of Length (Young's Modulus). — Consider a wire, of length l and cross-sectional area a, to be subjected to tension by the application of two equal and opposite forces F, F' to its ends, as a result of which the wire elongates an amount d. These quantities are depicted in Fig. 106. The strain in this case is the elongation d divided by the original length l, while the stress is equal to the force F divided by the cross-sectional area a. Therefore, strain = d/l and stress = F/a; consequently their ratio, which is a constant of the material of the wire, is

$$Y = \frac{\text{stress}}{\text{strain}} = \frac{\dfrac{F}{a}}{\dfrac{d}{l}} \tag{70}$$

This constant Y, the stretch modulus of elasticity, is called *Young's modulus*, after Thomas Young (1773–1829), English philosopher.

It can be shown that Young's modulus depends only upon the material tested and not upon the dimensions of the particular sample used. Suppose, for example, that a wire of the same material but having twice the length ($2l$) and twice the cross-sectional area ($2a$) is subjected to the same force (F) as before. The stress is now $\dfrac{F}{2a}$, which is half of the previous value. The elongation would be doubled because of the increased length of the sample and at the same time would be halved because of its increased area, consequently the elongation (d) remains unchanged and the strain becomes $\dfrac{d}{2l}$, which is half of the previous value. Thus, the stress and strain are changed in the same proportion, and therefore their ratio remains constant. This analysis shows that tests can be made on rods or wires of any convenient dimensions and all results for the modulus of any one material will be in agreement. The stress may be tensile or compressive with equal relevancy.

In British units the stress is often measured in pounds per square inch and the strain measured in inches of extension per inch of original length, consequently the unit for Young's modulus would be

$$Y = \frac{\dfrac{\text{lb.}}{\text{in.}^2}}{\dfrac{\text{in.}}{\text{in.}}} = \text{lb. per sq. in.}$$

In metric units the stress may be measured in dynes per square centimeter, in kilograms per square millimeter, or in similar units; the strain is usually measured in centimeters of extension or contraction per centimeter of original length. In this case also the unit for Young's modulus will be same as the unit for stress.

The numerical values of Young's modulus are very large in comparison with the values of the elastic limit and of the breaking stress. For example, for mild steel the stretch modulus of elasticity is 30,000,000 lb. per sq. in., the elastic limit is 35,000 lb. per sq. in., and the breaking strength is 60,000 lb. per sq. in. In designing structures, engineers allow a "unit stress" of perhaps 16,000 lb. per sq. in. to give an ample factor of safety.

As a numerical example, compute the elongation of a steel tie bar 24 ft. long, 4 in. wide, and $\frac{1}{2}$ in. thick, when subjected to a tensile force of 30,000 lb. The stress is 30,000 lb. $\div$ $(4 \times \frac{1}{2})$ sq. in. = 15,000 lb. per sq. in. By equation (70), the strain is found to be

$$\text{strain} = \frac{\text{stress}}{Y} = \frac{15,000 \dfrac{\text{lb.}}{\text{sq. in.}}}{30,000,000 \dfrac{\text{lb.}}{\text{sq. in.}}} = \frac{1}{2000}.$$

Since the strain is the elongation d divided by the original length l, it follows that the elongation is

$$d = l \times \text{strain} = 24 \text{ ft.} \times \frac{1}{2000} = 0.012 \text{ ft.} = 0.144 \text{ in.}$$

The small extensions which occur when a rod is placed under tensile loads may be measured by an *extensometer;* in one type two pairs of opposed pointed screws are pressed into the rod at a known distance apart, and a lever system with a short-focus microscope measures the elongation of that portion of the rod. In measuring the larger extensions of thin wires, sufficient accuracy is attained by placing at the end of the wire a small vernier, which moves along a suitably supported scale when the wire stretches.

96. Elasticity of Shape (Shear Modulus). — Often a body is subjected to a pair of equal forces which act in opposite directions but not along the same line, as in a couple [§ 62]. Such a pair of forces S, S is shown acting upon the upper and lower faces of a rectangular block *abcd* in Fig. 107, and would *shear* it into the parallelopiped *ab'c'd*, turning the end faces *ab* and *cd* through the small angle ϕ. Upon removal of the shearing forces the body will

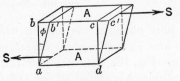

Fig. 107. Effect of shearing forces upon a block

resume its original shape, provided the elastic limit of the material was not exceeded. This type of elasticity is termed *elasticity of shape* or *of shear*, and is of great importance in structural design.

In order to study the behavior of materials under shear, it is usual to apply the general definitions for stress and strain to this particular kind of distortion. The block shown in Fig. 107 may be regarded as made up of a large number of horizontal sheets of area A, each of which is forced to slide along slightly with respect to its neighbors under the action of the shearing forces. The area A is obviously the surface which resists the shearing action caused by the force S, and hence the *shearing stress* is S/A, where A is the area of the upper or lower face of the block. *The strain is measured by the angle ϕ through which the end of the block is sheared;* it is expressed in radians.

Having suitable measures of shearing stress and of shearing strain, the constant ratio of the one to the other can be expressed by Hooke's Law as

$$E = \frac{\text{stress}}{\text{strain}} = \frac{\dfrac{S}{A}}{\phi} \tag{71}$$

This constant E is called the *shear modulus of elasticity*, and is also known as the *coefficient of rigidity*. Since the angle of shear is a

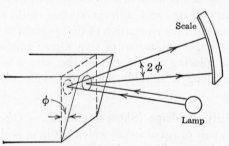

FIG. 108.   Measuring the angle of shear

pure numeric, the unit in which the modulus is expressed is the same as that used for the stress.

Fig. 108 indicates how the angle of shear can be measured. A mirror is affixed to one end face of the 'block and a ray of light from a lamp is reflected by the mirror upon the scale shown. As the face of the block turns through an angle ϕ the reflected ray of light will be turned through 2ϕ, (see § 365). If the scale is at a distance r from the mirror, and if the scale deflection due to shear is s, the angle $2\phi = s/r$. Consequently, measurements of r and s determine the angle of shear ϕ.

As a numerical example, assume a cube of brass, having faces 5×5 cm., to be subjected to a shearing force of 12,000 kg. The angle of shear is observed by the lamp-mirror-scale arrangement just mentioned and the reflected beam is shifted a distance of 9.0 mm. along a scale which is located 3 meters from the mirror affixed to the cube. What is the shear modulus of brass? In this problem, the angle of shear is $\phi = \dfrac{s}{2r} = \dfrac{9.0}{2 \times 3000} = 0.0015$ radian, and the shearing stress is $\dfrac{S}{A} = \dfrac{12{,}000 \text{ kg.}}{2500 \text{ mm.}^2} = 4.8 \text{ kg./mm.}^2;$ therefore the shear modulus of brass is $E = 4.8 \div 0.0015 = 3200 \text{ kg./mm.}^2$

97. Elasticity of Volume (Bulk Modulus).

When a body is subjected to normal forces pressing all over its surface, with the same amount of force acting on each unit of area, its shape remains unchanged but its volume decreases. Such action occurs when a body is submersed in a liquid, for the liquid pressure will be transmitted undiminished and will act perpendicularly to each portion of the surface, as described in the following chapter, the pressure being the force acting on unit area.

Consider a cube of some material under test to be subjected to hydrostatic pressure, equal forces f acting normally on all faces, as represented in Fig. 109. If the area of each face is a, then the stress set up within the material is equal to the *force per unit of normal area;* that is, stress $= f/a = p$, where p is the

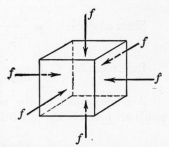

Fig. 109. Equal forces acting on a cube in all directions

pressure. The corresponding strain is defined as the *decrease of volume v divided by the original volume* of the body V; thus, strain $= v/V$. The ratio of the stress to the strain in this case is called the *bulk modulus of elasticity*, and is expressed as

$$B = \frac{\text{stress}}{\text{strain}} = \frac{p}{\dfrac{v}{V}} \tag{72}$$

The units in which the modulus B is expressed are the same as those used for the hydrostatic pressure p, since the denominator v/V is the ratio of two volumes or a numeric. This modulus is applied particularly to fluids; since they offer resistance only to change of volume [§ 104], they can have only a bulk modulus of elasticity.

The reciprocal of the bulk modulus of a substance is known as the *compressibility* of that material. The bulk modulus of elasticity of steel is 18,000,000 lb. per sq. in.; therefore its compressibility is 0.000000055 — meaning that a hydrostatic pressure of 1 lb. per sq. in. would decrease unit volume by this amount.

98. Summary of Elastic Moduli. — In the foregoing, the three moduli of elasticity were all derived from Hooke's Law, the stress in all cases being measured in force units per unit area, and the strain in all cases being a ratio of two like dimensions and therefore a numeric; consequently the unit in which the modulus is expressed is the same as that used for the stress. The expressions used for elasticity of length, shape, and volume are summarized here for convenience of reference:

$$\text{Young's modulus} = \frac{\text{longitudinal stress}}{\text{change of length per unit length}} = \frac{F/a}{d/l}$$

$$\text{Shear modulus} = \frac{\text{shearing stress}}{\text{angle of shear}} = \frac{S/A}{\phi}$$

$$\text{Bulk modulus} = \frac{\text{hydrostatic pressure}}{\text{change of volume per unit volume}} = \frac{p}{v/V}$$

Average values of the stretch and shear moduli of several solids are given below in British and metric units:

Elasticity of Solids

Material	Young's Modulus		Shear Modulus	
	lb. per sq. in.	kg. per sq. mm.	lb. per sq. in.	kg. per sq. mm.
Steel (mild)......	30,000,000	21,000	12,000,000	8500
Brass...........	14,000,000	10,000	4,500,000	3200
Aluminum.......	10,000,000	7,000	4,200,000	3000
Copper (rolled)...	17,000,000	12,000	6,000,000	4200
Iron (cast).......	12,000,000	8,500	8,000,000	5600
Glass (crown)....	10,000,000	7,000	3,600,000	2500
Timber..........	1,400,000	1,000	140,000	100

Representative values of the bulk moduli of several liquids are tabulated on the next page.

Elasticity of Liquids

Material	Bulk Modulus	
	lb. per sq. in.	kg. per sq. mm.
Water............	310,000	220
Alcohol...........	163,000	114
Ether.............	87,000	61
Mercury..........	4,000,000	2800

99. Elasticity and Vibratory Motion. — In Chapter IX harmonic motion was defined as the motion of a body in which its acceleration as well as its restoring force is proportional to the displacement of the body from its equilibrium position. In this chapter it has been pointed out that an elastic body sets up a restoring force which is proportional to the displacement from its position of rest. Consequently elastic bodies, when displaced from their normal positions, will vibrate with harmonic motion about those positions upon the removal of the displacing force. This vibratory motion will continue until the energy imparted to the body is completely dissipated in friction. The frequency of vibration of an elastic body, as well as the velocity at any point of its path, can be computed by applying the laws of harmonic motion, as given in §§ 86 and 87.

BEAMS AND RODS

* 100. Bending of a Beam. — An interesting application of elasticity is the bending of a beam of uniform section. At first sight it might appear to be an application of the shear modulus, but in reality the beam is to be regarded as composed of a number of longitudinal "fibers" some of which are in tension while others are in compression, and consequently Young's modulus, rather than the shear modulus, must be applied. The center line of the beam keeps its original length; it is called the *neutral axis*. The outer lines concentric with the neutral axis are lengthened and the inner lines are shortened, consequently the outer fibers of the beam are in tension and the inner fibers are in compression. The greater the distance of a fiber from the neutral axis the greater will be the fiber stress. With excessive loading, the stress of the outer fibers may equal the breaking strength of the material; when this occurs the beam will fail by developing cracks along the outer edge and bulges along the inner edge.

In order to find the maximum fiber stress in a simple beam, assume the beam, supported at its ends A and B, to be uniformly loaded by vertical forces and bent into the form illustrated in Fig. 110. By assuming this form as circular it becomes a simple matter to determine the change of length of any fiber and then to calculate its strain; thereafter an application of Hooke's Law yields the stress in that fiber.

Consider a fiber pp at a distance x from the neutral axis nn, and let its cross-sectional area be represented by a. The original

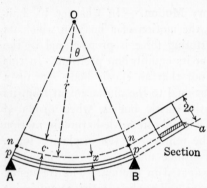

FIG. 110. Measuring the strain in a simple beam having a rectangular cross-section

length of this fiber is the same as the original length of all fibers of this beam, and since the neutral axis remains unchanged, the original length of fiber pp is the length of the neutral axis in the diagram, namely $r\,\theta$, where r is the radius of the neutral axis and θ is the angle subtended at the center O by the beam. The length of fiber pp in the bent beam is $(r + x)\theta$; therefore its change of length is $(r + x)\theta - r\theta = x\,\theta$. The ratio of this change of length $x\,\theta$ to the original length $r\,\theta$ of the fiber considered is the strain, namely x/r. The desired fiber stress F/a is now determined by using equation (70), which gives

$$\frac{F}{a} = Y\frac{x}{r} \tag{73}$$

The maximum fiber stress exists at the upper and lower edges of the uniform beam, and if the thickness of the beam is $2c$, the maximum stress is

$$S_m = \frac{Yc}{r} \tag{74}$$

Equation (73) shows that the stress at any cross-section of the beam at a distance x from the neutral axis is proportional to that distance; consequently the stresses may be plotted as in Fig. 111, the arrows showing the magnitudes and directions of the stresses at both sides of the section. It will be observed that the arrowheads lie on a straight line, and that these stresses collectively tend to produce a torque about point N on the neutral axis, which torque is clockwise in the figure. Since the beam is at rest it is evident that this torque does not produce rotation of the beam about the section under consideration, consequently the torque must be balanced by the *bending moment of the external forces* acting at that section. The bending moment must equal the algebraic sum of the moments of the forces F acting on the section, and is obtained from equation (73) as

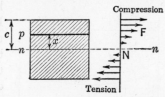

Fig. 111. Visualizing the bending stress at a cross-section of a beam under load

$$ M = \Sigma Fx = \Sigma \frac{Ya\,x}{r} \times x = \frac{Y}{r} \Sigma a\,x^2 $$

The summation Σax^2 is similar to the summation Σmr^2, which was defined in § 54 as the moment of inertia I of a mass about an axis. For this reason Σax^2 is spoken of as the *moment of inertia of cross-section*, and is also symbolized as I. Hence the bending moment at a section is given by

$$ M = \frac{YI}{r} \tag{75} $$

From equation (74) the fraction $\dfrac{Y}{r} = \dfrac{S_m}{c}$, and consequently the maximum bending moment may also be expressed as

$$ M = \frac{S_m I}{c} \tag{76} $$

where S_m is the maximum fiber stress at the upper and lower surfaces, c is the distance of the extreme fiber from the neutral axis, and I is the moment of inertia of cross-section about the neutral axis. The fraction I/c is called the *section modulus*.

The moment of inertia of cross-section of a rectangular-sectioned beam about its neutral axis is $\frac{1}{12}bd^3$, where b is the breadth and d is the depth of the beam (that is, $d = 2c$), and it is usually expressed in inches[4].

The ultimate fiber stresses of various kinds of timber average from 4000 to 6000 lb. per sq. in., but the working stresses range from 800 to 1300 lb. per sq. in. This allows a factor of safety of about 5.

In order to ascertain the maximum bending moment of external forces acting upon a simple beam, consider a weightless beam of length l to rest on knife-edges at its ends and to support a single

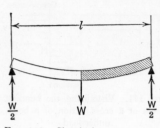

load W at the center, as shown in Fig. 112. Each knife-edge would then exert a reaction of $W/2$ upon the end of the beam. The conditions can be clarified by considering only half the beam (the shaded half) and regarding the left half embedded in a solid wall. It is obvious that the bending moment due to the load $W/2$ at the end will be a maximum at the wall, because the lever arm is

FIG. 112. Simple beam centrally loaded

the greatest possible; this moment equals

$$M = \frac{W}{2} \times \frac{l}{2} = \frac{Wl}{4} \qquad (77)$$

It can be shown similarly that if the load on the beam is uniformly distributed, the maximum bending moment will be

$$M = \frac{W}{2} \times \frac{l}{4} = \frac{Wl}{8} \qquad (78)$$

As an illustration, determine the maximum stress in a timber joist 2 in. wide and 6 in. deep having a span of 9 ft., and bearing a uniform load, including the weight of the beam itself, of 120 lb. per linear foot. In this problem, the maximum bending moment is $M = Wl/8$, the moment of inertia of the section is $I = \frac{1}{12} bd^3$, and the maximum stress is given by equation (76) as $S_m = Mc/I$. It follows that $M = 14,580$ lb-in., $c = 3$ in., $I = 36$ in.^{4}, and $S_m = 1215 \frac{\text{lb}}{\text{in.}^2}$. This is the stress to which the upper and lower fibers of the rectangular-sectioned joist would be subjected.

★ 101. Twisting of a Rod. — In order to determine how much a rod of given material will twist when subjected to a certain torque, it is necessary to apply the shear modulus of elasticity of that material. Imagine a cylindrical rod fastened rigidly at its left end and twisted at its right end by a torque T in the direction shown in diagram I of Fig. 113. An axial line AB drawn on the surface will then be shifted to a position such as AC, the angle of shift being indicated as ϕ; the radius OB of the right-hand cross-sectional area will be moved correspondingly to position OC, turning through an angle θ. The relation between the angle of shear ϕ and the angle of twist θ can be obtained readily by considering the small arc BC (of length $R\theta$) also to be the arc of a circle having a center at A and a radius of $AB = l$. Then $R\theta = l\phi$, and the angle of shear becomes

$$\phi = \frac{R}{l}\,\theta$$

In considering the angle of shear previously [§ 96] as a measure of strain, it was applied to a block, Fig. 107, and all parts of the block had the same stress and the same strain. This is not true for the cylindrical rod, and therefore it is necessary to consider the rod as made up of a series of telescoping tubes, and to ascertain their strains and stresses separately.

Imagine one such tube of mean radius r and of the small radial thickness x, as shown in diagram II of Fig. 113, to be subjected to

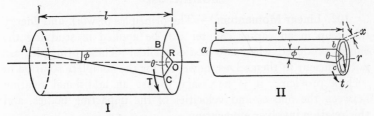

Fig. 113. Determining the stress and strain in a shaft under shearing forces

the torque t. An axial line ab on this tube will shift to position ac when the right-hand end of the tube twists through an angle θ. The line ab shifts through an angle ϕ', which is the angle of shear or the strain of the tube, and its value is $\phi' = r\theta/l$. This expression is similar to the foregoing one, but it involves the smaller radius r instead of the radius of the cylinder R which comprises the series of tubes.

Let f be the shearing force on the tube, acting over the entire end face, which has an area of $2\pi rx$; then the shearing stress on this tube is $f \div 2\pi rx$, and consequently the shear modulus, from equation (71), is

$$E = \frac{\dfrac{f}{2\pi rx}}{\phi'} = \frac{\dfrac{f}{2\pi rx}}{\dfrac{r}{l}\,\theta}$$

whence the torque twisting the tube is

$$t' = fr = 2\pi r^3 \frac{x\,\theta}{l}\,E \qquad\qquad (79)$$

The total torque T acting on the cylinder would then be the sum of a number of terms like the foregoing to include all tubes from the axis to the surface of the rod; such a summation is carried out by calling the elementary tube thickness $x = dr$ and integrating. Thus, the total torque becomes

$$T = \int_{r=0}^{r=R} 2\pi r^3 \frac{\theta}{l} E \, dr = \frac{\pi \theta E R^4}{2l} \tag{80}$$

This expression is used in computing the angular twist θ of a rod when its dimensions, its shear modulus E, and the applied torque T are known. When the dimensions are in inches and the modulus is in pounds per square inch, the torque will be in pound-inches.

MOMENTUM

102. Linear Momentum. — The principles of work and energy taken up in an earlier chapter can be applied in studying the effects produced when two bodies collide. These principles are not sufficient in themselves, however, for the complete solution of such a problem; it is necessary to use an additional relation between the masses and velocities of the impacting bodies, and this relation involves momentum.

The *momentum* of a body is defined as the product of its mass and its velocity, or symbolically: momentum = mv. It is a vector quantity, and has the same direction as the velocity. Since v represents the linear velocity of the body, the product mv is called its linear momentum. It is known from Newton's Second Law of Motion that when an unbalanced force F acts for a time t upon a body of mass m, changing the velocity of the body from v_o to v_f, the relation between these terms is given by equation (31) as $F = ma$ $= m \dfrac{v_f - v_o}{t}$. Rearranging terms, this expression becomes

$$Ft = mv_f - mv_o \tag{81}$$

When a force acts for a short time only, as in impact, the product of the force F and the time t is known as an *impulse*. An unbalanced impulse acting upon a body changes the momentum of the body, and equation (81) states that the change of momentum is numerically equal to the impulse.

Impact, or collision, between two bodies, occurs in a very short interval of time, but in this brief period the bodies become deformed and a certain amount of energy is used to change their shape. If the bodies are elastic, they will restore this energy upon springing back to their original shape; otherwise they will remain distorted, and the energy used in deforming them is not recovered.

In any collision between two bodies, whether elastic or not, Newton's Third Law of Motion states that the colliding bodies exert equal and opposing forces upon each other for the same short interval of time, that is, the impulses received by the two bodies are equal and opposite. Therefore, one of the bodies gains as much momentum as the other body loses, and the total momentum of the two bodies is not changed by the impact. This statement illustrates the *law of conservation of momentum*, which states that *for any collision, the vector sum of the momenta of the colliding bodies after collision equals the vector sum of their momenta before collision.*

Elastic impact may be exemplified by collision between two blocks of steel or other elastic material which slide together on a smooth horizontal surface. The velocities of the blocks after impact can be found by the principles just outlined.

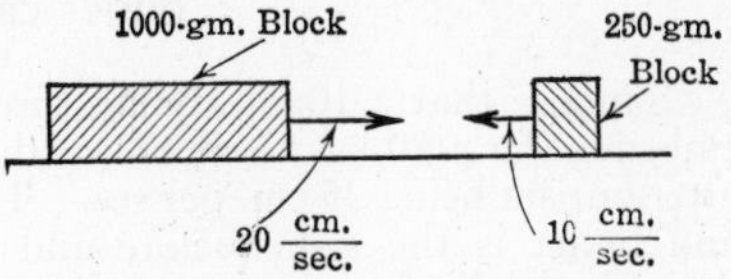

Fig. 114. Collision of elastic bodies

Suppose two blocks to be sliding together on a smooth level surface, as in Fig. 114. One block has a mass of 1000 gm. and a velocity toward the right of 20 cm. per sec.; the other has a mass of 250 gm. and moves toward the left at 10 cm. per sec. The velocities of the left and right blocks after impact will be designated respectively as v_1 and v_2. Since the total momentum of the two bodies is the same before and after impact,

$$(1000\,\text{gm.})\left(20\,\frac{\text{cm.}}{\text{sec.}}\right) + (250\,\text{gm.})\left(-10\,\frac{\text{cm.}}{\text{sec.}}\right) = (1000\,\text{gm.})\,v_1 + (250\,\text{gm.})\,v_2,$$

velocities to the right being considered positive. This expression when simplified becomes

$$4v_1 + v_2 = 70\,\frac{\text{cm.}}{\text{sec.}}.$$

Also, since the bodies are elastic, their total kinetic energy is the same before and after impact, whence,

$$\tfrac{1}{2}(1000\,\text{gm.})\left(20\,\frac{\text{cm.}}{\text{sec.}}\right)^2 + \tfrac{1}{2}(250\,\text{gm.})\left(-10\,\frac{\text{cm.}}{\text{sec.}}\right)^2$$
$$= \tfrac{1}{2}(1000\,\text{gm.})\,v_1{}^2 + \tfrac{1}{2}(250\,\text{gm.})\,v_2{}^2,$$

which reduces to

$$4v_1{}^2 + v_2{}^2 = 1700\left(\frac{\text{cm.}}{\text{sec.}}\right)^2.$$

Solving the two simplified expressions simultaneously, there result: $v_1 = +8$ cm. per sec., and $v_2 = +38$ cm. per sec., showing that the small block reverses its direction, and moves to the right with a speed of 38 cm. per sec., while the large block follows behind it at 8 cm. per sec.

Inelastic impact will be illustrated by a device known as the ballistic pendulum, which is sometimes used to determine the speed of

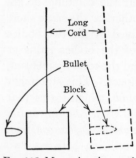

a bullet. The bullet is fired horizontally into a stationary wood block suspended by a long cord, as shown in Fig. 115, and the resulting velocity is determined, usually by calculation based on the height to which the block swings. Although in this collision energy is wasted in tearing apart the fibers of the block and in opposing friction, nevertheless the law of conservation of momentum still holds;

Fig. 115. Measuring the speed of a bullet

from this law the initial speed of the bullet can be obtained.

Suppose that a 10-gm. bullet, fired in the manner described, becomes embedded in a 20-kg. block of wood, the velocity of the block and bullet after impact being 25 cm. per sec. The combined momentum of the block and bullet is the same before and after impact; therefore, calling the desired initial velocity of the bullet v,

$$(10 \text{ gm.}) \ v + (20,000 \text{ gm.}) \ (0) = (10 \text{ gm.} + 20,000 \text{ gm.}) \left(25 \frac{\text{cm.}}{\text{sec.}}\right).$$

Solving this equation, v is found to be 50,025 cm. per sec., and this is accordingly the initial velocity of the bullet.

It is interesting to note that, although the mass of a body is commonly regarded as fixed, advanced theory shows that when a body moves its mass changes, but the change is inappreciable except with very high speeds, approaching that of light. Consequently, a more general statement of the expression for momentum, equation (81), would employ different symbols, m_f and m_o, to represent the final and initial values of the mass.

*103. Angular Momentum. — The close analogy between linear and angular quantities has been repeatedly pointed out, and is further illustrated by the study of momentum. The *angular momentum* of a body is defined as the product of the moment of inertia of the body and its angular velocity, the similarity between this quantity and linear momentum being apparent. Just as an unbalanced force exerted upon a body for a certain time causes a change in its linear momentum, so an unbalanced torque T

acting for a time t upon a body causes a corresponding change in its angular momentum, thus,

$$Tt = I_f\omega_f - I_o\omega_o \tag{82}$$

When the interval t is very short, as in angular collision, the product Tt is called an *angular impulse*. Equation (82) states that *an unbalanced angular impulse will cause a change in the angular momentum of a body*, and moreover, that *these two quantities will be numerically equal*.

A rotating body which is not subjected to any angular impulse tending either to accelerate or to retard it, will consequently maintain a constant angular momentum. For example, a wheel or other rigid object turning without any friction would continue to rotate with undiminished speed. It is interesting to observe, however, that if it is possible to alter the moment of inertia of such a rotating body, its angular velocity will change in an inverse manner, so as to keep the product $I\omega$ constant. This effect can be illustrated by setting a man into rotation on a piano stool which has only a small amount of friction in its bearings. If he extends his arms, thus increasing his moment of inertia, his speed will be reduced; but if he draws the arms in to his sides, this action will reduce the moment of inertia and the speed of rotation will increase.

PROBLEMS

1. A hard-drawn copper wire having a diameter of 0.128 in. is supported at one end and allowed to hang vertically; a load of 250 lb. is applied to the other end. The wire has an elastic limit of 28,000 lb. per sq. in. and a stretch modulus of 16,000,000 lb. per sq. in. Will the wire return to its original length upon removal of the load? What elongation will take place per foot of length when the load is applied?

2. A Monel-metal rod $\frac{3}{8}$ in. in diameter is subjected to a load of 2240 lb. by a testing machine. An 8-in. length of the rod is observed to increase its length by 0.0076 in. Compute Young's modulus of elasticity for the Monel-metal specimen.

3. A steel wire 7 meters long and 1 mm. in diameter is subjected to a tension of 30 kg., and its elongation is observed to be 1.21 cm. Find the strain, the stress, and Young's modulus for the specimen.

4. A load of 60 tons is carried by a steel column having a length of 24 ft. and a sectional area of 10.8 sq. in. What decrease in length will this load produce if the elastic modulus is 30×10^6 lb. per sq. in.?

5. Rubber suitable for use in tension has a stretch modulus of 240 lb. per sq. in. for moderate elongations. A sheet of it $\frac{7}{8}$ in. thick, 40 in. wide, and 20 in. long is stretched; what force will increase the length to 22 in.?

6. A copper wire 20 cm. long having a diameter of 2 mm. is used to support a weight of 2 kg. Find the stress, the strain, and the elongation of the specimen.

7. Fibers of spun glass are reported to be capable of sustaining unusually large stresses; a fiber 0.00035 in. in diameter was found to have a breaking strength of 0.385 oz. What is the breaking stress of this fiber?

8. A forged seamless boiler drum of steel, designed for high steam pressures, is 52 in. in inside diameter and 60 in. in outside diameter. When tested at double its normal pressure, the outer circumference of the drum expanded 0.095 in. Calculate the tensile force in the drum at the testing pressure, per foot of axial length.

9. A square plate of metal 4 ft. on a side and $\frac{1}{2}$ in. thick is subjected to a shearing stress which tends to twist the square surface into a rhombus. To apply this stress one edge is securely fixed, and a bar, fastened to the other edge, is pulled with a force of 180 tons. As a result the bar is observed to advance a distance of 0.069 in. in the direction of the pull. Find the shearing strain, the shearing stress, and the coefficient of rigidity of the plate.

10. An aluminum cube measuring 2 in. along each edge is subjected to a pair of parallel shearing forces applied to its opposite faces. How large must each of these forces be in order to shear the block through an angle of 0.01°?

11. Calculate the bulk modulus of glycerine, if a liter of this liquid contracts 0.21 cu. cm. when subjected to a pressure of 10,000 gm. per sq. cm.

12. A cubical block of fused quartz, measuring 8 cm. on an edge, is subjected to a hydrostatic pressure of 50 kg. per sq. cm. What will be its reduction in volume if the bulk modulus of the material is 1.4×10^8 gm. per sq. cm.?

*13. A square steel rod 1 in. on a side is to be bent into the arc of a circle. What is the smallest radius to which it can be bent (cold), assuming that the maximum stress is limited to 35,000 lb. per sq. in. and the modulus of elasticity (stretch) is 30×10^6 lb. per sq. in.?

*14. Find the dimensions of a timber beam that will carry the weight of three men (aggregating 500 lb.) at the center of a span of 15 ft., allowing a maximum fiber stress of 800 lb. per sq. in.

*15. A total load of 15,000 lb. (referred to as 15 "kips" by structural engineers) is distributed uniformly along a horizontal beam that has a span of 18 ft. What is the maximum bending moment of the beam?

*16. A cylindrical rod 8 ft. long and $\frac{3}{4}$ in. in diameter is rigidly supported at one end and carries at the other end a straight crank 10 in. long. Through what angle in degrees will the crank be turned when a force of 80 lb. is applied to its end perpendicularly to the crank and to the rod, assuming the material of the rod to have a shear modulus of 4.8×10^6 lb. per sq. in.?

17. The shear modulus of a thin wire can be determined experimentally by winding it into a helix, and then placing a weight upon one end while the other is supported rigidly, and finally observing the rate of up-and-down vibration of the weight. Theory shows that if R is the radius of the wire, r is the average radius of the helix, N is the number of turns on the helix, W is the weight supported by the helix, and T is the time of one complete vibration, then the shear modulus is determined by

$$E = \frac{16\pi^2 N W r^3}{T^2 R^4 g}$$

Determine an appropriate set of units for W, r, T, R, g and E.

18. What is the momentum of a 20-ton trolley car when traveling at 30 mi. per hr.?

19. A 5-gm. bullet is fired horizontally at 300 meters per sec. into an 8-kg. wood block resting on a smooth horizontal surface. Assuming that the bullet stays embedded in the block, find their joint velocity after impact.

20. Two elastic ivory balls, each of 200 gm. mass, are suspended by two cords each 20 cm. long, so that they rest in contact. If one ball is moved away as in a pendulum until its cord makes an angle of 60° with the vertical and is then released, find its velocity just before impact, and also the velocity of each ball after impact.

21. An 8-gm. bullet is fired horizontally into a 2-kg. block of wood suspended by a cord 1 meter long. The block swings because of the impact, deflecting the cord to a position 26° from the vertical. Find the initial speed of the bullet.

CHAPTER XI

LIQUIDS AT REST

104. The Liquid State. — Although most substances can be classified readily as to state; that is, as solid, liquid, or gaseous, the lines dividing these phases of a substance cannot always be sharply drawn. Thus, tar at ordinary temperatures can be fractured like a solid, and yet, to a slight extent, it flows like a liquid. Transitions frequently occur from one state to another, many solids becoming liquids when sufficiently heated, and liquids becoming solids when sufficiently cooled. Again, gases can be liquefied by sufficient cooling and compression, and liquids can be converted to gases by heating or, at ordinary temperatures, through the process of evaporation.

It is generally agreed that matter is composed of molecules which are in more or less violent agitation depending upon the temperature. In a solid the molecules are bound closer together than in a liquid, and their motion is more restricted, consisting of vibration over narrow ranges. In a gas the molecules are relatively far apart and move about with comparative freedom throughout the entire confining space. The liquid state is intermediate between the other two. Upon heating a solid such as iron, the molecules become more violently agitated and less closely bound together, and the molten or liquid state finally results.

The outstanding characteristics of a liquid are that it conforms readily to the shape of any containing vessel and that it has a free surface. When the liquid is at rest this surface is horizontal except at its edges [§ 115]. Although liquids have elasticity of volume, they do not possess elasticity of length in the usual sense of the term and have no elasticity of shape [Chap. X]. A *perfect liquid* is defined as a substance which is incapable of exerting a shearing stress, and which, if not completely confined, presents a free horizontal surface when at rest. Most liquids do not conform exactly to this definition, but are able to exert small shearing stresses. This effect will be neglected for the present, and will be considered in the following chapter under the subject of viscosity.

105. Liquid Pressure. — A liquid exerts a force against any surface with which it is in contact; the force which it exerts per unit area is defined as the *pressure*. The force exerted by a liquid is expressed in the usual force units, such as pounds and dynes, 980 dynes being the weight of an object which has 1 gm. of mass. Pressure is correspondingly stated in such units as pounds per square inch and dynes per square centimeter. In engineering practice, the term "pressure" or "total pressure" is frequently used with the meaning of "force" in the foregoing statement, and the expression "unit pressure" or "intensity of pressure" is used to mean "pressure" as above defined. To avoid confusion, however, in the present consideration of this subject, the term "pressure" will be used to represent the force exerted per unit area. When a force F acts upon a plane area A, the corresponding pressure is $p = F/A$; or, rearranging terms, the force can be expressed as

$$F = pA \tag{83}$$

When reference is made to the *pressure at a point* within a liquid, a question naturally arises as to the meaning of the term, since a point has no area. This expression should be taken to mean the force which would be exerted upon a plane surface of unit area placed at the point in question. A surface of unit area at point x in Fig. 116 supports the column of liquid directly above it, and the liquid pressure at x is equal to the weight of this column. The mass of the column is the product of its volume $h \times 1$ and its density d; and its weight may be expressed as $k \times h \times d$, where k is a constant showing the proportionality of the weight of the column to its mass. The pressure at the point x is accordingly

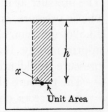

Fig. 116.　Illustrating pressure at a point

$$p = khd$$

In British units, for which the gravitational system is usually used, the weight of a body is numerically equal to its mass, and the proportionality constant becomes $k = 1$. Hence the pressure p in pounds per square foot is the product of the height h in feet and the density d of the liquid in pounds per cubic foot, or

$$p = hd \tag{84}$$

In metric units, using the absolute system, the column of mass m gm. has a weight of mg dynes, and the proportionality constant becomes $k = g \dfrac{\text{dynes}}{\text{gm.}}$. Therefore, the pressure p in dynes per square centimeter is found by multiplying this value of the constant k by the height h in centimeters and by the density d in grams per cubic centimeter, or

$$p = h\,d\,g \qquad\qquad (85)$$

The density of water is 1 gm. per cu. cm. or 62.4 lb. per cu. ft. Using these figures, the pressure at a point 100 cm. below the surface of water is 100 cm. $\times$ 1 gm./cm.^{3} $\times$ 980 dynes/gm. or 98,000 dynes per sq. cm.; the pressure at a point 100 ft. below the surface of water is 100 ft. $\times$ 62.4 lb./ft.^{3} or 6240 lb. per sq. ft.

The foregoing expressions give the pressure due to the liquid only; if the total or *absolute pressure* is desired, the atmospheric or other pressure on the surface of the liquid should be added to the value found. The effect of atmospheric pressure can be shown by withdrawing the air from the top of a glass tube suspended vertically with its lower end in a vessel of mercury. Under normal conditions the mercury will rise within the tube to a height of 76.0 cm. The pressure at the bottom of this column, which is normal atmospheric pressure, is found from equation (85) to be $p = 76.0$ cm. $\times$ 13.596 gm./cm.^{3} $\times$ 980 dynes/gm. $= 1,013,000$ dynes/cm.^{2}, or approximately 14.7 lb./in.^{2} In a similar manner, atmospheric pressure would raise a column of water to a height of about 34 ft.

The pressure at a point due to a liquid is seen to be determined by two factors only: the height of the liquid surface above the point, and the density of the liquid. This pressure is not affected by the depth to which the liquid may extend below the point in question, nor by the size or shape of the body of liquid in which the point is located. The direction of liquid pressure is governed by two laws, as follows:

(1) *The pressure exerted by a liquid at rest is normal to any surface with which the liquid is in contact.* For, suppose the pressure to be in some other direction, as in part I of Fig. 117, where p, the pressure of the liquid upon the wall at x, is (incorrectly) represented as inclined to the normal. Under these circumstances p could be resolved into two components n and t, these being respectively normal and tangent to the wall. But the component t cannot exist, otherwise the wall would exert a force equal and opposite to it on the adjacent layer of liquid, and the liquid would move, which is contrary to the assumption; hence the pressure p

must be normal to the surface. An experimental proof is indicated
in part II of the figure, where the liquid is observed to flow normally through small openings made in various surfaces with which
it is in contact.

(2) *The pressure at a point in a liquid at rest is the same in all
directions.* To verify this statement, consider a tiny plate to be
placed at the point; the forces exerted upon its two faces must be

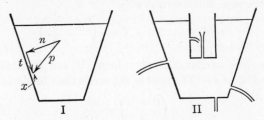

FIG. 117. Showing liquid pressure normal to surface

equal and opposite or it would move; and since the plate may be
imagined to occupy any position and to be indefinitely reduced in
size, the pressure at the point is equal in all directions.

106. Calculation of Force Due to Liquid. — The force due to
liquid pressure on any plane submerged surface can be calculated
from equation (83), $F = pA$. For a horizontal surface, since the
pressure is uniform throughout, p represents its value at any point.
For any other plane surface, *the same equation can be used, provided p represents the pressure at the center of the area subjected to
liquid pressure.* To verify this state-
ment, such a surface will be considered
as though it were divided into a number of elementary areas, upon each of
which the pressure is substantially
uniform; the foregoing expression may
then be used to find the force on each
individual area; and by adding the
forces thus found, the total force can be obtained.

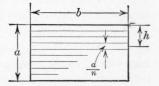

FIG. 118. Submerged surface
divided into horizontal strips

Consider a vertical submerged rectangle of area ab, as shown in
Fig. 118, with its upper edge in the surface of a liquid of density d,
to be divided into n slender horizontal strips each of width $\frac{a}{n}$.
Denoting the depths of these strips below the surface of the liquid
by h_1, h_2, h_3, $\cdots$ h_n, the total force acting upon the surface will

be the sum of the forces on the individual strips, thus:

$$F = h_1 d \frac{a}{n} b + h_2 d \frac{a}{n} b + \cdots + h_n d \frac{a}{n} b = \frac{dab}{n} \left[h_1 + h_2 + \cdots h_n \right]$$

The bracketed quantity consists of n terms, each greater than the preceding by an amount $\dfrac{a}{n}$, and thus forms an arithmetical progression, the sum of the series being

$$\left[h_1 + h_2 + \cdots h_n \right] = n \left(\frac{h_1 + h_n}{2} \right)$$

If the number of strips is very large, it can be assumed that $h_1 = 0$ and $h_n = a$. The sum of the series then becomes

$$n \left(\frac{0 + a}{2} \right) = \frac{na}{2}$$

and accordingly the force is

$$F = \frac{d a b}{n} \times \frac{n a}{2} = \frac{a^2 b d}{2}$$

This value can be expressed as $F = \left(\dfrac{a}{2} d \right) A$, where $A = a b$ is the area of the rectangle. But the term in parenthesis represents the pressure at the center of this area, and thus the force exerted by the liquid on the surface is

$$F = pA$$

where p represents the pressure at the center of the area in contact with the liquid. Students familiar with calculus will be able to simplify the foregoing treatment by using the method of integration. Although this proof was based on a vertical rectangle with its upper edge located in the surface of the liquid, the same method of treatment may be applied to surfaces having any shape, located anywhere, and inclined at any angle, provided only that the surface considered is plane, so that the pressure upon it varies uniformly from point to point.

107. Some Illustrations. — In designing and building tanks, dams, retaining walls, and other structures used to confine a liquid, it is necessary to know how much force the liquid will exert, in order that each surface may have the proper strength, weight, and bracing to withstand the applied load. In calculating such a force, the pressure is first determined, usually by equation (84),

$p = hd$, and the force can then be found from equation (83), $F = pA$.

An interesting example appears in Fig. 119, which shows a cross-section of three tanks having bases of equal area, the tanks being filled with water to the same depth. Upon calculation, the liquid will be found to exert the same force on the base of each

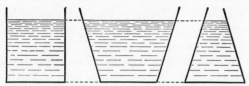

FIG. 119.   Force independent of amount of liquid

tank, thus showing that the force does not depend on the amount of liquid in the tank.

Consider next the force exerted by a liquid on a rectangular submerged surface, either vertical as represented in Fig. 118 or inclined as shown in cross-section in part I of Fig. 120. The center of area, x, is midway between the top and bottom edges, at a depth h below the liquid surface; the pressure at this point multiplied by the area gives the force desired. Having thus found the

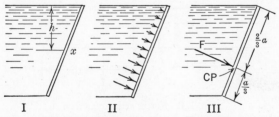

FIG. 120.   Force on submerged rectangle

magnitude of the force, and knowing its direction to be normal to the submerged surface, there remains only to be found its point of application, called the *center of pressure*. This point is easily located for a submerged *rectangle* which has its *upper edge in the surface of the liquid*. Although calculation gives a single value for the force acting upon such a rectangle, it is known that the liquid actually exerts a series of parallel forces upon the surface, these forces increasing in proportion to the depth, as indicated in part II of the figure. Hence the calculated force F, which replaces this series of parallel forces, must be their resultant, and its point of application can be found by the method described in § 63. By working out a numerical example, the student can show that this point of application is two-thirds of the way down from the upper to the lower edge, when the upper edge of the rectangle lies in the liquid surface. Taking a as the slant height, the center of pressure of this surface is located at CP in part III of the figure.

*108. Stability of a Dam. — The impounding of water for power, water supply and irrigation purposes is accomplished by dams, usually constructed of concrete. The cross-sectional shape of a dam is basically a right triangle with the vertical side in contact with water. Naturally, dams are designed to resist sliding downstream along their foundation as well as to resist overturning. These conditions of stability involve the principles of fluid pressure and equilibrium, and an example will emphasize their importance.

Consider a dam section having the dimensions shown in Fig. 121 and regard the width of the dam (perpendicular to the page) as 100 ft. for

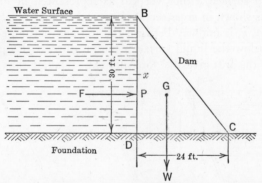

FIG. 121. Forces acting on a dam

simplicity. With the water level at the top of the dam, the center of area x of the water face is halfway along BD, being 15 ft. below B. The water pressure at this point is $p = hd = 15$ ft. $\times$ 62.4 lb./cu. ft. = 936 lb./sq. ft. The resultant force of the water on the dam is $F = pA = $ (936 lb./sq. ft.) $\times$ 30 ft. $\times$ 100 ft. = 2,808,000 lb.; it acts perpendicularly to BD at point P, two-thirds of the way from B to D.

Taking the density of concrete as 150 lb./cu. ft., the weight of the dam of this material is $W = \frac{1}{2}(30$ ft. $\times$ 24 ft.$) \times$ 100 ft. $\times$ 150 lb./cu. ft. = 5,400,000 lb., and it acts at the center of gravity of the section at G. Then, assuming that the coefficient of friction of the dam along its foundation is $\mu = 0.60$, the limiting force of friction [§ 45] will be 0.60 $\times$ 5,400,000 lb. = 3,240,000 lb. Since this force is greater than the force of 2,808,000 lb. exerted by the water, the dam will be safe against sliding.

To investigate the possibility of overturning the dam about the edge C, the moments of forces W and F are determined about this edge as axis.

Since the center of area G is $\frac{2}{3}$ the distance from the vertex B to the midpoint of the base CD, the vector W will be 16 ft. from C. Consequently, the torque due to W is 5,400,000 lb. × 16 ft. = 86.4×10^6 lb-ft. counterclockwise. Similarly, the torque due to F is 2,808,000 lb. × 10 ft. = 28.08×10^6 lb-ft. clockwise. The factor of safety against overturning the dam is the ratio of these torques and amounts to over 3. It can be shown that the resultant of the forces F and W upon the dam will pass through the base CD, at a point 10.8 ft. from C.

Engineers do not regard concrete as strong in tension unless reinforced by steel embedded in it. To eliminate the occurrence of tensile forces at the base of a dam without such reinforcement, it is designed so that the resultant of the forces upon it will be directed through the middle third of the base.

109. Transmission of Pressure; Pascal's Principle. — A number of principles in the mechanics of fluids are associated with the name of the French philosopher, Blaise Pascal (1623–1662). One of these is as follows: External pressure exerted upon a confined liquid is transferred undiminished to all surfaces in contact with that liquid. In other words, Pascal's Principle states that *an increase of pressure on any part of a confined liquid causes an equal increase throughout the liquid.*

This principle is employed in the hydraulic press, as used for compressing goods into bales, for forming the lead sheathing upon electric cables, and the like. An elementary diagram of this device is shown in Fig. 122, which represents a confined body of liquid connecting two cylinders of areas a and A respectively, each fitted with a piston. Upon applying a force f to the small piston, a

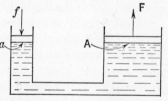

Fig. 122.   The hydraulic press

greater force F will be exerted by the large one, such that the pressures at the two pistons are equal, or $F/A = f/a$.

By this means a large force, exerted through a small distance, may be obtained by exerting a small force through a large distance. The mechanical advantage of this machine may be computed as described in § 80.

Hydraulic brakes on automobiles operate on the principle of liquid pressure. A pressure or master cylinder is mounted near the fulcrum of the foot-brake pedal and is connected by copper tubing and flexible hose connections to cylinders at each of the four wheel brakes, the entire system being filled with non-freezing liquid. When foot pressure is applied, the piston of the master cylinder is forced inward and the pressure is transmitted to the four wheel cylinders, forcing their pistons outward and tightening the brake bands against the drums.

110. Buoyancy; Archimedes' Principle. — It is well known that a stone can be lifted more easily in water than in air; that many objects float upon water; that a swimmer cannot sink in the Great Salt Lake; and that most metals will float upon mercury. Evidently a liquid exerts an upward force upon a body placed in it. Archimedes (*c*287–212 B.C.), Greek mathematician and inventor, determined how much this buoyant force is. The principle known by his name states that *a body submerged wholly or partially in a fluid is buoyed up by a force equal to the weight of the fluid displaced.*

To show how this principle can be verified *experimentally*, suppose that a metal body, having for example a volume of 27 cu. cm. and a weight in air of 189 gm., is lowered into a vessel filled to the top with water. The body naturally displaces its own volume of water, and this overflows and may be collected. The displaced water will be found to weigh 27 gm., and the apparent weight of the body when immersed in water will be found to be 162 gm. Thus, the loss in weight, namely 27 gm., is the same as the weight of the liquid displaced.

Archimedes' Principle can be proved *theoretically* by calculating the buoyant force acting upon a submerged body and also calculating the weight of the displaced liquid, and noting that these quantities are equal. Consider a block of rectangular cross-section, having a height h and having top and bottom faces of area a, immersed in a liquid of density d, as represented in Fig. 123.

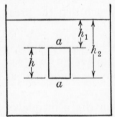

FIG. 123. Illustrating Archimedes' Principle

On the vertical faces, the liquid exerts horizontal forces which are balanced on all sides; on the top face it exerts a downward force $h_1 d a$, and on the bottom face an upward force $h_2 d a$. Since h_2 is greater than h_1, the liquid exerts a net upward force on the block amounting to $h_2 d a - h_1 d a = h d a$. However, the volume of the block, and hence that of the liquid displaced, is $h a$, and therefore the weight of the liquid displaced is $h d a$, which is identical with the buoyant force due to the liquid. Bodies of irregular shape may be considered as made up of a number of blocks as described; and thus it may be said that any body submerged in a liquid is buoyed up by a force equal to the weight of the liquid displaced.

This principle is employed in the control of submarines. In submerging the boat, sea water is admitted into tanks and the effect of the buoyant force is reduced. The boat is brought to the surface by expelling the water from these tanks with compressed air or with pumps.

111. Density and Specific Gravity. — The *density* of a substance has already been defined in § 9 as the amount of matter contained in unit volume of the substance; that is, *density is mass per unit volume*, or

$$d = \frac{m}{V} \qquad (86)$$

Density is usually expressed in pounds per cubic foot in British units, and in grams per cubic centimeter in metric units.

The specific gravity of a substance is the ratio of the density of the substance to that of water. This quantity is thus a pure numeric, and tells how many times a substance is as "heavy" (dense) as water. If a substance has a specific gravity of 5, one cubic foot of the substance has a mass of 5 × 62.4 or 312 lb. One cubic centimeter of this substance would have a mass of 5 × 1 or 5 gm. It will be noted that in the metric system of units, the specific gravity of a substance has the same numerical value as its

Specific Gravities

Liquids		Metals	
Alcohol, ethyl....	0.79 (0° C.)	Aluminum............	2.56– 2.58
Glycerine........	1.26 (0° C.)	Brass................	8.25– 8.70
Mercury........	13.596 (0° C.)	Copper..............	8.80– 8.95
Oils, lubricating..	0.90–0.93 (20° C.)	Iron, gray cast........	7.03– 7.13
Turpentine.......	0.873 (16° C.)	Lead.................	11.34–11.36
Water, pure.....	1.000 (4° C.)	Platinum.............	21.50
Water, sea.......	1.025 (15° C.)	Silver...............	10.4 –10.5
		Steel................	7.82– 7.85
		Uranium.............	18.7
Woods			
Balsa wood......	0.11–0.13	**Miscellaneous**	
Cedar..........	0.49–0.57		
Cork..........	0.22–0.26	Diamond.............	3.5 –3.6
Lignum-vitae....	1.17–1.33	Glass, common........	2.4 –2.8
Maple.........	0.62–0.75	Ice..................	0.88–0.91
Oak..........	0.60–0.90	Kapok (in pillows)......	0.05–0.10
Pine..........	0.35–0.85	Masonry.............	1.85–2.3

density, since the density of water is 1 gm. per cu. cm. Density
and specific gravity are independent of the size of the sample under
test, and depend only upon the substance of which it is made.
Some typical values of specific gravity are given in the accompanying table.

112. Measurement of Density. — The density of a solid can
usually be determined by direct measurement, its mass being
determined with an equal-arm balance, and its volume being found
either from its dimensions or by measuring the displacement it
produces when submerged in water. Knowing the mass and the
volume of the body, the density follows from equation (86).

An indirect method which offers some advantages consists of
weighing the body first in air and again when submerged in water,
and using Archimedes' Principle to calculate the density from the
data thus obtained.

Suppose, for example, that a body is found to weigh 420 gm. in air
and 350 gm. when submerged in water. The buoyant force is 420 − 350
or 70 gm., and by Archimedes' Principle, this equals the weight of the
water displaced by the body. Since 1 cu. cm. of water weighs 1 gm.,
neglecting slight variations due to temperature, it follows that the volume
of the displaced water, and hence the volume of the body, is 70 cu. cm.
As the mass of the body is 420 gm., and its volume is 70 cu. cm., its
density is 420 gm. ÷ 70 cu. cm. or 6.0 gm. per cu. cm.

The density of a liquid can be determined by several methods.
In one of these, a pyknometer or specific-gravity bottle of known
weight is filled with the liquid and the mass is determined with an
equal-arm balance. The volume of the container is usually known,
or may be determined by another measurement using water, and
the density of the liquid can then be calculated by a direct proportion. A second method for measuring the density of a liquid consists of weighing some solid body (1) in air, (2) when submerged in
water, and (3) when submerged in the liquid under test; and calculating the density of the liquid by use of Archimedes' Principle.

In measuring the density of alcohol by the method just described,
suppose that a body weighs 420 gm. in air, 350 gm. when submerged in
water, and 365 gm. when submerged in alcohol. The displaced alcohol
has a weight of 420 − 365 or 55 gm. and a volume of 420 − 350 or 70
cu. cm.; and therefore the alcohol has a density of 55 gm. ÷ 70 cu. cm.
or 0.79 gm. per cu. cm.

The density of a liquid can also be determined by means of a
hydrometer, Fig. 124. It consists of a hollow glass chamber
weighted at the bottom and having a graduated stem at the top.

The hydrometer has a constant mass and when floated on a liquid sinks until it displaces its own weight of liquid (see following section); the "lighter" the liquid, the deeper it settles before coming to rest. By suitably calibrating the scale of this instrument, the specific gravity of the liquid can be read directly at the point where the stem projects through the liquid surface.

Another method of theoretical interest for determining the density of a liquid is that of balanced columns. In this method, illustrated in Fig. 125, the arms of an inverted U-tube are dipped respectively into water and into the liquid under test. Upon removing part of the air from the tube through a valve at A, the two columns rise to heights h_w and h_x, which can be measured.

Fig. 124. Hydrometer

Since there is the same difference in pressure between the top and bottom of each column, it follows that $h_w d_w = h_x d_x$, where d_w represents the density of water and d_x that of the liquid under test. From this equation, the value of d_x can readily be found.

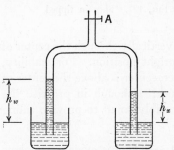

Fig. 125. Measuring density of liquid by balanced columns

113. Stability of Floating Bodies. — A floating body, as well as a submerged body, experiences an upward buoyant force equal to the weight of the liquid displaced, in accordance with Archimedes' Principle. A body floating at rest, moreover, is in equilibrium, and hence this buoyant force must be equal and opposite to the weight of the body. *A floating body when placed in a liquid sinks until it displaces its own weight of liquid.* A ship which displaces 20,000 tons of water also weighs this same amount. The forces acting upon such a ship are indicated in Fig. 126, where W represents the weight of the ship, acting downward through its center of gravity G, while B represents the equal buoyant force, which acts upward through C, the center of mass of the displaced water.

In order for a ship to be stable, it must tend to right itself when tipped to one side. Thus, the ship previously described is shown in Fig. 127 in a listed position. The weight W acts downward at G, as before, but the center of gravity of the displaced water is now shifted to C', at which point the upward force B acts. The forces B and W constitute a couple which tends to restore the ship to an upright position, and the ship is said to be stable. The stability of a ship is determined by the position of the *metacenter* M, this point being the intersection of two lines, one drawn vertically through the center of gravity of the displaced water, and the

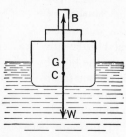

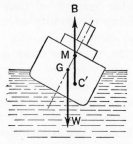

FIG. 126. Forces acting on   FIG. 127. Ship in tipped
           a ship   position

other being a line which was drawn vertically through the center of gravity of the ship when in an upright position. For stability, the design must be such that the metacenter is above the center of gravity of the ship, as in the figure; although in practice the *metacentric height MG* is kept reasonably small to provide riding comfort.

114. Action Between Molecules. — There is evidence to show that as two molecules approach each other, a separation is reached where their combined potential energy is a minimum. In this condition, work is needed to move them either nearer together or further apart, because of forces which are probably electrical. When molecules are very close together, these forces produce a tremendous repulsive effect, keeping the centers of the molecules at slight distances from each other. When the molecules are further apart, the force becomes one of attraction; such forces are known to be very great. It is this molecular attraction, for example, that holds a solid body together, enabling it not only to retain its shape but also to support large external loads. The attraction between molecules of the same substance is called *cohesion*, while the attraction between molecules of unlike substances is called *adhesion*.

The attraction between two molecules falls off rapidly as their separation increases. It is therefore convenient for discussion to imagine a tiny sphere around each molecule, called its *sphere of action*, and to say that this molecule exerts an attractive force upon other molecules which lie within this boundary, but not upon those which lie outside of it. This conception of molecular attraction being limited by a sphere is entirely artificial, but is of value in indicating that the forces of cohesion and adhesion are very small except for molecules which lie close together. The sphere of action is usually considered as having a radius smaller than one-millionth of a centimeter.

The theory of molecular attraction explains the interesting behavior of a liquid surface. In Fig. 128, the line *MN* represents a free liquid surface, and *A*, *B*, and *C* represent molecules of the liquid, each surrounded by its sphere of action. The molecule *A*, which is well within the body of the liquid, will, on the average, be attracted equally in all directions by other molecules within its sphere of action, and will be as likely to move in one direction as another. The molecule *B*, which is near the surface, will experience a downward force since there are more molecules in the lower half of its sphere of action than

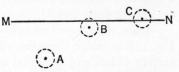

Fig. 128. Illustrating molecular sphere of action

in the upper half. Similarly, the molecule *C*, which is represented just above the free surface, will be acted upon by a considerable downward force. Hence a molecule which in its motion tends to rise above the surface is pulled downward. The surface acts like a stretched membrane, tending to shorten itself as much as possible, and assumes at each point a direction at right angles to the resultant forces acting on the surface molecules.

There is experimental evidence to show that the molecules of a body are in a state of eternal motion, this motion being entirely erratic and irregular, and depending only upon the temperature of the substance. The molecules themselves are, of course, too small to be visible, and indirect methods must be used to study their motion. The first observations were made in 1827 by the English botanist, Robert Brown (1773–1858), who noted that very fine particles placed in suspension in a liquid move about in an irregular and life-like manner. This action he attributed to uneven bombardment of the particles by the moving molecules of the liquid, and this hypothesis has been amply borne out by further research and mathematical study. These erratic motions, termed Brownian movements, can be observed with a high-power microscope by viewing fine particles of insoluble carmine or some similar substance suspended in water and properly illuminated.

115. Surface Phenomena. — The attraction between molecules, described in the foregoing section, is responsible for a number of effects which are usually referred to as surface phenomena, since they occur at the surfaces of liquids. These effects cannot be explained by the usual laws applying to liquids at rest, but follow at once when the forces acting upon the surface molecules are considered.

A small quantity of mercury or water poured upon a level surface does not spread out into a thin film, but assumes a globular shape. The liquid surface acts like a stretched membrane and becomes as small as possible; a sphere has the smallest surface for a given volume and, therefore, the drop becomes spherical except for a slight flattening due to gravity.

Again, the edges of a free liquid surface are usually curved, as in Fig. 129, in which the adhesive and cohesive forces acting upon a surface molecule of the liquid are shown. The force of adhesion A

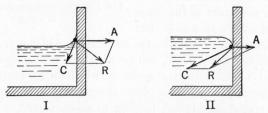

I   II

FIG. 129.   Angle of contact at edge of liquid surface

exerted by the wall is perpendicular to its surface; the force of cohesion C, which is due to the surrounding molecules of liquid, has the general direction shown; and their resultant R is at right angles to the surface of the liquid. The shape shown in part I of the figure is characteristic of those cases where the liquid wets the wall, the adhesion between the liquid and the solid being greater than the cohesion of the liquid. Here any liquid molecules near the wall which happen to rise above the free liquid surface are pulled toward the wall by the force of adhesion, causing the liquid to pile up along the edge. When the liquid does not wet the wall, as in the case of mercury and glass, the adhesion is less than the cohesion, and the liquid surface curves downward as in part II of the figure. The *angle of contact* at the edge of the liquid surface varies with the substances used, being 0° between water and glass, 90° between water and silver, and 132° between mercury and glass, when pure liquids and clean surfaces are used.

116. Surface Tension and Capillarity. — It has been pointed out that the surface of a liquid tends to assume the smallest possible size, acting in this respect like a membrane under tension.

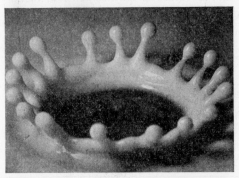

FIG. 130. Splash of a drop photographed in 1/100,000 second. (*Taken by Professors Edgerton, Germeshausen and Grier at Massachusetts Institute of Technology.*)

This is illustrated in Fig. 130, which shows an enlarged view of the splash produced by a drop of milk falling upon a surface of that liquid, and reveals the rebounding droplets just before becoming detached spheres.

Any portion of the liquid surface exerts a tension upon adjacent portions or upon other objects with which it is in contact. This force is in the plane of the surface and has different values for different liquids. For water, the *surface tension* is about 75 dynes per cm., at ordinary temperatures. Thus, if a line 1 cm. long is imagined in the surface of water, the surface on either side of this line exerts a force of 75 dynes upon the surface on the other side.

Surface tension occurs not only at the free surface of a liquid, but also at the boundaries or interfaces separating two liquids. By way of illustration,

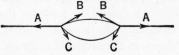

FIG. 131. Forces on floating oil drop

the forces acting upon a drop of oil floating on hot water are shown in Fig. 131. The surface tension *AA* of the water in contact with air tends to spread the drop out; while the surface tension *BB* of the oil in contact with air, and the surface tension *CC* of the oil in contact with water, tend to make the drop contract. Under the combined action of these forces, the drop assumes such a shape as to remain in equilibrium.

At lower temperatures, surface tension in general increases, although not equally for all substances. The drop shown in Fig. 131 spreads out into a thin film at ordinary room temperature because of the relatively great increase in the surface tension *AA*. Some approximate values of surface tension, based on measurements at ordinary room temperature, appear in the accompanying table.

Surface Tensions of Some Liquids

	In contact with	Dynes/cm.
Benzene.........	air	29
Glycerine........	air	63
Mercury.........	air	470
Mercury.........	water	392
Olive oil.........	air	35
Olive oil.........	water	19
Water...........	air	75

The surface tension of a liquid may be measured by observing the force needed to pull an inverted U-shaped wire upward through the surface. Suppose that in order to pull a wire of length *l* through the surface a force *F* in excess of its weight is required, as indicated in part I of Fig. 132. As the wire leaves the surface a

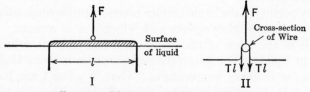

Fig. 132. Measurement of surface tension

film of liquid becomes attached to it, which, having two surfaces, exerts a downward force on the wire amounting to $2Tl$, where T represents the surface tension of the liquid. These forces are shown in the sectional diagram forming part II of the figure. To move the wire uniformly, the applied force must balance the downward pull, hence,

$$F = 2Tl \qquad (87)$$

from which the surface tension can be found.

The rise of liquids in fine-bore tubes is a result of surface tension and is called *capillarity*. When a tube of small radius r is dipped into a liquid which wets it, a concave meniscus is formed, and the adhesion of the glass, being equal and opposite to the surface tension T of the liquid, has a vertical component $T \cos \theta$ which pulls directly upward on the liquid. As a result, the liquid rises in the tube as shown in Fig. 133. Its elevation h will be such that the total upward force, which is $T \times \cos \theta \times 2\pi r$, just balances the weight of the column of liquid, which is $\pi r^2 h d g$, d being the density of the liquid and g being the acceleration due to gravity. Equating these forces and solving, the height of the column is found to be

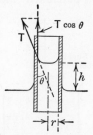

FIG. 133. Rise of liquid in small tube

$$h = \frac{2T \cos \theta}{r d g} \tag{88}$$

*117. Diffusion and Osmosis. — When two miscible liquids which do not react chemically are placed in the same vessel, the molecular motion of each makes it penetrate the other, and by a slow process called *diffusion*, the liquid eventually becomes uniform throughout. The rate of diffusion increases with increased concentration and with higher temperatures. Diffusion may be observed, for example, between a solution of copper sulphate in the lower part of a glass jar and a solution of zinc sulphate carefully poured in upon it. At first the liquids remain separated, with the denser copper sulphate solution at the bottom, as would be expected from the usual laws of liquids at rest; but gradually the sharp boundary between them disappears, and the liquids mix by diffusion.

Sometimes a liquid is able to pass through a membrane, presumably as a result of the bombardment of the membrane by the moving molecules of the liquid. Moreover, some membranes are selective in their action, allowing certain molecules to pass through them, but preventing others from doing so. Thus, a piece of animal membrane, such as parchment, when placed in contact with a sugar solution, permits the passage of the water molecules, but not of the larger and more complex sugar molecules. Such a process is called *osmosis*, and the membrane is termed a *semipermeable* membrane.

This action may be illustrated by the apparatus shown in Fig. 134, which represents an inverted thistle tube closed with a parchment membrane, the tube containing a small quantity of sugar solution, and the whole being dipped into a beaker of water. By molecular bombardment, the water molecules pass through the membrane in both directions, but more of them move upward than downward in a given time, since part of the upper surface of the membrane is obstructed by the sugar molecules inside the tube. As a result, the liquid rises in the tube, and the concentration of the sugar solution is reduced. An increased pressure being established within the tube, the rate at which the water molecules pass downward through the membrane is increased. Moreover, the reduced concentration of the sugar solution exposes more of the upper surface of the membrane, which also increases the rate at which the water molecules pass downward. When the upward and downward rates become equal, a state of equilibrium results, at which the pressure of the solute particles against the membrane has some maximum value determined by the conditions of the experiment. This value is termed the *osmotic pressure*.

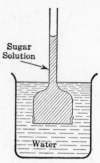

Sugar Solution →

Water

Fig. 134. Illustrating osmotic pressure

Osmotic pressure depends upon the solution used and upon its concentration; it increases with temperature and is independent of the material of the semi-permeable membrane. For dilute solutions, the osmotic pressure varies directly with the concentration, provided the solution is a non-conductor of electricity. Expressed mathematically,

$$\frac{p}{c} = \frac{p'}{c'} \tag{89}$$

where p and p' are any two osmotic pressures, and c and c' are the corresponding concentrations.

Osmosis is known to be an important factor in animal and vegetable life, owing to its influence on the transfer of liquids through membranes.

PROBLEMS

1. Calculate the liquid pressure at the base of a cubical tank measuring 8 ft. on a side when filled with water, and also find what force the water exerts on the base.

2. At what depth below the surface of water will the liquid pressure be 14.7 lb. per sq. in.?

3. Canyons have recently been discovered off the New England coast extending 8400 ft. below sea level. Calculate the pressure at this depth assuming the average density of sea water to be 64.2 lb. per cu. ft.

4. Convert a pressure of 1 lb. per sq. in. to the corresponding number of dynes per square centimeter.

5. A vertical dam 30 ft. long has a rectangular cross-section 10 ft. high and 6 ft. thick. When water just overflows the top, calculate the force which the water exerts on the dam, and also the torque with which it tends to overturn the dam.

6. A meter stick of negligible weight carries ten loads: 10 gm. being applied at the 5-cm. mark, 20 gm. at the 15-cm. mark, 30 gm. at the 25-cm. mark, and so on up to 100 gm. at the 95-cm. mark, this loading being somewhat like that shown in part II of Fig. 120. At what point will the meter stick balance in equilibrium? and what reaction will it experience there?

*7. A dam has a length of 40 ft. and a vertical height of 10 ft. Its cross-section is a right triangle of 6-ft. base. If water extends to the top of the dam, in contact with its sloping surface, calculate the force tending to slide the dam off its foundation, and find also the torque tending to overturn the dam.

*8. A concrete dam has a vertical height of 40 ft. Its cross-section is a right triangle of 20-ft. base. Water stands behind the dam in contact with its vertical surface to an elevation 4 ft. below the top. Calculate per foot of length (*a*) the moment due to the water tending to overturn the dam, and (*b*) the moment due to the weight of the dam tending to prevent overturning. Take the density of concrete as 150 lb. per cu. ft.

9. A hydraulic press has pistons of 2-in. and 12-in. radius respectively. If a force of 50 lb. is applied to the smaller piston, what force does the larger piston exert? Calculate also the theoretical mechanical advantage of this machine.

10. A large tank partly filled with water is balanced on a platform scale and is found to weigh 4800 lb. A cubic foot of granite suspended from a hoist directly above the tank is lowered until it is completely immersed in the water but does not touch the sides or bottom of the tank. Find the reading of the scale under this condition. Explain the answer.

11. A certain glass ball weighs 188 gm. in air, 116 gm. when immersed in water, and 125 gm. when immersed in turpentine. Calculate the density of the glass and the density of the turpentine.

12. A straight stick 1 in. in diameter weighs 1 lb. It is pushed straight down into water until its lower end is immersed 4 ft. What force is needed to hold it in this position?

13. A hydrometer, weighing 18.2 gm., has a cylindrical stem 15 cm. long and 1.00 cm. in external diameter. When floated in water it sinks to its zero mark near the upper end of the stem. What length of stem from its zero mark should project from the liquid surface when the hydrometer is floated in glycerine?

14. The method of balanced columns illustrated in Fig. 125 is used to determine the specific gravity of alcohol, a water column 4.9 cm. high balancing a column of alcohol 6.1 cm. high. Find the specific gravity of alcohol; and find also the pressure in the communicating tube above the columns.

15. An ice cube floats in a glass of water with $\frac{1}{10}$ of its volume projecting above the liquid surface. Calculate the specific gravity of ice. How will melting of the ice affect the level of the water in the glass?

16. A ship has a horizontal cross-section at the water line of 12,500 sq. ft. Assuming the sides to be vertical, how much load can be placed on board without causing the ship to sink more than 1 ft. in sea water?

17. A steel plate 1 cm. thick is floating on mercury. How much will the plate project above the surface? The specific gravity of steel is 7.85.

18. Osmium and lithium are the heaviest and lightest metals known, their specific gravities being 22.5 and 0.534 respectively. How many cubic centimeters of osmium attached to 10 cu. cm. of lithium would produce a combination that would just float completely immersed in mercury?

19. The S.S. Conte di Savoia has a displacement of 45,800 tons and a metacentric height of 2.2 ft. In still water it has a period of oscillation of 25 sec. Assuming the ship to roll in harmonic fashion through a small angle about a longitudinal axis through the metacenter, compute the moment of inertia of the ship about this axis.

20. The working surfaces of Johansson's gage blocks are plane within a fraction of a millionth of an inch. Two such blocks, each having surfaces measuring 0.70 × 0.70 in., when twisted tightly together, resisted a pull of 100 lb. without coming apart. With what force were the blocks held together (a) because of atmospheric pressure? (b) because of molecular attraction?

21. A fine wire formed into a loop of 1-cm. radius is placed horizontally in a liquid and pulled slowly upward through the liquid surface. If this operation requires a force of 465 dynes in addition to the weight of the wire, find the surface tension of the liquid.

22. A glass tube open at the ends and having an internal diameter of 0.5 mm. is placed vertically in a dish of mercury. Compute the depression of the mercury within the tube.

23. How high will water rise in a glass tube 0.5 mm. in diameter, at ordinary temperatures?

24. To determine the angle of contact between a given liquid and glass, two tests are made. First, a horizontal wire 5 cm. long is pulled slowly upward through the liquid surface, a force of 620 dynes in addition to the weight of the wire being found necessary. Next, an open glass tube of 2 mm. diameter is placed vertically in the liquid and the capillary rise is found to be 1.1 cm. The specific gravity of the liquid is 0.87; find its angle of contact against glass.

CHAPTER XII

LIQUIDS IN MOTION

118. Types of Liquid Pumps. — Liquids may be raised from one level to another by means of pumps. In this process the liquid gains potential energy with respect to its initial level, and this energy is supplied by the pump. An expression for this energy can be found by supposing that an open-top tank containing liquid is equipped at the bottom with a cylinder having a tight-fitting piston of area A, as shown in Fig. 135, and that an amount of work $E = Fs$ is done in pushing the piston inward a distance s by the application of a force F. The force required is $F = pA$, where p is the liquid pressure at the pump, and hence the work done is $E = pAs$. During this stroke of the piston the quantity of liquid pushed from the cylinder into the tank has a volume $V = As$, and hence, in forcing this volume of liquid

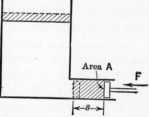

FIG. 135. Work done in pumping a liquid

into a region where the pressure exceeds that of the atmosphere by p, the work done is

$$E = pV \tag{90}$$

In order that the pump indicated in Fig. 135 may force more and more liquid into the tank during successive strokes, valves must be fitted into the piston or cylinder so that a new supply of liquid will be furnished for each stroke. The so-called lift pump and force pump accomplish this in the manner shown in Fig. 136. In the *lift pump*, while the piston is being drawn upward, valve 1 is closed and valve 2 open, and the pressure is lowered in the cylinder and pipe below it. Liquid rises into this space because of atmospheric pressure on the water surface below. When the piston is pushed downward, valve 2 closes and the imprisoned liquid passes through valve 1 to the upper portion of the cylinder. Upon the next upstroke the cylinder fills with liquid again through valve 2, and the liquid above the piston flows out of the spout into the elevated tank *U*.   The operation of the *force pump* can be described similarly, the liquid first being drawn into the cylinder by suction, after which it is forced to any desired height.   In raising water, valve 2 of either pump must be less than 34 ft. above the water

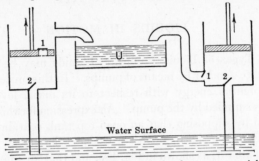

Fig. 136.   Lift (or suction) pump at left and force pump at right

surface, since atmospheric pressure cannot support a column of water higher than this.

Another form of pump depends for its operation upon centrifugal force.   In the *centrifugal pump*, water enters at the center of a rotating wheel, or impeller, provided with radial blades.   As the blades revolve, the water is thrown outward into the watertight housing of the pump, and thence into the discharge pipe.

119. Velocity of Efflux. — Liquid flowing through an orifice gives up potential energy and gains an equal amount of kinetic

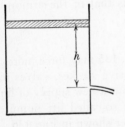

Fig. 137.   Flow through
an orifice

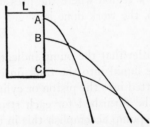

Fig. 138.   Paths of water flow

energy, assuming that no waste occurs during the process.   From this fact, the velocity of efflux can be calculated.   Consider a thin layer of liquid having a mass *m* and located in the liquid surface, at an average distance *h* above the orifice, as shown in Fig. 137. When an equal quantity *m* of liquid has flowed from the tank, this top layer has disappeared, and the potential energy is consequently reduced by an amount $m\,g\,h$. At the same time the gain in kinetic energy is $\frac{1}{2}\,m\,v^2$, whence

$$m\,g\,h = \tfrac{1}{2}\,m\,v^2$$

from which the velocity of the issuing stream is found to be

$$v = \sqrt{2\,g\,h} \qquad\qquad (91)$$

This result shows that, taking the acceleration due to gravity as constant, the velocity is dependent only upon the height of liquid above the orifice, and is proportional to the square root of this height.

To illustrate this relationship, consider a tank with three orifices A, B, and C, at different elevations, as shown in Fig. 138. If orifice A is 1 ft. below the liquid surface L, the liquid will come through the opening with a velocity of

$$v = \sqrt{2 \times 32\,\frac{\text{ft.}}{\text{sec.}^2} \times 1\ \text{ft.}} = 8\ \text{ft. per sec.}$$

Similarly, at orifice B, 4 ft. below the surface, the velocity of efflux will be 16 ft. per sec.; again at C, 9 ft. below the surface, the velocity will be 24 ft. per sec.

In all cases the velocity of efflux is normal to the surface. Since gravity acts on the liquid upon emergence from the tank, the jets of liquid in the problem just described will form trajectories [§ 33] as shown in the figure.

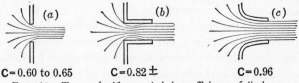

C=0.60 to 0.65   **C**=0.82 ±   **C**=0.96

Fig. 139.   Types of orifices and their coefficients of discharge

The volume of liquid discharged per unit time through an orifice can be calculated by geometry. For when an incompressible liquid flows at v cm./sec. through an orifice of area A sq. cm., the amount discharged in one second would fill a cylinder v cm. long and A sq. cm. in cross-section. Therefore, calling Q the volume discharged per second,

$$Q = A\,v \qquad\qquad (92)$$

This expression may also be used to calculate the rate of flow past a point in a pipe line.

The actual efflux velocities will be somewhat smaller than given by equation (91), because of friction. Also, the actual discharge will be smaller than given by equation (92), because of the contraction of the jet due to stream-line flow. To find the actual discharge, the theoretical value obtained from equation (92) is multiplied by a coefficient of discharge, C. Values of the discharge coefficient, based on experimental test, are given in Fig. 139 for some orifices.

120. Power from a Stream. — The water power which can be obtained from a stream depends upon the distance through which the water can fall, and upon the quantity of water available. The difference in elevation between the input and output water levels is termed the *head* of water. When 1 cu. ft. of water falls 1 ft., 62.4 ft-lb. of potential energy are transformed to kinetic energy, and consequently if Q cu. ft. of water drop per second through a head of h ft., energy is converted at the rate of 62.4 Q h ft-lb. per sec. By § 76 this represents a power of

$$\text{hp.} = \frac{62.4\, Q\, h}{550}$$

The value of Q can be estimated for a proposed water-power development from equation (92), by measuring the velocity of the stream from observations of a body floating downstream and by measuring the cross-section of the stream from observations of width and depth at various places.

The power of the stream expressed by the foregoing equation is made available by turbines, but, of course, some energy is wasted in the transformation by hydraulic and mechanical friction. For impulse wheels the best efficiency is about 82 per cent for all sizes, while for reaction turbines the efficiency ranges from 80 to 90 per cent with large sizes and from 60 to 80 per cent for small units.

121. Energy of a Moving Liquid. — When a liquid flows from one place to another it may undergo a change in potential energy or in kinetic energy, but if it moves without waste of energy due to friction, then its total energy remains unchanged, in accordance with the law of conservation of energy. Consider a liquid to flow steadily through a tube of any section as illustrated in Fig. 140, and imagine that the liquid is incompressible and frictionless, and that its velocity at any cross-section is uniform throughout that section. During a short interval of time, particles of liquid at section 1 and at section 2 will move as indicated by the arrows. Let the cross-sectional areas at these sections be respectively A_1 and A_2, the corresponding velocities of the liquid be v_1 and v_2, the elevations of the sections above a convenient datum plane be respectively h_1 and h_2, and the pressures of the liquid, as measured by manometers [§ 123] or pressure gages, be respectively p_1 and p_2.

Then since the liquid is incompressible, the same mass m will pass any section of the tube in a given time t; the volume of this mass will be $V = m/d$, where d is the density of the liquid. The work which must have been done on this mass of liquid to bring it to the conditions existing at section 1 consists of three parts: $m\,g\,h_1$ to elevate it to the height h_1 above the datum plane; $\frac{1}{2}\,m\,v_1^2$

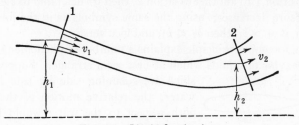

FIG. 140.   Liquid flow in pipes

to give it the velocity v_1; and $p_1 V$ or $p_1 m/d$ to force it into a region of pressure p_1, as given by equation (90). Since the liquid is frictionless, the same amount of work would be required to bring this mass of liquid to the conditions existing at section 2; consequently

$$m\,g\,h_1 + \tfrac{1}{2}\,m\,v_1^2 + p_1\,\frac{m}{d} = m\,g\,h_2 + \tfrac{1}{2}\,m\,v_2^2 + p_2\,\frac{m}{d}$$

The corresponding expression for the total work per unit weight of liquid at any section is obtained herefrom by dividing each term by the weight mg, thus

$$h_1 + \frac{v_1^2}{2g} + \frac{p_1}{d\,g} = h_2 + \frac{v_2^2}{2g} + \frac{p_2}{d\,g}$$

This summation is spoken of by engineers as *total head*, the respective terms being called, $h = $ *elevation head*; $\dfrac{v^2}{2g} = $ *velocity head*; and $\dfrac{p}{d\,g} = $ *pressure head*. If the pressure is determined by some height of liquid, say h', in a manometer tube, then $p = h'd\,g$, and the pressure head becomes h'. It may therefore be merged with the first term, reducing the equation to

$$H_1 + \frac{v_1{}^2}{2g} = H_2 + \frac{v_2{}^2}{2g} \qquad (93)$$

where $H = h + h'$ is now the head due to elevation and pressure.

122. Flow of Fluids; Bernoulli's Theorem. — Daniel Bernoulli (1700–1782) proposed the law dealing with liquid flow expressed by equation (93) which states that *if no work is done on or by an incompressible liquid as it flows, the total head remains unchanged.*

This relation shows that when a liquid speeds up in going from any position 1 to another position 2, then its head due to elevation or pressure decreases; using the same symbols as in the foregoing section, if $v_2 > v_1$, then $h_2 < h_1$, and vice versa.

The foregoing principle explains a number of phenomena about the behavior of liquids which at first seem strange.   Suppose two

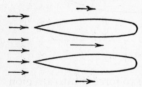

ships are steaming side by side in still water; the relative motion of the ships with respect to the water would be the same as if the ships were regarded as stationary and the water as flowing with the same speed in the opposite direction.

Fig. 141. Attraction of ships moving in the same direction

Fig. 141 shows that the water entrapped between the ships will speed up because of the narrower space.   In consequence the pressure in the water between the ships will be reduced and will become less than the water pressure on the far sides of the ships.   The excess pressure will cause the ships to come closer and closer together.   The application of Bernoulli's Theorem to gases is discussed in § 133.

* 123. Measurement of Liquid Flow. — The theorem of Bernoulli provides a means for measuring the flow of a liquid through a pipe.   A horizontal section containing a constriction or throat is inserted in the pipe line and the pressures are measured both at the throat and in the pipe by pressure gages or their equivalent. Fig. 142 shows the arrangement employing small tubes called manometers, in which the rise of liquid indicates the pressure. The pipe beyond the throat flares out slowly so that the velocity of the liquid can be reduced without disturbing stream-line flow.

Since the velocity of the liquid is greater at the throat than in the pipe, the pressure at the throat will be less than that in the pipe, as demanded by equation (93), and consequently the liquid in the throat manometer will not rise as high as in the pipe manometer. The difference in manometer elevations together with a knowledge of the cross-sections of pipe and throat permit the liquid flow to be measured. This device is known as a *Venturi meter*.

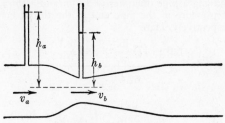

FIG. 142.   Venturi meter

Let the cross-sectional area of the pipe be A and the cross-sectional area of the throat be B. Further, let the velocities at these places be v_a and v_b respectively, and the heads be h_a and h_b respectively. Then from equation (93) for a frictionless liquid

$$h_a + \frac{v_a^2}{2g} = h_b + \frac{v_b^2}{2g}$$

Also, assuming the liquid to be incompressible,

$$A v_a = B v_b$$

Eliminating v_b between these equations,

$$h_a + \frac{v_a^2}{2g} = h_b + \frac{A^2}{B^2} \times \frac{v_a^2}{2g}$$

Transposing and multiplying by 2g,

$$\left(\frac{A^2}{B^2} - 1\right) v_a^2 = 2g(h_a - h_b)$$

from which the velocity of discharge is

$$v_a = \sqrt{\frac{2g(h_a - h_b)}{(A^2/B^2) - 1}}$$

Calling the difference of head $h_b - h_a = h$, the volume of liquid discharged in unit time is $Q = A v_a$, or

$$Q = A \sqrt{\frac{2 g h}{(A^2/B^2) - 1}} \tag{94}$$

The actual discharge of a Venturi meter is less than that obtained by using equation (94); with large tubes carrying water, the actual discharge may be 98 or more per cent of the theoretical value just given for perfect liquids.

As a numerical example, compute the discharge of water through a Venturi meter having a pipe diameter of 12 in. and a throat diameter of 6 in., the water pressure in the pipe and in the throat being 20 and 17 lb. per sq. in. respectively. Here

$$h = \frac{p}{d} = \frac{(20-17)\,\frac{\text{lb.}}{\text{in.}^2} \times 144\,\frac{\text{in.}^2}{\text{ft.}^2}}{62.4\,\frac{\text{lb.}}{\text{ft.}^3}} = 6.93\ \text{ft.},$$

$$A = \frac{\pi}{4}\,\text{ft.}^2, \qquad \frac{A}{B} = \frac{\pi/4}{\pi/16} = 4, \qquad \frac{A^2}{B^2} = 16.$$

Hence the discharge is

$$Q = \frac{\pi}{4}\,\text{ft.}^2\ \sqrt{\frac{2 \times 32\,\frac{\text{ft.}}{\text{sec.}^2} \times 6.93\ \text{ft.}}{16-1}} = 4.27\ \text{cu. ft. per sec.}$$

The flow of liquids is also measured in practice by the use of standard orifices, current meters, Pitot tubes, and weirs; these devices are described in books on Hydraulics.

★124. Viscosity of Liquids. — The property of a liquid that presents a resistance to flow is called *viscosity*. If two beakers, one containing some oil and the other some alcohol are tilted from side to side, much less mobility is observed in the oil than in the alcohol, and the oil is said to be the more viscous of the two liquids.

When a liquid flows over a flat surface, the layer of liquid particles in contact with the surface remains stationary because of adhesion, the next layer of particles moves slowly over the first, the third layer moves with respect to the second, and so on, the speed of each layer increasing with its distance from the solid surface. This distribution of speed causes a portion of the liquid that is cubical in shape at one instant to become rhomboidal at a later instant, as illustrated in Fig. 143.

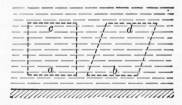

Fig. 143. Shearing action in a liquid

The layer of liquid forming the lower face of the cube travels from *a* to *b* while the upper face travels from *c* to *d*. If the speed of the upper face exceeds that of the lower face by the amount v, and if the vertical distance between these faces is h, the liquid may be looked upon as shearing at the rate v/h, and this rate will be constant as long as the shearing stress to which the liquid is yielding remains unchanged.

The shearing stress acting on the cubical portion of the liquid in Fig. 143 is measured by the force per unit area of the upper (or lower) face, and can be represented by F/A. Experiment shows that the rate of shear v/h is proportional in any liquid under like conditions to the shearing stress F/A which causes the liquid to flow; that is,

$$\frac{F}{A} \propto \frac{v}{h} \quad \text{or} \quad \frac{F}{A} = \eta \frac{v}{h}$$

where η (eta) is the proportionality constant. This constant is called the *coefficient of viscosity* of the liquid; its value is given by

$$\eta = \frac{\dfrac{F}{A}}{\dfrac{v}{h}} = \frac{Fh}{Av} \tag{95}$$

an expression which is similar to that for the shear modulus of elasticity [§ 96]. The viscosity of a liquid decreases with a rise in temperature.

Equation (95) affords a physical idea of what is meant by unit viscosity. Imagine a layer of liquid 1 cm. thick, and suppose a plane surface of large area to be drawn across the upper surface of the liquid with a speed of 1 cm. per sec. Then the force in dynes per sq. cm. of surface necessary to move this plane surface in the manner indicated is numerically equal to the coefficient of viscosity of the liquid under consideration. Its unit in the metric system is dyne-sec. per cm.^{2}, and is called the *poise*. The coefficients of viscosity for some liquids are given in the following table:

Coefficients of Viscosity

Alcohol, ethyl............. at	20° C.	0.012 poise
Benzene...................	20° C.	0.0065
Glycerine.................	20° C.	8.3
Mercury..................	20° C.	0.016
Oil, machine.............	19° C.	1.02
Water....................	20° C.	0.010
Water....................	100° C.	0.0028

The method of measuring viscosity described in the preceding paragraph is not easy to carry out directly. A more convenient method is to cause the liquid under test to flow through a vertical tube of small bore and to measure the rate of flow. Equation (95) must then be applied to each annular layer and the results integrated by the methods of calculus; the analysis yields the following equation for the rate of flow in cubic centimeters per second through a tube of length l cm. and radius r cm.:

$$Q = \frac{\pi P r^4}{8\eta\, l}$$

where P is the liquid pressure in dynes per square centimeter at the lower end of the tube. This relation is known as Poiseuille's Law, and is named after Jean L. M. Poiseuille (1799–1869). It applies to velocities of flow that will not set up eddies in the liquid.

The Saybolt viscosimeter is widely used in this country for practical measurements of viscosity. It operates on the principle that the time for a definite quantity of liquid to flow through a short small tube is proportional to the coefficient of viscosity. In the usual instrument the number of seconds for 60 cu. cm. of liquid to flow out is used as the measure of viscosity. Water at room temperature gives a reading of about 30 sec.

PROBLEMS

1. A tank 8 ft. deep has in the bottom a 2-in. orifice of the type shown in Fig. 139a, for which the discharge coefficient may be taken as 0.625. When the tank is full of water, with what discharge rate will it begin to empty?

2. At what pressure above that of the atmosphere is water emitted from "Old Faithful" geyser, if it rises to a height of 125 ft.?

3. A water tank has three discharge valves of different sizes at its base. With the tank completely filled, it is found that valve A alone can discharge all of the water in 15 min. Under the same conditions valve B alone can empty the tank in 30 min., and valve C likewise in 45 min. Determine the time required to discharge the tank full of water if all three valves are opened simultaneously.

4. What is the diameter of the orifice required to discharge at the rate of 20 gal. per min. from a water main into the atmosphere, if the gage pressure in the main is 80 lb. per sq. in.?

5. The pump of a fire engine, rotating at 3400 rev. per min., discharges 1000 gal. of water per min. at a gage pressure of 160 lb. per sq. in. It is driven by an engine revolving at 1540 rev. per min. through gears which consume in friction 4 per cent of the power supplied to them. If the engine delivers 123 hp. to the gears, what is the efficiency of the pump?

6. Calculate the horsepower developed by a liquid-circulating pump in lifting 190 gal. of water per min. against a 12-ft. head.

7. The World Power Conference defined the gross capacity of a water-power site as its full theoretical capacity at 100 per cent efficiency, expressed in kilowatts. Show that the gross capacity may be expressed as $0.085\, Q\, h$ when the flow Q is in cubic feet per second and the head h is in feet.

8. A stream has a flow of 2 ft. per sec. and the available head is 20 ft. The stream is 40 ft. wide and its depth measured at intervals of 8 ft. from bank to bank follows: 0, 3, 6, 8, 8, 0 ft. What is the maximum power which can be obtained from this stream?

9. Derive equation (91) from equation (93) by imagining an orifice at the bottom of a tank, and considering the kinetic energy of a frictionless liquid at the top of the tank to be zero, and the potential energy of the jet just outside the orifice to be zero.

10. Water at an elevation head of 20 ft. is moving at the rate of 12 ft. per sec. along an inclined channel. What is the velocity of the water at a place where the elevation head has half its former value, neglecting frictional losses?

11. A cylindrical tube 6 cm. in diameter has a constriction 4 cm. in diameter. When a liquid of specific gravity 0.9 flows through it, the pressure of the liquid in the tube exceeds that in the constriction by 16.2 gm. per sq. cm. Determine the velocity of the liquid in the tube.

*12. A Venturi meter having a 9-in. throat is inserted in a 1-ft. pipe. The pressures are observed to be 20 lb. per sq. in. in the pipe and 15 lb. per sq. in. at the throat when water flows through the meter at a certain rate. What is the discharge in cubic feet per second?

*13. A capillary tube 20 cm. long and with a bore of 2 mm. diameter is sealed to a funnel. The tube is placed upright and crude oil having a specific gravity of 0.87 is poured into the funnel to an elevation 25 cm. above the bottom of the capillary. Upon test 6.9 cu. cm. of the oil flows out in 30 min. What is the coefficient of viscosity of the oil?

CHAPTER XIII

MECHANICS OF GASES

125. Gaseous State of Matter. — The structure of a gas was described briefly at the beginning of Chapter XI, the accepted theory being that gas molecules are comparatively far apart and move about unceasingly throughout the entire space to which they are admitted. Gases differ from liquids in two respects: first, gases are very compressible; and second, they completely fill any closed vessel in which they are placed. In most other respects, however, gases resemble liquids, and since both are capable of flowing, they are designated by the common term *fluid*. Gases as well as liquids exert pressure upon surfaces with which they are in contact, and both exert upward buoyant forces in accordance with Archimedes' Principle; flowing gases conform to Bernoulli's Theorem, and the velocity of effusion through an orifice can be found as for a liquid; again, gases, like liquids, adapt themselves to the shape of the containing vessel and, having no elasticity of shape, are unable to exert shearing stresses, except those due to viscosity.

The term *vapor* is usually applied to a gas when not far removed from the liquefying temperature, although there is no hard and fast distinction between a vapor and a gas. Steam and carbon dioxide are usually called vapors, because they can be liquefied with comparative ease; but air, hydrogen and nitrogen are called gases.

126. Kinetic Theory of Gases. — Gases, because of their simple structure, are well adapted to mathematical study, and this fact has led to the development of a detailed theory of gas behavior called the *kinetic theory of gases*. Many results of this theory can be verified by test, and all are of theoretical interest.

Under the kinetic theory, a body of gas is composed of molecules which are all alike, and which behave like tiny elastic spheres. It is assumed that these molecules are comparatively far apart, on the average, and that they are in a state of motion, determined by the temperature, in which they continually strike against each other and against the walls of the container.   At a given instant, some molecules are moving one way and some another, some are traveling fast and some slow, and some are even at rest; and the combined effect of these varying velocities corresponds to the temperature of the gas.   Any appreciable volume contains so many molecules however, that, in accordance with the laws of probability, some intermediate velocity can be found which, if possessed by all the molecules, would correspond to the same temperature.   It is known that energy is needed to raise the temperature of a substance, and thus *the temperature of a gas is assumed to be directly proportional to the kinetic energy of the gas molecules.* The intermediate velocity v must, therefore, be such as to impart the same kinetic energy to N molecules, each of mass m, as that due to their individual velocities, $v_1, v_2, \cdots v_N$.   Hence,

$$N(\tfrac{1}{2}m\,v^2) = \tfrac{1}{2}m\,v_1{}^2 + \tfrac{1}{2}m\,v_2{}^2 + \cdots \tfrac{1}{2}m\,v_N{}^2$$

from which

$$v = \sqrt{\frac{v_1{}^2 + v_2{}^2 + \cdots v_N{}^2}{N}}$$

The varying individual velocities may therefore be replaced by a single velocity which is found by squaring the individual velocities, taking the mean of these squares, and then extracting the square root.   The result is known as the *root-mean-square* or r-m-s. velocity.

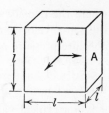

The r-m-s. velocity of the molecules of a gas can be found in terms of the pressure and density of the gas, by summing up the impulses of the molecules against one of the confining walls; this sum calculated for unit time and unit area is equal to the

FIG. 144.   Illustrating molecular velocities

pressure, and upon rearranging terms, the desired expression is obtained.   Consider a cubical box of volume $V = l^3$, as shown in Fig. 144, containing N molecules of gas each of mass m, and let the r-m-s. velocity of the gas molecules be v.   The actual motions of the molecules within the box can be resolved into three components, as though one-third of the molecules were moving perpendicularly between each pair of opposite faces. Such a group of molecules moving between face A and that opposite would encounter many collisions on the way.   Suppose the collisions to occur after traveling a small uniform distance x from A.

The number of molecules in a zone of this thickness would be $\frac{x}{l} N$, one third of which would strike A with a velocity v and rebound with a velocity $-v$. Each of these molecules thus undergoes a change of momentum of $2m\,v$, which is accordingly equal to the impulse imparted to the wall by collision [§ 102]. Including all the molecules striking face A, the impulse per impact is

$$Ft = \frac{1}{3} \times \frac{x}{l} N \times 2m\,v$$

The molecules travel a distance x before collision and travel back to face A, a total distance of $2x$ in a time $2x/v$, and thus strike the face $\frac{v}{2x}$ times each second. The total impulse exerted in 1 sec. is equal to the force, or

$$F = \frac{xN}{3l} \times 2m\,v \times \frac{v}{2x} = \frac{Nm\,v^2}{3l}$$

and the pressure exerted on the face is

$$p = \frac{F}{l^2} = \frac{Nm\,v^2}{3l^3} = \frac{Nm\,v^2}{3V} = \frac{d\,v^2}{3}$$

where the density of the gas is $d = Nm/V$. Rearranging terms, the r-m-s. velocity of the molecules, for a gas of density d under an absolute pressure p, is found to be

$$v = \sqrt{\frac{3p}{d}} \qquad (96)$$

As a typical value, the r-m-s. velocity of hydrogen molecules under normal atmospheric pressure [§ 105] is

$$v = \sqrt{\frac{3 \times 1{,}013{,}000 \text{ dynes/sq. cm.}}{0.000090 \text{ gm./cu. cm.}}} = 184{,}000 \text{ cm./sec.},$$

which is considerably more than the velocity of a rifle bullet.

One may well inquire, in view of such high molecular velocities, why it takes so long for illuminating gas, for instance, to penetrate the distant corners of a room after a gas jet is opened. The reason is that each molecule is continually impeded by collision with other molecules, thus altering its speed and direction. As a result the molecules zigzag about and their advance in a given direction is fairly slow. It can be shown that each of the hydrogen molecules referred to undergoes billions of such collisions each second, and that, on the average, it travels only about 0.00002 cm. between collisions. This distance is known as the *mean free path* of the molecules.

127. Atmospheric Pressure. — The earth is surrounded by a layer of air extending to great heights and held to the earth by gravitational attraction. This body of air, like all fluids, exerts a pressure determined by its height and density, in accordance with equation (84), $p = h d$. The existence of atmospheric pressure can be shown and its value measured by a mercury barometer, as in Fig. 145. In setting up this apparatus, a long glass tube sealed at one end is completely filled with mercury, and then placed in a

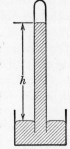

FIG. 145. Mercury barometer

vessel of mercury as shown. The mercury will settle down, leaving a vacuum above it. The height h of the mercury column is a measure of atmospheric pressure, the value 76.00 cm. at sea level at 0° C. being taken as normal or standard. The corresponding value of the pressure is 1,013,000 dynes/sq. cm. or about 14.7 lb./sq. in., as indicated in § 105.

The aneroid barometer is another device for measuring atmospheric pressure. This instrument consists essentially of a small sealed metal box from which most of the air has been removed, the box having a corrugated face which moves in and out as the atmospheric pressure varies. This slight movement is magnified by a system of levers and is communicated to a pointer which sweeps across a graduated dial or face plate.

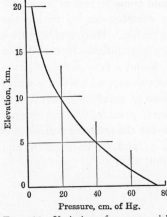

FIG. 146. Variation of pressure with altitude

On account of its compressibility, the air near the earth is weighed down and compressed by that above, and as a result the strata become rarer as the elevation is increased, although this effect is somewhat offset by the contraction due to cooling. Consequently the pressure does not vary uniformly with altitude, as it would in a medium of uniform density, but changes less and less rapidly at greater heights, as shown in Fig. 146, which is based on actual test.   The diagram shows also that the altitude of a point can be estimated from a knowledge of the corresponding atmospheric pressure.   This principle is used in the *altimeter* on aircraft; this device is essentially an aneroid barometer, calibrated to indicate altitude instead of pressure.

The force due to atmospheric pressure can be calculated by equation (83), $F = pA$, and is found to be very large, even upon a surface of moderate size.   In most cases, however, both sides of an object are subjected to the same pressure, and consequently the surface does not have to sustain a great load.

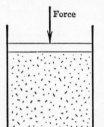

FIG. 147.   Illustrating pressure on a confined gas

128. Pressure of a Confined Gas; Boyle's Law. — One of the outstanding properties of a gas is compressibility.   It is known that if some gas is confined within a closed cylinder having a tight-fitting piston, as represented in Fig. 147, then upon applying a force as shown, the piston will move inward and come to rest at some new position where the pressure set up within the gas equals that exerted upon it by the piston.   During this process the gas is compressed and its volume is reduced.   Robert Boyle (1627–1691), an English philosopher, found a very simple relation between the pressure of a gas and its volume, which is known as Boyle's Law; namely, that *the volume of a confined body of gas varies inversely as the absolute pressure, provided the temperature remains unchanged*.   If p and V represent the pressure and volume of the gas under one condition, and p_1 and V_1 its pressure and volume under some different condition, then

$$V : V_1 = p_1 : p$$

whence

$$p V = p_1 V_1$$

The term "pressure" means either the pressure exerted by the gas or the external pressure applied to it, since these values are numerically equal.   A *perfect gas* will be defined for the present as one which conforms to Boyle's Law.

The kinetic theory, which pictures the pressure exerted by a gas as a continual bombardment of the enclosing walls by the moving molecules, may be used to derive Boyle's Law theoretically. Since the temperature of the confined gas remains unchanged, the mean kinetic energy of its molecules is assumed to be also unchanged. Using the notation of § 126, this equality of kinetic energies under the two conditions may be expressed by

$$\frac{m\,v^2}{2} = \frac{m\,v_1^2}{2}$$

Applying equation (96) for the molecular velocity, $v = \sqrt{3p/d}$, it follows that $\dfrac{3p}{d} = \dfrac{3p_1}{d_1}$. But the density of the gas is $d = \dfrac{M}{V}$, and similarly $d_1 = \dfrac{M}{V_1}$, where the mass M of the gas is the same under the two conditions. Therefore,

$$p\,V = p_1 V_1$$

as originally stated.

The pressure of confined gases can be measured by U-shaped manometer tubes containing mercury or other liquids, as shown in

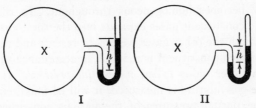

I   II

Fig. 148.   Open and closed manometers

Fig. 148.   The compressed gas in the container X forces the liquid down at the near side and up at the far side.   In the *open manometer*, the difference in height h between the two columns, multiplied by the density of the liquid, shows how much the gas pressure exceeds that of the atmosphere.   This value is known as the *gage pressure* to distinguish it from *absolute pressure*, which includes the pressure of the atmosphere.   In the *closed manometer*, the closed end of the tube contains air which is at atmospheric pressure when the columns are level.   As the liquid in the tube is forced to the position shown, this air becomes compressed, and the absolute pressure in the tank is found by adding the pressure of the air entrapped in the tube to that due to a liquid column of height h. The closed manometer is adapted to the measurement of higher pressures than the open type, but is not so sensitive, especially at high pressures.

The *Bourdon gage* is an instrument used extensively for industrial purposes, as in the measurement of steam pressures. The operating element of this device consists of a bronze tube of elliptical cross-section, the tube being curved into a circular arc. One end of the tube is fixed and the other is connected by a mechanical linkage to a toothed sector which engages the instrument pointer. When subjected to internal pressure, the tube tends to assume a circular cross-section, and in so doing uncoils slightly, moving the pointer over a scale.

129. Mixtures of Gases; Dalton's Law. — From the preceding section it is seen that a gas upon expanding undergoes a reduction in pressure. This fact will be of value in studying the mixture of several gases. Suppose that two or more closed vessels, originally containing different gases, are joined so that each gas has access to all the containers. Assuming that the gases do not react chemically, the molecular motion causes each gas to penetrate the entire volume of all the containers, and by diffusion the mixture eventually becomes homogeneous throughout. In this process, each of the constituent gases expands into the total available volume as though the other gases were not present, and the absolute pressure of each constituent is reduced, in accordance with Boyle's Law, to a lower value called its *partial pressure*. If the pressure of the gas mixture is measured, it will be found equal to the sum of the partial pressures of the various constituents. This relation, which was first established by John Dalton (1766–1844), English chemist and physicist, may be stated as follows: *A mixture of several gases which do not react chemically exerts a pressure equal to the sum of the pressures which the several gases would exert separately if each were allowed to occupy the entire space alone at the given temperature.*

As an illustration, suppose 1 liter of oxygen at a pressure of 2 atmospheres is allowed to mix with 3 liters of nitrogen at a pressure of 5 atmospheres. The oxygen in expanding from 1 liter to 4 liters will undergo a corresponding reduction of pressure, and in the final mixture its partial pressure will be $\frac{1}{4} \times 2$ or $\frac{1}{2}$ atmosphere. Similarly, the partial pressure of the nitrogen will be $\frac{3}{4} \times 5$ or $3\frac{3}{4}$ atmospheres. The pressure of the mixture will be the sum of the partial pressures, or $4\frac{1}{4}$ atmospheres.

130. Avogadro's Number; the Mol. — The Italian physicist Amadeo Avogadro (1776–1856) suggested that, at the same temperature and pressure, *equal volumes of different gases contain equal numbers of molecules.* This hypothesis has been verified experimentally and is called Avogadro's Law. Its agreement with the kinetic theory can be shown by considering two gases to have the same temperature and assuming that their molecules have the same mean kinetic energy. Using the symbols of § 126,

$$\frac{m_1 v_1^2}{2} = \frac{m_2 v_2^2}{2}$$

the subscripts being used to distinguish between the two gases. From equation (96) it follows that $\frac{m_1}{2} \times \frac{3p_1}{d_1} = \frac{m_2}{2} \times \frac{3p_2}{d_2}$. Replacing the density d by $\frac{Nm}{V}$, the equation becomes $\frac{m_1}{2} \times \frac{3p_1 V_1}{N_1 m_1} = \frac{m_2}{2} \times \frac{3p_2 V_2}{N_2 m_2}$. Under like pressure-volume conditions, $p_1 = p_2$ and $V_1 = V_2$, consequently $N_1 = N_2$, as stated in Avogadro's Law.

This law is frequently applied in Physical Chemistry to a particular quantity of a gas known as a *mol,* or gram-molecule. The mol of a substance is a mass in grams equal numerically to the sum of the atomic weights of the atoms in the molecule of that substance. The number of molecules in a mol of gas is known as *Avogadro's Number*; a mol of any gas contains 6.02×10^{23} molecules, and at 0° C. and 76 cm. pressure occupies a volume of 22.4 liters.

131. Density of Gaseous Media. — The density of a gas, as of any substance, is the amount of mass contained in unit volume. Since a body of gas has different volumes at different pressures, in accordance with Boyle's Law, the density of a gas is a function of the pressure, the density and pressure increasing in the same proportion. The density of a gas is also influenced by the temperature, it being known that gases expand when heated, and contract when cooled.

The density of air is of special importance, and has been determined with great care. One liter of air at standard temperature and pressure [0° C. and 76 cm. of mercury] weighs 1.293 gm., and thus the density of air is 0.001293 gm./cu. cm., which is equivalent to about 0.081 lb./cu. ft. The specific gravity of a gas is usually expressed with reference to air as a standard, instead of with reference to water, as in the case of solids and liquids. Thus, coal gas, which is only about four-tenths as dense as air, is said to have a specific gravity of 0.4 with respect to air.

It would be possible to measure the density of a gas directly, by weighing a hollow globe of known volume when filled with the gas and again when evacuated, but such a measurement would not be very precise, because a small volume of gas weighs so little. For industrial purposes, the *effusiometer*, Fig. 149, is used to compare the density of a gas with that of air. In this device the gas is admitted into a glass tube and is then forced out by water pressure through a tiny orifice, the time being measured during which the water pressure falls off a certain amount. A second measurement is then made under identical conditions, except that air is used instead of the gas. From the data thus obtained, the densities of the two gases can be compared, being directly proportional to the squares of the times of effusion. To prove this relation, it should first be considered that in forcing a volume V of gas into the tube under a gage pressure p, the work required is $E = pV$, as given for liquids in equation (90). An amount of potential energy pV is therefore given to the gas, the amount of potential energy per unit volume consequently being p. Upon effusion, this potential energy is transformed into kinetic energy, the kinetic energy of unit volume being $\frac{1}{2}m v^2 \div V = \frac{1}{2}d v^2$. Equating these energy values, $p = \frac{1}{2}d v^2$ or $v = \sqrt{2p/d}$. This expression gives the velocity of the stream issuing from the orifice, and should not be confused with equation (96), which applies to the unordered motion of molecules in all directions due to heat. From the equation just obtained, it is seen that if two gases are tested under the same conditions of pressure, their densities will prove to be inversely as the squares of their respective velocities of effusion. Thus, $d_1 : d_2 = v_2^2 : v_1^2$, where d_1 and d_2 are the densities of the gases, and v_1 and v_2 are the corresponding velocities. But the times of effusion for a given change in pressure are inversely proportional to the velocities, and therefore

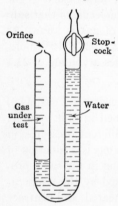

Fig. 149. The effusiometer

$$d_1 : d_2 = t_1^2 : t_2^2$$

where t_1 is the time of effusion for the gas of density d_1, and t_2 is the corresponding time for the gas of density d_2.

The densities and specific gravities of a few common gases are given in the accompanying table.   These values are for standard

Density and Specific Gravity of Some Gases

Gas	Density		Specific gravity
	gm./liter	lb./cu. ft.	
Air...........................	1.293	0.081	1.000
Carbon dioxide...............	1.977	0.123	1.529
Hydrogen....................	0.090	0.0056	0.069
Helium......................	0.179	0.011	0.138
Nitrogen.....................	1.251	0.078	0.967
Oxygen......................	1.429	0.089	1.105
Steam at 100° C.............	0.598	0.037	0.462

temperature and pressure unless otherwise noted.   The values for specific gravity are stated with respect to air as unity.

132. Buoyancy of the Atmosphere. — Archimedes' Principle, which was taken up in § 110 in connection with liquids, applies equally well to gases, and it may be said that *a body located in any fluid, whether liquid or gaseous, is buoyed up by a force equal to the weight of the fluid displaced.*   As applied to gases, interest in this principle centers in the buoyancy of the atmosphere.

A balloon filled with gas that is lighter than the surrounding air is raised by the buoyant force, but as it rises through strata of less and less density, the buoyant force becomes smaller and smaller. Finally a height is reached where this upward force is equal to the total downward force, which includes both the weight of the balloon and its load, and also the weight of the gas with which it is filled. The balloon is then in equilibrium and does not rise further.   During the ascent, some of the gas is allowed to escape through a valve, so as to keep its pressure about equal to that of the surrounding air, and thus prevent bursting of the envelope.   To reach greater heights, sand ballast is scattered overboard; and to descend, the light gas may be released.

Consider, for instance, a balloon of 35,000-cu. ft. capacity, designed to reach an altitude of 6000 ft. when filled with hydrogen, and calculate the allowable weight of the balloon and its load.   At a height of 6000 ft. [1.8 km.] the atmospheric pressure, from Fig. 146, is reduced from 76 to 60 cm. of mercury.   Neglecting temperature differences, the density of the air at this level is correspondingly lowered to 60/76 of its normal value, 0.081 lb. per cu. ft. [§ 131]. The buoyant force on the balloon is thus

$$35,000 \text{ cu. ft.} \times \frac{60}{76} \times 0.081 \frac{\text{lb.}}{\text{cu. ft.}} = 2240 \text{ lb.}$$

The hydrogen in the envelope is taken to have the same pressure as the surrounding atmosphere; its weight is 0.069 × 2240 lb. = 155 lb., and therefore the allowable weight of the balloon and load is 2240 lb. − 155 lb. = 2085 lb.

On account of the buoyancy of the atmosphere, it is sometimes necessary to apply corrections in precise weighing measurements, if the object being weighed is of different density than the weights with which it is being compared. In an equal-arm balance, the net downward force at the end of each arm is the true weight of the object there minus the buoyant force due to the atmosphere and, when the instrument is balanced, the net downward forces are equal; these facts make it possible to determine the true weight of an object.

Find the true weight w gm. of a sample of balsa wood [density = 0.12 gm./cu. cm.] which balances 100 gm. of brass weights [density = 8.5 gm./cu. cm.]. The volume of the wood is $w/0.12$ cu. cm., and the buoyant force upon it is 0.001293 $w/0.12$ gm. The volume of brass is 100/8.5 cu. cm., and the buoyant force upon it is 0.001293 × 100/8.5. Consequently,

$$w - 0.001293 \, w/0.12 = 100 - 0.001293 \times 100/8.5$$

whence the true weight of the wood is $w = 101.1$ gm.

133. Bernoulli's Theorem Applied to Gases. — It was implied in § 122 that Bernoulli's Theorem is applicable to gases as well as to liquids. The mathematical treatment, however, is complicated by the fact that gases are highly compressible, but the general effect is the same as previously described; namely, that

when a flowing stream of gas speeds up, its pressure decreases, and vice versa.

A tennis ball that is set spinning when served undergoes a curved flight as a result of the effect just described. Suppose a

I   II

FIG. 150.   Curved flight of ball

ball to be spinning in a clockwise direction while it is moving toward the left in still air, as indicated in part I of Fig. 150. The effect is the same as if the ball were spinning on a stationary axis in a wind directed toward the right, as in part II of the figure. As the ball spins, a layer of air clings to it and is carried around with it, and the velocity of the air at any point near the ball can be regarded as made up of two components, one due to the wind and the other due to the spinning of the ball. Above the ball, these components have the same direction, while below they have opposite directions. Thus, the velocity is greater at the top surface than at the bottom, and according to Bernoulli's Theorem, the pressure is increased at the bottom and reduced at the top. This unbalanced pressure causes the ball to rise as it moves forward.

The behavior of a ball supported in a jet of water or air is explained in a similar manner. Suppose a light ball to be placed directly in an inclined jet of air. The ball tends to move downward by the action of gravity to some position as in Fig. 151, whereupon the jet sets the ball into rotation as shown. There results a high air velocity over the surface *A*, with a corresponding lowering of the pressure at that place; and the larger pressure at *B* forces the ball back into the jet. By this means the ball may remain supported by the jet.

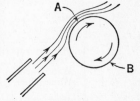

Fig. 151. Ball supported by jet of air

*134. Viscosity of Gases. — Molecular friction, or viscosity, is present in gases as in liquids, although to a smaller extent, as would be expected from the increased spacing of the molecules. This friction not only retards the motion of gases themselves in flowing through tubes, ducts, and the like; but also retards other bodies in moving through a stationary gas. Air friction increases with the velocity, and is an important factor in airplane construction, as evidenced by stream-lining designed to minimize its effects.

A study of scientific interest is the motion of a sphere falling through a viscous gas, such as a rain drop falling through the atmosphere. Suppose that such a drop starts falling with uniformly accelerated motion under the action of gravity; at first friction exerts only a small drag upon it, and it gains speed quickly, but as it does so the upward force of friction becomes greater and greater, until finally it equals the downward force of gravity. Thereafter the acceleration is zero and the drop descends with uniform motion. Sir George Stokes (1819–1903), British mathematician and physicist, found that for very small drops of radius *r* and density *d* the steady, or terminal, velocity acquired in falling through a medium having a coefficient of viscosity η, is given by the expression

$$v = \frac{2d\,g\,r^2}{9\eta} \tag{98}$$

g being the acceleration due to gravity. When c.g.s. units are used, the values of η will be in poises. The coefficients of viscosity for some gases are given in the following table:

Coefficients of Viscosity of Some Gases

Air....................	at 0° C.	173×10^{-6}
Air....................	99° C.	220×10^{-6}
Ammonia...............	0° C.	96×10^{-6}
Hydrogen..............	0° C.	87×10^{-6}
Mercury vapor.........	300° C.	532×10^{-6}
Oxygen................	0° C.	189×10^{-6}
Water vapor...........	0° C.	90×10^{-6}
Water vapor...........	100° C.	132×10^{-6}

It is interesting to note that a rise in temperature causes the viscosity of gases to increase; the reverse is true for liquids [§ 124].

135. Reduced Pressures. — When it is desired to exhaust the air from a vessel, a partial vacuum can be secured by the use of an *aspirator*. In this device, shown diagrammatically in Fig. 152,

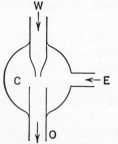

Fig. 152. The aspirator   Fig. 153. A vacuum gage

a stream of water, usually from the city mains, is admitted at W and flows through a small nozzle into the chamber C, which connects through a passage E to the vessel to be exhausted. The small size of the nozzle causes the stream to issue from it with high velocity, and the pressure in the chamber C is lowered in accordance with Bernoulli's Theorem. Thus, air is withdrawn from the vessel attached to E, and, mingling with the water, passes out at the outlet O. By using an aspirator, a reduction of pressure to about 3 or 4 cm. of mercury can be obtained; this corresponds to about one-twentieth of an atmosphere.

A higher vacuum can be secured with a *piston pump*, operating on the principle of an ordinary force pump, but arranged to withdraw air from the vessel instead of forcing it in. With the ordinary pump, however, there is a certain amount of dead space still left in the cylinder when the piston has advanced to the end of its stroke. Such dead spaces would make it impossible to secure a high vacuum, and are eliminated in the vacuum pump by covering the piston and valves with oil. Such an *oil pump* is capable of reducing the pressure inside a vessel of, say, 500-cu. cm. capacity to a small fraction of a millimeter of mercury in a few minutes.

Low pressures can be measured by a *vacuum gage*, a common type being represented in Fig. 153. This gage is actually a mercury barometer of small height mounted within an air-tight casing of glass which is attached to the system being exhausted. When the pressure is reduced to 10 or 12 cm. of mercury, the column falls away from the top of the closed tube, and lower pressures can be read directly from the graduated scale.

*136. High-vacuum Technique. — The quantity production of incandescent lamps, radio tubes, luminous-tube signs, vacuum bottles, and the like, all of which require a high degree of exhaustion, has led to the development of a more or less standard practice in the production of high vacua. As a preliminary step, it is customary to heat all glass parts to a high temperature, in order to drive off gases which cling to the surface of the glass or which are absorbed within its pores. Metal parts are baked in an atmosphere of hydrogen, which largely displaces the gases in the metal and which is itself given off readily during exhaustion. Heating is continued during the exhausting process, which is usually carried out by a diffusion pump. During the later stages of exhaustion, metal parts are heated by induced high-frequency currents to free them from gases. Finally, residual gases are removed by a minute amount of substance known as a "getter", that combines vigorously with them.

A type of *rotary pump* commonly used in high-vacuum work is represented in Fig. 154. This pump consists of an eccentric rotor *A* which revolves within a close-fitting cylinder *B*, a vane *C* being held tightly against the rotor by a spring, to separate the inlet tube *D* from the outlet port *E*. During each cycle the crescent-

shaped space F fills with air by expansion from the vessel connected
to D, and as the rotor turns, this air is compressed and forced
through the valve and out at the outlet
E. The entire pump is immersed in oil
to prevent leakage. These pumps are
quick acting and produce a vacuum of
perhaps 0.001 mm. of mercury.

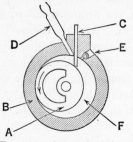

Fig. 154.   A rotary vacuum
pump

The modern *diffusion pump*, Fig. 155,
operates by means of the vapor which is
formed when mercury is heated. Gas
molecules passing by diffusion from the
vessel A being exhausted, enter the blast
of mercury vapor at B and are driven
down to C, where they are transferred to
the atmosphere by means of an auxiliary pump attached to the
outlet D. The mercury vapor is condensed by a water jacket E

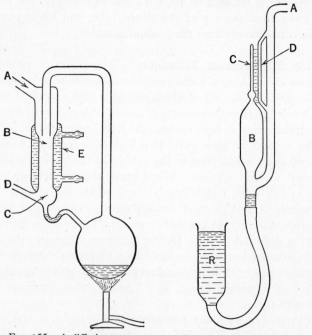

Fig. 155.   A diffusion pump   Fig. 156.   The McLeod gage

and returns to the heater where it is evaporated again. This
type of pump is very rapid in action and has no theoretical

lower pressure limit. Pressures as low as 10^{-8} mm. of mercury are reported to have been obtained by its use.

A standard instrument for the measurement of high vacua is the *McLeod gage*, shown in Fig. 156. The gage is attached at A to the vessel being exhausted, which is thus placed in communication with a chamber B of which the volume is accurately known. By raising the mercury reservoir R, a known volume of the gas at low pressure is isolated in B, and as the mercury surface is raised further, this gas is forced into a fine calibrated tube C. The pressure which this gas exerts when compressed in this manner is observed, and knowing the volume of B and of the tube C, the original pressure can easily be calculated by Boyle's Law. To avoid error due to capillarity a side-tube D is provided having the same diameter as the tube C.

It must not be thought, even with the highly developed technique now available, that it is possible to remove all of the gas molecules from a given space. Since under standard conditions there are 6.02×10^{23} molecules in a volume of 22.4 liters [§ 130], it can be appreciated that even at the low pressures reported for the diffusion pump, there are still hundreds of millions of molecules present in each cubic centimeter of space.

PROBLEMS

1. How long would it take a molecule of oxygen, moving with its r-m-s. velocity at atmospheric pressure, to travel a distance of 2×10^{-6} cm.?

2. Calculate the atmospheric pressure in pounds per square inch when the barometer stands at 75.0 cm.

3. What force is normally exerted by the atmosphere upon a table top measuring 3 ft. $\times$ 4 ft.?

4. Express normal atmospheric pressure in grams per square centimeter.

5. A cylinder having an internal diameter of 10 in. is supported vertically, and has its lower end closed by a 20-lb. piston to which a 200-lb. weight is attached. To what absolute value should the pressure within the cylinder be reduced in order that the piston and attached weight may be supported by atmospheric pressure? Assume no leakage.

6. A cylindrical carrier 2 in. in diameter travels at a speed of 1200 ft. per min. in a pneumatic tube. One end of the tube is kept at a gage pressure of 4 lb. per sq. in. and a vacuum is maintained at the other end having a pressure of 8 in. of mercury. Assuming the pressure difference at the ends of the carrier to be one-thirtieth of that between the ends of the entire tube, find the power expended in moving the carrier.

7. A piston 10 in. in diameter and weighing 150 lb. is placed in the top of a vertical cylinder 1 ft. high, containing air. Assuming that no leakage takes place, how far will the piston move downward in compressing the air before coming to rest?

8. Compute the gage pressure within a tank having a volume of 6 cu. ft. if it contains 5 lb. of neon at 32° F. The density of neon at this temperature and at atmospheric pressure is 0.056 lb. per cu. ft.

9. Compute the gage pressure and the absolute pressure in the tank of Fig. 148, part I, if the manometer contains water, the right-hand column being 14 in. higher than the other.

10. Compute the gage pressure and the absolute pressure in the tank of Fig. 148, part II, if the manometer contains mercury, the right-hand column being 10 cm. higher than the other, and extending to a point 5 cm. below the top of the closed tube.

11. A tank containing 2 cu. ft. of oxygen under a gage pressure of 350 lb. per sq. in. is connected directly to a closed cubical chamber measuring 3 ft. on a side which contains air at normal atmospheric pressure. Calculate the resulting absolute pressure.

12. Two cubical tanks, one measuring 2 ft. on each edge and the other measuring 3 ft. on each edge are joined together by a pipe having a length of 4 ft. and an inside diameter of 6 in., the pipe being provided with a valve at its midpoint. The smaller side of the system contains oxygen at a gage pressure of 25 lb. per sq. in. and the other side contains air at a gage pressure of 50 lb. per sq. in. Find the resulting gage pressure after the valve is opened.

13. Compute the velocity with which air will effuse through an orifice from a receptacle in which the gage pressure is 0.25 lb. per sq. in.

14. A paint-spray gun takes 7 cu. ft. of air per min. at a gage pressure of 90 lb. per sq. in. How much power is required on the part of the air compressor to operate it?

15. Calculate the buoyancy correction in weighing a cylinder of cork 5 cm. in diameter and 4 cm. high on an equal-arm balance, using brass weights of specific gravity 8.5. Take the specific gravity of cork as 0.24.

16. A captive balloon of 5000-cu. ft. capacity weighs 150 lb., not including the hydrogen with which it is filled. The balloon is blown horizontally by the wind and is held at a point not far above the earth by a rope which makes an angle of 70° with the level ground. Find the tension in the rope.

17. With what velocity does a rain drop 0.1 mm. in diameter fall at 20° C., if the coefficient of viscosity of air at this temperature is 181×10^{-6} poise?

18. Estimate the number of molecules remaining in 1 cu. cm. of hydrogen when the pressure is reduced to 10^{-8} mm. of mercury.

19. Calculate the total kinetic energy due to molecular motion in 1 cu. cm. of hydrogen at normal temperature and pressure; calculate also the average kinetic energy of a single molecule under these conditions.

$PV = N R_o T$ $PV = NRT$

HEAT

CHAPTER XIV

THE EFFECTS OF HEAT

137. Nature of Heat. — In the early days of science, heat was thought to be a weightless fluid called caloric. All substances were supposed to contain more or less of this fluid, and the passage of heat from one body to another was explained as a flow of caloric from the hotter to the colder body. Count Rumford (Benjamin Thompson, 1753–1814), a British-American scientist, was impressed by the large amount of heat produced in attempting to bore some cannon with blunt tools. Since the supply of heat appeared to be inexhaustible, he concluded that heat could not be a substance but must be related in some way to motion. His investigations resulted in the present theory, confirmed by other investigators and now accepted without question, that *heat is a form of energy*.

When heat is applied to a body, it increases the energy of that body, and since in general, no change can be detected in either the kinetic or the potential energy of the body as a whole, it appears that the energy must have been given to the molecules of which the body is made. Molecules are known to possess kinetic energy, for there is ample evidence of their incessant motion. Some molecules also possess potential energy; this is true for the molecules of a solid or of a liquid which has been expanded by heat, for work must have been done upon the molecules to separate them in opposition to the forces of cohesion. Gas molecules have but little potential energy, since they are relatively far apart and as a result have only a slight attraction for one another. Heat is, therefore, a form of energy which in gases is practically the kinetic energy of the molecules, and in solids and liquids also includes potential energy due to expansion.

When a gas is confined in a suitable vessel and the vessel is heated, the gas molecules striking the heated sides of the vessel in their incessant motion rebound with greater speeds; these molecules then strike others, and so on; in this way the entire gas is heated. When one end of a metal rod is placed in a fire, the entire rod becomes warmer and warmer as heat is gradually conducted along it. This action is explained in terms of the kinetic theory of heat by supposing that the molecules of the metal in the fire are set into more rapid vibration and that these in striking neighboring molecules impart kinetic energy to them, and so on throughout the rod.

138. Temperature Scales. — The application of heat to an object usually causes an increase in its *temperature*. The term temperature is used to express how cold or how hot an object is; cold implies a low temperature and hot a high temperature. A more definite idea of temperature can be realized by considering what occurs when a hot body is brought in contact with a cold one; for example, a hot steel forging plunged into cold oil. The forging becomes cooler and the oil warmer, the hot body giving up some of its energy to the cold one. This process continues until a state of thermal equilibrium is reached, in which the same temperature prevails throughout. A statement of the temperature of an object signifies that its molecules possess a particular amount of energy due to thermal agitation, an increase of temperature signifying a corresponding increase in molecular energy.

Terms such as cold, cool, warm, and hot, although used in everyday speech to suggest the temperature of a substance, do not allow a given temperature to be stated with definiteness, and this fact has led to the adoption of certain thermometric scales. Such a scale is constructed by choosing two standard temperatures, called fixed points, that can be reproduced easily; next, assigning arbitrary numbers to these temperatures; and finally, dividing the interval between them into an appropriate number of equal parts. The divisions are extended above and below the fixed points, and a unit division is called a *degree* (°). Four such temperature scales are in common use. For each, the fixed points are taken as the melting point of ice and the boiling point of water, both at the standard pressure of 76 cm. of mercury. The *fahrenheit scale*, which is used largely for engineering and household purposes, was named after the German physicist, Gabriel D. Fahrenheit (1686–1736), who made the first mercury-in-glass thermometer. The *centigrade scale* is due to Anders Celcius (1701–1744),

Swedish astronomer, and is universally used for scientific measurements. The *absolute scale* reckons temperatures from a value which is considered theoretically to be the lowest possible [§ 184]; it is used principally in thermodynamics. Such a scale based upon centigrade divisions is called the *kelvin scale* in honor of the English scientist, Lord Kelvin (William Thomson, 1824–1907), and the other based upon fahrenheit divisions is called the *absolute fahrenheit scale*. The data on which these scales are based appear in the following table:

Temperature Scales

	Fahrenheit	Centigrade	Kelvin	Absolute fahr.
Boiling point of water.........	212	100	373	671
Melting point of ice...........	32	0	273	491
Divisions between fixed points	180	100	100	180

These scales are shown aligned in Fig. 157 for comparison.

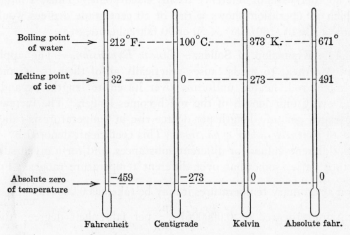

FIG. 157. Standard temperature scales

It is frequently necessary to convert temperatures from one scale to another. In doing so, it must be observed that a change of 180 fahrenheit degrees is equivalent to a change of 100 centigrade degrees, and that the melting point of ice which serves as the usual reference temperature is marked differently on the four scales.

For example, in converting a temperature of 60° F. to the centigrade scale, the degrees in excess of 32° F. are multiplied by 100/180, thus

$$(60 - 32) \times \frac{100}{180} = 15.6° \text{ C.}$$

The relation between fahrenheit and centigrade readings can be expressed by

$$\frac{F - 32}{180} = \frac{C}{100}$$

wherein the letters represent the corresponding temperatures.

To compare the absolute zeros on the centigrade and fahrenheit scales, the 273-degree range below 0 on the centigrade scale is multiplied by 180/100, yielding a range of 491 fahrenheit degrees, and this amount is subtracted from 32° F. to arrive at the result, namely −459° F. Again

$$\frac{F - 32}{180} = \frac{-273}{100}$$

from which $F = -459$.

A rise or fall in temperature can be converted from one scale to another without reference to any fixed point. Thus, a motor which in operation shows a rise of 50 centigrade degrees would show a rise of (180/100) × 50 or 90 fahrenheit degrees.

139. Expansion of Solids. — *Linear Expansion.* — The application of heat to solids causes practically all of them to expand. A metal rod, heated uniformly over its entire length, expands, and every unit length of the rod becomes longer. The increase in length per unit length per degree rise in temperature is called the *coefficient of linear expansion.* This coefficient, denoted by α, has different values for different substances, and for a given substance varies somewhat over different temperature ranges. For iron at ordinary temperatures it may be taken as $0.000012 \frac{\text{cm.}}{\text{cm.}}$ per centigrade degree or $0.0000067 \frac{\text{in.}}{\text{in.}}$ per fahrenheit degree; this means that a 1-cm. length of iron becomes 1.000012 cm. long when subjected to a temperature rise of 1 centigrade degree, and similarly a 1-in. length becomes 1.000012 in. long under the same temperature change. Some representative values of α are given on the next page.

The values tabulated apply to a range around 20° C. except where particular temperatures are listed. Knowing the coefficient of linear expansion and the length of an object at a given temperature, it is possible to compute the length at some other temperature. Calling L_1 the length at the lower temperature, the increase of length due to a temperature rise of t degrees will be $L_1 t \alpha$; consequently the length at the higher temperature will be $L_2 = L_1 + L_1 t \alpha$, or

$$L_2 = L_1(1 + \alpha t) \tag{99}$$

By way of illustration, suppose that a steel structure 1000 ft. long is to be designed to accommodate expansion over a range from $-20°$ C. to $+40°$ C. Assuming 1000 ft. to be its correct length at $-20°$ C., it follows that its length at $+40°$ C. will be

$$L_{40} = 1000 \text{ ft. } \left(1 + \frac{0.000011}{°\text{ C.}} \times 60° \text{ C.}\right) = 1000 \text{ ft. } \times 1.00066$$
$$= 1000.66 \text{ ft.}$$

An expansion sleeve of 0.66 ft. will take care of this change of length over the stipulated temperature range.

The linear expansion of a body could be neutralized by the application of a suitable compressive force. In effect, such neu-

Coefficients of Linear Expansion of Solids

	per C. degree	per F. degree
Aluminum....................	24×10^{-6}	13×10^{-6}
Brass or bronze...............	18 "	10 "
Copper.......................	17 "	9.5 "
Glass (soft to hard)...........	8 to 9.5 "	4.5 to 5.3 "
Ice (range $-10°$ to $0°$ C.).......	51 "	28 "
Invar steel (36% nickel).........	-0.3 to $+2.5$ "	-0.2 to $+1.4$ "
Iron (wrought)................	12 "	6.7 "
Lead.........................	29 "	16 "
Platinum.....................	9 "	5 "
Pyrex glass...................	3 "	1.7 "
Silica, fused ($0°$ to $30°$ C.).......	0.42 "	0.23 "
Silica, fused ($0°$ to $1000°$ C.)......	0.54 "	0.30 "
Silver.......................	19 "	11 "
Steel........................	11 "	6.1 "
Zinc.........................	26 "	14 "

tralization amounts to permitting the body to elongate a certain amount and then compressing it mechanically a like amount by a force according to equation (70) for Young's modulus of elasticity.

Several examples of linear expansion are illustrated in Fig. 158. In part I a strip of brass B and a strip of steel S are joined in one line; the total expansion due to heating will be the sum of the individual expansions of the two strips. The arrangement in part II of the figure shows these strips joined in another way to produce differential expansion. By properly choosing the lengths of the strips, the distance l between their free ends may be kept the same regardless of temperature changes. Such will be the case when the elongation $L_b\, t\, \alpha_b$ for the brass strip is equal to the elongation $L_s\, t\, \alpha_s$ for the steel strip over the same temperature range t. Under these conditions,

$$\frac{L_b}{L_s} = \frac{\alpha_s}{\alpha_b} = \frac{0.000011}{0.000018} = \frac{11}{18}.$$

This principle is made use of in designing clock pendulums to keep their periods of oscillation constant. In part III of the

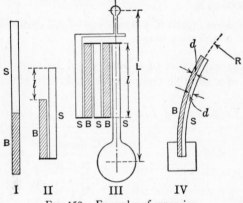

Fig. 158. Examples of expansion

figure is shown the left half of a clock pendulum made of steel and brass rods. In order to keep the length L of the pendulum constant at all temperatures, it is necessary for the lengths of brass and steel to be proportioned so that $2l\alpha_b t = (L + 2l)\,\alpha_s\, t$.

In part IV of Fig. 158 are depicted two strips of dissimilar metals, brass and steel, riveted or welded together side by side, their dimensions being the same at some initial temperature. The shape indicated is reached upon heating because brass expands more than steel. It can be shown that this shape is a circular arc having with a temperature elevation t a radius of curvature expressed by $R = d \div (\alpha_b - \alpha_s)t$, where d is the thickness of either brass or steel strip. In thermostats and similar appliances, the bending of a bimetallic strip is caused to make or break an electric contact and thereby control the operation of heaters or other apparatus.

A simple way of measuring the linear expansion coefficient of a metal is to use a rod of the material two or three feet long and place it within a pipe fitted with cork stoppers at each end to center the rod and to form an enclosure through which cold water or steam can be passed. The ends of the rod project slightly so that the length of the rod can be measured, the measuring device being equipped with a micrometer or a lever system to magnify the changes of length. The lengths observed with the rod in cold water and then in steam, together with the corresponding temperature readings, permit the computation for α to be made.

Surface and Volume Expansion.—The expansion due to heating affects all of the dimensions of a body. For an isotropic body, that is, one having the same physical properties in all directions, an expansion of 1 per cent in length is accompanied by an expansion of 1 per cent in width and 1 per cent in thickness.

To compute the expansion of a surface, consider a rectangular plate of dimensions a_1 and b_1 to have its temperature raised by an amount t. The dimensions then become $a_2 = a_1(1 + \alpha t)$ and $b_2 = b_1(1 + \alpha t)$, consequently the area of the surface at the higher temperature will be $S_2 = a_2 b_2 = a_1 b_1 (1 + \alpha t)^2 = S_1(1 + 2\alpha t + \alpha^2 t^2)$, where $S_1 = a_1 b_1$ is the area of the plate at the lower temperature. Neglecting the square of the small product αt, the final expression for the area of the plate becomes

$$S_2 = S_1(1 + 2\alpha t) = S_1(1 + \alpha' t)$$

where $\alpha' = 2\alpha$ is the *coefficient of surface expansion* of the material forming the plate.

Consider the expansion of a square plate of metal on which another square is marked out to form a frame of uniform width. Upon heating, the plate expands and the inscribed square expands proportionately. Had the inner square of metal been removed before heating, the expansion of the frame for the same temperature elevation would have been the same as though the plate were continuous.

The expansion of a volume can be expressed in a manner similar to that of a length or a surface. When a volume V_1 is heated through a temperature range t, it will assume a volume of

$$V_2 = V_1(1 + \beta t) \tag{100}$$

where β is the *coefficient of volume expansion* (sometimes called the cubical expansion coefficient) of the substance. By a development of the method used in calculating the expansion of a surface, the student can show that, as a close approximation,

$$\beta = 3\alpha \qquad (101)$$

It is important to remember this relation in seeking cubical expansion coefficients of solids in tables of physical constants since usually only linear coefficients of such bodies are listed.

The cavity in a hollow object expands as though it were a solid block of the same material. Thus, a liter flask of glass ($\alpha = 0.000008$ per C. degree) that is correct at 0° C. will have a volume of 1.0024 liter at 100° C., an increase of 2.4 cu. cm.

140. Expansion of Fluids. — Liquids, in general, follow the same law of expansion as that applicable to solids. The volume of a liquid at temperature t_2 in terms of its volume at temperature t_1 is

$$V_2 = V_1(1 + \beta t) \qquad (100)$$

where β represents the coefficient of volume expansion of the liquid, and t is the temperature difference $t_2 - t_1$. However, in measuring the expansion of a liquid it is usually necessary to consider the expansion of the containing vessel, and distinction must be made between the expansion observed and the true expansion of the liquid.

In the arrangement shown in Fig. 159, a glass flask contains the liquid under test originally at datum temperature t_1, at which

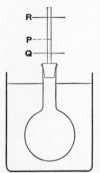

temperature the liquid extends into the capillary tube to level P. The flask is next totally immersed in a hot liquid of temperature t_2 contained in a large tank, as shown. If it were possible for the flask to attain the temperature t_2 before transmitting any heat to the liquid under test, the glass would expand and cause the liquid level to fall to some position Q. Subsequent heating of the liquid to temperature t_2 causes its level to rise to position R. The difference QR is an indication of the *true* or *absolute expansion* of the liquid

Fig. 159. True and apparent expansion compared

under test, while the difference PR measures its *apparent expansion.* Of course, position Q cannot be reached experimentally, because heat penetrates into the liquid before the flask has expanded its full amount. Consequently, it is necessary to deduce the true expansion from the observed apparent expansion of the liquid.

For definiteness, assume the flask to have a volume up to mark P of V cu. cm. at temperature $0°$ C., and the capillary to have a sectional area of A sq. cm. and to be calibrated in centimeters. (The expansion of the capillary will be neglected.) Let β_t and β_a be respectively the true and apparent coefficients of volume expansion of the liquid, and β_c the volume expansion coefficient of the container. Then, in expanding to temperature $t°$ C., the changes of volume in cu. cm. are

$$PQ \times A = V\beta_c t$$
$$QR \times A = V\beta_t t$$
$$PR \times A = V\beta_a t$$

Subtracting the first expression from the second,

$$PR \times A = V(\beta_t - \beta_c)\, t$$

and equating this to the third expression,

$$V\beta_a t = V(\beta_t - \beta_c)\, t$$

from which

$$\beta_t = \beta_a + \beta_c \tag{102}$$

Therefore, *to find the true coefficient of expansion of a liquid, add to its apparent coefficient as measured in a particular container, the cubical expansion coefficient of that container.* The accompanying table gives the true coefficients of volume expansion for a few liquids, these being average values over ranges of temperature around $20°$ C.

True Expansion Coefficients of Liquids

	per C. degree	per F. degree
Alcohol (methyl)....................	122×10^{-5}	68×10^{-5}
" (ethyl)......................	110 "	61 "
Ether (ethyl)........................	163 "	91 "
Glycerine...........................	53 "	29 "
Mercury............................	18.17 "	10.09 "
Sulfuric acid........................	57 "	32 "
Turpentine..........................	94 "	52 "

The density of a body is affected by temperature changes, since the volume increases with temperature and the mass does not. This is particularly important in dealing with liquids and gases for their expansion coefficients are much larger than those of solids. The volumes of a fluid of mass m at temperatures t_1

and t_2 are $V_1 = \dfrac{m}{d_1}$ and $V_2 = \dfrac{m}{d_2}$ respectively, where the corresponding densities are d_1 and d_2. Applying equation (100), it follows that

$$d_2 = \frac{d_1}{1 + \beta t} \tag{103}$$

showing that when the temperature of a body is raised, its density is reduced.

Gases as well as liquids follow the laws expressed by equations (100) and (103), provided they are tested at constant pressure, as was tacitly assumed in the case of liquids. The thermal behavior of gases is considered in Chapter XVII.

*141. Expansion of Water and Mercury. — Water and mercury are so often used in physical measurements that it is necessary to know exactly how they behave under changes of temperature. A table of densities at different temperatures (or a table of their reciprocals, called specific volumes) will be of great assistance in making volume calibrations. The following table gives the densities of these substances at a number of points over the temperature range from 0° to 25° C.

Density of Water and of Mercury

Temperature	Water	Mercury
0° C.	0.99987 gm./cu. cm.	13.5955 gm./cu. cm.
2	0.99997	13.5905
4	1.00000	13.5856
6	0.99997	13.5806
8	0.99988	13.5757
10	0.99973	13.5708
15	0.99912	13.5585
20	0.99823	13.5462
25	0.99705	13.5340

In calibrating a glass flask so as to have a volume of 250 cu. cm. at 20° C., there is poured in $250 \times 0.99823 = 249.558$ gm. of water at that temperature, and a mark is placed at the liquid surface. For accuracy, the shape of the flask should be such that the mark will come to a position where the area is small.

When water is cooled it contracts steadily until its temperature reaches 4° C. At this temperature it has its greatest density. As water is cooled further to 0° C. it *expands* and its density becomes slightly less. The irregular expansion of water can be observed in the foregoing table; it is also represented in Fig. 160. This behavior of water is of particular importance in that it causes the freezing of lakes and ponds to begin at the surface

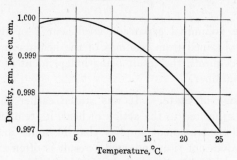

FIG. 160.   Anomalous expansion of water

rather than at the bottom. It is interesting to conjecture what would happen if the opposite were true.

Two French physicists, Pierre L. Dulong (1785–1838) and Alexis T. Petit (1791–1820), devised a method for measuring the expansion coefficient of a liquid without considering the expansion of the container. The method was improved by their countryman, Henri V. Regnault (1810–1878), and his apparatus for studying the expansion of mercury is represented in elementary form in Fig. 161. The mercury under test is contained in two upright pipes, which are maintained at different temperatures, say 0° C. and $t°$ C. by means of enclosing jackets. These pipes are joined at the bottom by a connecting tube which is made small so that but little heat will be conducted from one pipe to the other.

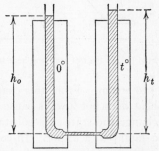

FIG. 161.   Measuring absolute expansion

It will be found in making a determination that the warm column of mercury, which has a lower density than the cold column ($d_t < d_0$), will extend to a greater height ($h_t > h_0$) than the other when a state of equilibrium is reached. This is explained by the fact that the two columns exert the same pressure at the bottom; consequently, by equation (85),

$$h_0 d_0 g = h_t d_t g$$

From equation (103), the density of mercury at the lower temperatures is $d_0 = d_t(1 + \beta t)$; therefore the expansion coefficient becomes

$$\beta = \frac{h_t - h_0}{h_0 t}$$

The absolute voluminal expansion coefficient β of the mercury can thus be obtained from readings of the heights and temperatures of the columns, the result being independent of the expansion of the container.

142. Change of State. — It was stated earlier that when a substance is subjected to the action of heat, its temperature usually rises. This statement implies that in some instances the temperature does not rise, and such a result is often experienced. For example, when heat is applied to a block of ice at 0° C., the ice melts, and the resulting water, remaining in contact with the ice, will stay at a temperature of 0° until all the ice is melted. This situation is represented by the horizontal line AB on the temperature chart, Fig. 162. If the heating is continued, the water will rise in temperature uniformly until the value 100° C. is reached. This change is shown on the same chart by the straight line BC. At the temperature mentioned, boiling occurs, and the temperature remains constant again (line CD) with the

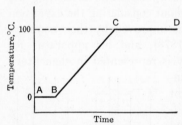

FIG. 162. Effect of applying heat to ice

application of heat until the water is completely converted into steam. From this example it is seen that the absorption of heat does not always cause a temperature rise, but may serve to change the state of a substance from a solid to a liquid or from a liquid to a vapor. In connection with the foregoing example, it might be mentioned that ice melts at 0° C. and water boils at 100° C. only when the pressure upon the substance has the normal value of 76 cm. of mercury, the boiling point especially being influenced by the pressure. This subject is discussed more fully in § 151.

143. Pyrometry. — So far, the effects of heat mentioned are: 1, change of temperature; 2, change of size; 3, change of state. Further, the application of heat to a body may produce: 4, incandescence, thereby causing the substance to emit light; 5, chemical changes, such as oxidation and reduction; 6, changes of electrical resistance; 7, generation of electromotive force at a junction of two dissimilar metals forming a thermoelectric couple. There are many other effects of heat, such as change of surface tension and viscosity, of magnetic properties, and of sound velocity; some of these will be considered elsewhere. Several of the effects enumerated are used for measuring temperature.

For the great majority of temperature measurements, change of size is the operating principle, as exemplified by the familiar mercury thermometer. For the measurement of high temperatures, say above 500° C., to which the name *pyrometry* is usually assigned, incandescence is made use of in the optical pyrometer. Resistance change is employed in the resistance thermometer,

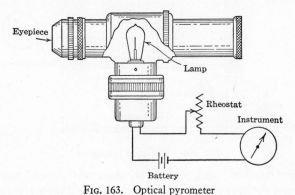

FIG. 163. Optical pyrometer

mostly within the range from −50° to +1000° C. Electromotive force generated in the thermocouple is utilized for measuring temperatures from very low values up to about 1500° C. Resistance and thermoelectric thermometers are considered in §§ 231 and 300.

The optical pyrometer is based on the principle that the brightness of a glowing body increases as its temperature is raised; the temperature of such a body is determined by comparing its brightness with that of a calibrated electric lamp. A commercial form of the instrument is shown in Fig. 163. A measurement is made by focusing the telescope on the incandescent object under test, thus bringing its image into the plane of the lamp filament, and then varying the current from a battery through the lamp until its filament appears to merge with the image of the hot body.

The temperature is then determined by the current through the filament; usually the indicating instrument is calibrated in degrees. To eliminate the effect of color on the observation, a filter is used which permits only the red rays to reach the eye.

In the radiation pyrometer, Fig. 164, the radiation emitted by the hot body, including the invisible heat rays as well as the visible light rays, is focused upon the disk of a thermocouple by a concave mirror, and the electromotive force generated is measured by a galvanometer which is graduated to read temperature directly. If the radiation proceeds from the interior of a uniformly heated enclosure, approximating what is known as a "black body," the radiation received upon the thermocouple disk is found to vary as the fourth power of the absolute temperature of the source [§ 189]. The galvanometer deflection is proportional to the

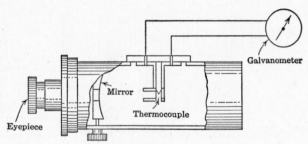

Fig. 164.   Radiation pyrometer

radiation received, and, moreover, does not depend upon the distance of the heat source from the pyrometer if there is no absorbing medium between.

144. Mercury Thermometry. — The mercury thermometer covers a very important range of temperatures, from −20° C. to 500° C. In this thermometer the temperature measurement is based upon the expansion of mercury, or more strictly, upon the relative expansion of mercury and glass. The thermometer, in its simplest form, is made by fusing a glass bulb to the lower end of a length of capillary glass tubing, mercury is next introduced through a funnel attached to the top of the tube, the thermometer is boiled and annealed, and the capillary is sealed at the top. The next process is to calibrate the thermometer at two or more points. Finally, the graduations and figures are etched on the stem. Since glass softens at about 400° C. and mercury boils at 356.7° C., it is usual to use thermometers for the higher temperatures that are made of boro-silicate glass and are filled above the mercury column with an inert gas under pressure. For low temperatures, the use of mercury is limited by its freezing point, $-38.8°$ C. In thermometers of similar construction the range may be extended downward by using toluol or pentane instead of mercury; these liquids freeze at $-97°$ C. and $-200°$ C. respectively.

The *clinical thermometer*, used by physicians, has a fine constriction in the stem near the bulb. Upon heating, the mercury expands through this opening and rises properly on the scale; but upon cooling, surface tension prevents the mercury beyond the constriction from returning to the bulb. This arrangement permits the indication to be read at any time after the thermometer is used; vigorous shaking is required to restore the mercury to the bulb.

The *Beckmann thermometer* devised by Ernest O. Beckmann is another interesting type; it is used for precise measurements of small temperature changes, particularly in physical chemistry. The device carries a small reservoir of mercury in a pocket at the top of the stem, from which more or less mercury as desired may be admitted into the bulb to suit the particular temperature range of a test. A typical instrument of this type covers any 5-degree range from $-25°$ to $+200°$ C. and its scale divisions indicate hundredth of a degree.

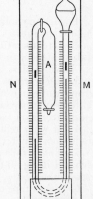

The *maximum and minimum thermometer*, shown in Fig. 165, employs glycerine as the thermometric substance, and mercury as an indicator. When subjected to a temperature rise, the glycerine in chamber A expands, causing the mercury column at M to rise. A fall of temperature causes the glycerine in A to contract, and the mercury at N to rise. Small steel indicators in the glycerine above the ends of the mercury column are raised by the motion of the columns as described, and are held at their highest positions by small springs. If this thermometer is exposed to varying temperatures, readings taken after the test showing the positions of the lower ends of the

Fig. 165. Maximum and minimum thermometer

indicators in M and N will give the maximum and minimum temperatures which occurred during the test. The indicators may be restored by a small magnet.

Most mercury thermometers are calibrated for complete immersion of the mercury, but in actual use a portion of the stem containing mercury often projects into a region which is cooler than the bulb. Under these conditions a "stem-exposure" correction must be added to the reading, since the exposed mercury did not expand as much as allowed for in the calibration. This correction may be calculated from the observed thermometer reading t by noting the length of the exposed mercury column n, in degrees, and measuring its temperature t_2 with an auxiliary "stem thermometer" held near its mid-point. The correction will be the amount that the exposed mercury would expand if heated from t_2 to t; namely,

$$\text{correction} = n\,\beta\,(t - t_2)$$

where β is the apparent coefficient of volume expansion of mercury in glass.

For precision measurements with mercury thermometers, it is sometimes necessary to correct for a temporary depression of the zero point which occurs after a thermometer has been exposed to a high temperature, and also for slight errors due to pressure on the thin wall of the thermometer bulb.

PROBLEMS

1. Mercury solidifies at $-38.8°$ C. and vaporizes at $356.7°$ C. Express these temperatures on the fahrenheit scale.

2. A temperature of approximately $39°$ F. prevails throughout most of the waters of the deep sea. Express this temperature on the centigrade and kelvin scales.

3. Safety rules specify that electric wiring shall not be subjected to temperatures in excess of $49°$ C. for rubber insulation, $75°$ C. for varnished-cloth insulation, or $90°$ C. for slow-burning insulation. Express these temperatures on the fahrenheit scale.

4. At what temperature are the readings of a fahrenheit and a centigrade thermometer the same numerically?

5. If steel rails are laid when the temperature is $35°$ F., the length of each rail being 40 ft. at this temperature, what should be the separation between successive rails to allow for expansion up to $120°$ F.?

6. A steel tape correct at $0°$ C. is used to measure a parcel of land when the temperature is $25°$ C. What is the percentage error in the measurement of length due to the expansion of the tape?

7. Given a solid bronze sphere 2.00 in. in diameter at $20°$ C.; to what temperature must it be raised in order that it may just pass through a ring 2.01 in. in diameter? The coefficient of linear expansion may be taken as 22×10^{-6} per centigrade degree for the temperature range involved.

8. With what force must a steel measuring tape $\frac{1}{4}$ in. wide and 0.011 in. thick be pulled in order to compensate for a temperature drop of

20 fahrenheit degrees? Take 30×10^6 lb. per sq. in. as Young's modulus for steel.

9. A copper bar 1 in. square and 12 in. long at $0°$ C. is set between two fixed supports so that no clearance exists at the ends of the bar. If the bar is heated to $65°$ C., what force will it exert against the supports?

10. A steel rivet, 0.75 in. in diameter, was used to fasten together two pieces of structural steel, each 0.5 in. thick. If the rivet was headed over while hot, and if its temperature at the end of the riveting process was $200°$ C., find the tension in the rivet at $20°$ C.

11. A 5-in. length of thermostatic metal (bimetallic strip) has a differential linear expansion coefficient $(\alpha_1 - \alpha_2)$ of 10^{-5} per centigrade degree and a total thickness of 0.05 in. Its free end makes electrical contact between two terminals. What will be the movement of this free end of the strip if it is designed to move from one terminal to the other with a temperature elevation of 5 centigrade degrees?

12. A 20-ton disk of boro-silicate glass, which was cast in 1934 for a telescope mirror, was cooled at the rate of 1 centigrade degree every 30 hr. Taking the specific gravity of the glass as constant at 2.24 and its coefficient of linear expansion as 0.00000245 per centigrade degree, compute the rate of shrinkage in cubic inches per hour.

13. Iron is poured into a spherical mold 5 in. in diameter at its melting point of $1530°$ C. In solidifying it shrinks 3 per cent in volume, and as it cools to $20°$ C. it contracts further. Assuming α for cast iron to have the average value of 0.000016 per centigrade degree over this temperature range, find the volume of the casting at $20°$ C.

14. A spherical aluminum shell was used by Professor Auguste Piccard as his cabin in the 1932 balloon ascent into the stratosphere; it measured 7.0 ft. in diameter at $70°$ F. At an altitude of 10 miles the temperature was observed to average $-70°$ F. Assuming the aluminum to have the latter temperature throughout, how much has the volume been reduced in reaching that temperature?

15. A Pyrex glass flask is fitted with a capillary tube having a sectional area of 1 sq. cm. At $20°$ C., 500 cu. cm. of glycerine are placed in the flask, the free surface of the liquid being in the capillary tube. If the flask and its contents are heated to $60°$ C., how far will the glycerine advance in the tube? Neglect the expansion of the capillary tube.

16. A steel tank is filled with turpentine when the temperature is $40°$ F., at which temperature its volume is 70 gallons. How much of the liquid will overflow when the temperature becomes $105°$ F.?

*17. In carrying out Regnault's method for determining the absolute expansion of mercury, the two tubes of this liquid were maintained at temperatures of $0°$ C. and $100°$ C. and the top of the cold column stood 149.5 cm. above the horizontal connecting tube. What should be the reading at the top of the column of hot mercury?

18. A mercury thermometer which is used to measure the temperature of a steam bath reads $98.4°$ C. If the thermometer stem above the $30°$ mark projects into a region where the temperature is $25°$ C., compute the true temperature of the bath. The thermometer is made with Jena glass having a cubical expansion coefficient of 0.253×10^{-4} per centigrade degree.

CHAPTER XV

CHANGE OF STATE

145. Heat Units. — Among the various effects produced by heat, two of the most important are change of temperature and change of state. Either of these effects might be used to establish units for quantity of heat. As a matter of convenience, heat units are based upon the change of temperature of definite quantities of water.

It is common experience that more heat is needed to bring a kettleful of water to the boiling point than a cupful, starting in both cases with cold water at the same temperature. Further investigation shows that the quantity of heat required to produce a given rise of temperature is directly proportional to the amount of water heated. Again, to increase the temperature of any given amount of water through, say 60 degrees, takes more heat than to raise the same amount through 30 degrees; in fact, it takes twice as much. Thus, the heat required is proportional to the *amount of water* and to the *rise of temperature*. In consequence, the unit of heat is chosen as the quantity of heat needed to raise the temperature of a unit mass of water through one degree.

Two units of heat are in common use: the calorie (cal.) and the British thermal unit (B.t.u.) The *calorie* is the quantity of heat required to raise the temperature of 1 gm. of water through 1 centigrade degree. The *British thermal unit* is the quantity of heat required to raise the temperature of 1 lb. of water through 1 fahrenheit degree. It can be shown readily that there are 252 cal. in 1 B.t.u. Having established the units of heat, it is a simple matter to compute the amount of heat needed to produce a given temperature elevation in any mass of water. Thus, to raise 5 kg. of water from 10° C. to 70° C. requires $5 \times 1000 \times 60 = 300,000$ cal., and to raise 50 lb. of water from 40° F. to 200° F. requires $50 \times 160 = 8000$ B.t.u.

While the foregoing statements are sufficiently exact for most practical purposes, actually, the quantity of heat required to raise unit mass of water through one degree varies slightly from point to point along the thermometer scale. The *mean calorie* is defined as one one-hundredth part of the heat required to raise 1 gm. of water from 0° to 100° C.; the heat required to raise 1 gm. of water from 15° to 16° C. is very close to the mean value.

146. Melting and Freezing. — The change of state which occurs when matter is transformed from the solid to the liquid phase is called *melting* or *fusion*. When ice melts, the change of state occurs at a fixed temperature, as described in § 142, it being assumed that the pressure remains constant. The property of having a fixed melting point is generally characteristic of crystalline substances; in contrast, amorphous substances, such as tar and glass, pass imperceptibly from one state to the other. During the process of melting, the heat energy supplied is used in separating the molecules against the forces of cohesion, and the melted substance has a greater energy content than the same substance in the solid phase. Fusion is the opposite of freezing or solidification. A solid which has been heated to its melting point will melt at this temperature upon the further application of heat; the corresponding liquid when cooled to this same temperature will freeze as more heat is withdrawn.

If a substance is melting and no heat is supplied to it deliberately, it must be absorbing heat from its surroundings; thus melting is sometimes referred to as a cooling process. Conversely, a liquid in freezing must give up heat to its surroundings; thus, freezing is sometimes called a heating process. A gram of ice in melting abstracts a definite quantity of heat from its surroundings, and a gram of water in freezing gives up the same quantity of heat to its surroundings. It is reported that this latter fact is utilized in fruit cellars by placing large vats of water near the fruit; should the temperature fall dangerously low, the water would freeze, and the consequent liberation of heat would prevent freezing of the fruit.

Most liquids contract in the process of freezing, but there are some important exceptions. Water undergoes a remarkable expansion when freezing, ice at 0° C. having a density only 0.91 that of water at the same temperature. This expansion accounts for the bursting of water pipes when the water in them freezes. Type metal, an alloy containing antimony as the principal constituent, also expands upon freezing (solidifying); this action fills the mold and produces a good casting.

The quantity of heat that must be given to unit mass of a solid to melt it without change of temperature is called the *heat of fusion*. Representing the heat of fusion of a solid by L, the quantity of heat Q needed to melt a mass m at constant temperature will be

$$Q = mL \qquad (104)$$

This expression shows the number of calories which must be imparted to melt m gm. of the solid or which must be abstracted to solidify m gm. of the corresponding liquid, if the heat of fusion L is being expressed in calories per gram. If m is expressed in pounds, then L must obviously be in British thermal units per pound in order that Q may be in British thermal units.

Under normal atmospheric pressure, the melting point of ice is 0° C. or 32° F. Experiment shows that 1 gm. of ice in melting under these conditions absorbs 80 cal. from its surroundings; conversely, 1 gm. of water in freezing dissipates 80 cal. to its surroundings. This means that under normal pressure the heat of fusion of ice is 80 cal. per gm.; this is equivalent to 144 B.t.u. per lb. The ratio of these quantities is 5 to 9.

The accompanying table gives the values of the heat of fusion for a number of substances, all at a normal pressure of 1 atmosphere.

Heats of Fusion

	Cal./gm.	B.t.u./lb.
Aluminum	92.4	166
Bismuth	13.0	23.4
Copper	43	77
Ice	80.0	144.0
Lead	5.4	9.7
Mercury	2.8	5.0
Silver	22	40
Tin	14.6	26.3

147. Effect of Pressure on Freezing. — The freezing point of a liquid is affected by the pressure to which it is subjected, but only to a small extent. For liquids which contract upon freezing, an increase of pressure raises the freezing point; for liquids which expand upon freezing, such as water, an increase of pressure lowers the freezing point. This statement follows from the fact that pressure on a body tends to prevent its expansion, and consequently an increase of pressure upon a liquid that expands upon freezing would tend to prevent its solidification by lowering the freezing point.

The behavior of water is represented graphically in Fig. 166, in which pressure is plotted against temperature. The curve slopes upward to the left and a pressure increase of 100 atmospheres lowers the freezing point by less than 1 centigrade degree.

A curve such as that shown represents a state of equilibrium between the solid and liquid states of the substance in question. Consider a mixture of ice and water, for example, at 0° C. and 76 cm. pressure, to be represented by point A on the curve. To raise the temperature of the mixture at this pressure, say to temperature B, it would be necessary first to supply heat to melt all of the ice present, and then more heat to cause the desired temperature rise.

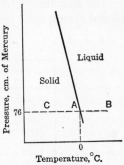

FIG. 166. Influence of pressure on the freezing point of water

Similarly, to lower the temperature of the mixture, say to temperature C, heat must first be abstracted to freeze all of the water present and thereafter a lowering of temperature is possible. In the diagram, therefore, the region to the right of the curve represents the liquid state and that to the left of the curve represents the solid state.

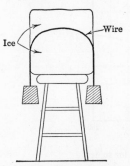

FIG. 167. Regelation experiment

The line itself shows the relative conditions of temperature and pressure under which ice and water can coexist in equilibrium.

The effect of increased pressure in lowering the melting point of ice is well illustrated by a classical experiment in which a small wire, weighted at the ends, is placed across a cake of ice as in Fig. 167. The wire gradually melts its way through the ice, and as it does so, the groove formed above becomes solid ice again, leaving the cake intact. This process, known as *regelation*, is explained as follows: The pressure beneath the wire is greater than atmospheric, causing the melting point of the ice there to be slightly below 0° C. But since that ice is at 0°, it is momentarily above its melting point and a little of it melts, causing a slight reduction of temperature; the wire settles down and the water formed is squeezed into the region above it. Here the pressure is normal and the water, which is now slightly below 0°, freezes again.

The melting (or freezing) points of a number of substances at normal atmospheric pressure are given in the following table:

Melting Points

	° C.	° F.
Aluminum.........	657	1215
Copper............	1080	1975
Gold..............	1063	1945
Hydrogen.........	−259	−434
Iron..............	1530	2790
Lead.............	327	621
Mercury..........	−38.8	−37.8
Platinum..........	1755	3190
Silver............	960.5	1761
Tin..............	232	450
Tungsten..........	3300	5950

*148. Fusion of Mixtures. — The presence of impurities usually has the effect of lowering the melting point of a substance.

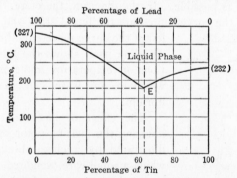

Fig. 168.   Melting-point diagram for solder

In calibrating a thermometer at 0° C. by immersion in a mixture of ice and water, it is necessary to use distilled water to prevent errors from this cause. The addition of salt to ice (1 part NaCl to 2 parts of ice by weight) lowers the melting point from 32° F. to about 0° F., and forms a useful freezing mixture.

In a mixture of two metals to form an alloy, the presence of each constituent lowers the melting point of the other. Fig. 168

is a melting-point diagram for solder composed of lead and tin in various proportions by weight. The different alloys thus formed start to melt at various temperatures as shown, the minimum being 181° C. for an alloy composed of 63 per cent of tin and 37 per cent of lead. The alloy having the lowest melting point E is known as an *eutectic mixture* and its melting point is called the *eutectic temperature*.

When an eutectic mixture is allowed to solidify slowly, its components crystallize out in the proportions in which they are

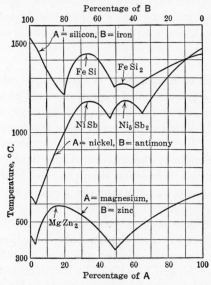

Fig. 169. Melting-point diagrams for some alloys

present in the liquid, and thus the liquid remains unchanged in composition as solidification progresses. Other mixtures do not have this property. If a mixture of 80 per cent of tin and 20 per cent of lead, for example, is completely melted and slowly cooled, some tin will crystallize out starting at 215° C. (see curve), and the remaining liquid if examined at 200° will be found to consist of 72 per cent of tin and 28 per cent of lead. The same conclusion is reached for alloys in which the lead predominates. A mixture of 20 per cent of tin and 80 per cent of lead when melted and slowly cooled will start to solidify at 305° C., and the liquid remaining at 200° will consist of 57 per cent of tin and 43 per cent of lead. In this case, the material which solidifies contains a little tin with the lead and forms a homogeneous substance; for this reason it is called a *solid solution* of tin in lead. As solidification progresses the concentration of tin in the solid solution increases until point E on the curve is reached. Only the eutectic alloy solidifies completely at a constant temperature and without change of composition in either the liquid or solid phases as freezing progresses.

The behavior of the tin-lead alloys depicted in Fig. 168 is relatively simple. Some alloys, in which one or more compounds separate out on freezing, have more complex melting-point diagrams, as shown for three alloys in Fig. 169. Each curve shows several eutectic points, with intermediate points of maximum melting temperature.

149. Process of Evaporation. — Changing a substance to the vapor state is a process called vaporization. The term vaporization is a general one and includes: (1) *evaporation*, which is a conversion from the liquid to the vapor state that occurs only at the surface; (2) *boiling*, which is similar to evaporation but which takes place throughout the interior of the liquid; and (3) *sublimation*, which is a conversion from the solid to the vapor state directly without passage through the liquid state. Boiling and sublimation are considered later in this chapter.

Evaporation goes on at all temperatures, and continues until the liquid disappears or until the space above the liquid has become saturated with the vapor. In the process of evaporation a liquid is gradually transformed to a vapor by loss of molecules at its surface. The molecules of a liquid are regarded as in a state of continual but disordered motion, moving about in all directions and with various speeds. In this motion there will be many instances where a molecule is approaching the liquid surface with a sufficient velocity to carry it beyond the range of attraction of the surface molecules; this molecule then leaves the liquid and becomes a molecule of vapor.

It will be inferred from such a conception of evaporation that the molecules which succeed in escaping through the surface are those having the higher velocities, and that consequently the average molecular velocity in the liquid is lessened by evaporation. Such is the case, for evaporation lowers the temperature of the liquid. This agrees with the experience that evaporation is a cooling process; for example, water placed in a porous jar is cooled by evaporation through the walls, and the skin is cooled by evaporation of perspiration. A person uncomfortably warm through fever may be sponged with alcohol to afford relief.

150. Saturated Vapor. — A saturated vapor can be produced by allowing a liquid to evaporate into a confined space, as illustrated in Fig. 170. As the process of evaporation continues, more and more molecules leave the liquid and assume the vapor state. These molecules of vapor are also in motion, and some of them strike the liquid surface and return to the liquid. The number which reenter will increase as evaporation continues, until finally a state of equilibrium is reached

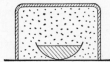

FIG. 170. Production of saturated vapor

wherein the same number of molecules pass from the liquid into the vapor as from the vapor back into the liquid in a given time. The space above the liquid is then said to be *saturated* with the vapor. Sometimes an unconfined space may become virtually saturated with vapor, as occurs with the atmosphere on a humid day, but ordinarily the conditions necessary for the production of saturated vapor are: (1) *the presence of the generating liquid*, and (2) *a confined space*.

In the evaporation process, the vapor above the liquid becomes more dense and the pressure due to this vapor becomes greater, reaching a maximum value at the point of saturation. The maximum vapor pressure of a liquid is called the *saturated vapor pressure*. Thus, for water at 20° C. the vapor pressure would build up to a maximum value of 1.75 cm. of mercury; this value is the saturated vapor pressure of water at this temperature.

Assuming that no chemical reactions occur, the value of the saturated vapor pressure is unaffected by the presence of other gases. Referring again to water at 20° C., if the evaporation occurs in a vacuum, the pressure builds up to the value 1.75 cm. of mercury; but if the enclosure contains dry air at the normal pressure of 76.0 cm. of mercury, the pressure builds up to an absolute value of 76.0 + 1.75 or 77.75 cm. of mercury, of which 76.0 cm. is the partial pressure due to dry air and 1.75 cm. is the partial pressure due to water vapor [§ 129]. Evaporation continues, regardless of other gases, until a partial pressure due to the vapor is established which is equal to the saturated vapor pressure of the liquid at the existing temperature.

In describing the production of a saturated vapor, no reference was made to the size of the enclosure in which the evaporation occurred. The various effects mentioned take place whatever the size of the enclosure, the only difference being that the larger the enclosure, the longer the time required for saturation.

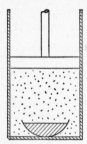

FIG. 171. Saturated vapor in cylinder

The pressure of a saturated vapor is, then, independent of the volume occupied by the vapor. If the evaporation were to take place in an otherwise empty cylinder of variable volume, as in Fig. 171, the piston might be moved up or down without affecting the pressure in the cylinder. These considerations show that it is impossible to change the pressure of a saturated vapor by varying the volume. If the volume of the vapor is reduced, some of the vapor will condense to a liquid, and if the volume is increased, some of the liquid will vaporize, but the pressure remains constant and its value depends only upon the material and the temperature. In this respect a saturated vapor behaves quite differently from a perfect gas [§ 128], the pressure of which, in accordance with Boyle's Law, increases to double value when its volume is halved. The curves shown in Fig. 172 contrast the behavior of a saturated vapor and of a perfect gas on a pressure-volume diagram. The temperature is assumed constant in both cases.

It is found by test that the saturated vapor pressure of a liquid has materially different values when measured at different temperatures. For example, the saturated vapor pressure of water

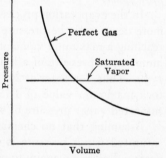

FIG. 172. Saturated vapor contrasted with perfect gas

when measured at 20° C. is 1.75 cm. of mercury, at 30° C. it has the value 3.17 cm., at 50° C. it is 9.23 cm., and at 100° C. the saturated vapor pressure is 76.00 cm. of mercury or exactly 1 atmosphere. These pressure-temperature values are plotted to definite scale in Fig. 173.

The saturated vapor pressure of a few liquids at various temperatures is given in the following table:

Saturated Vapor Pressure of Several Liquids

	Temperature	Pressure
Alcohol (ethyl).......	20° C.	4.4 cm. Hg
"	50	22.0
"	78.3	76.00
Mercury............	20	0.00011
"	100	0.0276
"	250	7.58
"	356.7	76.00
"	450	323
Water..............	0	0.458
"	20	1.75
"	50	9.23
"	100	76.00
"	150	356.9

151. Boiling. — Evaporation has been described as the escape of molecules from the liquid to the vapor state at the surface of a liquid. Boiling consists of evaporation throughout the body of the liquid, bubbles of saturated vapor being formed within the liquid which gather additional molecules and so increase in size as they rise to the surface.

The bubbles which are produced in the process of boiling would be unable to form if the pressure exerted upon them from the outside were greater than their own internal pressure. The external pressure consists of the atmospheric or gas pressure on the liquid surface plus whatever pressure is due to the liquid above the bubble. The internal pressure is the saturated vapor pressure

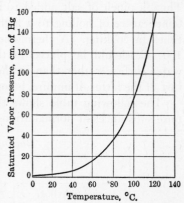

Fig. 173. Saturated vapor pressure of water

of the liquid at its existing temperature. Hence, *a liquid cannot boil unless the vapor pressure of the liquid is equal to* (or infinitesimally greater than) *the pressure exerted on the liquid.*

Boiling can be brought about either by *increasing the temperature* until the corresponding vapor pressure is equal to the pressure on the liquid (see Fig. 173), or by *reducing the pressure* on the liquid to the value of the saturated vapor pressure. Water, initially at 50° C., will serve as an illustration. When it is heated in the open air it will boil at 100° C., at which temperature the saturated vapor pressure will be 76.0 cm. of mercury or 1 atmosphere. Or, it may be made to boil at 50° C. by lowering the pressure upon it to 9.23 cm. of mercury, which is the value of the saturated vapor pressure of water at 50° C. From these considerations it is seen that the curve, Fig. 173, may also be called a boiling-point curve, since it shows the relation between boiling point and applied pressure. The difficulty of cooking by boiling at high altitudes, where low pressures prevail, may be inferred from this curve.

As in the case of the freezing-point curve, Fig. 166, the boiling-point curve, Fig. 173, represents a condition of equilibrium between two phases of a substance, in this case between the liquid and vapor states of water. The region to the left of the curve represents the liquid state and that to the right of the curve represents the vapor state.

The boiling point of a liquid is also influenced by the presence of impurities in it, impurities tending to raise the boiling point. Thus, a pinch of salt added to a kettleful of water will raise the temperature of boiling to a higher value, an effect desired sometimes in cooking. A thermometer which is being calibrated at 100° C. should be placed in the saturated steam close to the water surface rather than in the boiling water, for the temperature of the latter, if impure, is somewhat uncertain.

The following table shows the boiling points of a number of pure substances at normal atmospheric pressure:

Boiling Points

	° C.	° F.
Alcohol (ethyl)........	78.3	140.9
Copper..............	2310	4190
Helium..............	−269	−452
Hydrogen...........	−252.7	−422.9
Iron................	2450	4440
Lead................	1620	2950
Mercury............	356.7	674.5
Oxygen.............	−183.0	−297.4
Sulphur.............	444.6	832.3
Tin.................	2270	4020

152. Heat of Vaporization. — The process of vaporization requires that a definite quantity of heat be supplied to vaporize a certain amount of substance. The quantity of heat which must be given to unit mass of a liquid to convert it to vapor without change of temperature is called the *heat of vaporization*. The equation used in § 146 for calculating heat quantities during fusion, namely

$$Q = mL \qquad (104)$$

may also be used to determine heat quantities during vaporization if L is used to represent the heat of vaporization. This equation shows how much heat must be imparted to a mass m of liquid to vaporize it at constant temperature, or abstracted from that mass of vapor to condense it under the same conditions.

The heat of vaporization depends on the temperature at which change of state occurs, and the temperature in turn is determined by the pressure. The values of the heat of vaporization L for a few liquids at normal atmospheric pressure are given in the following table:

Heats of Vaporization at Normal Boiling Points

	Cal./gm.	B.t.u./lb.
Alcohol (ethyl)........	208	374
Carbon disulfide......	86	155
Mercury.............	68	122
Water..............	539	970
Oxygen.............	51	92

If heat is applied to some water in an open beaker, the pressure remaining at 76 cm. of mercury, the water will boil at 100° C. and the heat of vaporization will be 539 cal. per gm. If instead, water in a beaker at 0° C. is placed in the receiver of an air pump, and the air pressure therein is reduced to 0.46 cm., the water will boil at that temperature and the heat of vaporization will be 599 cal. per gm. For water boiling at high pressures and temperatures, the heat of vaporization is less than the values mentioned, while at the critical temperature [§ 169] the heat of vaporization will be zero.

153. Sublimation. — Under the proper conditions of temperature and pressure, a substance can pass directly from the solid to the vapor state, without liquefying as an intermediate step. Iodine crystals vaporize in this manner under ordinary room conditions, and the same is true of naphthalene moth balls, and "dry ice" (solid carbon dioxide). It has been found recently that carbon behaves similarly at 3800° K. These are illustrations of sublimation.

The relation between sublimation, freezing, and boiling is illustrated for water in Fig. 174. The line *FX* is a redrawing of the freezing-point curve; *BX* is likewise a redrawing of the boiling-point curve; and *SX* is a corresponding curve representing equilibrium between the solid and vapor states, that is, the sublimation curve. If the pressure on a block of ice is reduced to a value below *A'* and maintained at this value, the ice will be transformed directly into vapor by the application of heat, and the process is represented by a line such as *MN*. At an appropriate higher pressure the effect of applying heat to ice is represented by the line *QR*, the ice being converted to water and this in turn being converted to vapor.

The point of intersection *X* of the three curves is of special interest. Every point on the curve *FX* represents a state of equilibrium between the liquid and solid states; similarly every point on *BX* represents a state of equilibrium between the liquid and vapor states; consequently, the intersection point *X* denotes a state of equilibrium among all three states. This point is called the *triple point*, and represents a condition of pressure and temperature at which the water can freeze and boil simultaneously. To reach this point the temperature is lowered sufficiently to cause freezing, and at the same time the pressure is lowered sufficiently to cause boiling. The triple point for water occurs when the pressure is reduced to 0.46 cm. of mercury and the temperature is lowered to +0.0075° C.

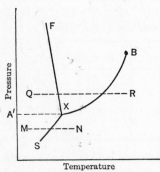

Fig. 174. Triple-point diagram for water

The upper portion of the freezing-point curve *FX* has been investigated by Professor Percy W. Bridgman. At high pressures the curve is found to undergo some marked changes of shape, and several varieties of ice are formed having properties different from those of ice at atmospheric pressure. For one variety the freezing-point line shifts to the right at extremely high pressures, to such an extent that at about 20,000 kg. per sq. cm. water may be frozen at 70° C.

The boiling-point curve, *BX*, comes to a definite end at a point *B*, for which the temperature is 365° C. This is the critical temperature of water [§ 169]; at higher temperatures steam cannot be condensed into water, however great the applied pressure.

It might be mentioned that although freezing normally occurs at some point on the curve *FX*, water which is quiescent and free from impurities may be cooled several degrees below its freezing point without solidification. This phenomenon, called *supercooling* or *undercooling*, represents a condition of unstable equilibrium. Upon dropping particles of ice into the supercooled liquid, solidification takes place immediately, and the temperature rises rapidly to the normal freezing point. Similarly, under certain conditions water may be *superheated* several degrees above its boiling point, but when boiling starts the temperature falls to the normal value. This use of the term "superheated" should not be confused with the common use of the word in connection with steam. Steam is superheated by removing it from its source and heating it; the steam then becomes a vapor that is above its liquefaction temperature and acquires the behavior of a perfect gas. Supercooling and superheating are also observed with other substances.

PROBLEMS

1. How many calories are needed to heat 500 gm. of water from 15° to 80° C.?

2. How many British thermal units are needed to heat 1 cu. ft. of water from 70° F. to 180° F.?

3. An electric heater supplying 65 cal./sec. is placed in 0.5 liter of water for 6.2 min. Calculate the temperature rise, assuming that all of the heat is expended in heating the water.

4. Find the temperature of 1 gallon of water initially at 40° F. after supplying it with 500 B.t.u.

5. Heat is supplied to 2 kg. of cracked ice at 0° C. at the rate of 85 cal. per sec. Neglecting heat losses, how long will it take to melt all of the ice?

6. How much heat does 1 cu. ft. of ice absorb in melting at 32° F.?

7. Determine how much heat is liberated by 5 kg. of mercury when it freezes, the temperature remaining unchanged.

8. How much heat is needed to convert 5 lb. of ice at 32° F. to water at 70° F.?

9. What result is produced by supplying 100,000 cal. to 1 kg. of ice at 0° C.?

10. Heat is supplied to 1 lb. of ice at 32° F., converting it to steam at 212° F. Plot a graph to scale showing energy supplied as ordinates and temperatures as abscissas.

*11. A mixture composed of equal parts of tin and lead is completely melted and cooled slowly. At what temperature will the mixture start to solidify? Describe the composition of the liquid remaining at 200° C.

*12. Determine the eutectic temperatures for the three alloys represented by the melting-point diagrams of Fig. 169.

13. Find the result of abstracting 12,000 B.t.u. from 10 lb. of steam at 100° C.

14. Determine how much heat is required to vaporize 15 gm. of ethyl alcohol at its normal boiling point.

15. If 70,000 cal. are abstracted from 100 gm. of steam at 100° C., what will be the result?

16. How much heat is needed to convert 5 gm. of ice at 0° to steam at 100° C.?

17. If 0.3 lb. of steam at the normal boiling point of water is changed to ice at 32° F., how much heat will be liberated?

CHAPTER XVI

CALORIMETRY

154. Measurement of Heat Quantities. — The measurement of heat quantities, called calorimetry, is frequently carried out by the so-called "method of mixtures." This method makes use of the following principles: 1. When two bodies, initially at different temperatures, are placed in good thermal contact with each other, *the hot body gives up heat and the cold body gains heat*, the system finally reaching a condition of equilibrium at some temperature which is uniform throughout. 2. *The heat given up by the hot body is equal to that taken on by the cold body*, provided no heat is gained from, or given to, the surroundings. The application of these facts makes it possible to determine some unknown factor of an experiment in which several substances at different temperatures are brought together.

Suppose it is desired to find the temperature that results when 500 gm. of water at 80° C. are mixed with 200 gm. of water at 10° C. The resulting temperature x will be such that the heat released by the 500 gm. of water in falling from 80° to $x°$ is equal to that absorbed by the 200 gm. of water in rising from 10° to $x°$. Thus,

$$500 \times (80 - x) = 200 \times (x - 10),$$

from which the temperature of the mixture is found to be $x = 60°$ C.

155. Thermal Capacity and Specific Heat. — One calorie of heat will raise one gram of water through one centigrade degree. It should be noted that this statement applies only to water, for the amounts of heat needed to raise one gram of various substances are peculiar to them. For copper, only about 1/11 cal. is needed to raise 1 gm. through 1 centigrade degree, while for platinum about 1/30 cal. is sufficient, and so on. This quantity of heat is a characteristic property of matter to which the term *thermal capacity* is applied. per gram

The thermal capacity per gram *of a substance is the number of calories needed to raise 1 gm. of it through 1 centigrade degree*, or, what amounts to the same thing, *the number of British thermal units needed to raise 1 lb. of the substance through 1 fahrenheit degree.*

Thus, the thermal capacity of copper is 0.093 cal./(gm. °C.) or
0.093 B.t.u./(lb. °F.).   For water, the value is, of course, 1 cal./
(gm. °C.) or 1 B.t.u. /(lb. °F.).   The thermal capacity of any
substance varies somewhat with its temperature.

The ratio of the thermal capacity of a substance to the thermal
capacity of water is called the *specific heat* of the substance.
Specific heat is a ratio like specific gravity [§ 111], and therefore
has no unit; numerically it has the same value as thermal capacity for a given substance.

The specific heats of some solids and liquids are given in the
following table, these being average values for the temperatures
listed:

Specific Heats

	Temperature	Specific Heat
Alcohol (ethyl)........	0–40° C.	0.59
Aluminum...........	0–100	0.21
Copper.............	0–100	0.093
Glass, ordinary.......	10–50	0.14
Ice.................	−20–0	0.50
Iron...............	0–1000	0.15
"	0–100	0.11
Lead...............	0–300	0.032
Mercury...........	0–100	0.033
Platinum...........	20–100	0.032
Tin................	0–100	0.060

The definition of thermal capacity shows that in order to raise
a mass m of a body having a thermal capacity c through a temperature range t, the quantity of heat required is

$$Q = m c t \qquad (105)$$

This expression also shows the quantity of heat which must be
removed from the body to lower its temperature by t degrees.   In
this equation t stands for *change* of temperature, say from t_1 to t_2
degrees, an interval small enough to permit the specific heat value
to be regarded as constant.

Thus, 30 gm. of tin in being raised from 10° to 100° C., will absorb
$30 \times 0.060 \times 90 = 162$ cal.   Again, if 10 lb. of iron are cooled from
800° F. to 30° F., the heat lost will be $10 \times 0.15 \times 770 = 1155$ B.t.u.

156. Determination of Specific Heat. — The method of mixtures, described in § 154, is commonly used in calorimetry for the
determination of specific heat.   One form of apparatus used for
this purpose is shown in Fig. 175.   A test sample P of known mass

is heated in a steam-jacketed compartment S to a measured high temperature; the calorimeter R, a heat-insulated metal vessel containing a known amount of water at a known temperature, is pushed directly under the heated compartment and the sample is allowed to drop into it, whereupon the calorimeter is quickly moved away to prevent its gaining heat from the jacket, and the resulting temperature of the mixture is noted. To find the specific heat of the test sample from the data thus obtained, equate the heat released by the sample to that gained by the water and calorimeter, using equation (105) to express each of these heat quantities.

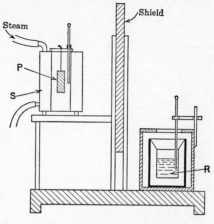

Fig. 175.   Apparatus for measuring specific heat

In a particular test, a 300-gm. sample of unknown thermal capacity c was heated to 98.5° C. and dropped into 600 gm. of water at 19.0° C. contained in a 140-gm. copper calorimeter, the resulting temperature being 22.4° C. The heat equation follows:

$$300 \times c \times (98.5 - 22.4) = 600 \times 1 \times (22.4 - 19.0) +$$
$$140 \times 0.093 \times (22.4 - 19.0) = (600 + 13.0) \times 3.4,$$

from which the value of c is found to be 0.091. The thermal capacity of the sample under test is 0.091 cal./(gm. ° C.) and its specific heat is 0.091.

The product of the mass of a calorimeter and its thermal capacity, called its *water equivalent*, is a quantity that is useful in calorimetric computations. In the foregoing illustration, the 140-gm. calorimeter is equivalent to $140 \times 0.093 = 13.0$ gm. of water, which means that 13.0 gm. of water would experience the same temperature rise as the 140-gm. copper calorimeter for the same supply of heat.

157. Calorimetry Involving Change of State. — When substances at different temperatures, and possibly in various states, are mixed and allowed to settle to equilibrium, some of them may vaporize, condense, melt, or freeze during the process. These changes either require or liberate heat, and this heat energy must be accounted for in applying the principles of the method of mixtures. A hypothetical problem will illustrate the procedure.

Suppose 5 lb. of steam at atmospheric pressure, superheated to a temperature of 250° F., together with 10 lb. of ice at 20° F., to be introduced simultaneously into a copper calorimeter weighing 4 lb. and containing 60 lb. of water at 70° F. The thermal capacities in British thermal units per lb. per fahrenheit degree are as follows for the temperature ranges involved: steam, 0.48; ice, 0.50; and copper, 0.093. The heats of fusion and vaporization for water are respectively 144 and 970 B.t.u. per lb. Calculate the resulting temperature of the mixture, neglecting heat losses to other bodies.

The problem will first be solved by equating the heat lost by the steam to that gained by the ice, water, and calorimeter, assuming the resulting temperature x to be between 70° and 212° F. The heat lost by the steam consists of three parts: $5 \times 0.48 \times (250 - 212) = 91$ B.t.u. in cooling to 212° F.; $5 \times 970 = 4850$ B.t.u. in condensing into water at 212° F.; and $5 \times (212 - x)$ B.t.u. in cooling to the final temperature x. Similarly, the heat received by the ice consists of three parts: $10 \times 0.50 \times (32 - 20) = 60$ B.t.u. in rising to 32° F.; $10 \times 144 = 1440$ B.t.u. in melting; and $10 \times (x - 32)$ B.t.u. in rising to the final temperature. For the water and calorimeter, the heat gained is $(60 \times 1 + 4 \times 0.093) \times (x - 70) = 60.37 \times (x - 70)$ B.t.u. Equating:

$$91 + 4850 + 5 \times (212 - x) = 60 + 1440 + 10 \times (x - 32) +$$
$$60.37 \times (x - 70),$$

from which $x = 120°$ F.

This problem will now be solved by a different method, which involves calculating first the total heat content of the system before mixture with regard to some convenient reference state, and then the effect that this quantity of heat will produce on the system after mixture.

Choosing as the reference state water at 32° F., the heat contents are found to be:

in steam:	$5 \times 0.48 \times (250 - 212) = +\quad 91$	
	$5 \times 970 = + 4850$	
	$5 \times (212 - 32) = +\quad 900$	$+ 8135$ B.t.u.
in water:	$60 \times 1 \times (70 - 32) = + 2280$	
in calorimeter:	$4 \times 0.093 \times (70 - 32) = +\quad 14$	
in ice:	$-10 \times 0.50 \times (32 - 20) = -\quad 60$	-1500
	$-10 \times 144 = - 1440$	

$$+6635 \text{ B.t.u.}$$

This total heat content of 6635 B.t.u. is to be distributed among $5 + 10 + 60$ or 75 lb. of water and 4 lb. of copper. Since the 4-lb. copper calorimeter is the equivalent of $4 \times 0.093 = 0.37$ lb. of water, the 6635 B.t.u. will be imparted to 75.37 lb. of water. This will cause a temperature rise of

6635 ÷ 75.37 = 88 fahrenheit degrees. Thus, the final temperature will be 88 + 32 = 120° F.

The second method is of advantage in that it is not necessary to make any assumption as to the probable final temperature. This method would also be helpful in solving a problem where the resulting temperature is 32° F. with some ice unmelted (total heat content of system above water at 32° F. would be negative), or where the resulting temperature is 212° F. with some steam uncondensed (total heat content of system sufficient to raise entire system to 212° F., leaving a surplus to vaporize part of the water). In such cases the calculation will show the amount of ice unmelted or the amount of steam uncondensed.

158. Measurement of Heat of Fusion. — The value of the heat of fusion of ice, given in § 146 as $L = 80$ cal. per gm., can be verified in the laboratory by measuring the temperature change when a measured amount of ice is dropped into a measured amount of hot water, and equating the heat lost by the water to that gained by the ice.

In such a test, some surface-dried ice at 0° C. was dropped into a calorimeter containing water at 55° C., the mass of water (including the water equivalent of the calorimeter) being 250 gm. After the ice was melted, the temperature was found to be 45° C. and the calorimeter was observed to have 20 gm. of water more than previously. In this test the hot water lost 250 × 10 cal., the heat required to melt the ice is 20 × L cal., and the water thus formed gained 20 × 45 cal. in coming to the final temperature. Consequently, neglecting any effects due to the surroundings, 250 × 10 = 20 × L + 20 × 45; whence $L = 80$ cal. per gm.

159. Measurement of Heat of Vaporization. — The heat of vaporization of water can be determined by passing saturated steam into cool water within a calorimeter, and thereby condensing it. The amount of steam condensed is found by weighing the contents of the calorimeter before and after the test, and the temperature rise of the calorimeter and its contents is measured by a thermometer. If m gm. of water are raised from t_1 to t_2° C. as a result of admitting M gm. of steam at T° C., the heat absorbed by the water will be $m(t_2 - t_1)$ and must equal that liberated by the steam, namely, $M[L + (T - t_2)]$. From this relation, the heat of vaporization L at temperature T can be found readily.

The heat of vaporization can also be measured by means of a steam calorimeter devised by John Joly, in which the heat liberated by condensing steam is used to raise the temperature of a known mass of metal. The elements of the apparatus are shown in Fig. 176. A sphere S with collecting pan P is suspended

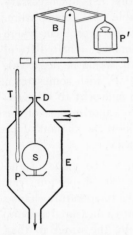

within an enclosure E by a fine wire extending from one arm of a balance B. It is counterbalanced at room temperature (indicated by thermometer T) by weights placed in pan P' on the other arm of the balance. The wire passes through a small hole in a free cover disk D of light metal; this construction prevents the escape of steam but does not hinder balancing the sphere. When steam is passed through the enclosure, some will condense on S and the water will collect in pan P; additional weights must be placed on P' to restore balance when temperature equilibrium has been reached.

FIG. 176. Joly calorimeter for measuring heat of vaporization

Knowing the mass, specific heat, and temperature elevation of the sphere S, and the change in reading of the weights on P', the heat of vaporization can be obtained.

Engineers frequently use "steam tables" in determining the performance of boilers. These tables include the temperature at

Properties of Saturated Steam

Absolute pressure, lb. per sq. in.	Temperature, ° F.	B.t.u. in 1 lb. above 32° F.		
		In water	Heat of vaporization	Total heat
1	101.8	70	1035	1105
2	126.1	94	1022	1116
5	162.3	130	1000	1130
10	193.2	161	982	1143
14.7	212.0	180	970	1150
20	228.0	196	960	1156
50	281.0	250	923	1173
75	307.6	277	904	1181
100	327.8	298	888	1186
150	358.4	330	863	1193
200	381.8	355	843	1198
250	401.0	376	824	1200
300	417.3	394	808	1202
400	444.6	424	780	1204
500	467.0	450	754	1204

which change of state occurs, the heat units in the water, the heat of vaporization, and the total heat (or sum of the two preceding). A few scattered entries from such a table will show the variation of the heat of vaporization with the temperature at which change of state occurs.

160. Heat of Combustion. — When a substance is burned or oxidized it produces heat, and the amount of heat evolved per unit mass upon complete oxidation is called its *heat of combustion.* The heats of combustion of several fuels are tabulated in round numbers as follows:

Heats of Combustion

	Cal. per gm.	B.t.u. per lb.
Coal (anthracite)............	7,600 to 8,400	13,500 to 15,000
Coke......................	6,900	12,600
Gasoline...................	11,000 to 11,400	20,000 to 20,500
Illuminating gas.............	5,500 to 6,400	9,900 to 11,500
Wood (various).............	4,000 to 4,500	7,000 to 8,000

The heats of combustion of carbon and of a few organic compounds are given below expressed in calories per mol, § 130. Considering methane (marsh gas) as an illustration, the molar weight of this compound is $12 + 4(1) = 16$ gm., and therefore its

Heats of Combustion

	Formula	Cal. per mol
Carbon............	C	97,300
Methane............	CH_4	212,000
Acetylene..........	C_2H_2	310,000
Methyl alcohol.......	CH_3OH	182,000
Ethyl alcohol........	C_2H_5OH	341,000
Carbon disulfide......	CS_2	265,000

heat of combustion per gram will be $212,000 \div 16 = 13,250$ cal. In engineering, heats of combustion are usually considered positive. In thermochemistry, the opposite practice is generally followed, heat evolved in a reaction being regarded as negative, and heat absorbed positive. The use of signs is conventional, and need cause no confusion.

Measurements of heat of combustion are made in combustion calorimeters, one type of which is shown in section in Fig. 177. The substance to be tested is placed in a platinum crucible *C* mounted within a strong steel container S lined with platinum, gold or porcelain to prevent corrosion. Oxygen under a pressure of several atmospheres is admitted at O and next the bomb is tightly sealed. It is then placed in a calorimeter containing water, and an electric current is passed through a small heating coil H which dips into the test substance. When the wire becomes incandescent, combustion takes place and the rise of temperature of the water is observed.

A different procedure is used for measuring the heat of combustion of gaseous fuels. The gas is burned at a constant rate within a chamber through which water is circulating uniformly. The

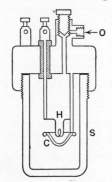

temperatures of the water as it enters and leaves the chamber, together with the rate at which the water passes through it, permit the determination of the heat evolved per unit volume or per unit mass of the fuel.

In some fields of study heat quantities are expressed in terms of the *kilogram-calorie;* this is equal to 1000 calories. Food values are stated in the larger unit for convenience; thus, the fuel value of the foods consumed by the average American per day is 3250 kilogram-calories ($3\frac{1}{4}$ million calories).

Fig. 177. Bomb of a combustion calorimeter

★161. Heat of Formation. — Every chemical reaction is attended by a definite exchange of heat. Thus, when elements unite to form a compound, the number of calories evolved or absorbed per mol of compound produced is called the *heat of formation* for the temperature prevailing. The following table gives the heats of formation for a few compounds at approximately 20° C., heat evolved being regarded as negative.

The heat of combustion of a fuel can be calculated from a table of heats of formation, and the fact that compounds are not usually made directly from their elements does not detract from the usefulness of such a table. Let it be required to find the heat of combustion of methane, according to the equation

$$CH_4 + 2O_2 \rightarrow CO_2 + 2H_2O$$

If the heat of formation of 1 mol of CH_4 is subtracted from the heats of formation of 1 mol of CO_2 and 2 mols of H_2O, the remainder is the heat involved in combustion. Hence the heat of combustion of methane is $(-94,400) + 2(-68,400) - (-19,200)$ $= -212,000$ cal. per mol. This result agrees with the value listed in the preceding section, with proper regard for signs.

Heats of Formation

	Formula	Cal. per mol
Acetylene	C_2H_2	$+ 54,400$
Carbon dioxide	CO_2	$- 94,400$
Copper sulfate	$CuSO_4$	$-183,000$
Hydrochloric acid (gas)	HCl	$- 21,800$
Methane	CH_4	$- 19,200$
Sulfur dioxide (gas)	SO_2	$- 69,300$
Sulfuric acid	H_2SO_4	$-189,800$
Water (liquid)	H_2O	$- 68,400$
Water (vapor)	H_2O	$- 57,800$
Zinc sulfate	$ZnSO_4$	$-230,000$

Substances for which the heat of formation is positive have a peculiar interest. Acetylene (C_2H_2), for example, liberates the heats of combustion of the carbon and hydrogen in burning, and in addition surrenders 54,400 cal. for each mol in decomposing. It is because of this augmented heat evolution that such compounds make superior fuels.

It will be observed that water has a larger heat of formation than water vapor. The difference between these values is the heat liberated by the condensation of the vapor, and is equal to the heat of vaporization per mol of water at 20° C.

PROBLEMS

1. How much heat is necessary to raise the temperature of a block of iron weighing 2.7 kg. from 10° to 150° C.?

2. How much heat is lost by 140 gm. of ethyl alcohol in cooling from 38° to 16° C.?

3. Ice at 0° C. and water at 90° C. are mixed in equal parts by weight. Determine the resulting temperature.

4. One pound of mercury at 100° C. is poured into 1 lb. of water at 20° C. Neglecting the effect of the container, determine the resulting temperature.

5. Two pounds of ice at 0° C. are placed in a bucket that is capable of holding 10 lb. of water. Water is added until the bucket will hold no more, and it is found that half of the ice melts. What was the temperature of the water, neglecting the thermal effect of the bucket and ignoring losses?

6. A glass beaker weighing 120 gm. contains 360 gm. of water at 16.3° C. Into the water is placed a 154-gm. mass of lead, originally at a temperature of 99.2° C. Compute the final temperature.

7. A 160-gm. sample of an alloy is heated to 100° C. and then dropped into a cavity in a large block of ice. If 24 gm. of ice are melted, find the specific heat of the alloy.

8. An electric heater supplying 75 cal. per sec. is buried in 1000 gm. of cracked ice at 0° C. Find the temperature at the end of 30 min., disregarding the heat absorbed by the heater itself.

9. In determining the specific heat of a metal, a 150-gm. sample of it is heated to 99.5° C. and is dropped into 225 gm. of water at 18.0° C. contained in a copper calorimeter weighing 160 gm. The resulting temperature is 22.4° C.; find the specific heat of the sample.

10. A copper calorimeter weighing 150 gm. contains 300 gm. of water at 20° C. Into this are placed 100 gm. of lead and 200 gm. of iron, both at 75° C. Find the resulting temperature of the mixture.

11. How many calories will be required to change 1 gm. of ice at −35° C. to steam at 130° C. under atmospheric pressure? Take the specific heat of steam as 0.48.

12. Diphenyloxide, $(C_6H_5)_2O$, is a substance used in some steam generating stations for reheating steam and for recovering heat otherwise wasted. It melts at 27° C. and boils at 258° C. under normal pressure. Its specific heat in the liquid phase averages 0.50 and its heat of vaporization at 258° C. is 78 cal./gm. Calculate the total heat content of one gram of the substance as a vapor at the latter temperature with respect to its heat content as a liquid at the melting point. Also express the result in B.t.u. per lb.

13. Solve the problem cited in § 157 using 2 lb. of steam and 35 lb. of ice instead of the 5 and 10 lb. quantities of these substances.

14. Some steam at 100° C. under atmospheric pressure is passed into 300 gm. of water at 15° C. When the temperature of the water has reached 25° C. the test is stopped and it is found by weighing that 4.9 gm. of steam have been condensed. Compute the heat of vaporization of water at 100° C. as given by this test, neglecting the effect of the container.

15. How much coal is needed to heat a 40-gal. tank full of water from 50° to 130° F.? Assume that the heat of combustion of the coal is 15,000 B.t.u. per lb., of which 60 per cent is useful in heating the water.

16. Illuminating gas is used to heat the 6 cu. ft. of water required for a tub bath. The water is to be heated from 55° to 100° F. The heat of combustion of the gas is 600 B.t.u. per cu. ft. and it costs 95 cents per thousand cu. ft. How much does it cost to heat the bath water, assuming that 70 per cent of the fuel heat is delivered to the water in the tub?

17. An industrial process requires that 3000 gal. of water per hour be heated from 40° F. to 140° F. To do this, steam from a boiler at an absolute pressure of 100 lb. per sq. in. is passed into a coil immersed in the water. The steam condenses and is returned to the boiler as water at 150° F. How many pounds of steam are required each hour?

18. The steam-heating plant in a small house uses 1 ton of coal fortnightly in supplying steam at atmospheric pressure to the radiators. Assuming that the heat of combustion of the coal is 15,000 B.t.u. per lb., of which 60 per cent is useful in heating water in the boiler, how much condensed steam at a temperature of 150° F. will be returned daily from the radiators to the boiler?

19. A gasoline engine has its cylinders cooled by circulating water through a jacket surrounding them. The engine consumes 7 gal. of gasoline per hr. and loses 23 per cent of the energy input to the cooling water. At what rate must the water be circulated in order to limit its tempera-

ture rise to 50 fahrenheit degrees? For gasoline, take the heat of combustion as 20,000 B.t.u. per lb. and the specific gravity as 0.68.

20. An eight-room frame house is heated by illuminating gas having a fuel value of 540 B.t.u. per cu. ft. The monthly gas consumption in cubic feet during the heating season follows: October 14,000, November 33,600, December 56,400, January 68,000, February 78,000, March 46,100, April 37,000, and May 11,400. The monthly charge is determined by the following rate schedule:

First	600 cu. ft. or less	$1.00	
Next	2,400 cu. ft.	9.5 cents per 100 cu. ft.	
Next	3,000 cu. ft.	7.0 " " "	
Next	4,000 cu. ft.	6.0 " " "	
Above	10,000 cu. ft.	5.0 " " "	

Determine the annual cost of heating the house and the average cost per million B.t.u. of heat supplied. *Ans.* 95.9 cents.

CHAPTER XVII

THERMAL BEHAVIOR OF GASES

162. Pressure, Volume, and Temperature Relations. — The condition of a gas is completely determined by three variables: the *pressure* which it exerts, the *volume* that it occupies, and its *temperature*. For a given amount of a gas, if two of these variables are given, the value of the third becomes known; or if some one variable is kept constant, the relation between the other two can be found. These relationships for actual gases are complicated by the interaction of their molecules, particularly near the temperatures of liquefaction. The analysis is simplified by imagining a so-called "perfect gas," § 165; such an ideal gas will be assumed in the following analysis of the three gas variables. Air, hydrogen, and other fixed gases, behave very nearly like the perfect gas over wide temperature ranges.

Constant Temperature.—A mass of gas enclosed in a cylinder having a piston, part I of Fig. 178, will occupy a volume at some

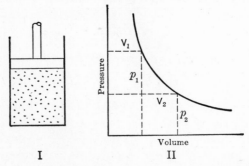

Fig. 178. Pressure-volume relation at constant temperature

definite temperature that depends upon the pressure exerted by the piston. If provision is made to keep the temperature constant, the volume of the gas will vary inversely with the absolute pressure, in accordance with Boyle's Law [§ 128]. This relation is indicated mathematically for any two pressure-volume conditions by the equation

$$p_1 V_1 = p_2 V_2 \tag{106}$$

and is represented by the hyperbola in part II of the figure.

Constant Pressure.—A mass of gas may be kept at constant pressure by enclosing it in a chamber equipped with a freely moving piston, as indicated in part I of Fig. 179, for the slightest change of pressure will cause the piston to move in or out, keeping the pressure inside of the container constant at the value existing on the outside. Upon heating a gas under these conditions, the volume is found to increase with rising temperature in

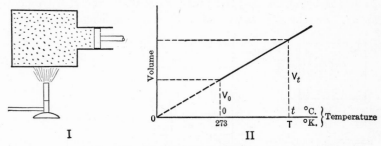

Fig. 179.   Gas heated at constant pressure

accordance with the relation discovered by the French mathematician and physicist, Jacques A. C. Charles (1746–1823), which is

$$V_t = V_o (1 + \beta t) \qquad (107)$$

where V_o and V_t represent the volumes of the gas at 0° C. and t° C. respectively, and β is the coefficient of volume expansion of the gas. This variation of volume with temperature is expressed in exactly the same way as for solids and liquids, but the coefficient β for gases is much larger than for those substances, and moreover, has almost exactly the same value for all gases. This value is $\beta = 0.00367(= 1/273)$ per centigrade degree, which means that a given amount of gas at 0° C. will expand 1/273 of its volume when heated 1 degree, and will contract by the same amount when cooled 1 degree. Note carefully that this value for β applies only when V_o is the volume at 0° C.

Expressing 0° C. as 273° K, it is seen that an increase of 1/273 in the volume corresponds to an increase of 1/273 in the absolute temperature. The volume of a fixed mass of gas thus varies directly with the absolute temperature, as shown in the curve forming part II of Fig. 179, which, if extended, would meet the axis of abscissas at 0° K.

Constant Volume.—To keep a mass of gas at constant volume, it may be confined in a tight container, as represented in part I of Fig. 180, the container being made of some material having negligible expansion. The application of heat causes the pressure to increase in a manner similar to that for the change of volume at constant pressure, namely,

$$p_t = p_o(1 + \beta't)$$

p_o and p_t being the absolute pressures at $0°$ C. and $t°$ C. respectively. Herein β' is the so-called pressure coefficient of the gas,

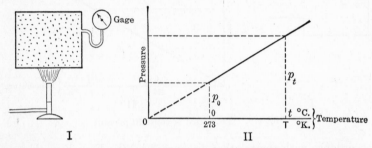

FIG. 180.   Gas heated at constant volume

and represents the change in pressure per unit pressure per centigrade degree change of temperature.

It can be shown that the voluminal expansion coefficient β and the pressure coefficient β' have the same values for a perfect gas. Imagine a fixed quantity of gas to occupy a volume V_o and to exert a pressure p_o at $0°$ C., and suppose this gas to be heated to some temperature $t°$ C. at constant pressure. Its new volume will be $V_t = V_o \times (1 + \beta t)$ and its pressure will be the same as it was originally, or $p_t = p_o$; hence by multiplying terms, $p_t V_t = p_o V_o (1 + \beta t)$. Suppose, next, that the gas is again heated from its original condition, that is, p_o and V_o, to the same temperature $t°$ C., this time at constant volume. Its new pressure will be $p'_t = p_o(1 + \beta't)$, and its volume will remain unchanged, or $V'_t = V_o$. Multiplying these terms gives the expression: $p'_t V'_t = p_o V_o (1 + \beta't)$. Since in these two tests the same mass of gas has been brought to the same temperature, the products $p_t V_t$ and $p'_t V'_t$ must be equal in accordance with Boyle's Law; consequently,

$$p_o V_o (1 + \beta t) = p_o V_o (1 + \beta't)$$

which proves that the coefficients β and β' are equal.

The numerical equality of the two coefficients for a perfect gas makes it unnecessary to distinguish between them, and hereafter β will be used to represent either. The equation for gas pressure at any temperature may therefore be written as

$$p_t = p_o(1 + \beta t) \tag{108}$$

It follows that the pressure of a given mass of gas at constant volume varies directly as the absolute temperature, as indicated in part II of Fig. 180.

163. The Gas Thermometer. — The gas thermometer utilizes the change of pressure caused by heating or cooling a gas at constant volume as a means for measuring temperature. The thermometer, Fig. 181, consists essentially of a thin-walled bulb B of glass or porcelain, in which the gas is confined, and to which is attached a flexible tube containing mercury. By keeping the top of the left-hand mercury column at a constant level A the volume of the gas is kept constant, and the pressure is obtained by reading the difference in height of the two columns A and C on the scale S. The gas thermometer is somewhat awkward to manipulate and is not direct-reading, but it is used as a basic standard for the calibration of thermometers to serve as secondary standards. The gas used in the thermometer bulb is usually hydrogen; for measurements at very low temperatures helium is preferable.

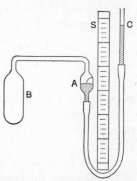

FIG. 181. Gas thermometer

To show how the gas thermometer is used for temperature measurement, suppose that the pressure of the gas in the bulb is p_o at $t_o°$ C., p_1 at $t_1°$ C., and p_2 at $t_2°$ C. The volume of the gas being constant, it follows from the foregoing that a change in temperature will produce a proportional change in pressure, whence

$$(t_1 - t_o) \propto (p_1 - p_o)$$

and

$$(t_2 - t_o) \propto (p_2 - p_o)$$

Since the proportionality is the same in both,

$$\frac{t_2 - t_o}{t_1 - t_o} = \frac{p_2 - p_o}{p_1 - p_o}$$

Taking, for example, the pressure of the gas to be p_o when the bulb is placed in melting ice ($t_o = 0°$ C.), to be p_1 when the bulb is surrounded by steam under standard conditions of temperature and pressure ($t_1 = 100°$ C.), and to be p_2 at some unknown temperature $t_2°$ C., then the value of the latter temperature becomes

$$t_2 = 100 \frac{p_2 - p_o}{p_1 - p_o}$$

in terms of the observed gas pressures.

164. General Gas Law. — The relation between the pressure, volume, and temperature of a fixed mass of gas developed in § 162, namely

$$p_t V_t = p_o V_o (1 + \beta t) \tag{109}$$

is of great importance and merges the relations discovered by Boyle and Charles. Herein, by way of summary, p_t and V_t are respectively the absolute pressure and the volume of the gas at $t°$ C.; p_o and V_o are the corresponding values at $0°$ C., and β is the mean coefficient of expansion of the gas over the range from $0°$ to $t°$ C.

It will be of value to express the foregoing equation in terms of the absolute temperature. To do so, first factor the quantity β from the parenthesis in equation (109), and then replace $1/\beta$ by 273, yielding

$$p_t V_t = p_o V_o \beta \times (1/\beta + t) = p_o V_o \beta(273 + t)$$

The product $p_o V_o \beta$ for a known mass is constant and will be called MR, where M is the mass of the gas under consideration and R is a constant. Further, $(273 + t)$ may be replaced by the corresponding absolute temperature T. Making these substitutions and dropping subscripts, the expression becomes the General Gas Law, namely:

$$pV = MRT \tag{110}$$

A still simpler form of this law may be obtained by making use of the fact that for a given mass of gas the quantity MR in equation (110) is constant, hence the values of p, V, and T must be so related that $\dfrac{PV}{T} = MR$ under all conditions. Using subscript 1 to denote one particular condition of pressure, volume, and temperature, and subscript 2 for some different condition, it follows that

$$\frac{p_1 V_1}{T_1} = \frac{p_2 V_2}{T_2}$$

(111)

an expression which shows the relation between the absolute pressure and the volume of a fixed mass of gas at different absolute temperatures.

This law of gases confirms the theory that the temperature of a gas is directly proportional to the kinetic energy of the gas molecules [§ 126]. It was there shown that the pressure exerted by a gas is $p = Nm\,v^2/3V$, where N/V is the number of gas molecules per unit volume, m is the mass of each molecule, and v is their r-m-s. velocity. Herefrom $pV = Nm\,v^2/3$, or $pV \propto m\,v^2$. But from equation (110), $pV \propto T$; therefore

$$T \propto m\,v^2 \propto m\,v^2/2 \propto \text{K.E.}$$

which shows the desired proportionality between the absolute temperature and the kinetic energy of the gas.

The Gas Constant.—The numerical value of the *gas constant R* referred to ahead can be computed readily, since its equation is

$$R = \frac{p_o V_o \beta}{M}.$$

The constant R has a particular value for each gas. For example, air at 0° C. and standard pressure has a density $M/V = 0.001293$ gm./cu. cm., whence the value of the gas constant for air is

$$R = 1,013,000 \frac{\text{dynes}}{\text{cm.}^2} \times \frac{0.00367}{\text{°K.}} \div 0.001293 \frac{\text{gm.}}{\text{cm.}^3} = 2.87 \times 10^6 \frac{\text{ergs}}{\text{gm.°K.}}$$

While this value was computed for the standard conditions, it is the same for air under all conditions of pressure, volume and temperature.

As a typical problem involving the gas constant, find the volume occupied by 1000 gm. of air at 100° C. when subjected to a pressure of 10 atmospheres. From equation (110)

$$V = \frac{MRT}{p} = \frac{1000 \text{ gm.} \times 2.87 \times 10^6 \frac{\text{ergs}}{\text{gm. °K.}} \times 373° \text{ K.}}{10 \times 1,013,000 \frac{\text{dynes}}{\text{cm.}^2}} = 106,000 \text{ cu. cm.}$$

By expressing the mass of a gas in mols [§ 130] instead of grams, the gas constant R is given a single value which is the same for all gases.   Since 1 mol of any gas at 0° C. and 76.0 cm. of mercury occupies a volume of 22.4 liters, it follows that this universal value is

$$R = 1{,}013{,}000 \, \frac{\text{dynes}}{\text{cm.}^2} \times \frac{0.00367}{\text{°K.}} \times \frac{22{,}400 \text{ cm.}^3}{\text{mol}} = 83.1 \times 10^6 \frac{\text{ergs}}{\text{mol °K.}}$$

The value of the gas constant per molecule is obtained herefrom by dividing by Avogadro's number, thus, $83.1 \times 10^6 \div 6.02 \times 10^{23}$ $= 1.38 \times 10^{-16}$ ergs per °K.

165. Free Expansion. — A gas is said to undergo *free expansion* when it is allowed to expand without external opposition.   For example, suppose that a tank of gas under pressure is piped to a second tank from which the air has been evacuated, Fig. 182, and imagine the valve between the tanks to be opened suddenly; the gas then expands freely into the vacuum.   An experiment of

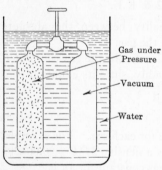

this kind was conducted by the French chemist and physicist, Joseph L. Gay-Lussac (1778–1850) and was afterwards improved by Joule in 1844, to determine whether any temperature change would occur during free expansion.   The tanks were immersed in a water bath, and the temperature of the water was observed before and after the valve was opened.   In this test the temperature appeared to remain

Fig. 182. Illustrating free expansion

unchanged, which would indicate that a gas is neither cooled nor heated by free expansion.   The experiment was not entirely convincing, however, because the bath contained so much water that a slight temperature change of the gas might readily escape notice.   In a later and more delicate experiment conducted by Joule and Thomson, the gas was allowed to escape slowly through a porous plug from a region of high to one of low pressure, a thermoelectric couple being used to detect any temperature change during the process.   Most gases were found to undergo a slight cooling upon expansion.   Hydrogen appeared at first to be an exception, but when tested at appropriate temperatures, was also found to become cooled.

As a consequence of the free-expansion experiment, a perfect or ideal gas can now be fully defined, and some distinctions made between perfect and actual gases. A *perfect gas* is one which *fulfils the General Gas Law*, $pV = MRT$, and which *does not exhibit cooling during free expansion.* These considerations show that in a perfect gas, the molecules exert no force on one another. For, suppose the molecules of such a gas did exert a slight attraction for one another; then in freely expanding to a greater distance apart, work would have to be done upon them, and this work, being taken from the internal energy of the gas, would result in a lowering of the temperature. The same reasoning shows that in an actual gas there is almost no force action among the molecules, and that the small force which does exist is one of attraction.

Further, since a perfect gas shows no temperature change during free expansion, it is evident that no energy is abstracted from it, although both its pressure and its volume are changed. From this fact an important principle follows, namely: *the internal energy of a perfect gas remains constant regardless of changes in pressure and volume, provided the temperature is not changed.*

The kinetic theory offers a picture of what takes place when an actual gas expands through a small opening into a region of lower pressure. Supposing the gas molecules to exert a force of attraction on one another, a molecule passing through the orifice will be attracted by such other molecules as are within its sphere of action. Those ahead of it will attract it forward and those behind it will attract it backward. The predominating effect, however, will be due to the molecules behind it since the pressure, and consequently the molecular density, is greater in that region. The result is a slowing down of the molecule as it passes through the orifice, and this implies a reduction of its kinetic energy and a lowering of temperature. This theory shows that whenever an actual gas expands, its temperature will fall on account of the attraction among its molecules. At ordinary temperatures, this cooling is very small, but as the temperature is lowered the molecules come closer together (assuming the pressure unchanged) and the cooling effect is greatly increased.

166. Constrained Expansion. — When a gas under pressure is allowed to expand against a back pressure, the expansion may be termed *constrained* to distinguish it from free expansion into a vacuum. During constrained expansion either a perfect or actual gas does work in pushing back the atmosphere or other surrounding gases. Suppose that a cylinder, Fig. 183, contains gas under absolute pressure p, and that the gas pushes a piston of area A back a distance s. During this process, the confined gas exerts a force $F = pA$ and does an amount of work $E = Fs = pAs$. The product As is the increase in volume of the gas and may be denoted by v, whence the work done by the gas during expansion becomes

$$E = p\,v \qquad (112)$$

This expression is true for any change in volume v which is sufficiently small so that during the change, the pressure p may be considered constant.

If no energy is supplied to the gas during this expansion, the work $p\,v$ will necessarily be done at the expense of the internal energy of the gas, as a result of which its temperature will fall. When an actual gas expands against a back pressure, it is cooled by doing external work, and also by the internal work of separating its own molecules.

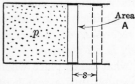

FIG. 183. Work done during expansion

In the commercial manufacture of ice, the refrigeration is brought about by allowing anhydrous ammonia to pass through an expansion valve into a region of reduced pressure. The evaporation of the liquid and the consequent expansion of the vapor are both cooling processes; together they lower the temperature of the ammonia sufficiently to freeze water placed nearby.

In a similar manner it can be shown that the compression of a gas causes it to become hotter. The heating of air in a tire pump is a familiar example. In the Diesel engine [§ 181] air drawn into the cylinder is compressed and thereby heated to about 1000° F., which is sufficient to cause the fuel to ignite as it is sprayed into the cylinder.

The kinetic theory again offers a mental picture of these processes. The gas molecules in the cylinder, Fig. 183, are supposed to be continually striking against the cylinder walls and piston and rebounding from these surfaces. If the piston is moving outward, as during expansion, the molecules in rebounding from this receding surface will lose velocity. If, however, the piston is moving inward, as during compression, the molecules upon striking this advancing surface will gain velocity upon rebound. Thus, expansion lessens the velocity of the gas mole-

cules, reduces their kinetic energy, and lowers the temperature
of the gas; compression produces the opposite effect.

167. Thermal Capacity and Specific Heat of Gases. — The
thermal capacity of a gas, as of any substance, is the amount of
heat necessary to raise the temperature of a unit mass of it one
degree. The specific heat of a gas is the ratio of the thermal
capacity of the gas to the thermal capacity of water. In the case
of a gas the thermal capacity is not single-valued but may have a
range of values depending upon the constraints that are imposed
upon the gas while it is being heated. The heat required to raise
1 gm. of gas 1 centigrade degree would be quite different if the
gas were kept at *constant volume* than if it were kept at *constant
pressure*, and still different values would be obtained if variations
were allowed in both volume and pressure. The most important
values of the thermal capacity of a gas are those at constant volume, c_v, and at constant pressure, c_p.

For solids and liquids the change in volume is so small that it
need not be considered as affecting the thermal capacity, but such
is not the case for gases, as the following consideration will show.
When 1 gm. of gas is confined so that its volume cannot change,
as illustrated in Fig. 180, the quantity of heat needed to raise its
temperature 1 centigrade degree is its thermal capacity at *constant volume*. The heat supplied increases the internal energy of
the gas and is completely accounted for in the increased velocity
of the gas molecules. On the other hand if 1 gm. of gas is enclosed
in a cylinder with a freely moving piston, as in Fig. 179, the quantity of heat needed to raise its temperature 1 centigrade degree is
its thermal capacity at *constant pressure*. In this case the heat
energy supplied must not only increase the velocity of the gas
molecules, but a considerable amount must be expended in doing
external work in pushing back the surrounding gases, and also a
small (often negligible) amount must be expended in the internal
work necessary to overcome the slight cohesion of the molecules
as the gas itself expands. Consequently, *the specific heat of a gas
at constant pressure exceeds its specific heat at constant volume*.

The following table gives the specific heats of several gases at
constant pressure c_p (for atmospheric pressure) and at constant
volume c_v:

It is natural from the foregoing statements to expect that the
difference between the two specific heats of a gas will be virtually

Specific Heats

	Temperature	c_p	c_v
Air......................	0–100° C.	0.242	0.173
Argon.....................	0–100	0.123	0.074
Carbon dioxide..............	0–100	0.208	0.159
Hydrogen..................	0–100	3.40	2.40
Oxygen...................	0–800	0.246	0.176
Water vapor...............	100	0.48	0.34

the external work done by the confined gas in pushing back the
surrounding gases. To derive this relationship, suppose 1 gm. of
air to be heated from 0° to 1° C. at a constant pressure of 1 atmosphere. The initial volume of the air is 1/0.001293 = 775 cu. cm.,
and the increase in volume v during a temperature rise from 0° to
1° C. is (1/273) × 775 = 2.83 cu. cm. The external work done
during expansion, by equation (112) is:

$$E = pv = 1,013,000 \frac{\text{dynes}}{\text{cm.}^2} \times 2.83 \text{ cm.}^3 = 2,870,000 \text{ ergs} = 0.287 \text{ joule}$$

In § 174 it will be shown that this result is equivalent to 0.068 cal.
From the foregoing table, for air $c_p - c_v = 0.242 - 0.173 = 0.069$
cal., the two results being in approximate agreement. For a perfect gas, the agreement would be exact, and the difference between
c_p and c_v would be due entirely to the external work done in its
expansion.

It can also be shown that for a perfect gas, the quantity $c_p - c_v$
is equal to the constant R in equation (110) which expresses the
General Gas Law. Suppose 1 gm. of gas to be heated through a
small temperature range t in two different ways: first, at constant
volume, and second, at constant pressure. Since the temperature
limits are the same, the internal energy of the gas will be increased
by the same amount in each test. In the first of these, the energy
input is $c_v t$, all of which increases the internal energy of the gas.
In the second test, the energy input is $c_p t$, but out of this an amount
$p v$ is expended in external work; consequently the increase in
internal energy is $c_p t - p v$. Equating these values gives $c_v t = c_p t$
$- pv$, and remembering that the increase in volume is $v = V_o \beta t$
from equation (107), it follows that

$$c_p - c_v = \frac{p v}{t} = p V_o \beta$$

The resulting product $pV_o \beta$ is expressed in § 164 as R times the mass of gas under consideration; consequently, for unit mass

$$c_p - c_v = R \tag{113}$$

all terms being expressed in the same unit. Thus, the difference between the two specified specific heats of a gas is equal to the gas constant R per unit of its mass.

168. Isothermal and Adiabatic Processes. — An expansion or contraction of a gas which occurs without change of temperature is said to be *isothermal*. This process has already been considered in connection with Boyle's Law; the relation between pressure and volume for a perfect gas when kept at constant temperature is shown in Fig. 178 and is given by the expression $p_1 V_1 = p_2 V_2$; or, more simply, the equation of an isothermal process is

$$pV = \text{a constant.} \tag{114}$$

Since expansion is a cooling process, it follows that heat must be supplied to a gas during an isothermal expansion. This action will take place automatically if the gas is allowed to expand slowly while in good thermal contact with some source of heat which is maintained at the temperature of the gas. The cooling tendency during expansion will be offset by a flow of heat from the source into the gas, keeping its temperature constant. Also, since the internal energy of the gas remains constant at constant temperature, the heat supplied during an isothermal expansion must be equivalent to the work done by the gas during expansion. Similarly, during an isothermal compression, heat must be continuously withdrawn from the gas in order to keep the temperature constant, the heat abstracted being equal to the work done in compressing the gas. Since heat must pass into or out of the body of gas during these processes, isothermal changes usually take place somewhat slowly.

When a gas expands or contracts without the transfer of heat to it or from it, the process is called *adiabatic*. Such a process would result if the gas were contained in a cylinder completely surrounded by a perfect heat insulator, so that no heat could enter during expansion or escape during compression. During an adiabatic expansion some of the heat energy of the expanding gas is converted into mechanical work and the temperature of the gas is lowered. Again, during an adiabatic compression the work done upon the gas causes its temperature to rise. Actual expansions and compressions are neither isothermal nor adiabatic, but are intermediate between these processes.

To permit comparison between isothermal and adiabatic processes, an isothermal curve XI and an adiabatic curve XA are drawn on the same pressure-volume diagram in Fig. 184. The two curves start from point X, which represents a certain initial condition of pressure and volume of the gas under consideration. The gas, if expanded adiabatically to some lower pressure p', at point M, will be cooler and will therefore occupy less volume than if heat had been supplied to expand it isothermally to the same

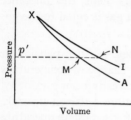

Fig. 184. Isothermal and adiabatic processes compared

pressure at point N. Consequently, the curve representing the adiabatic process is steeper than that for an isothermal process.

A family of isothermal curves I_1, I_2, I_3, and a family of adiabatic curves A_1, A_2, A_3, are shown in Fig. 185. Since an increase of temperature tends to increase both the volume and the pressure of a gas, it is seen that isothermal curves for higher tempera-

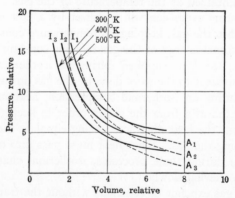

Fig. 185. Families of isothermal and adiabatic curves

tures occupy positions farther from the origin than those for lower temperatures.

The equation of the adiabatic curve can be found by considering an adiabatic expansion to be made up of very small steps, expressing the energy relations over one such step, and summing up the result for the entire curve. The result of carrying out such a procedure yields the following relationship between volume and pressure:

$$pV^\gamma = \text{a constant,} \tag{115}$$

where the symbol γ is used to represent the ratio c_p/c_v.

The numerical value of γ depends upon the molecular structure of the gas. Most of the common gases, such as hydrogen, oxygen, and nitrogen, are *diatomic*; that is, the molecule is composed of two atoms; while the inert gases, such as helium and argon, are chiefly *monatomic*, the molecule consisting of a single atom. It can be shown theoretically that for diatomic gases $\gamma = 1.40$ and for monatomic gases, $\gamma = 1.66$. For air, which is largely composed of diatomic gases, $\gamma = 1.40$.

169. Liquefaction of Gases. — Essentially a liquid differs from a gas in that its molecules are closer together; it is natural, then,

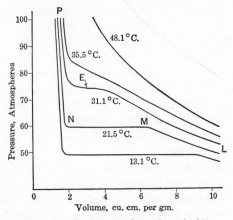

Fig. 186. Isothermals for carbon dioxide

that in attempting to liquefy a gas, the gas should be subjected to low temperature and high pressure, both of which cause it to contract. The behavior of a gas as it approaches liquefaction can be studied by investigating the relation between its pressure and its volume as the temperature is held at lower and lower values. Such a series of tests was conducted on carbon dioxide by Thomas Andrews (1813–1885), Irish chemist and physicist, with results as plotted in Fig. 186.

In one test, the tube containing the carbon dioxide was maintained at a constant temperature of 48.1° C. while the volume of the gas was reduced from a large to a small value; during this process the pressure increased approximately in accordance with Boyle's Law, as shown by the uppermost curve in the figure. A similar test at a lower temperature, 35.5° C., showed a noticeable departure from Boyle's Law. For tests at still lower temperatures, the departure became more marked, and the curve for the test at 31.1° C. shows a definite point of inflection at E. The curve for any temperature below this value exhibits a horizontal portion, signifying the presence of liquid as well as vapor, as described in § 150. In this temperature region, a curve such as $LMNP$ shows that as the volume of the gas is reduced the pressure at first increases (LM), much as for a perfect gas; next the point of saturation is reached and liquid begins to form (M); a further reduction in volume causes more and more of the vapor to liquefy, the pressure remaining constant (MN); eventually the liquefaction is complete (N); and from this point on a great pressure (NP) is required to produce a small change in volume. The point E is called the critical point, and the corresponding properties of the substance under test are referred to as the critical values.

The *critical temperature* is that temperature above which a gas cannot be liquefied, no matter how much pressure is applied; for carbon dioxide it has the value 31.1° C. The *critical pressure* is the absolute pressure (of gas and liquid) at the critical temperature. The *critical volume* is the volume of gas at the critical temperature and pressure which at 0° C. and 76.0 cm. of mercury would have unit volume.

An experiment on critical temperature may be conducted using some liquid carbon dioxide sealed in an evacuated tube, the tube having heavy glass walls which will withstand high pressures and still allow the interior to be seen. At room temperature the liquid will rest at the bottom of the tube and the space above it will be filled with saturated vapor. As the tube is heated, the liquid will expand and its density will decrease, while that of the vapor will increase. If the amount of liquid used is in the proper proportion to the volume of the tube, the critical point will be passed through when the temperature reaches 31.1° C. At this point the line of demarcation between the liquid and vapor will disappear and the tube will present a uniform appearance throughout. The liquid and vapor then have the same density; and the two states cannot be differentiated.

All gases show the same general behavior with reference to liquefaction as has just been described for carbon dioxide. The values of critical temperature, pressure, and volume, are, however, quite different for different substances, as tabulated below:

Critical Values

	Temperature	Pressure in atmospheres	Volume
Air......................	$-140°$ C.	39	0.0047
Alcohol (ethyl)............	243	62.7	0.0071
Ammonia.................	130	115	0.0048
Carbon dioxide............	31.1	73	0.0066
Helium..................	-268	2.3	0.0030
Hydrogen................	-239.9	12.8	0.00264
Methane.................	-82	46	0.0049
Oxygen..................	-118	50	0.00426
Sulfur dioxide............	155.4	79	0.0075
Water...................	365	195	0.00386

★170. Behavior of Actual Gases; Van der Waals' Equation. — It has long been recognized that Boyle's Law, although used as a criterion for a perfect gas, is not followed exactly, even by the so-called fixed gases; and the curves in Fig. 186 show how widely a gas departs from this law as it approaches the liquid state. Numerous attempts have been made to formulate an expression which would agree more closely with the facts of experiment; one of these is due to the Dutch physicist, Johannes D. van der Waals (1837–1923). He considered that in an actual gas the attraction of the molecules for one another, which is ignored in the concept of a perfect gas, would be equivalent to a slight increase in the pressure applied to the gas. Any given molecule is affected by a number of others within its sphere of action, and this number will be proportional to the density of the gas. Further, for a given amount of gas, the number of molecules affected will also be proportional to the density. Hence the correction should be proportional to the square of the density or inversely proportional to the square of the volume V. For this reason van der Waals replaced the pressure p in Boyle's Law by a term $\left(p + \dfrac{a}{V^2}\right)$. He also considered that the volume, which is to be regarded as the volume into which the gas can expand, would be reduced in an actual gas because of the space occupied by the molecules themselves, and should be replaced by a smaller term $(V - b)$. Making these corrections to Boyle's Law, the following relationship is established between the absolute pressure p and the volume V of a mass of actual gas at constant temperature:

$$\left(p + \frac{a}{V^2}\right)(V - b) = \text{a constant,} \tag{116}$$

where a and b are constants which can be evaluated for various gases. For large values of p and V the corrections have but little effect, and the equation is represented by a curve which is nearly hyperbolic. For smaller values of p and V, the curve takes the form shown by the full line in Fig. 187. It conforms almost perfectly to the experimental curve *LMNP* of Fig. 186 except that the horizontal portion is replaced by a sinuous line.

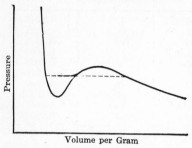

FIG. 187. Graph of van der Waals' equation

The relation between pressure and volume may therefore be found by van der Waals' equation for either the gaseous or the liquid state of a substance, and the transitional region in which the equation does not apply, is known to be one of constant pressure.

It can be shown for a fluid which satisfies van der Waals' equation that the values of critical temperature, pressure, and volume are given respectively by

$$T_c = \frac{8a}{27br}, \ p_c = \frac{a}{27b^2}, \ \text{and} \ V_c = 3b$$

in terms of the constants a and b of equation (116)

171. Atmospheric Humidity. — As a result of evaporation, the atmosphere always contains some moisture in the form of water vapor. This moisture does not consist of tiny particles of liquid held in suspension in the air, but is an invisible vapor as truly gaseous as the air with which it mixes. The weight of water vapor contained in a unit of volume is known as the *absolute humidity*, and is usually expressed in grains per cubic foot (15.432 grains = 1 gm.) or in pounds per cubic foot.

Since the atmosphere is a mixture of dry air and water vapor, the total atmospheric pressure p has two components: the partial pressure due to dry air, p_a, and the partial pressure due to the water vapor, p_w; in accordance with Dalton's Law [§ 129],

$$p = p_a + p_w \tag{117}$$

Water evaporates into the atmosphere until the partial pressure due to the vapor is equal to the saturated vapor pressure of water at the existing temperature [§ 150]; at 20° C., for instance, evaporation will continue until $p_w = 1.75$ cm. of mercury. At this point the atmosphere is *saturated*; that is, it contains all of the water vapor possible at that temperature, and evaporation ceases. Such a condition is uncomfortable in warm weather because perspiration cannot evaporate and the desired cooling effect is absent. The pressure of water vapor at saturation can be read for various temperatures from the curve in Fig. 173, but in the calculation of atmospheric humidity it is more convenient to use pressures in inches of mercury and temperatures in degrees fahrenheit. A similar curve in which these units are used is given for the lower temperature range in Fig. 188, the data from which it is plotted being listed in the first two columns of the following table. The absolute humidity at saturation and the heat of vaporization are also stated at the various temperatures.

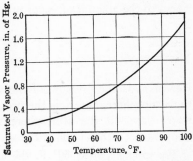

FIG. 188. Pressure of saturated water vapor

Water Vapor

Temperature, °F.	Pressure of saturated vapor, in. of Hg	Weight of saturated vapor, grains per cu. ft.	Heat of vaporization, B.t.u. per lb.
0	0.0375	0.472	
10	0.0628	0.772	
20	0.1027	1.237	
30	0.1646	1.943	
35	0.2036	2.380	1076
40	0.2478	2.868	1073
45	0.3003	3.442	1070
50	0.3624	4.113	1067
55	0.4356	4.895	1064
60	0.521	5.80	1061
65	0.621	6.86	1058
70	0.739	8.07	1055
75	0.874	9.46	1052
80	1.031	11.06	1049
85	1.212	12.89	1046
90	1.421	14.96	1043
95	1.659	17.32	1040
100	1.931	19.98	1037

Usually, the atmosphere does not contain the full amount of water vapor which would produce saturation. The ratio between the amount of water vapor actually present and the amount necessary to produce saturation at the existing temperature is called the *relative humidity*; in equation form, this ratio becomes

$$\text{Relative humidity} = \frac{\text{amount of water vapor present}}{\text{amount of water vapor for saturation}} \quad (118)$$

this ratio is usually multiplied by 100 and expressed as a percentage. The relative humidity can also be expressed in terms of pressure, since the pressure due to the vapor is approximately proportional to the amount of vapor present; thus, the relative humidity is

$$h = \frac{p_w}{p_s} \times 100 \quad (119)$$

Herein p_w is the pressure of the water vapor actually present in the atmosphere, and p_s is the pressure which would be exerted by water vapor if the atmosphere were saturated at the existing temperature; that is, p_s is the saturated vapor pressure of water.

For example, if at 60° F. the atmosphere contained 3.442 grains of water vapor per cu. ft., then the relative humidity would be $h = (3.442/5.80) \times 100 = 59$ per cent. Or, using the corresponding pressures, $h = (0.3003/0.521) \times 100 = 58$ per cent, a result which agrees sufficiently with the foregoing.

With a given moisture content, if the temperature of the atmosphere rises, the relative humidity will be lowered, because the saturated vapor pressure has higher values; thus, the atmosphere feels drier, although the amount of water vapor remains the same. On the other hand, a fall of temperature increases the relative humidity for the same moisture content. If the temperature falls to a sufficiently low value the atmosphere becomes saturated and the vapor begins to condense, forming dew; accordingly, this value of the temperature is called the *dew point*. Condensed vapor suspended in the air is familiar to the observer as fog when at the surface of the earth, and as a cloud when it is at greater altitudes. Upon further cooling the water particles grow in size as more and more moisture condenses on the nuclei, and the drops so formed fall to the earth as rain. Condensation of water vapor at temperatures below the freezing point forms frost and snow.

The dew point of the air can be measured by cooling a very small portion of it so that it will become saturated, and observing the temperature at which condensation occurs. The device for making the measurement is called a condensing hygrometer; it consists primarily of a glass plate so arranged that one face can be cooled either by circulating cold water or by evaporating ether until dew is observed to form on the other face that is exposed to the atmosphere. The corresponding temperature of the air, which is assumed to be the same as that of the plate in contact with it, is the dew point.

The relative humidity of the atmosphere can be calculated from a knowledge of the dew point and a reference to a vapor pressure curve like Fig. 188. The pressures read from this curve at the temperature of the dew point and of the air under test are called p_w and p_s respectively, and their ratio gives the relative humidity according to equation (119).

The relative humidity can be determined experimentally with a psychrometer which consists of two suitably-mounted thermometers; one has its bulb exposed to the atmosphere (dry bulb) and the other is wrapped with muslin and kept moist with water (wet bulb). The dryer the atmosphere, the more rapid will be the evaporation of water from the muslin, and the lower will be the reading of the wet-bulb thermometer. Tables are available which give the percentage humidity in terms of the dry-bulb reading and the depression of the wet-bulb temperature.

The humidity of the atmosphere can also be measured conveniently, but only roughly, with the hair hygrometer. This instrument depends for its action upon the absorption of moisture by a hair (or by a strip of other hygroscopic substance) and upon the change of its length brought about by this absorption. A pointer moves across a dial as the length changes and indicates the condition of the atmosphere as moist, dry, and very dry.

*172. Air Conditioning. — The treatment of the atmosphere within rooms or buildings to control its temperature, moisture content, purity, and circulation, is called air conditioning. Its purpose is to provide air conditions that are conducive to human comfort and health, or that are best suited to the processing or manufacture of certain products. Air conditioning involves the use of apparatus for heating or cooling the atmosphere and for supplying or removing moisture. The process of supplying moisture is termed *humidification* and that of removing moisture is termed *dehumidification*. In addition, blowers or ventilating fans are needed for circulating the air. The various air conditioning equipments differ in the type of apparatus used for the different functions and in the methods used to achieve automatic control of temperature and moisture.

To find the amount of water needed to bring the humidity of the air to any desired value, use is made of the General Gas Law to express the weight of water vapor in terms of the partial pressures of water vapor and air. Applying equation (110) that expresses this law, and introducing density $d = M/V$, the gas constant becomes

$$R = \frac{p}{Td} \qquad (120)$$

and for convenience the pressure p will be reckoned in inches of mercury, the absolute temperature T in degrees fahrenheit, and the density d in pounds per cubic foot.   Taking the density of dry air at 32° F. and atmospheric pressure (30 in. of mercury) as 0.081 lb./ft.³, the gas constant for dry air becomes

$$R_a = 30 \div [(459 + 32) \times 0.081] = 0.754.$$

Similarly, taking the density of saturated water vapor at the normal boiling point (212° F.) and under atmospheric pressure as 0.037 lb./ft.³, the gas constant for water vapor becomes

$$R_w = 30 \div [(459 + 212) \times 0.037] = 1.21.$$

Herefrom the masses of dry air and of saturated water vapor per cubic foot at any temperature $t°$ F. will be

$$M_a = \frac{p_a}{0.754\ (459 + t)}$$

$$M_w = \frac{p_w}{1.21\ (459 + t)}$$

Consequently, the weight of water vapor in pounds mixed with one pound of dry air is

$$M = \frac{\dfrac{p_w}{1.21\ (459 + t)}}{\dfrac{p_a}{0.754\ (459 + t)}} = 0.622\ \frac{p_w}{p_a}$$

where p_a and p_w are the partial pressures due respectively to dry air and water vapor expressed in inches of mercury, and t is the temperature in degrees fahrenheit.

As an illustration, consider that air is to be maintained at 65° F. with a relative humidity of 50 per cent at a time when the external atmosphere is at 20° F. with a relative humidity of 70 per cent, the barometric pressure being 29.85 in. of mercury. Using the table of saturated vapor pressures in the preceding section, the actual vapor pressures are found to be $p_w = 0.50 \times 0.621 = 0.311$ for the conditioned air, and $p_w = 0.70 \times 0.1027 = 0.072$ for the external air, both expressed in inches of mercury. Hence, the weight of water vapor per pound of dry air in the conditioned air should be $\dfrac{0.622 \times 0.311}{29.85 - 0.311} = 0.00655$ lb., and in the external air is $\dfrac{0.622 \times 0.072}{29.85 - 0.072} = 0.00150$ lb.; consequently the amount of water vapor to be supplied is 0.00505 lb. per lb. of dry air.

The amount of heat to be furnished to or removed from the atmosphere in conditioning it can be calculated by the methods used in Chapter XVI.

To determine the heat required per pound of air for conditioning the atmosphere in the preceding problem, assuming the intake water to be at 50° F., take the specific heats at constant pressure to be 0.24 for dry air and 0.45 (average) for water vapor, and the heat of vaporization of water at 65° F. to be 1058 B.t.u. per lb., and proceed as follows:

To heat the dry air $= 0.24 \times 1 \times (65 - 20)$ $= 10.80$ B.t.u.
To heat the water vapor $= 0.45 \times 0.00150 \times (65 - 20) =$ .03   "
To heat the added water $= 0.00505[(65 - 50) + 1058]$ $= 5.42$ "

Total heat required per pound of dry air $= 16.25$ "

Humidification may be accomplished by injecting steam or water mist into the air, by mixing with it air of higher absolute humidity, and by evaporation from water in pans, wicks or sprays. Dehumidification may be effected by absorption of moisture by anhydrous solids such as silica gel, by condensation on refrigerated surfaces or into water sprays, or by adding dry air. In many installations air to be conditioned is drawn by fans through a chamber in which a number of spray nozzles discharge water to form a sheet through which the air must flow. The desired humidity is obtained by supplying heat to or abstracting heat from the air, or water spray, or both. The sprays also serve to "wash" the air, that is, to free it from dust.

Much experimentation has been carried out to determine the dependence of human comfort and physiological efficiency upon the temperature, humidity and air motion of the atmosphere. A composite index of these three elements is termed "effective temperature" and serves as an arbitrary measure of the warmth or cold experienced by the body. Its numerical value for a particular air condition expresses the temperature of saturated air which at a velocity of 15 to 25 ft. per min. induces a temperature sensation like that of the given condition. For example, an air condition is said to have an "effective temperature" of 70, when in practically still air it induces a sensation of warmth like that felt by the body in air at 70° F. saturated with water vapor and moving at the speed stated. Laboratory tests show that the average comfort zone has an "effective temperature" ranging from 63 to 75 depending upon the amount of clothing worn and upon the rate of working; mean values are 66 for winter and 71 for summer.

PROBLEMS

1. A hand pump with a cylinder 14 in. long is being used to pump air into a tire in which the gage pressure is 20 lb. per sq. in. at the beginning of the stroke. Assuming the temperature to remain constant, how far must the piston be pushed down before air can enter the tire?

2. A tank of compressed air has a volume of 5 cu. ft. and its pressure gage indicates a pressure of 350 lb. per sq. in. If the valve on the tank is opened until the gage reading goes down to 250 lb. per sq. in., how many cubic feet of air, reckoned at atmospheric pressure, will escape from the tank? Assume that the temperature remains constant.

3. When the piston of a pump is completely pushed in, there remains between it and the cylinder head a certain so-called dead space [§ 135]. Solve Problem 1, assuming that this dead space together with the tube which extends to the tire has a volume of 1 cu. in., and that the piston has a diameter of $1\frac{1}{4}$ in.

4. A tank of compressed air has a volume of 10 cu. ft. and its pressure gage indicates 200 lb. per sq. in. What volume would this air occupy at atmospheric pressure, if its temperature remained unchanged?

5 Some hydrogen which occupies 80 cu. cm. at 15° C. is heated at constant pressure to 40° C. What volume will it then occupy?

6. An automobile tire can just withstand a gage pressure of 65 lb. per sq. in. The tire has a constant volume of 1335 cu. in. and is pumped up to a gage pressure of 30 lb. per sq. in. at 20° C. If the temperature of the tire were then raised, at what temperature would it burst?

7. A steel tank contains compressed air at a gage pressure of 100 lb. per sq. in. when the temperature is 20° C. Find the pressure which would be developed if the tank were subjected to a temperature of 1500° C. in a fire. Neglect the expansion of the tank.

8. If a gas has a volume of 3 cu. ft. at a gage pressure of 100 cm. of mercury and at a temperature of 60° F., what volume will it occupy when the gage pressure is doubled and the temperature is raised to 200° F.?

9. Taking the volume of an automobile tire to be constant at 25 liters what volume of air at 14.7 lb. per sq. in. and 20° C. must be pumped into the tire to increase the pressure gage reading from 25 lb. per sq. in. to 35 lb. per sq. in.? Assume all the air to be heated 5 centigrade degrees during the process.

10. Compute the weight of air in the tire described in Problem 6. See table in § 131.

11. A 3-liter container of hydrogen under an absolute pressure of 125 gm. per sq. cm. and a 2-liter container of nitrogen under an absolute

pressure of 83 gm. per sq. cm. are connected. (*a*) What is the absolute pressure of the mixture when equilibrium is reached, assuming that the temperature remains constant at 0° C.? (*b*) If the temperature of the mixture is raised to 40° C., what absolute pressure will result?

12. In the 1935 stratosphere flight, 225,000 cu. ft. of helium at atmospheric pressure were admitted to the balloon "Explorer II" while collapsed on the ground at a temperature of −14° C. A portion of this gas was allowed to escape during the $13\frac{3}{4}$-mi. ascent, but sufficient gas was retained to expand the balloon to its full volume of 3,700,000 cu. ft. at the "ceiling." At this point the gas temperature was 0° C. and its pressure (assumed equal to that outside) was 30.1 mm. of mercury. What per cent of gas used was allowed to escape during the ascent?

13. A piston placed in the top of an upright cylinder at 20° C. compresses the air beneath it isothermally and settles to rest at an intermediate position between the top and bottom of the cylinder. To what temperature should the air be heated in order to restore the piston to its initial position? The piston weighs 40 lb., is 6 in. in diameter, and is assumed to operate without leakage or friction.

14. Air under standard atmospheric pressure and at 32° F. has a density of 0.081 lb. per cu. ft. Compute the value of the gas constant for air in British units.

15. If a tank of oxygen having a volume of 3 cu. ft. shows a gage pressure of 60 lb. per sq. in. at a temperature of 80° F., how many pounds of oxygen does the tank contain?

16. A metal cylinder has a volume of 5 cu. ft. Find the gage pressure in this cylinder after 6 lb. of oxygen have been compressed into it at a temperature of 25° C.

17. Heat is applied to some air as indicated in Fig. 179, the pressure remaining constant at 1 atmosphere. How much external work does the gas do while its temperature is being raised from 0° to 5° C., if it occupies a volume of 2 liters at the lower temperature?

18. A certain gas, having a density of 0.00125 gm. per cu. cm. under a pressure of 1 atmosphere and at a temperature of 0° C., occupies a volume of 8 liters under these conditions. If 30 cal. are required to raise the temperature of this gas to 15° C. at constant pressure, find the specific heat of the gas at constant pressure and also that at constant volume.

19. What volume does 1 gm. of air occupy at 0° C. and 76 cm. of mercury? Find the volume of this air when compressed isothermally to twice this pressure, and to three times this pressure. Repeat such computations for adiabatic compression using logarithms in the calculation. Plot the isothermal and adiabatic curves to scale for these compressions.

20. A liter of oxygen at normal atmospheric pressure is compressed to a volume of 500 cu. cm. Find the resulting absolute pressure of the gas (*a*) if the compression is isothermal, and (*b*) if the compression is adiabatic.

21. Find the relative humidity for a day when the temperature is 70° F. and the dew point is 50° F.

22. For a day when the temperature is 70° F., the relative humidity 60 per cent, and the barometer reading 77 cm. of mercury, find what portion of the atmospheric pressure is due to dry air.

*23. It is desired to cool air at 80° F. and 60 per cent humidity to 55° F. with the same relative humidity. Assuming atmospheric pressure to be 30.10 in. of mercury, find the weight of vapor which will condense on cooling one pound of the air, and the quantity of heat to be removed if the condensate is ejected at 55° F.

CHAPTER XVIII

WORK AND HEAT

173. Laws of Thermodynamics. — The recognition of heat as a form of energy implies that transformations involving heat obey the principle of energy conservation. Thus, heat can be transformed into mechanical work or mechanical work into heat, and while some energy may be wasted in such transformations, none will be destroyed.

The science of thermodynamics is based upon two laws, the first of which deals with energy transformations, and follows at once from the foregoing considerations. The *First Law* may be stated as follows:

Whenever heat energy is transformed into any other kind of energy, or vice versa, the quantity of energy which disappears in one form is exactly equivalent to the quantity which is produced in the other form.

The second of these laws deals with the direction in which a transformation will take place. It has been expressed in many forms and its full significance involves the study of thermodynamics. For present purposes, the following statement of the *Second Law* will suffice:

Heat does not pass from one place to another place that has a higher temperature unless work is done to accomplish this result. Heat naturally flows down a "temperature hill," so to speak, but work must be expended to take it up that hill. In a steam engine, heat flows from a high-temperature boiler to a low-temperature exhaust and does work in the process. In keeping a room cool by refrigeration, on the other hand, heat is transferred from that room to a place of higher temperature outside, but work must be done to effect the transfer.

174. Transformation of Work into Heat. — Every observer is familiar with the production of heat from other forms of energy; heat is produced from mechanical energy in an automobile brake, from electrical energy in an electric heater, and from chemical

298

energy in many reactions. Heat is also produced as a by-product in most energy transformations, and in many of these much is wasted.

The numerical relation between heat and mechanical energy, which is implied in the first law of thermodynamics, was determined about 1845 by Joule, using several independent methods. In one of these a paddle wheel was placed in a vessel containing a known amount of water and was rotated by means of descending weights. The work done in turning the paddle wheel could be readily measured; this work was converted to heat by friction in stirring the liquid, and caused a rise in temperature. By measuring the energy E supplied to the paddle wheel and the heat Q produced in the water, it was found that these quantities varied in direct proportion to each other; their ratio $J = E/Q$ is known as the *mechanical equivalent of heat*. Joule's original results have been slightly modified in subsequent investigations; the accepted values follow:

Relation of Heat to Mechanical Work

Quantity of heat	Equivalent amount of mechanical work
1 cal.	$\begin{cases} 4.186 \times 10^7 \text{ ergs, or} \\ 4.186 \text{ joules} \end{cases}$
1 B.t.u.	778 ft-lb.
0.239 cal.	1 joule

Whenever a specified amount of work is transformed into heat, the quantity of heat produced can be determined at once from the values given above. Thus, the number of heat units corresponding to 2,870,000 ergs, or 0.287 joule, of mechanical work mentioned in § 167 is

$$Q = \frac{E}{J} = \frac{0.287 \text{ joule}}{4.186 \frac{\text{joules}}{\text{cal.}}} = 0.068 \text{ cal.}$$

As an example illustrating the conversion of mechanical energy into heat, consider a 15-ton trolley car moving at 30 mi. per hr. (that is, 44 ft. per sec.) which is brought to rest by the brakes. The kinetic energy of the car, by § 72 , is

$$\frac{Wv^2}{2g} = \frac{30,000 \text{ lb.} \times \left(\frac{44 \text{ ft.}}{\text{sec.}}\right)^2}{2 \times 32 \frac{\text{ft.}}{\text{sec.}^2}} = 908,000 \text{ ft-lb.}$$

This mechanical energy is transformed into 908,000/778 or 1170 B.t.u. of heat.   Supposing half of this heat (585 B.t.u.) to be expended in heating 8 iron brake shoes weighing 30 lb. each, their temperature rise (assumed uniform) would be found by equation (105) to be $t = Q \div mc = 585 \div (8 \times 30 \times 0.11) = 22.2$ fahrenheit degrees, wherein 0.11 is the thermal capacity of iron in B.t.u. per lb. per ° F.

175. Transformation of Heat into Work. — The transformation of heat into mechanical work, which is the reverse of the process just described, is fundamental to the operation of every heat engine.   This type of transformation is usually accomplished by heating a gas and causing it to do work as it expands.

The external work *done by* a gas in expanding by an amount v is given by equation (112) as $E = p\,v$, provided the pressure p stays constant during the expansion.   The same expression can also be used to show how much work must be *done upon* the gas in order to compress it a like amount under the same pressure.

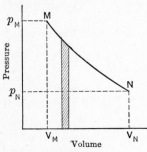

FIG. 189. Work done by expanding gas

Usually, as a gas expands, its pressure becomes lower. Fig. 189 indicates on a pressure-volume diagram the behavior of a gas which expands from M to N, its pressure falling from p_M to p_N as its volume increases from V_M to V_N. Obviously, the pressure of this gas cannot be considered constant, and the work done during expansion cannot be found directly from the expression $E = p\,v$. Such an expansion can be regarded, however, as composed of a number of smaller expansions, one of these being represented in the figure by the shaded strip over which interval the pressure may be assumed constant. The work done in expanding will then be the product of this pressure and the increase in volume. Since this pressure is represented by the height of the shaded strip and the increase in volume is represented by its width, the work done in this elemental expansion will be represented by the shaded area. Considering the entire area beneath the curve to be divided into similar vertical strips, each of which represents the work done during a small expansion, it is apparent that the area under the complete curve, namely MNV_NV_M, represents the work done during the entire process from M to N. In general, if the expansion or compression of a gas is represented as a pressure-volume curve, the area under this curve will represent either the work done by the gas during expansion or the work which must be done upon it during compression. Such an area may be measured with the planimeter, or may be computed by calculus if the equation of the curve is known. The work done, ascertained in these ways, will generally be expressed in mechanical units, such as joules or foot-pounds, but can be converted to heat units as shown in § 174.

When a gas is expanded and is compressed subsequently so as to return exactly to its initial condition, it is said to have completed a *cycle*. Consider a cycle in which the gas, initially in a condition represented by M, Fig. 189, is first heated so as to expand as represented by the curve MN, and is then compressed in exactly the reverse manner, so that the curve is retraced from N to M, completing the cycle. In such a process, the work done by the gas in expanding from M to N is exactly equal to the work done upon it in compressing it from N to M; consequently, over the entire cycle, the net amount of work done is zero. Naturally, there is no object in carrying a gas through a cycle in which the expansion and compression curves coincide. To accomplish a useful purpose, the gas must do more work in expanding than is done upon it during compression. In the ordinary heat engine the average pressure is higher during expansion than during compression, and the cycle is represented by a loop. The area of this loop is a measure of the mechanical work that the engine delivers in return for the heat supplied.

176. The Ideal Engine; Carnot Cycle. — The French physicist, Sadi Carnot (1796–1832), described an *ideal engine*, the efficiency of which cannot be exceeded by any heat engine working within the same temperature limits. This engine and its operating cycle will be explained with the aid of Fig. 190. The engine consists of a cylinder C containing a perfect gas as the working substance, a source of heat at a high temperature T_1, a so-called refrigerator at a lower temperature T_2, and an insulating stand I. The cylinder walls and piston are supposed to be perfect insulators of heat [§ 186]; and the bottom, or head, of the cylinder is a perfect conductor, through which heat will flow when the inside and outside temperatures differ by the slightest amount. The engine is also assumed to operate without friction.

Starting with the cylinder standing upon the source of heat and the piston held at rest near the bottom of the cylinder, the gas at temperature T_1 occupies a small volume at high pressure, as indicated by point A on the diagram. Upon reducing slightly the pressure applied to the piston, the gas is allowed to expand, and a quantity of heat Q_1 flows into it from the source, maintaining the temperature constant. The expansion is represented by the isothermal curve AB. Next, the cylinder is transferred to the insulating stand I and the gas is allowed to expand further. This expansion BC is adiabatic, and the temperature falls until at point C it reaches the value T_2. When the gas reaches this condition,

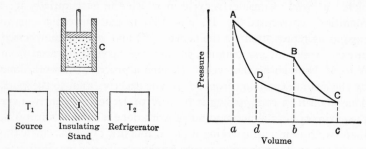

Fig. 190.   Ideal engine and Carnot cycle

the cylinder is placed on the refrigerator and by slightly increasing the pressure on the piston the gas is compressed. The heat generated, Q_2, flows into the refrigerator and the compression CD is isothermal at the lower temperature T_2. At a certain point D the cylinder is again moved to the insulating stand and further work is done on the gas, compressing it adiabatically along DA, thereby completing the Carnot cycle.

Remembering that the mechanical work in any process is measured by the area under the corresponding pressure-volume curve, it is seen that during expansion the gas does an amount of work equivalent to the area $ABba + BCcb = ABCca$, and that during compression the work done upon it is given by the smaller area $CDdc + DAad = CDAac$. The gas, therefore, does more work than is done upon it, and the net work done by the gas during the cycle amounts to $ABCca - CDAac = ABCD$, which is the area of the closed loop.

Summarizing, the ideal engine receives during a cycle an amount of energy Q_1 from the source in the form of heat; of this an amount Q_2 is wasted in the refrigerator, and the balance, which is transformed into mechanical work, is represented by $ABCD$ in mechanical units or $(ABCD)/J$ in heat units. Since friction is assumed absent, the latter amount represents the output of the engine, which is consequently $(ABCD)/J = Q_1 - Q_2$, using heat units for all terms. The efficiency of any device is the ratio of its output to its input; for the ideal cycle this becomes

$$\text{Efficiency} = \frac{(ABCD)}{JQ_1} = \frac{Q_1 - Q_2}{Q_1}$$

and is independent of the working substance used in the engine.

In the ideal engine, work is done by the gas during expansion, and a smaller amount of work is done upon it during compression. It would be possible, theoretically, to store energy during the expansion portion of the cycle and to use part of the energy during the compression portion, the remainder being available to drive an external load. In the actual steam engine this result is accomplished by using a flywheel. In the ideal engine, however, mechanical and thermal difficulties are encountered, so that this engine is to be considered a theoretical ideal to which the actual engine should approach as closely as feasible.

Throughout the Carnot cycle the gas does not depart appreciably from a state of equilibrium. The slightest increase of external pressure during expansion would compress the gas and cause heat to be delivered to the source, and the slightest reduction of pressure during the compression *CD* would allow the gas to expand, removing heat from the refrigerator. It would be possible, therefore, by slight changes of pressure during the cycle, to operate the engine in the reverse manner, abstracting heat from the refrigerator and delivering heat to the source. Under such conditions there would be a net amount of mechanical work done on the gas rather than done by it during the cycle. A cycle which can be reversed in this manner is called a *reversible cycle*. If such a cycle is reversed at any point and returned to its initial state, everything connected with the process is restored exactly to its original condition. In practice, this ideal is never attained, one reason being that friction, which is always present, causes the dissipation of some energy. Actual cycles are thus *irreversible cycles*.

177. Thermodynamic Temperature Scale. — Lord Kelvin used the concept of an ideal engine to establish a theoretical temperature scale which would not depend upon the physical properties of any particular substance. Imagine a series of one hundred ideal engines to be so arranged that the first receives heat at the temperature of boiling water, the last releasing heat at the temperature of melting ice, and each intermediate one having as its source the refrigerator of the one preceding. By assuming, further, that the output of each of these engines is the same, temperatures between the two fixed points may be assigned by considering the difference in temperature between the source and refrigerator of each engine to be the same. If the respective engine outputs are $Q_1 - Q_2 = Q_2 - Q_3 = \cdots$, and the corresponding temperature intervals are $T_1 - T_2 = T_2 - T_3 = \cdots$, then

$$\frac{T_1}{Q_1} = \frac{T_2}{Q_2} = \frac{T_3}{Q_3} = \cdots \cdot \tag{121}$$

The temperature scale constructed in this manner is based solely on thermodynamical principles, and is called the absolute or thermodynamic scale. Absolute zero on this scale is that refrigerator temperature at which the ideal engine would release no heat; its value corresponds to $-273°$ C. The thermodynamic scale is followed very closely by the gas thermometer, and for engineering purposes may be considered identical with the Kelvin or absolute scale described in § 138.

178. Efficiency of the Ideal Engine. — The efficiency of the Carnot cycle, which was shown in § 176 to be $(Q_1 - Q_2)/Q_1$, can be expressed in terms of temperatures, by making use of the proportionality stated in equation (121), whence

$$\text{Carnot Efficiency} = \frac{T_1 - T_2}{T_1} \tag{122}$$

where T_1 and T_2 are the respective *absolute temperatures* of the working substance as received and as released by the engine. Evidently, the efficiency can be increased by raising the temperature at which the working substance is received or lowering the temperature at which it is exhausted. Since the efficiency depends only upon these temperatures, all ideal engines operating between the same temperature limits would have the same efficiency.

Thus, for an engine supplied with saturated steam at an absolute pressure of 100 lb. per sq. in. and exhausting into the atmosphere, the steam table in § 159 gives the supply and exhaust temperatures as 327.8° and 212° F., whence by equation (122), it appears impossible to convert more than $\dfrac{(327.8 + 459) - (212 + 459)}{327.8 + 459} = 0.147$ or 14.7 per cent of the heat energy into mechanical form.

179. Carnot Vapor Cycle. — The Carnot cycle previously described, in which a perfect gas was used as the working substance, does not apply directly to the ordinary engine using saturated steam, owing to the different behavior of these substances [§ 150]. The engine parts are the same as before, Fig. 190, but the cylinder is assumed at the start to contain liquid at the boiling point T_1. This corresponds to point A in

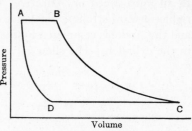

Fig. 191.   Carnot vapor cycle

the Carnot cycle for vapor as represented in Fig. 191.   The addition of a quantity of heat Q_1 from the source causes boiling at constant temperature and under constant pressure, as indicated by line AB; when the vaporization is complete the cylinder is transferred to the insulating stand and adiabatic expansion follows (BC) with lowering of temperature to T_2; the cylinder is then moved to the refrigerator and the volume is reduced at constant pressure (CD), liquefaction taking place meanwhile without change of temperature, and the heat of vaporization Q_2 escaping to the refrigerator; at a certain point D the cylinder is again moved to the insulating stand and further pressure is applied, causing adiabatic compression (DA) and completing the cycle.

This vapor cycle, like the gas cycle previously described, is reversible, and is, moreover, a close approximation to that of the actual steam engine.

180. The Reciprocating Steam Engine. — The reciprocating steam engine, associated with the name of the Scottish engineer, James Watt (1736–1819), utilizes the expansion of steam for the production of mechanical work.   The simple engine, represented in Fig. 192, has a cylinder C with ports A and B, entrance to which is controlled by the slide valve V.   These ports lead either to the steam chest S or to an exhaust pipe entering from the side at E.   The piston P within the cylinder is joined to the cross head H, and thence, through the connecting rod R and crank D, to the main driving shaft of the engine.   Upon this shaft is mounted the flywheel F and also an eccentric G which controls the slide valve.

Steam enters the steam chest under high pressure from a boiler, and, at the instant shown, is admitted through port A to one end of the cylinder; the other end is connected simultaneously through port B to the low-pressure exhaust. The piston is thus subjected to an unbalanced or "effective" pressure which drives it to the right (forward stroke); the valve closes port A at a suitable point and the stroke is completed by the expansion of the steam enclosed in the cylinder. The slide valve next interchanges the port con-

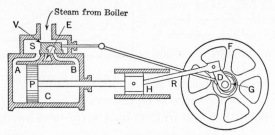

FIG. 192.   A simple steam engine

nections, joining port A to the exhaust and port B to the steam chest. With this position of the valve, the steam drives the piston in the opposite direction (return stroke). This cycle is repeated over and over, the reciprocating motion of the piston being converted to rotary motion of the driving shaft and flywheel.

A diagram showing the relation between the pressure and volume in an engine cylinder throughout a cycle can be obtained by an *indicator*. This device is piped to the cylinder like a pressure gage, and has a tracing point which moves up and down as the pressure changes. The point rests against a card which

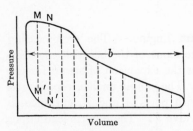

FIG. 193.   Steam-engine indicator card

follows the forward and backward motion of the piston to a reduced scale. The vertical motion of the tracing point combined with the horizontal motion of the card results in a diagram of the form shown in Fig. 193. The student should correlate the different portions of the diagram with the various steps of the actual cycle as described at the beginning of the section, and should also note the similarity between this diagram and that of the Carnot vapor cycle. As before, the area of the indicator card represents that portion of the energy supplied during a cycle which is available for mechanical work.

It will be observed that in the ordinary steam engine the same ports are used alternately to admit the high-temperature steam and to exhaust this steam at a lower temperature after expansion. The repeated heating and cooling of the ports is a wasteful process, and is avoided in a recent development known as the *uniflow* engine. In this engine steam is admitted at the ends of the cylinder and is exhausted at the center, the piston serving as an exhaust valve by covering and uncovering the exhaust ports at the proper times.

181. Internal Combustion Engines. — In the internal combustion engine, fuel is burned directly in the cylinder, and its chemical energy is converted into kinetic energy of the moving piston. This type of engine, as used for automobile propulsion, usually has six or eight cylinders of the form represented in Fig. 194. The water-cooled cylinder C, fitted with mechanically operated valves I and E, and with a spark plug A, encloses a piston P which is connected by a piston rod to the crank shaft S. The fuel used is gasoline, which is atomized and mixed with air in a carburetor so as to form an explosive mixture.

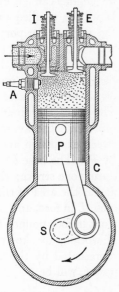

FIG. 194. Internal combustion engine

The complete cycle consists of four strokes. The figure shows the piston starting downward on the first stroke; the inlet valve I is open and a charge of fresh fuel is drawn in through it from the carburetor. When the piston has reached the bottom of its stroke and starts back, the inlet valve closes and the piston compresses the charge in the upper part of the cylinder. As the piston reaches the end of its upward stroke, the compressed charge is ignited by an electric spark at the points of the spark plug A. The resulting explosion drives the piston downward during the next, or working, stroke. On the return upward stroke of the piston, the exhaust valve E opens and the piston forces the burned gases out through the exhaust pipe, leaving the cylinder ready for the beginning of a new cycle. At each explosion, the heat of combustion of the gasoline consumed [§ 160] is liberated and this energy is partially converted into mechanical work.

The Diesel engine, invented by the German engineer, Rudolph Diesel (1858–1913), uses fuel oil and no spark plugs. Air is drawn into the cylinder and is highly compressed, thus raising it to a high temperature. A charge of fuel oil is then sprayed into the cylinder under high pressure, and ignites spontaneously as it mixes with the hot compressed air. Burning takes place without explosion, and the fuel supply is so regulated that the pressure remains almost constant during combustion.

182. Engine Horsepower and Efficiency. — The horsepower of an engine can be obtained quite easily from its indicator card. It will be recalled that of the heat energy supplied each cycle to the engine, the portion which becomes available for mechanical work is represented by the area of its indicator diagram. Since the area of any figure is the product of its average height and its base, for an indicator diagram as in Fig. 193 the area is the average of all the ordinates MM', NN', etc. multiplied by the base b. The average ordinate is known as the *mean effective pressure*, and represents the average difference in pressure in the cylinder between expansion and compression; this value will be represented by P. The base b represents the volume swept out by the piston during one stroke; that is, $b = LA$, where L is the length of stroke and A the area of the piston. Expressing P in pounds per square inch, L in feet, and A in square inches, the product PLA gives the work in foot-pounds for each working stroke. Supposing there are N working strokes per minute, the horsepower of the engine as represented by the indicator card, known as the *indicated* horsepower, will be

$$\text{i.hp.} = \frac{PLAN}{33,000} \tag{123}$$

In practical testing, the mean effective pressure P is calculated from the indicator card, and the remaining quantities are obtained by direct measurement.

The actual engine may be regarded as a heat engine combined with a mechanical engine. As a heat engine, the input is the heat absorbed from the source, which per unit time may be expressed in horsepower, and the output is the indicated horsepower. The ratio of this output to the input is known as the *indicated thermal efficiency*, and will be less than the efficiency of an ideal engine operating over the same temperature range.

Considering the engine as a mechanical device [§ 79], the input is the indicated horsepower, and the output is the horsepower as measured by a brake, called the brake horsepower (b.hp.). Hence,

$$\text{Mechanical efficiency} = \frac{\text{b.hp.}}{\text{i.hp.}}$$

For the purpose of assigning horsepower ratings to automobile engines, standard conditions have been adopted that are equivalent to the following: a mean effective pressure of 67.2 lb. per sq. in., and an average piston speed of 1000 ft. per min. In the automobile engine [§ 181] the piston travels $4L$ ft. for each working stroke, consequently, $4LN = 1000$. Using these values, equation (123) yields the rated horsepower per cylinder as

$$\text{hp.} = \frac{PLAN}{33{,}000} = \frac{67.2 \times \dfrac{1000}{4} \times \dfrac{\pi d^2}{4}}{33{,}000} = \frac{d^2}{2.5}$$

where d is the piston diameter in inches. For an automobile engine having C cylinders, the rating is

$$\text{hp.} = \frac{d^2 C}{2.5} \tag{124}$$

183. The Steam Turbine. — The steam turbine utilizes the kinetic energy of a jet of steam, rather than the expansion of a vapor as in the cylinder of a reciprocating engine. High-velocity jets are formed by passing the steam through a set of fixed nozzles; these jets impinge against a series of curved vanes or blades evenly spaced around the rim of a rotary disk and set the disk into rapid motion. Typical turbine construction is shown in Fig. 195.

The energy of the steam jets cannot be absorbed by a single row of blades without involving excessive speeds. In the arrangement shown,

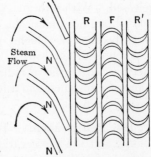

Fig. 195. Arrangement of blades in a turbine

the steam issues from the fixed nozzles NN, and after passing one row of rotating blades R, strikes a corresponding row of fixed blades F, and is redirected against a second row of rotating blades R' mounted on the same rotor. In a turbine having several *stages*, the rotor consists of a number of disks with blades, mounted on the same shaft, and the disks are separated by stationary diaphragms so that each disk is housed in a separate compartment within the casing.

The theoretical output developed by a turbine is equal to the reduction in kinetic energy of the steam in passing through the machine. Suppose that in t sec. W lb. of steam are supplied to the blades at a velocity v_1 ft. per sec. and are discharged at a velocity v_2 ft. per sec. The reduction in energy, by equation (50), is $\dfrac{Wv_1^2}{2g} - \dfrac{Wv_2^2}{2g}$ ft-lb., and this represents the theoretical energy output of the turbine. The corresponding *power output* in foot-pounds per second is consequently

$$P = \frac{W}{2gt}(v_1^2 - v_2^2)$$

and can be converted to horsepower by dividing by 550.

In some turbines, the blading is so designed that the steam expands, and thus gains speed, while passing through the moving blades. By this means, the blades, upon discharging the steam, experience a reactive force which assists their forward motion.

As suggested in § 178, an improvement in efficiency can be achieved by raising the temperature at which the working substance is received or lowering the temperature at which it is released. With saturated steam, intake temperatures much above 600° F. are not practicable because the corresponding vapor pressures become very high. With mercury, however, the absolute vapor pressure at 850° F. is only about 75 lb. per sq. in. This fact has led to the introduction of mercury as the working substance for turbines, and a few large installations of this type have already been made.

184. Refrigeration. — The manufacture of ice, the cooling of rooms, and the preservation of food in cold-storage spaces, are processes which require apparatus for the production of low temperatures. Heat must be taken away from the articles under refrigeration and delivered to regions at higher temperatures.

The evaporation of a liquid and the expansion of a gas or vapor are known to be processes in which heat is absorbed. These actions can be illustrated in the making of carbon-dioxide snow, by allowing some liquid carbon dioxide at the pressure of its saturated vapor to escape from the containing cylinder through a small opening into the atmosphere. The resulting evaporation and expansion take sufficient heat from the issuing stream to cause the CO_2 to solidify as snow.

In the commercial manufacture of ice, mentioned in § 166, anhydrous ammonia circulates continuously around a closed system, such as represented in Fig. 196. The vapor is compressed in a compressor cylinder P and passes through the coils of a condenser C. In these coils, which are cooled by water, the vapor liquefies and the liquid flows to an expansion valve A at the freezing tank D. Here the liquid vaporizes into an evaporator or brine coil B and is thereafter drawn into the compressor to repeat

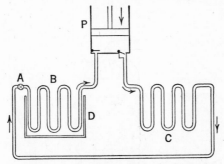

Fig. 196. Compression system of refrigeration

the cycle. The evaporation and expansion which occur at the expansion valve cause the absorption of heat from the brine within the freezing tank, and lower its temperature. Cans filled with water are placed in the brine tank and their contents are frozen. This system may be regarded as a reversed heat engine, operating as described at the end of § 176. The working substance (ammonia vapor) absorbs heat from the refrigerator (freezing tank) and delivers it to the higher-temperature source (condenser), work being done (in driving the compressor) on the vapor during the process.

Household Refrigerators.—The electric refrigerator for household use operates as a compression system, essentially like the ice machine of Fig. 196, but with certain modifications to adapt it to domestic purposes. Sulphur dioxide and ethyl chloride are commonly used as the refrigerants; the evaporator coils are located in the food compartment, and the condenser coils, which

are air cooled, are outside. The compressor is driven by an electric
motor, arranged with a thermostatic switch to start and stop as
needed.

The gas refrigerator for household use receives its energy from
a small gas flame and has no mechanical moving parts. The
principles of operation will be explained by reference to Fig. 197.
The refrigerant, ammonia vapor, is originally dissolved in water
in the generator *G*, but is driven off as a vapor by heat from the
flame, and is cooled and condensed at the condenser *C* into pure
ammonia liquid. The liquid trickles into the evaporator *E*, which

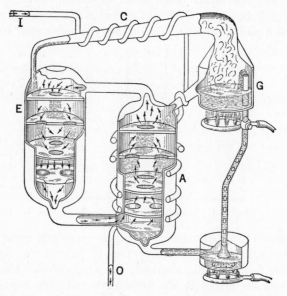

Fig. 197. Electrolux gas refrigerator

is located in the food compartment, a large amount of hydrogen
entering the evaporator at the same time. Here the liquid
evaporates, producing the desired refrigeration, and the vapor and
hydrogen sink to the bottom and pass together to the absorber *A*.
There the ammonia vapor is absorbed in a water solution, thus
freeing the hydrogen, which rises again to the evaporator. The
solution in *A*, having absorbed the ammonia, is returned to the
generator and the process begins over again. The operation of
the refrigerator involves only a slow motion of liquids and gases in
various parts of the enclosure.

The hydrogen, which is confined to the absorber-evaporator system during operation, plays an important part in the refrigeration process. The pressure within the enclosure is fairly high because of the large amount of hydrogen present, and is substantially uniform throughout, as evidenced by the fact that the liquids and gases move about slowly. In the condenser, the pressure is due only to ammonia vapor, and is sufficiently high to produce condensation. In the evaporator, the pressure is made up chiefly of the partial pressure of the hydrogen, and to a much smaller extent of the partial pressure of the ammonia vapor, in accordance with Dalton's Law. The partial pressure of the ammonia vapor is sufficiently low to cause the liquid ammonia to evaporate [§ 150] even at the low temperature of the evaporator, and in so doing it extracts heat from its surroundings.

The gas flame performs two functions; it drives off the ammonia vapor from the solution in the generator as described, and it also serves to return the solution from the absorber to the generator. This latter result is attained by raising a column of liquid and gas somewhat as in a coffee percolator. In the apparatus described, the condenser and absorber are cooled by a stream of water which enters at the inlet *I* and leaves at the outlet *O*. In a more recent type air is used as the cooling medium instead of water.

Liquefaction of Gases.—The cooling due to expansion is utilized in the liquefaction of gases. For the so-called fixed gases, however, the critical temperatures are too low to be attained by simple expansion, and this fact makes it necessary to resort to some cumulative cooling action. This procedure was perfected by Karl R. von Linde (1842–1934), German technologist. In liquefying air by this process, the air is compressed to about 200 atmospheres, next cooled by means of a freezing mixture, and then passed through a long tube from the end of which it is allowed to expand to a pressure of about 15 atmospheres. The air is appreciably cooled by this expansion, and is then allowed to expand again, this time to atmospheric pressure, which results in a further lowering of its temperature. Some of the air which has been cooled by each expansion circulates around the tube from which it issued, in order to cool the air stream before expansion cools it further. Thus, as the system operates, the cooling action is progressively intensified, and finally the temperature is lowered sufficiently to cause a small portion of the air to liquefy as it leaves the tube. The liquid air is collected in large containers resembling thermos bottles so that it can be transported to places where extremely low temperatures are desired.

By somewhat similar processes it has been possible to liquefy all known gases. Helium presented the greatest difficulty in liquefaction, but was eventually liquefied in 1908 at −268° C. by the Dutch physicist, H. Kamerlingh Onnes (1853–1926). By evaporating liquid helium, lower and lower temperatures have been attained by many investigators; the lowest temperature reached is only a small fraction of one degree above the absolute zero, −273.1° C. These low temperatures can be measured by changes in the magnetic properties of certain salts. [§ 270].

PROBLEMS

1. A paddle is used to stir 2 gallons of water, and 0.3 hp. is supplied to it continuously. Assuming that the water receives the entire energy supply, calculate its temperature rise in 30 min.

2. Knowing that 4.186 joules are equivalent to 1 cal., show that 778 ft-lb. are equivalent to 1 B.t.u.

3. A glass tube 1 meter long, closed at the ends, contains 250 gm. of lead shot, the remainder of the tube being filled with 1 liter of water. The tube is held vertically and then inverted, causing the shot to fall the entire length of the tube. How many times must this action be repeated to produce a temperature rise of 1° C.? Neglect the heat supplied to the glass.

4. A brake shoe exerts a frictional force of 18 lb. on the rim of a wheel 3 ft. in diameter, bringing it to rest after 21.4 rev. Find the heat generated.

5. How many kilowatt-hours are required to melt 1 ton of copper at its melting point of 1975° F.?

6. A motor delivers 10 hp. continuously for 8 hr. at an efficiency of 85 per cent. Calculate the quantity of heat wasted in the machine during this time.

7. A blunt drill is used in attempting to bore a hole in a 500-gm. block of iron initially at 20° C. The drill is rotated 5000 times, the average torque exerted upon it being 5,000,000 dyne-cm. If the iron block receives $\frac{3}{4}$ of the mechanical energy supplied, find its resulting temperature.

8. Steam is supplied to a large turbine at a temperature of 910° F. and is exhausted at a temperature of 540° F. for use with lower pressure prime movers. Determine the maximum theoretical efficiency of the turbine.

9. Find the efficiency of an ideal engine which receives saturated steam from a boiler at an absolute pressure of 500 lb. per sq. in. and exhausts it into the air at a pressure of 1 atmosphere.

10. A turbine operates with saturated mercury vapor from a boiler at 840° F., exhausting into a condenser at 350° F. Find the maximum efficiency possible with an ideal heat engine operating under these conditions.

11. Find the indicated horsepower of a simple steam engine which runs at 120 rev. per min., if the piston has a diameter of 10 in. and a stroke of 14 in., and is subjected to a mean effective pressure of 24 lb. per sq. in.

12. A reciprocating steam engine having a stroke of 6 in. develops 15 hp. at a speed of 480 rev. per min. Assuming a mean effective pressure of 60 lb. per sq. in., calculate the diameter of the piston.

13. An automobile having 6 cylinders of $3\frac{5}{16}$-inch bore runs 18 mi. on 1 gal. of gasoline (specific gravity 0.70), at an average speed of 35 mi. per hr. Assuming an indicated thermal efficiency of 25 per cent, calculate the indicated horsepower of the engine and compare it with the rated horsepower.

14. Calculate the indicated thermal efficiency of a four-cycle gas engine which consumes 24 cu. ft. of gas per indicated horsepower per hour, the gas having a heating value of 540 B.t.u. per cu. ft.

15. A gasoline engine driving a water pump (see Problem 5 of Chapter XII), takes 580 lb. of gasoline in an 8-hr. test at uniform load, while delivering 123 hp. (*a*) What weight of fuel does the engine use per hp-hr. of output? (*b*) If the gasoline has a heat of combustion of 20,000 B.t.u. per lb., what is the thermal efficiency of the engine?

16. What is the overall efficiency of an electric generating station if it develops 1 kw-hr. of energy per pound of coal burned? The heat of combustion of the fuel is 14,000 B.t.u. per lb.

17. How much torque does a 600-hp. airplane engine develop at a speed of 2600 rev. per min.? Assuming the mechanical efficiency of the engine at this speed to be 92 per cent, what is its indicated horsepower?

18. Compute the horsepower rating of the automobile engine referred to in Problem 20 of Chapter I.

CHAPTER XIX

TRANSFER OF HEAT

185. Methods of Heat Transfer. — Heat energy may be transmitted from one place to another in various ways. The method called *conduction* is a point-by-point process in which one part of a body is heated by direct contact with a source of heat, and neighboring parts become heated successively. Thus, if one end of a metal rod is placed in a hot furnace, the heat travels along the rod by conduction. This is commonly explained by considering the molecules of the rod within the furnace to be in violent vibration and these, in bumping against their neighbors, to set the latter into more rapid motion, and so on throughout the rod. The process of conduction is more properly explained on the basis

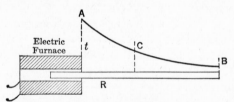

FIG. 198.   Illustrating conduction of heat

of electronic motion.   Good conductors of heat are also good conductors of electricity, and since the conduction of electricity is explained by a drift of the free electrons that are present in such conductors, it is rational to ascribe heat conduction primarily to the mobility of the free electrons. The electron theory will be discussed more fully in connection with the subject of electricity.

Heat will flow between any two points on the rod if there is a difference in temperature between them; consequently the temperature along the rod must be lower at points more remote from the heated end. This is shown in Fig. 198 where a rod *R*, stuck partially into an electric furnace, serves as the base of the temperature graph *ACB*. The difference in temperature between two points on the rod that are close together, divided by the distance between these points, is called the *temperature gradient* at that particular place. If at some place along the rod there is a temperature difference of 0.6 C. degree between points 0.5 cm. apart, then the temperature gradient there is 0.6 ÷ 0.5 = 1.2° C. per cm. The gradient at point A where the temperature is t is greater than that at C since the slope diminishes in approaching the end of the rod B.

The method of heat transfer called *convection* involves a bodily movement of the material heated and applies to mobile substances, that is, to liquids and gases. The motion is brought about by changes of density that accompany the heating process. Water in a kettle on the kitchen stove is heated by convection, as is also the air in a room from a hot stove. The ordinary water heater, Fig. 199, comprising a tank, a heating coil C, and the connecting pipes A and B, forms a circulating system, all being filled with water. When the water in coil C is heated by the gas flame, it becomes less dense and rises, entering the tank through pipe B; meanwhile cold water from the bottom of the tank enters the coil through pipe A. This process continues and all the water in the tank becomes heated by circulation or convection.

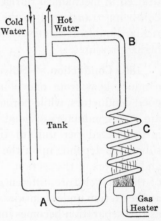

FIG. 199.   Illustrating convection of heat

The transfer of heat by radiant energy is called *radiation*. The process involves the conversion of heat energy into radiant form at the heater, and the reversion of radiant energy into heat wherever the radiation is absorbed. The electric radiator is an appliance operating on this principle, which has a heating element mounted at the focus of a parabolic reflector. When heated by an electric current, the element emits not only "light waves" that stimulate the eye, but also "heat waves" which do not. When waves of either kind are absorbed by a body, they are converted into heat and produce the various effects mentioned in Chapter XIV. The purpose of the reflector is to concentrate the heat waves into a beam, just as a searchlight reflector concentrates light waves into a beam, so that the intensity of radiation will not diminish rapidly in receding from the source.

The process of heating a house through the use of steam radiators involves boiling water in the cellar and condensing the resulting steam in the rooms above. When a pound of water is boiled at the normal boiling point it receives 970 B.t.u. from the coal fire [§ 152] and changes to steam at atmospheric pressure; and when that pound of steam is condensed within the radiators of the rooms, its heat of vaporization is given up to heat the air in the rooms by convection. This method of *evaporation and condensation* is also utilized in mechanical refrigeration, the heat from foods in the ice box being transferred to the surrounding air by evaporating particular liquids at relatively low pressures and condensing them at higher pressures.

186. Conduction. — Substances differ widely in their ability to conduct heat from one point to another; metals are relatively good conductors, while porous substances in which air is entrapped are poor conductors or good insulators. The amount of heat that is conducted per unit of time through any cross-section of a substance depends upon the temperature gradient at that section and the area of the section. The temperature gradient is the ratio of the temperature difference between two parallel planes located at the section under consideration to the separation of these planes, as this separation becomes infinitesimally small; for a temperature difference dt over a distance ds this ratio may be written as $\dfrac{dt}{ds}$. Calling the sectional area A, the rate of heat transfer is

$$q = k \frac{dt}{ds} A \qquad (125)$$

where k is a constant called the *thermal conductivity* of the substance. When the temperature gradient is expressed in centigrade degrees per centimeter, and the area is expressed in square centimeters, then to have the rate of heat transfer q in calories per second, the conductivity k must be expressed in cal./sec. per ° C. per cm. Using these units, k is the number of calories of heat which would be transmitted per second through a sample of the material one square centimeter in cross-section and one centimeter long, when the opposite faces are maintained at a temperature difference of one centigrade degree.

In many commercial calculations of heat conduction, the temperature gradient is expressed in fahrenheit degrees per inch, the area is expressed in square feet, and the rate of heat transfer q

is expressed in B.t.u. per day; with these units the conductivity k will be the number of B.t.u. which will be transmitted in 24 hours through one square foot section of the material, one inch in thickness, when the opposite faces are kept at a temperature difference of one fahrenheit degree. Average values of thermal conductivities of a number of substances at ordinary temperatures in the metric and British units are listed below:

Thermal Conductivities (k)

	Calories per cm. per sec. per °C.	B.t.u.-inches per sq. ft. per day per °F.
Air	0.000054	3.8
Aluminum	.49	34,000
Brass	.26	18,000
Cement	.0007	50
Copper	.91	63,000
Cork	.0001	7
Cotton	.0005	35
Glass	.002	140
Ice	.005	350
Iron	.15	10,400
Lead	.08	5,600
Platinum	.17	11,900
Silk	.0002	14
Silver	.99	69,000
Slate	.005	350
Steel	.11	7,700
Water	.0015	105

To measure the thermal conductivity of a substance, it is necessary to observe the rate at which heat passes through a given cross-section of it under a known temperature gradient. In testing metals, since their conductivity is relatively high, satisfactory precision can be attained by using specimens in the form of rods. In the usual method, the rod under test is fitted with a steam jacket at one end and with a coil of several turns of small metal tubing wound around the other end. Between these parts are placed two thermometers in good thermal contact with the rod and located some distance apart. Thermometers are also used to measure the temperature of water entering and leaving the coil of tubing. The entire rod is placed in hair felt to reduce the emission of heat from the surface of the rod. When steam is passed through the jacket and all four thermometers have attained steady readings, the heat given to the rod is conducted along its length and transferred to the water.

In a typical experiment, a copper rod of 10 sq. cm. cross-section has thermal contacts 12 cm. apart. When one end is heated the thermometers indicate steady readings of 78 and 52° C. at these contacts. At the other end 3.9 gm. of water are heated each second through 5.0 centigrade degrees. The average temperature gradient over the rod length under test, say G, is $(78 - 52) \div 12 = 2.17°$ C./cm. and the heat transmitted along the rod is $q = 5.0 \times 3.9 = 19.5$ cal./sec. Therefore, the heat conductivity of the copper specimen is $k = q/GA = 19.5 \div (2.17 \times 10) = 0.90$ cal./(sec. cm. °C.).

In measuring the thermal conductivities of poor conductors of heat, accuracy requires that specimens in the form of sheets be used so that the heat path will be short and of large sectional area, but in other respects the method of test is the same as for good conductors. Liquids and gases are poor conductors of heat. Air in finely divided form serves as a good insulating substance since its thermal conductivity is very low and because circulating currents are almost entirely eliminated. Textiles, such as wool and felt, are good heat insulators primarily because of the air entrapped in them. Saw dust, granulated cork, loose asbestos, and similar porous materials are used in the walls of refrigerators, frame buildings, and ice houses for heat insulation.

187. Convection. — The transfer of heat by convection refers to the movement of warmed fluids, and is brought about by changes of density that accompany changes of temperature. This process is important in heating systems and ventilation. The heating of houses is accomplished by placing heating units at certain points, and by circulating the air which comes in contact with these units by convection. The so-called radiator (steam or hot-water) does transfer some heat by radiation but it transfers far more by convection. In the hot-water system of heating residences, the water is heated in a furnace located in the cellar and flows through the various radiators by convection. In hot-air heating systems, the air heated in the cellar furnace is delivered to the various floors through large ducts with outlets near the floor. Convection also causes the draft in a stove or in a chimney. The heated gases in a chimney weigh less than a corresponding column of cold air, consequently the mass of gas in the chimney is buoyed up according to Archimedes' Principle [§ 110].

The trade winds are caused by the continued heating of the air near the equator and its movement away from the earth's surface. Cooler air from the tropical belts rushes to take its place, flowing from the north in northern latitudes and from the south in southern latitudes, and convection currents are set up which blow in the same direction for long periods. The rotation of the earth causes the deflection of these winds somewhat from the directions mentioned.

*188. Heat Transfer Through Cylindrical Walls. — Passage of heat through the walls of a tube or pipe is of considerable impor-

tance, and is interesting because the heat flow takes place through layers of varying area. Consider a pipe, shown in section in Fig. 200, to carry steam at temperature t_1, the surrounding temperature being t_2. The heat conducted through the walls is determined by expressing the temperature difference over an annular element of radius r and thickness dr, and summing up the result for all such elements of the pipe from the inner radius r_1 to the outer radius r_2.

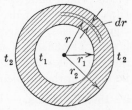

Fig. 200. Conduction of heat through a pipe

Applying equation (125) to the element of thickness dr, and considering unit length of pipe, the rate of heat conduction is

$$q = k \frac{dt}{dr} A$$

where k is the thermal conductivity of the pipe material, dt is the temperature difference over the element, and A is the area normal to the flow of heat, namely, $2\pi r$. The temperature difference over the element is consequently

$$dt = -\frac{q \, dr}{2\pi r k}$$

the minus sign being introduced to show that an increase in the radius of the element corresponds to a decrease in the temperature. Integrating over the full thickness of the pipe, the temperature difference between the steam and the surroundings is

$$\int_{t=t_1}^{t=t_2} dt = -\frac{q}{2\pi k} \int_{r=r_1}^{r=r_2} \frac{dr}{r}$$

whence

$$t_2 - t_1 = -\frac{q}{2\pi k} \log_\epsilon \frac{r_2}{r_1}$$

and therefore the heat conducted through the walls per unit time is

$$q = \frac{2\pi k(t_1 - t_2)}{\log_\epsilon \dfrac{r_2}{r_1}}$$

In transferring heat through walls by conduction and transferring it further by convection through solids or liquids in contact with the walls, cognizance must be taken of thin films of these media which cling to the surfaces. Heat is transferred through these films principally by conduction, and since they have low conductivities, the temperature gradient over them is relatively large. The effects of such films can be allowed for through experimentally determined coefficients, but no corrections for them will be made in the problems on conduction.

189. Radiation. — Energy reaches the earth from the sun by radiation, that is, by waves transmitted through the intervening space. In full sunlight, the energy received above the earth's atmosphere is about 2 cal. per min. on a surface 1 cm. square held perpendicular to the sun's rays; about one-third of this amount is absorbed in passing through the atmosphere. These waves are electromagnetic waves and pass through the vacuum which exists over most of the distance from sun to earth; they have the same character as light and electric waves; see Chapter XXX. Radiation impinging on a body may be reflected from it, transmitted through it, or absorbed by it. Substances which absorb radiation become heated, so the presumption is that the molecular and electronic motions within these substances are augmented by the waves.

An instrument often seen in opticians' shops and called a radiometer illustrates the absorption and reflection of radiant energy. It consists of a delicately pivoted rotating element of four small vanes within a partially evacuated glass bulb. Each vane has one side polished and the other blackened. When radiant energy from the sun or other intense source falls upon a polished face it is reflected, and when the radiation falls upon a blackened face it is absorbed and that face becomes hot. As the air molecules in the bulb dart about some will impinge upon the vanes; those that strike the hot blackened faces will rebound with increased velocities and cause the pivoted element to rotate.

All bodies radiate energy, whether they are hot or cold; the hotter a body is the greater its radiation will be. Further, all bodies receive radiation from others. This exchange of radiant energy goes on continuously. Accordingly, a body that remains at constant temperature is not considered as having stopped radiating, but rather as receiving energy at the same rate that it loses energy by radiation. A body that is a good radiator of energy is also a good absorber of energy. A black rough surface, such as that provided by a coating of lampblack, is an excellent radiator (as well as an excellent absorber) of radiant energy. A highly polished surface has opposite characteristics.

Intensity of radiation is defined as the energy radiated or absorbed per unit time per unit area. The radiation intensity of a body depends upon the surface characteristics of the body and particularly upon its temperature. The relation between the intensity of radiation I and the absolute temperature T of the body was found empirically by the Austrian physicist, Josef Stefan (1835–1893), and later deduced theoretically by his countryman, Ludwig Boltzmann (1844–1906). The relationship is called the Stefan-Boltzmann Law and applies to the ideal case of a "black body," that is, a perfect radiator or perfect absorber; it is

$$I = \sigma T^4 \qquad (126)$$

where σ (sigma) is a constant depending on the units used for expressing I and T. Thus, if the absolute temperature of a body is doubled, its radiation will increase sixteen fold. Experiment shows that when I is in calories per second per square centimeter, the value of σ is 1.36×10^{-12}.

Consider a radiating body at the center of a spherical enclosure, as represented at O in Fig. 201. If the sphere has a radius r_1, the intensity of radiation at the surface of the enclosure will be

$$I_1 = \frac{E}{4\pi r_1{}^2}$$

where E is the energy radiated per second. If the sphere were replaced by one of different radius, say r_2, the intensity of radiation at that surface would be expressed similarly, or

$$I_2 = \frac{E}{4\pi r_2{}^2}$$

By division

$$\frac{I_1}{I_2} = \frac{r_2{}^2}{r_1{}^2} \qquad (127)$$

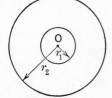

Fig. 201. Illustrating the Inverse Square Law

which states that the intensity of radiation at any surface varies inversely as the square of the distance of that surface from the radiating body. This relation is commonly referred to as the Inverse Square Law.

This law explains the statement in § 143 that in making a temperature measurement with a radiation pyrometer it does not matter how far the instrument is from the radiating source as long as absorbing media are absent. It is understood that the image of the source upon the receiving disk of the thermocouple will always be greater in size than the disk. If, then, the telescope of the instrument is sighted upon the glowing source, the area visible through the eyepiece increases as the square of its distance away, while the intensity of radiation varies inversely as the square of this distance. Hence the total radiation received upon the thermocouple disk, and the deflection of the instrument, will be unaffected by the location of the pyrometer.

The temperature of the sun can be estimated with the aid of the Stefan-Boltzmann Law on the assumption that the sun is a black body radiator. Taking T_s as the absolute temperature of the sun, the intensity of radiation of its surface will be $1.36 \times 10^{-12}T_s^4$ cal. per sec. per sq. cm. This radiation will spread radially, and at the average distance of the earth from the sun its intensity will be given by the Inverse Square Law as $\left(\dfrac{433,000}{92,900,000}\right)^2$ $\times 1.36 \times 10^{-12}T_s^4$, where the sun's radius and the earth's solar distance are expressed in miles. The intensity of radiation from the earth is $1.36 \times 10^{-12}T_e^4$, where T_e is its absolute temperature. The net intensity of the radiation received from the sun by the earth in calories per second per square centimeter is therefore

$$S = 1.36 \times 10^{-12} \times \left[T_s^4\left(\frac{433,000}{92,900,000}\right)^2 - T_e^4\right]$$

The value of the solar constant S has been found by many investigators to average 0.033 cal. per sec. per sq. cm., which agrees with the value previously given, and $T_e = 288°$ K.; consequently the effective temperature of the sun is found to be 6150° K.

The rate at which a body loses heat to its surroundings, when its temperature elevation is not large, is proportional to the temperature elevation. This statement, ascribed to Newton, is called Newton's Law of Cooling, and is often used in correcting calorimetric measurements for radiation.

190. Granular Character of Radiation. — The radiation emitted by a heated body takes the form of waves in space and the lengths of these waves from crest to crest cover a wide range. The long ones are perceived by an observer as heat and the shorter ones as light. The energy of radiation is distributed over the range of wave length in a manner that depends upon the temperature of the radiating body and the nature of its surface. Fig. 202 shows the distributions of energy radiated by a black body as obtained by experiments conducted at two temperatures, namely 1250° and 1450° K. The curves represent the relative intensities at the various wave lengths up to 0.0006 cm. Radiation which affects the eye as light extends roughly from 0.00004 to 0.00008 cm., and is marked on the diagram as the visible range. The region to the right of this visual zone is termed the infra-red, and to the left is termed the ultra-violet. The relation between the length λ (lambda) of the waves emitted by a source of radiation and the frequency f of the vibrating source [§ 322] is given by

$$\lambda = \frac{V}{f}$$

showing that for a constant wave velocity V the frequency of vibration varies inversely with the length of the waves. The total energy radiated is indicated by the area under the curves. The Stefan-Boltzmann Law, presented in the preceding section, shows that this energy for a black body is proportional to the fourth power of the absolute temperature.

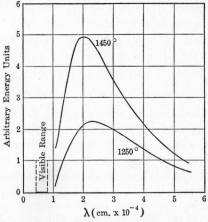

Fig. 202. Distribution of radiation energy among the various wave lengths

Increase of temperature causes not only an increase in total radiation but also shifts the peak of the radiation curve toward the shorter wave lengths. It is this effect which serves as the operating basis of the radiation pyrometer described in § 143. The shift in wave length has been formulated by the German physicist, Wilhelm Wien (1864–1928), and is known as Wien's Displacement Law. It states that the product of the wave length λ_m at which the energy density is a maximum and the absolute temperature T of the radiating body is a constant. This wave length in centimeters is given by the equation

$$\lambda_m = \frac{0.2885}{T}$$

Much attention has been directed toward an explanation of the shapes of radiation curves such as Fig. 202. Max Planck, formerly professor at the University of Berlin, introduced the idea in 1900 that a radiating body behaves as though it contained harmonic oscillators, each of which responds to one frequency of vibration and corresponds to the radiations which it is capable of absorbing or emitting, and he assumed these oscillators to absorb or emit energy in small steps rather than continuously. This has been interpreted to mean that energy is granular in nature, an idea that is radically different from that held since the time of Newton, namely, that the energy of a body can change from one value to another through every conceivable intermediate value. According to the newer theory, each oscillator can absorb or emit one or more of these "grains" of energy, each of which is called a *quantum*. The magnitude of a quantum of energy for an oscillator which has a frequency f is given by the following equation:

$$E = hf \tag{128}$$

where E is the energy in ergs, f is the frequency in vibrations per second, and h is a constant that has the value 6.63×10^{-27} erg-sec. It will be evident herefrom that quanta are extremely tiny grains of energy, and that the quantum is smaller for low frequencies (long wave lengths) than for high frequencies (short wave lengths). The symbol ν (nu) is often used to represent the frequency.

*191. The Quantum Theory. — The theory based upon the granular picture of energy, called the *quantum theory*, has been modified by many investigators, and now affords not only a satisfactory explanation of the radiation of energy, but also of the photoelectric effect, the structure of atoms, and all collision phenomena; these are treated later.

The quantum explanation of the shape of the radiation curves for black bodies is an involved one and makes use of rather difficult mathematical steps. It will suffice here to give Planck's equation for the energy per cubic centimeter associated with the wave length interval from λ to $\lambda + d\lambda$ cm., namely

$$E \, d\lambda = \frac{8\pi ch \, d\lambda}{\lambda^5 (\epsilon^{ch/k\lambda T} - 1)}$$

where the velocity c of the waves is very nearly 3×10^{10} cm. per sec. [§ 362], and k is the gas constant per molecule, namely 1.38 $\times$ 10^{-16} ergs/° K. [§ 164].

Planck's theory was applied by Professor Einstein to explain the variation of the specific heats of solids with temperature, and was later modified by Professor Debye to secure closer agreement with experimental results. These analyses indicate that the product of the specific heat and atomic weight of a substance falls to zero as the absolute zero of temperature is approached and that the product has a nearly constant value at relatively high temperatures. The ultimate value averages 6.3 cal. per gram-atom per degree for a large number of elements.

PROBLEMS

1. A room measuring 15 $\times$ 30 $\times$ 12 ft. is insulated on all surfaces by a 4-in. covering of glass wool having a thermal conductivity of 6 British units. It is desired to maintain the temperature inside the room at 75° F. while that outside is 30° F. How much heat must be supplied to this room per hour to offset the loss by conduction?

2. A box measuring 2 ft. along each edge containing 50 lb. of ice at 32° F. is to be maintained at this temperature while that of the surroundings is 100° F. For this purpose it is covered on all surfaces with "Celotex," a material having a thermal conductivity of 8.2 British units. How thick should the covering be in order that the ice may last 2 days?

3. The space within an ice box measures 2 $\times$ 3$\frac{1}{2}$ $\times$ 1$\frac{1}{2}$ ft., and the wall is 2 in. thick. How much ice must be melted per day in order to keep the contents at an average temperature of 45° F. with a surrounding temperature of 75° F.? Assume the walls to be made entirely of cork for which the conductivity is 7 British units, and that the melted ice drips out.

4. Ice on a pond is 1.5 in. thick and the temperature of the water below it is 32° F. At what rate does the ice become thicker when the air temperature is 0° F.?

5. A method for measuring the thermal conductivity of liquids employs two concentric cylinders with the liquid under test between them, the inner cylinder being heated by an electric current through a wire at its center. With cylinders 10 in. long, having an annular space between them $\frac{1}{64}$ in. thick and 1$\frac{1}{4}$ in. in circumference filled with benzene, a steady power input of 1.92 watts produces a temperature difference of 0.60° C. between the cylinders, when tested at about 30° C. Compute the thermal conductivity of benzene from these data.

6. A house of frame construction measures 40 ft. by 20 ft. and is 20 ft. high. The walls consist of $\frac{3}{4}$-in. clapboard, 1-in. rough boarding, 4-in. studding, and lath and plaster covering; for this type of wall the heat transmitted per sq. ft. per day is 9.5 B.t.u. for one fahrenheit degree dif-

ference of temperature between the outer and inner faces. (*a*) Neglecting the correction for floor, window and door areas and considering heat conduction through the roof the same as that through the walls, compute the number of B.t.u. per day necessary to maintain a temperature difference of 30 fahrenheit degrees between house and outdoor temperatures. (*b*) If the house is to be heated by gas having a heating value of 542 B.t.u. per cu. ft., and costing 75 cents per thousand cubic feet, how much will it cost to maintain the temperature difference assumed as an average during a heating season of 200 days?

7. Water is being converted into steam at an absolute pressure of 100 lb. per sq. in. in a steam boiler. How long will it take to vaporize 1 lb. of water for each square foot of boiler surface if the boiler walls are of iron $\frac{1}{2}$ in. thick, the outside being maintained at a temperature of 1800° F.?

8. Glass thermos bottles consist of double-walled flasks joined only at the neck, with air at very low pressure between the walls. The glass faces which bound the evacuated zone are silvered and polished. Explain fully why such flasks transfer little heat from the substance contained in them to the surroundings, or vice versa.

9. How many horsepower are received per square yard of the earth's surface from the sun, assuming perpendicular incidence of full sunlight and neglecting absorption by the earth's atmosphere?

10. In a solar engine conceived by Dr. C. G. Abbot, the sun's radiation falling upon a mirror is focussed upon a black liquid where it is absorbed, the energy being used to generate steam and operate a small engine. With a mirror 30 sq. ft. in area, arranged for perpendicular incidence of the radiation, an overall efficiency of 15 per cent is predicted; what horsepower will the engine develop under these conditions?

11. At what rate will heat be emitted from a spherical body 10 cm. in diameter which has a temperature of 650° C., assuming that the radiation constant in the Stefan-Boltzmann Law is 1.1×10^{-12} cal. per sec. per sq. cm.?

12. A sphere 4 cm. in diameter is made of solid iron having a specific gravity of 7.7 and a specific heat of 0.15. At a particular temperature, the sphere radiates energy at the rate of 30 cal. per sec.; at what rate is its temperature falling?

13. Two like bodies, one at temperature 60° C. and the other at 40° C., are located in a room having a temperature of 17° C. Compare their rates of cooling on the basis of the Stefan-Boltzmann Law for net radiation, $I \propto (T_1{}^4 - T_2{}^4)$, where T_1 is the temperature of either radiating body and T_2 is the temperature of the surroundings. Recompute by applying Newton's Law of Cooling, and determine the percentage departure from the previous result.

14. From the Inverse Square Law, estimate the intensity of the solar radiation upon Neptune, when this planet is 2.793×10^9 mi. from the sun.

15. A calorimeter is found to cool from 30.2° C. to 29.7° C. in 1 min., the surrounding temperature being 20.0° C. As the cooling continues, how long will it take the calorimeter to cool from 24.0° C. to 23.0° C.?

16. Explain why in summer the prevailing winds tend to blow from sea to land, while in winter they are oppositely directed.

17. Plot a curve showing the wave lengths at which the maximum radiation occurs for black bodies at various temperatures up to 5000° K.

ELECTRICITY AND MAGNETISM

CHAPTER XX

ELECTRIC CHARGE

192. Electrostatic Attraction and Repulsion. — The earliest electrical experiment ever recorded is probably that due to the Greek philosopher Thales (640–546 B.C.), who observed that a piece of amber when rubbed with cloth was able to attract light objects placed near it. Nowadays, the act of rubbing, or of bringing about a very close contact between the amber and the cloth, is said to give the amber a *charge of electricity*, and the attraction is called an electric or *electrostatic attraction*. The term electricity is derived from *elektra*, the Greek word for amber.

Many other substances can be charged in the same manner. A charge can be produced on a glass rod by rubbing it with silk. A hard-rubber rod rubbed with fur becomes highly charged; it can exert sufficient force upon a meter stick to turn it horizontally about a pivot at its midpoint.

The forces due to electric charges can be demonstrated best by using very light objects because the effects produced can be observed readily. Two pith balls, each suspended by a thread, and hung a few centimeters apart, will serve very well. When both are brought in contact with a charged glass rod they fly apart and remain separated; they act the same way when both are touched to a charged hard-rubber rod. But if one pith ball which has been touched to the glass rod is brought near one which has been touched to the rubber rod, then they will approach each other. From these tests it is evident that there is some difference between the electricity on the glass and that on the hard rubber; and quite arbitrarily, the glass rod is said to be charged *positively* and the rubber rod *negatively*. Furthermore, these tests show a fundamental fact of great importance, namely, that *like charges of electricity repel each other, and unlike charges attract each other.*

The presence of an electric charge on a body can be detected by an *electroscope*, the construction of which is indicated in Fig. 203.

Two leaves, ordinarily of aluminum or gold foil, hang side by side from a metal rod which terminates in a metal knob outside of the case. If the metal knob is touched with the charged body, the leaves will acquire electricity of the same sign and will repel each other, as represented in the figure. It is evident that a larger quantity of electricity will cause a greater separation of the leaves.

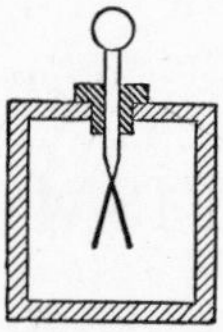

Fig. 203. A simple electroscope

193. The Constitution of Matter. — The student of Chemistry is familiar with the subdivision of matter into molecules and atoms, and has learned to appreciate the simplification that is brought about by being able to reduce a multitude of substances to terms of only about ninety elements. For a number of years the atoms of all elements were regarded under the so-called *electron theory* as composed of only two component parts: *electrons*, each of which has a definite charge of negative electricity, and *protons*, which are heavier particles each having an amount of positive electricity equal to the negative charge of the electron. Although both of these particles are inconceivably tiny, it is known that their sizes are of the same order of magnitude but that the mass of the proton is about 1800 times that of the electron. Recent research has demonstrated that the atom also contains uncharged particles, called *neutrons*, each of which has about the same mass as the proton. Further developments have shown the existence of *positrons*, which are particles of positive electricity having about the same mass as the electron, and at present there is much speculation in regard to the fundamental positive charge; it may develop that the proton will be found to be a combination of a neutron and a positron, or the neutron a combination of an electron and a proton.

The actual structure of the atom is naturally a matter of conjecture, but many facts of Physics and Chemistry can be explained by an imaginative atomic structure proposed some years ago by the British scientist, Lord (Ernest) Rutherford (1871–1937), and developed by the Danish physicist, Niels Bohr. More recently the ideas about the atom have been modified through the discovery of the neutron by Rutherford's associate, James Chadwick. The atom is pictured as consisting of a central *nucleus* together with one or more electrons whirling around it in the same way that the planets revolve about the sun, most of the region "occupied" by the atom being empty space, as in the solar system. The simplest atom is that of hydrogen; according to this picture it has a single proton as its nucleus and one planetary electron, the two being held together by mutual attraction. Next in order of simplicity is the helium atom, composed of a nucleus and two planetary electrons, the nucleus being regarded as a stable combination of two protons and two neutrons. The more complex atoms have more and more protons and neutrons in the nucleus, with a corresponding increase of planetary electrons, the total amount of positive and negative charge being equal in any uncharged or *neutral* atom. The electrons are supposed to occupy shells around the nucleus, their arrangement under normal conditions being as follows:

The hydrogen (H) atom has its one electron in the first shell, and the helium (He) atom has both its electrons in that shell. This shell accommodates only two electrons. The lithium (Li) atom, with a total of three planetary electrons, has one of them in the second shell; beryllium (Be) has two in the second shell, boron (B) three, carbon (C) four, nitrogen (N) five, oxygen (O) six, fluorine (F) seven, and neon (Ne) eight, the last number filling the second shell. The sodium (Na) atom has a total of eleven planetary electrons, of which two fill the first shell, eight fill the second shell, the remaining one being in a third shell. By continuing the foregoing process, and supposing the electrons to be arranged in shells of various sizes, the Periodic Table of the Atoms may be constructed (see Appendix). The *atomic number* for any atom is the number of positive charges (protons) in its nucleus; it is also equal to the number of planetary electrons, supposing the atom to be uncharged.

Certain elements are quite inert and it is concluded that their atomic structures are inherently stable. Perhaps because of compactness or symmetry, such stability is regarded as involving electron shells that are completely filled. The helium atom with its first shell complete, the neon atom with the first and second shells complete, and other atoms similarly located in the table (argon, krypton, xenon and niton), are chemically inactive.

The ability of atoms to combine and form molecules is determined by the planetary electrons, and the tendency in combining is apparently to form arrangements in which the electron shells are completely filled. A lithium or sodium atom, with one electron in its outer shell, is in a condition which is favorable to the loss of this electron, while a fluorine or chlorine atom, with one electron less than is needed to complete its outer shell, is in a state which favors annexing one. When sodium and chlorine are allowed to mingle, each sodium (Na) atom joins a chlorine (Cl) atom, forming sodium chloride (NaCl), in which process the loosely held electron of the sodium atom is transferred to the chlorine atom, thus filling the electron shells of both atoms. The measure of the ability of atoms to form molecules by combining in this manner is known as *valence*; for example, sodium, which has one electron more than is needed to fill its outer shell, is said to have a *valence number* of $+1$, and chlorine, which has one electron less than is needed to fill its outer shell, is said to have a valence number of -1.

Atomic quantities are much too small to be measured directly, but from indirect measurements results of great precision have been obtained. For example, the hydrogen atom, which is composed of a proton and an electron, has a mass of 1.662×10^{-24} gm. Of this amount, the electron forms only a small part; its mass when at rest is 9.11×10^{-28} gm. The dimensions of the hydrogen atom are of the following order of magnitude, assuming its components as spherical: radius of nucleus and radius of electron, each about 2×10^{-13} cm.; least radius of electronic orbit, about 0.5×10^{-8} cm. A better appreciation of the relative proportions of these quantities can be obtained by imagining the atom to be magnified until the electronic orbit is as large as that of the earth about the sun. The electron would then be represented by a sphere about the size of the earth itself, and would rotate around a nucleus of equal size.

194. Production of Electric Charge. — The process of charging a body by rubbing it with another material may be viewed as a stripping of electrons from some of the atoms at the contacting surface. Certain atoms release electrons with comparative ease, and other atoms are in a state which favors annexing them. A neutral or uncharged body contains equal amounts of positive and negative electricity; when electrons are added to it, it becomes negatively charged, and when electrons are removed from it, it becomes positively charged. Applying this explanation, a hard-rubber rod, when brought into intimate contact with fur, gains electrons and becomes negative and the fur loses these electrons and becomes positive to an equal extent.   A glass rod rubbed with silk loses electrons and becomes positive, while the silk gains these electrons and so becomes negative.

Examples illustrating the production of electric charge are familiar to everyone. The effect may be observed by passing a rubber comb through the hair or by shuffling the feet on a woolen carpet. A leather belt traveling on iron pulleys may acquire sufficient electricity to produce a spark to a person's finger held near it. The paper in a printing press sometimes manifests a charge when it is separated from the rollers, and means must be provided to dissipate the charge. A tank truck carrying gasoline is usually grounded by a dangling chain to allow any accumulated electricity to escape to the earth, so that the flammable vapors may not be ignited by a spark.

195. Insulators and Conductors. — It is possible to charge a body from one that is already charged by simply bringing the two into contact. Thus, a metal sphere will gain negative electricity if it is touched with a negatively charged rubber rod, Fig. 204. It appears that some electrons leave the rod at the point of contact by virtue of their mutual repulsion and attach themselves to the sphere, making it negative also. Or, if the sphere had been touched with a positively charged glass rod it would have become positive, because electrons would have been attracted away from it to the rod at the point of contact. It is assumed that the sphere is so supported that the electricity accumulated upon it will not leak away. This can be done by suspending the sphere by means of a dry silk string or by supporting it on props of mica or glass. Evidently charges are not transferred or conducted to an appreciable extent from one point to another in materials like these, and they are called *insulators* or *dielectrics*. If the sphere had been suspended by a metallic wire or mounted upon a metal support, practically the entire charge on it would have escaped to the earth. It can be concluded that metals are good *conductors* of electricity. Many substances are neither good insulators nor good conductors but may be classed in an intermediate group as fair electrical conductors; for example, the human body, a piece of damp wood, or the earth.

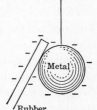

Fig. 204. Charging a metal sphere by contact

196. Motion of Electric Charge; Electric Current.—The transfer of electric charge within a medium, spoken of as conduction of electricity, takes place differently through solids, gases, and liquids. A consideration of conduction through liquids will be deferred to Chapter XXIII.

Conduction in Solids.—The closeness of the atoms to one another in solids makes it possible for the outer electron orbits of neighboring atoms to overlap. Moreover, most conducting solids are metals in which the atom has only a few electrons in the outer shell (see Periodic Table), a condition which favors the loss of these electrons. Under these circumstances, and possibly because some electrons serve in a double capacity in two adjoining atoms, it is believed that a large number of electrons are comparatively free to move.

When one end of a conducting wire is maintained negative by supplying it with electrons and the other end is maintained positive by withdrawing electrons from it, the *free electrons* within the wire are repelled from the negative end and attracted toward the positive end. These electrons acquire a definite drift from atom to atom toward the positive end of the wire. It is this flow of electrons which constitutes an *electric current.* The particles of electricity in a body are pictured as being in a state of unceasing, unordered motion, depending upon the temperature. The directed *drift* motion which occurs in the electric current is superposed upon the motion of thermal agitation.

It is interesting to note that in solids the positively charged atoms remain fixed in position except for thermal agitation, and that the *current is attributed entirely to a movement of electrons.* The free electrons are also believed to assist in the conduction of heat, as well as of electricity, through solids.

In insulating solids the electrons are not readily detachable from the atoms. If one surface of a glass plate, for example, is maintained negative and the other positive, the electrons in the dielectric do not drift through it, but undergo only a slight shift or *displacement.*

Conduction in Gases.—To demonstrate the flow of electricity through gases, suppose that an electroscope has been charged so that its leaves stand apart as in Fig. 203, and that the flame of a gas jet is brought near the electroscope knob. It will be found that the leaves fall together promptly, showing that the electroscope has lost its charge. The molecules of the heated gases collide with each other and with air molecules so forcibly as to knock some electrons out of the atoms. As a result, the neutral molecules become interspersed with molecules carrying negative and positive charges. These are called *ions* (go-ers), a term which is applied to atoms or atomic groups when electrically charged. If the electroscope is positive it will attract the negative ions, and if negative it will attract the positive ions. Its charge in either case will be neutralized, and the air around it will be *ionized*.

Again, if a charged electroscope is exposed to the radiation from uranium, radium, or other radioactive substance, the electroscope will be found to lose its charge, because the radiation has ionized the air. Ionization of the air is also produced by x-rays and ultra-violet light, as well as by cosmic radiation received by the earth from remote sources. It is found that from various causes, any sample of air will include some ions.

The flow of electricity through air and other gases can be studied in a glass tube fitted with sealed-in electrodes and attached to a vacuum pump as shown in Fig. 205. One electrode *A* is maintained positive and the other one *C* negative; these are called the *anode* and *cathode* respectively. At atmospheric pressure nothing happens, but as the pressure is reduced gradually, the following effects may be observed.

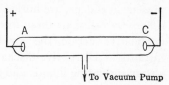

Fig. 205.   Gaseous discharge tube

First, a noiseless discharge takes place in the form of a purplish wavy thread between the electrodes. Next, this discharge broadens and fills the entire cross-section of the tube, being accompanied by a noticeable glow near the cathode. At still lower pressures the glow moves away from the cathode, leaving a dark space between them, and a second comparatively dark space forms beyond the glow; the remainder of the tube is then occupied by a luminous column in which striations of luminosity often appear. When the exhaustion is carried to about 0.001 mm. of mercury, the luminous column disappears and the walls of the tube exhibit a fluorescent glow.

At moderate pressures, the discharge in the tube is attributed to the ions present in the enclosed air, which move in accordance with their attraction or repulsion by the electrodes. At low pressures, however, the discharge is in the nature of a radiation directed away from the cathode, to which the name *cathode rays* is given. These rays cause certain substances to glow, and have electromagnetic properties by which they are recognized as a stream of high-velocity electrons. Conduction through the tube is explained by supposing that the bombardment of positive ions knocks electrons out of the cathode, particularly at reduced pressure, and that these electrons have sufficient energy to ionize the air within the tube by collision. At moderate pressures the tube is so crowded with air molecules that the emitted electrons do not gain sufficient velocity to produce much ionization, and at very low pressures the air molecules are so widely spaced that the collisions are comparatively infrequent. The maximum conduction of gas occurs at some intermediate pressure value.

When two strongly charged points separated by air at ordinary pressure are brought sufficiently close to each other, a *spark* will jump between them, this *disruptive discharge* being accompanied by a sharp, quick snap or crackle. The lightning flash with its accompanying clap of thunder is a familiar example of this effect on a huge scale. In these cases the few ions which are always present in the air, are hurled along so violently that they produce others by collision; these in turn produce still more, and by this cumulative action the air becomes highly conducting almost instantly. Disruptive discharge may occur not only in gases but also in insulating liquids and solids.

197. Charging by Induction. — A method of charging a metallic object from another initially charged body that does not involve contact between the two is much used; the method is called *induction*. The procedure follows: (1) bring the charged body close to, but not in contact with, the object to be charged; (2) ground the object by touching it with the finger; (3) remove the ground connection; and (4) remove the initially charged body. The object will then have acquired a charge that is opposite in sign to the original one.

To explain this process, suppose a brass tube, which is mounted on a glass support for insulation, is to be charged by induction from a rubber rod; the steps in the process are illustrated in Fig. 206. (1) When the negatively charged rod is brought near the tube, it will repel some of the electrons of the tube, thus making the distant end of the tube negative, and leaving the adjacent end positive. A state of equilibrium will soon be reached in which any other electrons that are repelled by the rod, are prevented from moving to the distant end of the tube by the negative electricity which has accumulated there. (2) When the tube is grounded, a path is provided for some of the electrons to escape, and there will be a flow of electrons through the ground connection to the earth. (3) Upon removing the ground connection the body is again isolated and it will have a positive charge, since it has lost some electrons. Finally, (4) the removal of the inducing charge allows the charges on the tube to distribute themselves in a normal manner, and the tube becomes positive over its entire surface.

A similar explanation will make it clear why the charged rod attracts the meter stick as mentioned in § 192. The negative

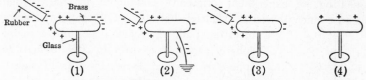

Fig. 206. Charging a metal tube by induction

inducing charge repels the electrons in the stick, and while they cannot move bodily throughout the stick, since it is an insulator, they are slightly displaced, leaving the adjacent surface of the stick positive, and thus accounting for the attraction.

198. Distribution of Charge on Conductors. — The shape of a conducting body has a marked effect on the distribution of electricity over it, and in general the amount of charge per unit area will not be uniform over its surface. The amount of the charge at any spot can be determined by using a *proof plane*, consisting of a small metal disk fastened to one end of an insulating rod, together with an electroscope. The disk of the proof plane is applied to the spot under test and then to the electroscope; the resulting separation of the electroscope leaves becomes a measure of the *surface density of charge*. In testing a charged conducting sphere, whether hollow or solid, the proof plane will produce the same separation of the leaves after being touched to any point on the spherical surface, provided the sphere is isolated so as to be uninfluenced by its surroundings; this test indicates that the surface density is uniform. On an elongated conductor, such as a rod or tube, this density will be found greater at the ends than at the middle, a result which shows the tendency of the individual charges to repel one another to the greatest possible distance. If a conductor has a sharp point, a large part of its charge will pass to the point, and the few ions already present in the neighboring air will be accelerated so strongly that they create more ions by cumulative collision thus permitting the electricity to escape from the conductor. A similar effect is produced by bringing a pointed object *near* a charged conductor, because of the charge which is induced on the point. The discharge from pointed electrodes is accompanied by a glow which may be seen in the dark, and is called a *brush discharge* or *corona*. To minimize such leakage, rounded knobs are used instead of sharp points on electrostatic apparatus.

Electric charges and their distribution can be studied by repeating an experiment originally conducted by the British chemist and physicist, Michael Faraday (1791–1867), using a

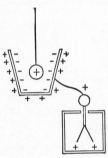

metal ice pail, an electroscope, and a metal sphere, arranged as in Fig. 207. When the sphere is charged from an outside source and lowered into the pail the leaves of the electroscope diverge. The sphere may then be moved around inside the pail, touched to its inner surface, and removed, without causing any further change in the electroscope. After touching the sphere to the pail and removing it, both the sphere itself and the inner surface of the pail will be found entirely free from charge.

FIG. 207. Faraday's ice-pail experiment

To explain this result, assume a positive sphere lowered to the position shown. It attracts the free electrons in the metal pail to the inner surface, and consequently the outer surface, together with the electroscope, are left positive. Upon touching the sphere to the pail the induced charge on the inside of the pail and the inducing charge on the sphere neutralize each other. The charge on the outside of the pail, which before contact was as large as that on the inside, must therefore be equal to the initial amount on the sphere, and of the same sign. Consequently it may be concluded that *a charge induces an equal and opposite charge on the surrounding surface*. It is also seen that *a charge cannot exist inside of a conductor*, unless this region also contains an equal and opposite charge, *but will reside on the outer surface*. In conducting the experiment, it is desirable to have the opening in the receptacle as small as possible, for theoretically, the action will not be complete unless the hollow conductor is completely enclosed.

199. Electrostatic Generators. — For the operation of discharge tubes, the production of x-rays of high penetration, and the acceleration of charged particles for research on the atomic nucleus, use is often made of electrostatic generators to accumulate electricity on suitable terminals. Such machines have been built for many years with rotating glass plates equipped with metal disks for carrying the charges produced by induction, but a new type of generator has been developed by Robert J. Van de Graaff in which the charges are transported on a traveling belt.

A recent design is represented diagrammatically in Fig. 208. It consists essentially of a hollow metal terminal T mounted on an insulating column C, within which a motor drives an endless belt B of insulating material for conveying electricity between the terminal and ground. The terminal may be made either positive or negative; the operation will be described for the latter case.

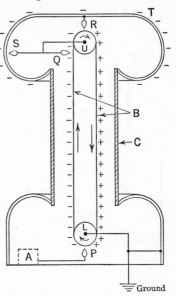

A row of metal points represented by P is directed toward the lower metal pulley L and receives continuously a small supply of negative electricity from an auxiliary source A. The air in the vicinity of the points becomes ionized and the negative charges are repelled toward the pulley and deposited on the intervening insulating belt. This neutralizes the

FIG. 208. Van de Graaff type of electrostatic generator (*Unit 4 ft. high develops up to 500,000 volts with a rubber-fabric belt 10 in. wide driven at 5000 ft. per min.*)

positive charge that may be on the belt from its downward run and leaves a net negative charge to be carried to the upper terminal.

The collector Q transfers this charge partly to the upper insulated pulley U and partly (through suitable control devices not shown) to the point S and thence to the terminal. The charges are so distributed as to make the pulley more negative than the terminal itself, and thus the pointed electrode R connected to the terminal may now be regarded as positive with respect to the pulley. In consequence, the region between the two becomes ionized and positive charges are attracted to the pulley and deposited on the belt. This action neutralizes the negative charge remaining on the belt and leaves a residue of positive charge to be carried downward. Thus, as the machine is driven, there is a continuous transfer of negative electricity up one side of the belt and positive electricity down the other side, as the result of which the terminal acquires a large negative charge.

200. Forces Exerted by Charges upon Others. — It has been shown that charges of like sign repel and those of unlike sign attract each other, but nothing has been said so far about the

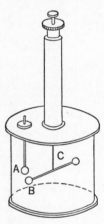

magnitudes of the forces of repulsion or attraction. The first quantitative measurements of these forces were conducted by the French physicist, Charles A. Coulomb (1736–1806), using a *torsion balance* as shown in Fig. 209. In this device, the repulsion between the charged spheres A and B twists the supporting wire C, and the moving system comes to rest when the opposing torques acting upon it are equal. These investigations, confirmed in various ways by Cavendish and others, showed that the force between two charges, whether of repulsion or attraction, varies directly as the product of the charges, varies inversely as the square of the distance between them, and is influenced by the surrounding medium. For

Fig. 209. Torsion balance

charges concentrated at points, the exact value of the force in dynes which either one exerts upon the other is given by the expression:

$$F = \frac{Q_1 Q_2}{K r^2} \tag{129}$$

where Q_1 and Q_2 are the values of the charges and r is the distance between them. The constant K is called the *dielectric constant* of the medium surrounding the charges; its value is taken as unity for a vacuum, and is found to be very nearly unity (1.000586) for air at normal temperature and pressure.

The foregoing expression is the foundation of a system of electrostatic units (e.s.u.), and serves to define unit charge in that system. *The electrostatic unit of charge is a quantity of electricity which when placed 1 cm. in a vacuum from an equal one will be acted upon by a force of 1 dyne.* For practical purposes, the force may be considered the same in air as in a vacuum. There is no special name for this unit; it is called an e.s.u. of charge, or merely *unit charge.*

201. The Electric Field. — The region about a charged body is referred to as an electric field of force, or briefly, an *electric field,* because any other charge located in this region will experience a force, either of attraction or repulsion. The amount of force acting upon a unit charge is taken as a measure of the strength or intensity of the field. *The intensity of an electric field at any point is defined as the force which would be exerted upon a unit positive charge placed at that point,* and the electrostatic unit of field strength is the *dyne per unit charge.* If, at a particular point in an electric field, a unit of positive electricity experiences a force of say, 1000 dynes toward the right, this signifies that the field intensity at that point is 1000 dynes per unit charge and is directed toward the right. In general, if Q units of electricity located in an electric field are acted upon by a force of F dynes, the intensity of the field $\mathcal{E}$ at that place is given in dynes per unit charge by the expression

$$\mathcal{E} = \frac{F}{Q} \tag{130}$$

In this expression, Q represents a charge placed at some point in an already existing field, and $\mathcal{E}$ is the field strength at that point before Q was introduced.

Consider now the region around a charge of $+Q$ units, and suppose for simplicity that this electricity is concentrated at a point, as at O in Fig. 210. The direction and strength of the electric field which it produces at any point in the region is found by assuming a *unit positive* charge to be placed there and determining the force acting upon it. The directions of the field at four points A to D are shown in the figure by arrows all of which are radially outward from Q. The force on a unit charge at, say,

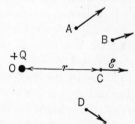

Fig. 210. Radial field around a point charge

point C is found from equation (129) to be $F = \dfrac{Q \times 1}{K r^2}$, where r is the distance from O to C. Hence, the field intensity at any point distant r from a charge of Q units is

$$\mathscr{E} = \frac{Q}{Kr^2} \qquad (131)$$

where Q represents the charge which establishes the field, and $\mathscr{E}$ is the strength of the field in dynes per unit charge. Summarizing, the field intensity due to a point charge varies inversely with the square of the distance from it, and is directed radially outward from a positive charge and radially inward toward a negative one.

The region around an electric charge is represented conventionally by *lines of dielectric flux* directed along the field at every point. The region near two spheres, one positive and the

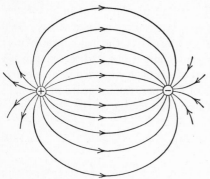

other negative, is represented in this manner in Fig. 211. The flux lines show the direction in which a positive charge would move if free to do so; they start at a positive charge and end at a negative one. Ordinarily, the flux extends through air, which has practically the same dielectric constant as a vacuum. Under these circumstances

FIG. 211.   Lines of dielectric flux

it is customary to represent a particular value of field intensity by that same number of lines drawn perpendicularly through 1 sq. cm. of area. Thus, if the field intensity at a particular point in air is $\mathscr{E}$ dynes per unit charge, then $\mathscr{E}$ lines per square centimeter are imagined at that place. For any other medium of dielectric constant K, the number of lines per square centimeter is increased to $K\mathscr{E}$.

Maps of the flux distribution about charged bodies may be obtained experimentally by sprinkling tiny bits of straw or hair on an insulating plate held between them.

The amount of flux extending from a charge Q can be evaluated by imagining a sphere of radius r about it as center; the field is perpendicular to the spherical surface at all points and has the same intensity $\mathscr{E} = Q/Kr^2$ all over. The flux through each square centimeter of the spherical surface is $K\mathscr{E} = Q/r^2$, and consequently the total flux extending from the central charge Q through the entire surface of area $4\pi r^2$ is $4\pi r^2 \times Q/r^2$ or $4\pi Q$.

Since electric field intensity has direction as well as magnitude, it is a vector quantity [§ 18], and consequently field intensities can be resolved or combined in the same way as velocities or forces. When the field intensity at a point is due to several point charges, its value can be determined by computing the field intensity at the point due to each in turn, and then finding the resultant of these individual values. In Fig. 212, the field intensity at point P has one component directed radially away from the positive charge Q_1 and another component directed radially toward the negative one Q_2; the resultant field intensity at this point is shown at $\mathscr{E}$.

FIG. 212. Field due to two point charges

As an illustrative example, consider that the charges shown in Fig. 212 are $Q_1 = +1000$ units and $Q_2 = -1000$ units, these being 12 cm. apart, and that the point P is located 5 cm. directly below Q_2. This point will then be 13 cm. away from Q_1. The component of $\mathscr{E}$ due to Q_1 is $\frac{1000}{(13)^2} =$ 5.9 dynes per unit charge, and that due to Q_2 is $\frac{1000}{(5)^2} = 40.0$ dynes per unit charge. The angle $\theta = \tan^{-1} 12/5 = 67.4°$, and therefore, by the Law of Cosines,

$$\mathscr{E}^2 = (5.9)^2 + (40)^2 - 2(5.9)(40) \cos 67.4°;$$

from which $\mathscr{E} = 38.1$ dynes per unit charge. Using the Law of Sines, the direction of this resultant field intensity is found to be 8.2° to the right of the vertical.

202. Electric Potential. — It is known that an electric field exerts a force upon a charge located within it. From this fact, it is evident that work must be done upon such a charge in moving it against this force. If the field is uniform in intensity, the work done will be the product of the constant force and the distance the charge moves, provided it moves along the line of force action. If the field is not uniform, the force will vary from point to point, and the determination of work done becomes more involved.

In order to simplify such computations, the idea of "electrical level" will be found serviceable, and this concept is called *potential*. In mechanics, if a body is to be moved from one level to a higher one, work must be done upon it, and in electricity, if a +charge is to be moved from one potential to a higher one, work must be done upon it. Thus, points in space near charged objects have definite potentials, and by convention the numerical value of *the potential at any point is the work which must be done upon a unit positive charge in order to move it from an infinitely great distance up to the point in question.*

To derive an expression for potential, consider an electric field about a charge $+Q$ located at point O in Fig. 213, and compute the amount of work to be done upon a unit positive charge in moving it from an infinitely great distance up to a point R that is distant r cm.

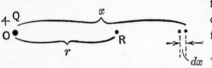

FIG. 213. Illustrating electric potential

from O. When the unit charge is at a distance x cm. from O, it is repelled by Q with a force of $\dfrac{Q}{Kx^2}$ dynes, and an equal and opposite force is required to hold it at this position. Hence, the work done in moving it an infinitesimal distance dx toward Q is $-\dfrac{Q}{Kx^2}\,dx$ ergs.

The total work done in moving the unit charge from an infinitely great distance to R is found by integrating this expression between the limits $x = \infty$ and $x = r$, giving

$$\int_{x=\infty}^{x=r} -\frac{Q}{Kx^2}\,dx = \left.+\frac{Q}{Kx}\right|_{\infty}^{r} = \frac{Q}{Kr}$$

Consequently, the potential at a point R distant r cm. from a point charge of Q units is

$$V = \frac{Q}{Kr} \tag{132}$$

and is expressed in electrostatic units of potential, or ergs per unit charge.

The difference in potential between two points would be found by subtracting the potential at one point from that at the other point. This difference represents the work done in moving a unit positive charge from one point to the other. In practice, difference in potential is used more often than absolute values.

Potential is completely expressed by a statement of magnitude; it is therefore a scalar quantity. The potential at a single point due to several charges would be found by adding algebraically the individual potentials due to the several charges.

The work done in transferring a quantity of electricity from one point to another in an electric field can now be determined readily. Since the work done in transferring unit charge between two points is equal to the potential difference V between the points, the work done in transferring any charge Q between these points is

$$W = Q V \qquad (133)$$

It will be clear that if Q is expressed in units of charge and V is in ergs per unit charge, the work will be in ergs.

Suppose that two charges of $+600$ units and $+500$ units are spaced 12 cm. apart in air, and that it is desired to compute the work needed to reduce their separation to 10 cm. Supposing the 600-unit charge to remain at rest, the potential which it establishes at a point 12 cm. away is $V_{12} = 600/12 = 50$ and at a point 10 cm. away is $V_{10} = 600/10 = 60$, both expressed in ergs per unit charge. The work needed to move the 500-unit charge through the potential difference of 10 ergs per unit charge is $500 \times 10 = 5000$ ergs. The same result can be obtained by supposing the 500-unit charge to be fixed and to establish a potential difference through which the 600-unit charge is then moved.

Work must be done to move a positive charge from a point of low potential to one of high potential; under the same circumstances a negative charge would move of itself, if free to do so, and would do work in the process. Thus, the free electrons in a conductor will move, producing an electric current, if there is a potential difference between any two points on the conductor. Further, if a conductor bears a charge which is not moving to produce a current, its surface must have the same potential at all points. Such a surface is called an *equipotential* surface, and it follows from the definition of potential that no work would be required to transport electricity from one point on it to another.

A conductor isolated in space and charged with an amount Q will have an equipotential surface and its potential V will be proportional to Q. The relationship between these two factors can be expressed as

$$Q = C V \qquad (134)$$

where C is a constant determined by the size and shape of the particular conductor and called its *capacitance*. For a charged sphere mounted so as to be undisturbed by neighboring charges, the capacitance can be evaluated easily. The field about such a body extends radially from the sphere and has the same outward appearance as though its charge were concentrated at the center. The potential at any distance r from such a concentrated charge in a vacuum ($K = 1$) is given by equation (132) as $V = \dfrac{Q}{r}$, and this would necessarily be the potential of the surface of a concentric sphere of radius r. It follows that the capacitance of the sphere is

$$C = \frac{Q}{V} = \frac{Q}{\dfrac{Q}{r}} = r;$$

in the electrostatic system of units the capacitance of an isolated conducting sphere is equal to its radius in centimeters. The capacitance of a conductor is increased by bringing a second conductor near it. Such a combination forms a *condenser* and will be treated in a later chapter.

203. Field between Parallel Charged Plates. — The electric field between two parallel plates, charged as in Fig. 214, is uniform, having the same intensity at

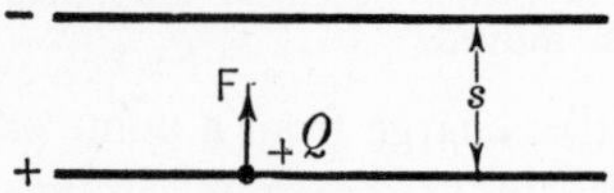

Fig. 214. Field between parallel plates

all points, except at the edges, and the edge irregularities may be neglected if the plates are large compared with the distance between them. Under these conditions, the field intensity can be computed by considering the work done by a charge in moving from one plate to the other. Thus, in the figure, the work done by the charge $+ Q$ in moving from the positive plate to the negative one in the direction of the field will be some force F multiplied by the distance s between the plates. This amount of work can also be expressed as QV from equation (133), where V is the potential difference between the plates. Hence $Fs = QV$, or $F/Q = V/s$. But F/Q, being the force per unit charge, is the field intensity, by equation (130). Whence, the field between the plates has an intensity given by

$$\mathscr{E} = \frac{V}{s} \qquad\qquad (135)$$

If V is in ergs per unit charge and s is in centimeters, $\mathscr{E}$ will be in dynes per unit charge, as previously.

204. Measurement of the Electronic Charge. — An achievement of fundamental importance concerning the nature of electricity was the determination of the charge of the electron by Robert A. Millikan in 1913. His method consists essentially of

charging a tiny oil drop, placing it in an electric field so directed
as to urge the droplet upward against the pull of gravity, and regulating the field strength so as to hold the droplet stationary.
Under this condition the upward force due to the field will equal
the downward force of gravity, a fact which permits the quantity
of electricity on the droplet to be computed.

Millikan's apparatus, shown in Fig. 215, consists of a closed
chamber C containing near the top an atomizer A, and near the
bottom a pair of parallel plates PP which can be connected across
the battery B. The plates are separated by a few insulating
blocks, not shown, and the air between them is ionized by x-rays

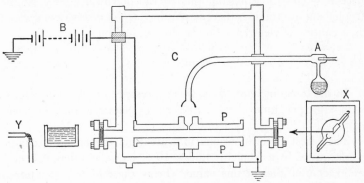

FIG. 215.   Millikan's oil-drop apparatus

from the tube X.   The central region between the plates is illuminated by the arc lamp Y, and observations are made there by
means of a telescope at the front.

Oil is sprayed from the atomizer into the chamber and falls as a
mist, some of the droplets entering the space between the plates,
the upper one of which is pierced with a pinhole for this purpose.
After a droplet is singled out, a preliminary measurement is made
with the plates uncharged to determine its velocity of free fall;
this is done by noting the time required to fall a small known
distance. A knowledge of this velocity makes it possible to
determine the radius of the droplet from Stokes's Law [§ 134],
which gives the radius of the droplet as

$$r = \sqrt{\frac{9\,\eta\,v}{2\,d\,g}}$$

where η is the coefficient of viscosity of the air, d is the density
of the oil, g is the acceleration due to gravity, and v is the velocity

of the droplet. The mass m of the droplet can then be found from its radius and density, namely,

$$m = \tfrac{4}{3}\pi\, r^3 d$$

The plates PP are next connected across the battery, and the potential difference between them is adjusted to a value V such that the droplet under investigation will remain stationary at some convenient point between the plates. The electric field strength under this condition will be $\mathscr{E} = V/s$, where s represents the separation of the plates. If the droplet has acquired an amount of electricity Q from the ionized air, it will experience an upward force $F = QV/s$. Equating this to the downward force on the droplet due to gravity, there is obtained $QV/s = m\,g$, from which the quantity of electricity on the droplet becomes

$$Q = \frac{m\,g\,s}{V}$$

In the foregoing equations, Q is expressed in units of charge, V is in ergs per unit charge, and all mechanical quantities are expressed in the c.g.s. system of units.

The latest determinations indicate that the smallest charge ever acquired by a droplet is 4.80×10^{-10} e.s.u., and that all others are exact multiples of this value. From these facts it is inferred that electricity consists of tiny discrete charges, and that the elementary quantity, the charge of the electron, is $e = 4.80 \times 10^{-10}$ e.s.u. No electrical charge smaller than this has ever been discovered.

205. Some Ionization Effects in Gases. — The process of ionization whereby a gas becomes conducting was described in § 196. Some of the effects produced by this action will serve to illustrate the principles of electrostatics.

Under certain atmospheric conditions the clouds gather electricity, either by contact of electrically dissimilar layers of air or by the falling of charged rain drops, and this induces a charge of opposite sign on the surface of the earth below. If the intervening electric field is sufficiently intense, a disruptive discharge will occur as a stroke of lightning. To protect buildings and other structures from damage which may result from lightning strokes, they are equipped with *lightning rods*. These are large conductors, well grounded at the bottom and terminating in sharp points at the top, arranged to form as complete an enclosure of the building as is practicable. Such an arrangement tends to prevent the interior of the building from becoming electrically charged, since it forms at least a partial conducting shell around it. It also allows the electricity induced on the neighboring portion of the earth to escape from the sharp points and in this way tends to prevent the accumulation of sufficient charge to result in a lightning stroke. In the event of a stroke, the large conductors provide a low-resistance path for the current and tend to divert it from the building. Although there is no doubt that buildings equipped with lightning rods have been injured by lightning, nevertheless, a well designed and properly installed system of lightning rods is recognized as a valuable safeguard against such injury.

Gaseous ionization is utilized in electrostatic precipitation. In the *Cottrell process* for smoke elimination a long negatively charged wire is suspended vertically within the column of rising smoke. A wire of small diameter is purposely used so that it will have a large surface density of charge, and an intense field will be set up in the region directly around it. Here the gas becomes ionized by collision and the suspended carbon particles acquire negative charges by contact with the gaseous ions. They are then repelled by the negative wire and deposited on the surrounding walls.

Luminous tube lamps and many rectifier and electron tubes also depend upon ionization for their operation.

*206. Isotopes. — Not all atoms of a chemical element are alike, for some are heavier than others. Elements containing atoms that have the same atomic number but different atomic weights are called *isotopes*, the difference between them depending upon the number of neutrons in the atomic nucleus. Most elements consist of two or more isotopes. Chlorine has two isotopes, of atomic weights 35 and 37, mixed in a proportion which yields an average of 35.46. Similarly, lithium has stable isotopes of atomic weights 6 and 7, the average being 6.94. The chemical properties of the isotopes of an element are of the same kind but there are differences in the rate or extent to which certain reactions take place. Isotopes are not given special names except in the case of hydrogen; its isotope of atomic weight 1 is called hydrogen, and that of atomic weight 2 is called deuterium.

Many isotopes have been formed by bombarding atoms with tiny high-speed particles like neutrons and the nuclei of hydrogen and helium. If a nucleus of deuterium, called a *deuteron*, strikes the nucleus of a lithium atom of atomic weight 6, the impact may produce a lithium nucleus of atomic weight 7. The reaction may be expressed as

$$_3\text{Li}^6 + {}_1\text{H}^2 \rightarrow {}_4\text{Be}^8 \rightarrow {}_3\text{Li}^7 + {}_1\text{H}^1$$

where the subscripts represent the atomic numbers and the super-scripts the atomic weights. Thus, the deuteron and the lithium nucleus combine producing a beryllium nucleus with a great deal of excess energy, which immediately breaks up to form the heavy isotope of lithium and a proton. A different result is obtained if a deuteron strikes a lithium nucleus of atomic weight 7. The deuteron is absorbed by the struck nucleus forming beryllium of atomic weight 9, which then disintegrates, the reaction being

$$_3\text{Li}^7 + {}_1\text{H}^2 \rightarrow {}_4\text{Be}^9 \rightarrow {}_2\text{He}^4 + {}_2\text{He}^4 + {}_0\text{n}^1$$

where n represents a neutron. The result is not another isotope but another element; a heavy lithium nucleus is *transmuted* into two nuclei of helium.

PROBLEMS

1. Two small objects carrying positive charges of 10 e.s.u. and 100 e.s.u. respectively are spaced 5 cm. apart in a horizontal plane, the surrounding medium being air. How much force does each exert upon the other?

2. The practical unit of electric quantity, called the coulomb, is equal to 3×10^9 e.s.u. of charge. If it were possible to bring a charge of 1 coulomb to a point in air 1 cm. away from another just like it, what force in tons would these charges exert upon each other?

3. A charge of $+1000$ e.s.u. is situated 100 cm. in air from a charge of -800 e.s.u. Compute the force upon each.

4. At what speed must the electron in the hydrogen atom revolve to prevent it from being pulled in to the nucleus by electrostatic attraction, if the radius of its orbit is taken as 0.5×10^{-8} cm.?

5. A charge of $+40$ e.s.u. experiences a downward force of 500 dynes at a certain point in an electric field. Find the field intensity at that point.

6. A charged body which weighs 0.01 gm. is held stationary in space by placing it in an upwardly directed electric field having an intensity of 10 dynes per unit charge. Find the charge on the body.

7. (a) Find the field intensity and the potential at a point midway between the charges described in Problem 1. (b) Find the field intensity and the potential at a point 4 cm. vertically below the smaller charge.

8. Find the potential at a point 20 cm. from a charge of $+1000$ e.s.u. in a vacuum, and also at a second point 10 cm. from this charge. How much work would be necessary in order to move a quantity of $+5$ e.s.u. from one of these points to the other?

9. Referring to the charges described in Problem 3, find the field intensity and also the potential at a point 75 cm. away from the 1000-e.s.u. charge and on the line connecting the two.

10. A charge of $+10$ e.s.u. is located 20 cm. in air from another of $+1000$ e.s.u. How much work is needed to move either one a distance of 10 cm. toward the other?

11. Two horizontal plates, each 12 cm. in diameter, are spaced 0.3 cm. apart in air. A drop of oil of radius 0.00006 cm. and of density 0.86 gm./cm.^{3} is introduced into the region between the plates. If the drop carries 3 electrons, what potential difference must be maintained between the plates in order to hold the drop at rest?

12. A particle of radius r carrying a charge Q is located in an electric field of intensity $\mathscr{E}$, the surrounding medium having a coefficient of viscosity η. Show by means of Stokes's Law that the velocity of the particle due to the field can be expressed as $v = \dfrac{\mathscr{E}Q}{6\pi\,\eta\,r}$.

13. Suppose a charged dust particle of 0.001 mm. diameter to be located in a horizontal electric field having an intensity of 5 dynes per unit charge, the surrounding medium being air at 20° C., for which the coefficient of viscosity may be taken as 181×10^{-6} poise. Using the expression developed in Problem 12, find the number of electrons on the dust particle if it travels a horizontal distance of 2 cm. in 0.68 sec.

CHAPTER XXI

MAGNETISM

207. Magnets. — A *magnet* is a body which has the property of attracting iron and steel, and which if suspended freely will turn so as to point in a definite direction. The magnet will also attract certain other materials, such as nickel and cobalt, although rather feebly. Any material which a magnet attracts is known as a *magnetic substance*.

The property of magnetism has been known for centuries. Ancients recognized that a black mineral ore called lodestone or magnetite exhibited this property, and there is evidence to show that the word magnetism was derived from the name of a district in Asia Minor, Magnesia, where the ore was plentiful. The approximate composition of this natural magnet is Fe_3O_4.

A bar of steel can be made into a magnet very simply; it is only necessary to rub it with a piece of lodestone or with another magnet. It can be magnetized much more strongly, however, by placing it within a coil of wire carrying an electric current. When the bar is of hard steel, it holds its magnetism for long periods of time and becomes a *permanent magnet*. Soft iron does not have such permanence. If a soft-iron bar is placed inside the coil just mentioned, forming what is known as an *electromagnet*, it will be magnetized strongly while there is a current in the winding, but will lose almost all of its magnetism as soon as the current is interrupted, retaining only a small amount known as *residual* magnetism. The magnetizing action of the electric current is explained in § 249.

208. Magnetic Poles. — Experiment shows that magnetism is not exhibited uniformly over the surface of a magnet; the regions where its effects are pronounced are called *poles*. A straight magnet, for example, if dipped in iron filings will attract them in large clusters near its ends and will show practically no attraction at its center; thus such a magnet as ordinarily made has two poles. Precise tests reveal the fact that *the two poles of a magnet have exactly the same strength.*

It is also found that when a bar magnet or a magnetized needle is suspended or pivoted it rotates to a general north-and-south direction, and the same end always points toward the north. This fact suggested appropriate names for the two magnetic poles. The magnet pole which points to the arctic region of the earth is termed the north-seeking pole, or briefly the *north* (N) pole of the magnet; the other is termed the *south* (S) pole.

If a bar magnet is brought near another, it will be observed that the north pole of one attracts the south pole of the other, that the two north poles repel each other, and that the two south poles repel each other. In short, *unlike magnetic poles attract each other; like poles repel.*

The magnitude of the force between two magnetic poles was measured by Coulomb in 1785, using a torsion balance as in the study of electrostatic forces, but substituting magnetic poles for the electric charges. His results, later confirmed with greater accuracy, showed that the force is proportional to the pole strengths and inversely proportional to the square of the distance between the poles. Thus, if two magnetic poles have strengths of m_1 and m_2 units, and if the distance between them is r cm., then the force action between them in dynes is

$$F = \frac{m_1 m_2}{\mu \, r^2} \qquad (136)$$

whether the action is one of attraction or of repulsion. The constant μ depends on the medium in which the two poles are located, and is called the *permeability* of the medium. Its value is unity for a vacuum and but slightly different from unity for air. The equation assumes that the poles are concentrated at points.

This equation not only shows the factors which determine the force of one pole upon another, but serves also to define the unit of pole strength. Thus, *a unit magnet pole is one of such strength that it will exert a force of 1 dyne upon an equal pole in vacuum (or air) when placed 1 cm. away from it.* There is no characteristic name for this unit of pole strength, it is merely called *unit pole.*

As an application of the Inverse Square Law of magnetic action, equation (136), consider two bar magnets 10 cm. long placed in one line with their N poles 5 cm. apart and their S poles 25 cm. apart. Assume that each pole has a strength of 200 units, that it is localized in a central point on the end face of the magnet, and that the medium is air. There will be four force actions:

Repulsion $\dfrac{200 \times 200}{(5)^2} = 1600$ dynes; $\dfrac{200 \times 200}{(25)^2} = 64$ dynes.

Attraction $\dfrac{200 \times 200}{(15)^2} = 178$ dynes; $\dfrac{200 \times 200}{(15)^2} = 178$ dynes.

Thus, the net force will be a repulsion of $1600 + 64 - 2(178) = 1308$ dynes.

209. The Magnetic Field. — The region about a magnet where its influence can be detected is called a *magnetic field*. Throughout this region forces will act upon magnetic substances or magnet poles. The force that is experienced by any given pole within the field will vary in direction and in amount as that pole is moved about, and this fact indicates that the magnetic field must have a certain direction and a particular intensity at every point. *The direction of a magnetic field is that of the force acting upon an isolated* N *pole*; the idea of an isolated pole is a convenient concept which implies that the companion pole of the magnet is too far away to affect the resulting action appreciably. *The intensity of the magnetic field at any point is defined as the force that would be exerted upon a unit pole placed there.*

The unit of field intensity is called the *oersted*, and is named after Hans Christian Oersted (1777–1851), the Danish physicist who discovered electromagnetism. It was formerly called the gauss [§ 254], and the change was made by the International Electrotechnical Commission in 1930. *The oersted is the intensity of a magnetic field in which a unit magnet pole experiences a force of 1 dyne.* From this definition it follows that if at any point in a magnetic field, a pole of strength m units experiences a force of F dynes, the field intensity at that point in oersteds will be

$$H = \frac{F}{m} \tag{137}$$

Thus, if an isolated pole of 20 units strength placed at some point in a magnetic field is acted upon by a force of 240 dynes, the field intensity at that point is $240 \div 20 = 12$ oersteds.

The foregoing facts explain the behavior of a suspended magnet in seeking a position of equilibrium within a magnetic field of uniform intensity. The magnet, of length l cm. between poles, is shown in the plan view of Fig. 216 to be displaced at an angle θ from the direction of the field, the field being represented by the light arrows. From equation (137) the N pole of the magnet is acted upon by a force $F = mH$, where m is the pole strength and H is the field intensity. The torque of this force to produce rotation about the center is $Fd = F\dfrac{l}{2} \sin \theta$. The force on the S pole produces a torque of the same value and direction, consequently the total torque is

$$T' = 2mH\frac{l}{2} \sin \theta = MH \sin \theta$$

where $M = ml$ is a constant of the magnet called its *magnetic moment*. This torque tends to lessen the angle θ, and the magnet, because of its inertia, will oscillate until friction brings it to rest in the direction of the field.

If a light magnet is mounted on a piece of cork and floated on water in a uniform magnetic field, it will be observed to rotate in the manner described. Furthermore, it will have no motion of translation, showing that the uniform field acts equally but oppositely upon the two poles. This result confirms a previous statement that the two poles of a magnet are equal in strength.

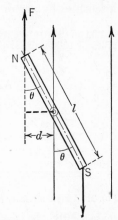

FIG. 216. Magnet oscillating in a magnetic field

210. Field Near a Magnet Pole.—Upon exploring the region around a magnet pole it is found that the magnetic field is not uniform, but diminishes rapidly in intensity as the distance from the pole is increased. Suppose that the intensity of a field around a pole of strength m is to be determined at any point distant r from the pole, and imagine a test pole of N polarity and of strength m_1 to be placed at this point. If the field there has an intensity H, as yet unknown, the test pole will experience a force Hm_1. It is apparent that pole m_1 is separated from pole m by a distance r and that the force action between them can also be expressed by equation (136) as $F = \dfrac{m\,m_1}{\mu r^2}$, both poles being regarded as point poles. Since the two foregoing expressions must represent the same force, they may be equated, giving as the field intensity at the point in question:

$$H = \frac{m}{\mu r^2} \tag{138}$$

This expression shows that the field intensity produced by a magnet pole varies inversely with the square of the distance from the pole; specifically, it gives the field intensity in oersteds due to an isolated pole of strength m units at a point r cm. away in a region of permeability μ.

The direction of the field, being that in which a free N test pole would move, is radially outward from a N pole and radially inward toward a S pole. The intensity and direction of the field at any specified point due to a magnet can be obtained by applying equation (138) to both poles, and combining the component intensities by vector addition.

As an illustrative problem, suppose that the bar magnet in Fig. 217 has poles of 1600 units strength spaced 10 cm. apart, and that it is desired to compute the field intensity at point A in the surrounding air, this point being 10 cm. from N and 8 cm. from S. The field intensity at A has two components, $\frac{1600}{(10)^2} = 16$ oersteds directed away from N, and $\frac{1600}{(8)^2} = 25$ oersteds directed toward S. Since the triangle NAS is isosceles, the angles at A and S will each be $\cos^{-1} 4/10 = 66.4°$, as indicated in the figure; consequently the angle between the two field components will be $180° - 66.4° = 113.6°$. The resultant field intensity at A is given by equation (8) as $H = \sqrt{(16)^2 + (25)^2 + 2 \times 16 \times 25 \cos 113.6°} = 23.6$ oersteds. Application of the Law of Sines shows the resultant to make an angle of $38.1°$ with the component toward S; it is therefore directed at an angle of $66.4 - 38.1 = 28.3°$ down from the horizontal datum.

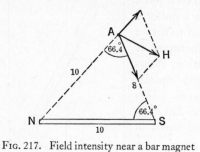

FIG. 217.   Field intensity near a bar magnet

211. The Earth's Magnetic Field.

The fact, mentioned in § 207, that a suspended magnet orients itself in a particular direction at every point on or near the earth, shows that the earth is surrounded by a magnetic field. The distribution of the field is such as might be produced by a huge bar magnet within the earth, located about 17° away from its axis and having a length much less than the earth's diameter. The two places at the earth's surface where the field is vertical are called the magnetic poles. The magnetic pole in the northern hemisphere is on Boothia Peninsula in Northern Canada (latitude 70° N., longitude 96° W.), and the one in the southern hemisphere is near Ross Sea, Antarctica (latitude 72° S., longitude 157° E.). The magnetic equator is

an irregular line varying in latitude from 15° S. in South America
to 20° N in Africa.

The alignment of a light pivoted magnet with the earth's magnetic field makes possible its use as a *compass* for guidance in travel
and navigation.   Such use dates back a number of centuries, and
there is evidence to show
that pieces of lodestone
were suspended for this
purpose by the Chinese
perhaps as far back as ten
centuries B.C.   A modern
magnetic compass is shown
in Fig. 218.   At the center
of the card carrying the
scale is a spheroidal air
vessel to buoy the card
and magnets, which are
immersed in a mixture of
water and alcohol that
entirely fills the bowl.
The magnets are visible

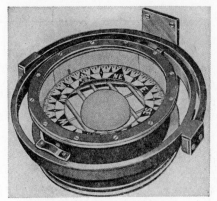

FIG. 218.   Liquid-type compass
(Courtesy of E. F. Ritchie & Sons)

below the card and are formed of sealed cylindrical tubes filled
with magnetized steel wires.

Naturally the N pole of a compass points to the earth's magnetic pole in the northern hemisphere; this terrestrial pole must
have south polarity in order to attract the N pole of the compass
needle, but this fact need cause no confusion.   Since this magnetic
pole is far away (about 1400 miles) from the north geographic pole,
the compass will not point true north, and the angle that it makes
with the geographic meridian is called the *declination* of the compass.   A compass at New York City points $11\frac{1}{2}$° west, and at San
Francisco points 18° east, of geographic (true) north.   Fig. 219
shows a chart on which points of equal magnetic declination are
connected by lines, the amount and direction of declination being
indicated; these lines are called *isogonic lines.*   The isogonic line
for which the declination is zero is indicated by a heavy line;
it is called an *agonic line.*   At a place through which an agonic
line passes, a compass needle will point true north.

The declination at any place does not remain the same year
after year, but changes somewhat over long periods of time.
Besides these so-called *secular changes,* there are variations within

the year and also changes of small extent throughout the day. Large erratic variations occur during "magnetic storms"; these are often concurrent with the appearance of sun-spots. Much work has been done in attempting to explain terrestrial magnetism and to account for its variations, but too little is known at present about the magnetic sources within the earth and about atmos-

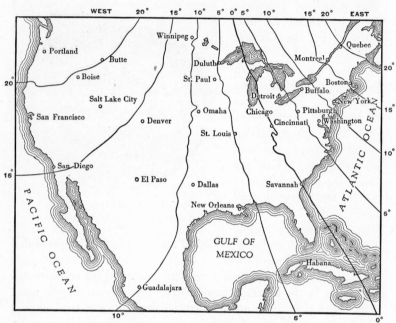

FIG. 219.   Isogonic lines for the United States (1935)
(*Courtesy of U. S. Department of Commerce*)

pheric currents to establish a satisfying theory of the earth's magnetism.

The direction of the earth's magnetic field is not horizontal (except at the magnetic equator), as can readily be observed by balancing a magnetized needle on a horizontal spindle, and placing it so that its vertical plane of movement includes the direction of the field.   At New York such a *dip needle* would point downward at an angle of 72° with the horizontal.

Calling the intensity of the earth's field H_e, and the angle of dip β, the horizontal and vertical components of the earth's field become respectively

$$H_h = H_e \cos \beta \quad \text{and} \quad H_v = H_e \sin \beta$$

It is the horizontal component which is most frequently utilized in magnetic measurements.   Its greatest value is 0.40 oersted in the Gulf of Siam, and its value in the United States ranges from 0.14 to 0.28 oersted.

212. The Magnetometer. — Theoretically, the intensity of a magnetic field can be measured by observing the force acting upon an isolated magnet pole of known pole strength placed in it, and then applying equation (137); but since magnet poles do not exist singly, it is customary to make measurements of field intensity with an instrument called a *magnetometer*.   In this device, a small magnetic needle is delicately pivoted or suspended without appreciable torsional control, and the needle is provided with a pointer, or a mirror and scale arrangement is used, in order to observe the deflection.   A measurement is made by comparing the field to be measured with another that is taken as a standard;   the latter may be the earth's field if its value is definitely known, or else may be produced by an electric current [§ 250].

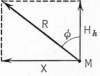

To measure the magnetic field X shown in the plan view, Fig. 220, it is arranged horizontally to be at right angles to the earth's field of known horizontal intensity H_h.   The needle of the magnetometer placed at M will point in direction H_h when the unknown field X is

FIG. 220. Measurement of a magnetic field

absent, and will point in the direction of the resultant R of the two fields when both act upon the instrument   The angle of deflection of the needle from one position to the other is observed. Calling this angle ϕ, it follows that the intensity of the field under test is expressed in terms of the known intensity H_h as

$$X = H_h \tan \phi \qquad (139)$$

This method was applied years ago to the measurement of current in an instrument called the tangent galvanometer.

The rate of vibration of a magnetic needle in a field also gives a measure of the intensity of that field, for it can be shown in a manner similar to that for a physical pendulum [§ 90] that the time of one vibration of small amplitude is

$$T = 2\pi \sqrt{\frac{I}{MH}}$$

where I is the moment of inertia of the magnet about its center, and M is its magnetic moment.

213. Magnetic Lines of Force. — The configuration of a magnetic field can be observed by placing a sheet of glass or cardboard in the region being surveyed and sprinkling it with iron filings. Upon tapping the sheet, the filings align themselves with the field and form strings or chains, as are represented in Fig. 221 for a bar magnet. Such tests indicate that the space around a magnet is in a peculiar magnetic condition. Faraday regarded it to be in a state of stress, whereby it is able to exert a force on any pole brought into it. Lines drawn along the direction of the field will indicate the directions of the forces and are called appropriately *lines of force*. The iron filings in the test just described lie along such lines.

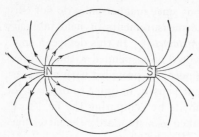

Fig. 221.   Lines of force about a bar magnet

Lines of force are directed *away from the* N *pole* of a magnet and *toward the* S *pole*, and since the field can have only one direction at a given point, the *lines of force never cross one another*. The magnetic stresses produced by the field can be pictured by imagining that the lines tend to shorten themselves (like stretched elastic bands) and that lines extending side by side exert a sidewise thrust upon one another. The attraction or repulsion between two magnets can then be ascribed to the interactions of lines of force in the intervening field. The concept of lines of force has its chief value in directing attention to the important part played by the medium surrounding the magnet poles in determining their force actions.

214. Theory of Magnetism. — An explanation of magnetism is suggested by a simple test which consists of breaking a magnet in two, then breaking one of these parts in two, and so on. As far as actual tests like this have been carried out the parts of the original magnet are always found *to be magnets themselves*, so it is presumed that if the breaking process were continued until parts of molecular magnitude were reached, each minute part would prove to be a magnet. The hypothesis that a magnetic substance is composed of molecular magnets, not necessarily that each molecule be a magnet, is called the *molecular theory of magnetism*.

According to this theory, when a substance is unmagnetized its molecular magnets point in all conceivable directions and form small stable groups that exhibit no outside magnetism. When placed in a magnetic field, the molecular magnets align themselves more and more in a definite direction as the intensity of the field is increased, and magnetic poles of increasing strength are produced in the substance. Hard steel requires a more intense field than soft iron to produce a given magnetization, because its molecular magnets turn with greater difficulty; for the same reason, upon withdrawal of the field most of the molecular magnets of the steel retain their positions, while most of those of the iron again assume random positions. This explains the difference in behavior of permanent magnets and electromagnets, and accounts for residual magnetism in the latter.

If a bar of unmagnetized steel is held in the direction of the earth's field and jarred by striking it repeatedly, some of the molecular magnets will align themselves with the field, and the bar will become permanently magnetized. On the other hand, if a permanent magnet is heated to a dull red, the increased motion of the molecules will throw them out of their orderly arrangement, and the magnet will lose its magnetism.

Again, if a piece of unmagnetized iron or other magnetic substance is placed in a magnetic field, its molecular magnets will align themselves with the field to a certain extent, and poles are *induced* in the specimen so long as it remains in the field. It is because of these induced poles that a magnet attracts a piece of unmagnetized iron.

A more complete theory attributes magnetism to the motion of electrons within the atom, for it is known that a moving electron constitutes an electric current and that an electric current produces a magnetic effect. It is believed from spectrum analysis that the planetary electrons in the atom not only revolve about the nucleus but also that each electron spins about an axis through its center, and that in the crystals of highly magnetic substances each atom has more electrons spinning in one direction than in the other. Throughout a tiny region called a "domain" these uncompensated spins have the same directions in the atoms of all the crystals, and the entire magnetic specimen is composed of a large number of such domains, these being highly magnetized but turned at random with respect to one another. When a small external field is applied, the direction of magnetization of the individual crystals is shifted toward that of the field and the specimen becomes slightly magnetized. Upon increasing the strength of the applied field, a value is reached at which the domains themselves are rotated until the axes of magnetization of all crystals lie along the direction of the field. Beyond this point, an increase in the applied field produces no further effect.

PROBLEMS

1. A magnet 12 cm. long has poles of 300 units strength at its ends. It is suspended horizontally over an identical magnet that is located directly below it on a table. What is the vertical force between the magnets when they are 9 cm. apart and in the same vertical plane?

2. Two bar magnets, one 10 cm. long and having poles of 300 units strength and the other 12 cm. long and having poles of 400 units strength, are placed in a straight line with their N poles 3 cm. apart and their S poles 25 cm. apart. Compute the force between the magnets.

3. An isolated N magnet pole of 10 units strength experiences a force to the right of 80 dynes at a certain point in a magnetic field. Compute the field intensity at that point.

4. A compass needle 6 cm. long and weighing 1.2 gm. is pivoted at its midpoint to swing in a horizontal plane. When the needle is twisted to an east-west position and held there, one of its ends experiences a force of 20 dynes toward the north and the other end experiences an equal force toward the south because of the magnetism of the earth. With what acceleration will the needle start to move when released? Take the moment of inertia of the needle about its midpoint to be one-twelfth of its mass multiplied by the square of its length.

5. Calculate the magnitude of the magnetic field intensities at points along the axis of a bar magnet 10 cm. long, the points being 5, 10, and 20 cm. beyond one end of the magnet. The magnet has poles of 500 units strength.

6. Find the field intensity at a point midway between the N poles of the magnets described in Problem 2.

7. At the Kew Observatory, near London, the horizontal and vertical components of the earth's field were found to be 0.1843 oersted and 0.4336 oersted respectively. Find the intensity and inclination of the earth's field at this point.

8. At Sitka, Alaska, the components of the earth's magnetic field are 0.156 oersted horizontal, and 0.556 vertical. Compute the total intensity and the inclination of the field.

9. A pivoted magnet makes 1 vibration in 3 sec. in a field having an intensity of 0.2 oersted. What is the field intensity in a region where this magnet makes 2 vibrations per sec.?

10. Assuming that each pole of the suspended magnet described in Problem 1 is directly above one having like polarity of the magnet below it, find the field intensity at a point between the magnets and equally distant from all four poles.

11. Suppose a bar magnet 16 cm. long and having a magnetic moment of 8000 units to be supported in a horizontal position; find the field intensity at a point in space 10 cm. vertically above its N pole.

12. Determine the intensity of the magnetic field produced by a given electric current if this field, when arranged horizontally at right angles to the earth's field of horizontal intensity 0.22 oersted, displaces a compass needle through an angle of 55°.

13. If the compass needle described in Problem 4 has poles of 100 units strength, compute the frequency with which it will oscillate in coming to rest in a magnetic field of horizontal intensity 0.2 oersted.

CHAPTER XXII

CURRENT AND RESISTANCE

215. Electric Current. — When the potential at one end of a conducting wire is different from the potential at the other, the free electrons in it will undergo a drift or flow. Such a flow takes place in an electric lamp, for example, when a potential difference is applied across its terminals, and the lamp is said to have an *electric current* in its wire filament. In order for this flow to continue, the potential difference must be maintained by some electrical *source*, such as a battery or generator, connected across the ends of the filament. The source and lamp together with the connecting wires form a complete conducting path, or *circuit*; the part external to the source is called the *external circuit*.

The current is capable of producing a number of effects in electric circuits; the principal ones, familiar to most observers, are *heat*, *magnetism*, and *electrolysis*. A current in a lamp heats the filament to incandescence, and thereby produces illumination. A current in the electromagnet of a telegraph sounder magnetizes the iron core and causes a pivoted piece of iron to be attracted, thereby producing a click. A current in acidulated water (H_2O)

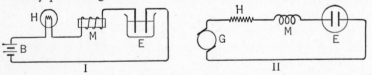

FIG. 222. Circuit to show the three effects of an electric current

causes the liberation of the component gases, hydrogen and oxygen, by electrolysis.

216. The Simple Circuit. — A circuit in which the effects of the current may be demonstrated is shown in Fig. 222. In part I a battery B supplies current to a lamp H, a coil or electromagnet M, and an electrolytic cell E, these circuit elements being shown pictorially. Part II shows a generator G in a circuit having the same elements represented conventionally.

A battery or direct-current generator urges the electrons continuously in one direction. If it is desired to have them flow in the opposite direction in the external circuit, the terminals of that circuit must be reversed with respect to the battery or generator terminals. For this reason, these sources of electricity are said to have fixed polarity, and one terminal of the source is called positive and the other negative.

From the early days of electrical science, current has been considered to flow in the external circuit from the positive terminal of the source to its negative terminal. It is now known that a current is actually a movement of electrons, and since these are negative, they travel around the external circuit from the negative terminal to the positive terminal. The flow of electrons is, therefore, opposite to the conventional direction of the current, making it necessary, in order to avoid confusion, to distinguish one direction from the other by name. It is customary to speak of *electron flow* as taking place from negative to positive, and *current flow* from positive to negative. Strictly speaking, the expression "current flow" is a poor one for the word "current" itself means flow; it will be heard often because of its rather common use in engineering.

Most electric generators are of the alternating-current type, that is, they urge the electrons in one direction around a circuit for a brief interval and then in the other direction for a corresponding interval, the reversals of direction taking place many times per second and as long as the circuit is closed. Alternating currents produce the same effects as direct currents, but the electrolysis developed for one direction of flow will neutralize that for the other direction, consequently there is no purpose in having electrolytic cells in circuits carrying such currents. On the other hand, these circuits often include *condensers*, which consist of two sets of metal plates separated by some insulating material; these store electrical energy momentarily for purposes that will be explained later.

The characteristics of the various circuit elements above mentioned will be considered in the chapters to follow, and attention will first be given to the study of direct currents.

217. The Coulomb and the Ampere. — The electrostatic unit of charge is so small a quantity of electricity that for practical purposes a larger unit called the *coulomb* is used. *A coulomb is a* *quantity of electricity equal to 3 × 10⁹ electrostatic units of charge;* the reason for using this particular number will be apparent after the magnetic effect of the current has been considered [§ 250]. Since the charge of the electron is 4.80×10^{-10} e.s.u. of charge, it follows that a coulomb is a charge of $3 \times 10^9 \div 4.80 \times 10^{-10}$ or 6.25×10^{18} electrons.

The magnitude of an electric current in a circuit expresses the rate at which electrons drift through it, that is, *the time rate of flow of electric charge.* The unit of flow is appropriately taken as the transfer of one coulomb of charge per second of time past some point in the circuit. Because the concept of current is so commonly used, a shorter name is applied; the unit is called the *ampere* (abbreviated amp.) and is named after the French scientist, André M. Ampère (1775–1836). *The ampere is a rate of flow of electric charge of one coulomb per second.* If electricity flows at a uniform rate such that Q coulombs pass a point in t sec., the current at that point, expressed in amperes, is

$$I = \frac{Q}{t} \tag{140}$$

The current in a circuit is measured by an instrument called an *ammeter.*

Electric current is sometimes confused with electric charge. The difference can be explained through analogy with hydraulics, by assuming a pump to circulate water in a pipe line, just as a battery or generator circulates charges in an electrical circuit. The quantity of water would be reckoned in gallons while the charge would be in coulombs. The rate of flow of water past any point in the piping would be expressed in gallons per second while the flow of electricity would be in coulombs per second (or amperes).

218. Electromotive Force and Potential Drop; the Volt. — In the study of electrostatics it was found that work is always done in moving an electric charge between two points which have different potentials. The work done is equal to the product of the charge and the potential difference, in accordance with equation (133). This statement applies also to the circulation of charge around an electric circuit. The *charge does work* in traversing the circuit, as evidenced by the evolution of heat and the operation of electromechanical devices; the *charge has an equal amount of work done upon it* as it moves through the battery or other source of electrical energy. The battery or other source is said to have an *electro-*

motive force (abbreviated e.m.f.), which is measured by the work done upon each unit of charge as it passes through the source.

A source within which a charge Q has an amount of work W done upon it has an electromotive force given by

$$E = \frac{W}{Q} \tag{141}$$

Also, the work done by a unit charge in passing between two points of a circuit is equal to the *potential drop* between those points. If W is now taken to represent the work done by the charge Q in moving between two such points, the potential drop between the points is

$$V = \frac{W}{Q} \tag{142}$$

The term *potential difference* applies to both e.m.f. and potential drop; the practical unit is the *volt*. *The potential difference between two points is one volt if a charge of one coulomb either requires or expends one joule of energy in moving from one point to the other.* This unit was named after the Italian physicist, Alessandro Volta (1745–1827). In equations (141) and (142), if E and V are expressed in volts, W is in joules, and Q is in coulombs.

To give a practical idea of the volt, a few illustrations will be cited. The e.m.f. of the familiar dry cell is 1.5 volts. Practically all electric lamps are illuminated by direct or alternating current supplied at 110 to 120 volts. Many direct-current railways are operated on 500 to 600 volts. For long-distance transmission of electrical energy, values over 100,000 volts are often employed.

Since the energy which the charge receives from the source must be the same as that which it expends throughout the circuit, it follows that the e.m.f. of the source must equal the sum of the potential drops around the circuit.

The difference of potential between two points in an electric circuit is measured by an instrument, called a *voltmeter*, by merely connecting the instrument across the points under consideration.

219. Electrical Energy and Power. — It was shown in the foregoing section that the electrical energy supplied to a circuit by a source of e.m.f. E is given by $W = E\,Q$, but this result can be expressed more usefully in terms of the current I rather than the charge Q. Since the quantity of charge transferred is equal to the average current multiplied by the time of transfer, or $Q = It$, the energy may be expressed as

$$W = EIt \qquad (143)$$

Also, in any portion of a circuit, across which the potential drop is V, the energy liberated is

$$W = VIt \qquad (144)$$

In these expressions the energy W is expressed in joules, the e.m.f. E or potential drop V is in volts, the current I is in amperes, and the time t is in seconds. The energy may appear in any form, such as heat, mechanical energy, and chemical energy.

The rate of expending energy in a circuit is the *power* supplied to it; this is found by differentiating the foregoing expressions with respect to time. Thus, the power supplied to the entire circuit is

$$P = \frac{dW}{dt} = EI \qquad (145)$$

and to a portion of the circuit is

$$P = \frac{dW}{dt} = VI \qquad (146)$$

In these equations the unit in which power is expressed is the joule per second, or watt.

220. Ohm's Law; the Ohm. — Experience with metallic circuits shows that the current established in such a circuit is directly proportional to the e.m.f. of the source, assuming that no other e.m.f.'s are acting in the circuit. Thus, the current I varies directly with the e.m.f. E, and introducing a proportionality constant to form an equation, the expression for the current becomes

$$I = \frac{E}{R} \qquad (147)$$

This relation was first given by Georg S. Ohm (1787–1854), a German physicist, in 1827, and is known as Ohm's Law. The quantity symbolized by R is called *resistance*. It is a property of the circuit somewhat analogous to friction in mechanics and is responsible for the production of heat.

The law states that the current in a circuit equals the e.m.f. in that circuit divided by the resistance of the circuit. Each of the symbols in the equations should be interpreted as applying to the entire circuit, thus R stands for all the resistance of the circuit, including the internal resistance of the source.

Ohm's Law may also be stated for part of a circuit as follows: The current in any part of a circuit equals the potential drop across that part of the circuit divided by the resistance of that part. In symbols

$$I = \frac{V}{R} \tag{148}$$

This equation further serves to establish the unit in which resistance is expressed. Thus, if the potential drop across a resistance is 1 volt when the current in it is 1 ampere, then the resistance must have unit value; this unit is called the *ohm*. *The ohm is a resistance across which there is a potential drop of one volt when the current in it is one ampere.*

A few examples will serve to give an approximate idea of the unit of resistance. A copper wire 1000 ft. long and 0.1 in. in diameter (No. 10 American wire gage) has a resistance of 1 ohm. A copper wire 2.4 ft. long and 0.005 in. diameter (No. 36 A.w.g.) has the same resistance. An iron rod 1 km. long and 1 cm. square also has a resistance of 1 ohm.

The resistance of a wire or device can be determined by connecting it in a circuit to a battery and using an ammeter to measure the current in it and a voltmeter to measure the potential drop across it, as shown in Fig. 223. If the current is I and the potential drop is V, the value of the resistance is $R = V \div I$. The instrument connections shown are also suitable for measuring the

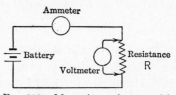

Fig. 223. Measuring resistance with ammeter and voltmeter

power expended in the resistance, this being the product of the ammeter and voltmeter readings, as indicated by equation (146).

The current in a resistance is 0.25 amp. when a potential difference of 120 volts is applied across its terminals. Find the value of the resistance and also the power expended. By Ohm's Law, the resistance is $\frac{120}{0.25} = 480$ ohms. Also, from equation (146), the power expended is $120 \times 0.25 = 30$ watts.

Ohm's Law is one of the most frequently used expressions in electrical work, and it is important to remember that all quantities in the equation must apply to the same circuit or to the same part of a circuit.

221. Joule's Law of Heating. — The flow of electricity through a wire or other conductor of electricity always produces heat. The quantity of heat produced in a given conductor naturally depends upon the duration of flow and upon the value of the current. That twice as much heat will be produced by a given current in 20 seconds as in 10 seconds is to be expected, but how the quantity of heat varies with the current cannot be predicted so simply. Experiment shows that doubling the current *quadruples* the heat developed under like conditions, and that, in general, the heat produced is proportional to the square of the current. Still another factor is involved, namely, the resistance of the conductor. If the same current prevails for equal intervals of time through pieces of wire having the same dimensions, one of copper and the other of iron, the iron will become hotter than the copper; consequently, iron is said to offer more opposition to the current and to have a higher resistance than copper. Summing up, the *heat produced in a conductor is proportional to the resistance of the conductor, to the square of the current, and to the time.* This statement is known as Joule's Law of electric heating.

The amount of energy W converted into heat in a time t, by a current I, in a conductor of resistance R is given by this law as

$$W = R I^2 t \qquad (149)$$

If R is expressed in ohms, I in amperes, and t in seconds, then the energy will be given in joules. The heat developed can be determined in calories by using a constant from § 174 so that

$$H = 0.239 \, R I^2 t$$

When a current of 1 amp. flows for 1 sec. through a conductor of 1 ohm resistance, the amount of heat produced is exactly 1 joule, or 0.239 calorie.

The correctness of these expressions can be verified by using a calorimeter containing oil or other insulating liquid and immersing the conductor in it as shown in Fig. 224. The current can be measured by an ammeter, and the duration of the test by a stop watch. The heat liberated by the conductor is obtained by measuring the water equivalent of the calorimeter and its contents, and observing the change of temperature that occurs during the test [§ 156].

In the experiment just described the electrical energy supplied to the immersed coil is all converted into heat. If the source produces a potential difference of V volts at the heater with a current of I amp., the energy it supplies to the heater in t sec. is VIt, and this must equal the heat energy as expressed by equation (149). Consequently, $VIt = RI^2t$, and

$$V = RI$$

which, of course, is Ohm's Law.

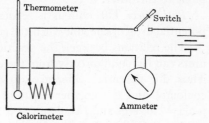

Fig. 224.   Measuring the heat produced by a current

Since the energy appearing as heat is given in joules by $W = RI^2t$, the *power* expended in heat is given in watts by

$$P = RI^2$$

The same expression applies equally well to an entire circuit or to any part of it.

Compute the rating of an electric heater in kilowatts which will heat 10 liters of water from 20° C. to 80° C. in 15 min., assuming that no heat is wasted. What current must be supplied to this heater if its resistance is 5 ohms?   The heat needed is 10,000 × (80 − 20) or 600,000 cal. or 600,000 ÷ 0.239 = 2,511,000 joules.   The power expended is 2,511,000 ÷ (15 × 60) = 2790 joules per sec. or watts; this is equivalent to 2.79 kw. It follows that 2790 = 5 × I^2, from which I = 23.6 amp.

222. The Practical Electrical Units. — For convenience of reference the electrical quantities so far dealt with are summarized below, together with their practical units and the definition of each.

Quantity or charge: The coulomb is a quantity of electricity equal to 3 × 10⁹ electrostatic units of charge.   The e.s.u. of charge is defined in terms of its force action upon an identical charge at unit distance in a vacuum [§ 200].   The coulomb equals 6.25 × 10¹⁸ electrons.

Current: The ampere is a unit of current which is equal to a rate of flow of electric charge of one coulomb per second.

Energy: The joule is an amount of work or energy equivalent to 10⁷ ergs.   The erg [§ 69] is defined as the work done by a force of one dyne exerted through a distance of one centimeter.

Power: The watt is the power expenditure of one joule per second.

Electromotive force and potential drop: The volt is the difference in potential between two points when a charge of one coulomb either requires or expends one joule of energy in moving from one point to the other.

Resistance: The ohm is a resistance across which there is a potential drop of one volt when the current in it is one ampere.

The relations between the practical units and the electrostatic units can be found directly from the definitions in the two systems. Thus, for potential difference, to compare the volt (joule per coulomb) and the erg per e.s.u. of charge [§ 202], note that 1 joule = 10^7 ergs and 1 coulomb = 3×10^9 e.s.u. of charge, whence 1 erg per e.s.u. of charge = 300 volts.

Certain prefixes are commonly used with these units when large or small values are referred to. These include: meg = 10^6, kilo = 10^3, milli = 10^{-3}, and micro = 10^{-6}. Thus, 1 megohm = 1,000,000 ohms, and 1 microvolt = 0.000001 volt.

223. Factors Affecting Resistance. — The resistance of an electrical conductor opposes the flow of electricity in somewhat the same way that friction in a pipe line opposes the flow of water. As might be expected from this similarity, electrical resistance is directly proportional to the length of the conductor and inversely proportional to its cross-sectional area. Further, it is found that two conductors of the same dimensions will have different resistances if made of different substances. This effect is ascribed to their different resistivities, the *resistivity* being the resistance of a sample of the substance having specified unit dimensions. Consequently, a conductor of length l, cross-sectional area A, and resistivity ρ (rho), has a resistance R which is given by the equation

$$R = \rho \frac{l}{A} \qquad (150)$$

When the length l is expressed in centimeters, the cross-section A in square centimeters, and the resistance R in ohms, the unit for resistivity will be

$$\rho = \frac{RA}{l} = \frac{\text{ohm} \times \text{cm.}^2}{\text{cm.}} = \text{ohm-cm.}$$

Copper has a resistivity of 1.72×10^{-6} ohm-cm., and this means that a specimen of copper 1 cm. long and 1 sq. cm. in cross-section will offer 1.72×10^{-6} ohm resistance between opposite faces of the cube.

To illustrate the calculation of conductor resistance, consider a copper wire having a diameter $d = 0.1$ cm. and a sectional area $A = \pi d^2/4 = 0.00785$ sq. cm. A length of 100 cm. of this wire will have a resistance of

$$R = \rho \frac{l}{A} = 1.72 \times 10^{-6} \text{ ohm-cm.} \times \frac{100 \text{ cm.}}{0.00785 \text{ cm.}^2} = 0.0219 \text{ ohm.}$$

224. Resistances of Wires. — In calculating the resistances of wires for industrial purposes, it is common practice in this country to express the length of the wire in feet, and the cross-section in circular units of area called *circular mils* (abbreviated C.M.). One circular mil is the area of a circle 0.001 in. (1 mil) in diameter. Since the area of a circle varies as the square of its diameter, a wire having a diameter of 2 mils will have an area of 4 C.M., one having a diameter of 3 mils will have an area of 9 C.M., and so on. Thus, *to find the cross-section of a wire in circular mils, express the diameter in mils and square this number.* The circular mil is a convenient unit of area for round wires because it avoids the use of the factor $\pi/4$ in the calculation.

When the length of a wire is expressed in feet and its cross-section in circular mils, the corresponding unit for resistivity in equation (150) is the ohm-circular mil per foot. Thus, copper has a resistivity of 10.4 ohm-C.M. per ft., meaning that a specimen of copper 1 ft. long and 1 C.M. in cross-section will have a resistance of 10.4 ohms. This specimen is shown in Fig. 225, together with that representing the ohm-centimeter.

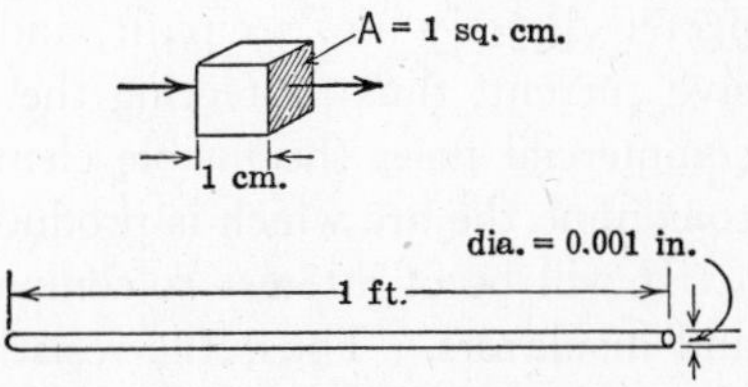

FIG. 225. Shapes on which resistivity values are based

The following table lists the resistivities of a number of common materials. The resistivity of a substance is affected somewhat by temperature changes, and the values shown apply to temperatures around 20° C. By comparing this table with that in § 186, it will be observed that those substances which are good conductors of heat usually have low resistivity and are, therefore, good conductors of electricity as well.

Low resistivity is necessary in wires that are used for transmitting electricity efficiently from place to place. On the other hand, conductors of moderately high resistivity are used when the primary purpose of the current is the production of heat. Thus, electric heaters are wound with wire of Nichrome or of

Resistivities of Conductors

Substance	Microhm-cm.	Ohm-C.M. per ft.
Aluminum...........................	3.21	19.3
Carbon.............................	4000 to 7000	24,000 to 42,000
Constantan (Cu 60%, Ni 40%).........	49	295
Copper.............................	1.72	10.4
Iron...............................	12 to 14	72 to 84
Lead...............................	20.8	125
Manganin (Cu 84%, Ni 4%, Mn 12%)...	43	258
Mercury............................	95.76	575
Nichrome (Ni 60%, Cr 12%, Fe 26%, Mn 2%).........................	110	660
Platinum...........................	11.0	66
Silver..............................	1.65	9.9
Tungsten...........................	5.5	33
Zinc...............................	6.1	36.7

similar alloy, and lamp filaments are made of tungsten. For electric fuses, a relatively high resistivity is desired, combined with a low melting point; lead alloy is frequently used for this purpose. The fuse consists essentially of a metal strip connected directly into a circuit, and is designed to melt upon excessive current, thus protecting the circuit against overheating. In commercial fuses the fusible element is mounted within a casing to confine the arc which is produced upon melting.

It will be of interest to compare the resistivities of conductors and insulators. Thus, the resistivity of gutta percha is 2×10^9 ohm-cm. and that of mica is 9×10^{15} ohm-cm.

For the wiring of electric circuits and the windings of electrical apparatus, copper is used almost exclusively, on account of its low resistivity and moderate cost. In this country, copper wire sizes are standardized in terms of the American wire gage, also called the Brown & Sharpe gage. A few entries from copper wire tables are listed on the next page; the resistances are carried only to three places since this precision is sufficient for most practical purposes. The resistances are based on the International Annealed Copper Standard, and the allowable current-carrying capacities are as published by the Fire Underwriters in the National Electrical Code. The complete gage extends to wires as small as No. 40 and as large as No. 0000. Larger sizes than this are designated by their cross-sections in circular mils.

225. Calculation of Wire Size. — The wires in an electric light or power circuit form a line connecting the generator with the lamps, motors, or other load. The line wires are kept small for the sake of economy, but if they are too small, their resistance will be unduly high. As a result, the potential drop along the line will be excessive, leaving too low a potential difference across the load to operate it properly. It is common practice to restrict the

Table for Copper Wire

A.w.g. No.	Diameter, mils	Cross-section, C.M.	Resistance, ohms per 1000 ft.	Allowable carrying capacity, amp.		
				Rubber insulation	Varnished-cloth insulation	Other insulation
2	258	66,400	0.156	90	110	125
3	229	52,600	0.197	80	95	100
4	204	41,700	0.249	70	85	90
5	182	33,100	0.313	55	65	80
6	162	26,300	0.395	50	60	70
8	129	16,500	0.628	35	40	50
10	102	10,400	0.999	25	30	30
12	81	6,530	1.59	20	25	25
14	64	4,110	2.53	15	18	20

potential drop along the line wires to 3 per cent on lighting circuits and to 5 or 10 per cent on power circuits. A second objection to undersized line wires is the excessive heating which the current would produce in them. To prevent deterioration of the insulation surrounding the wires, the allowable carrying capacities, as listed in the foregoing table, should not be exceeded.

As an illustrative problem, consider an installation of lamps requiring 30 amp. and located in a room 200 ft. away from a generator which maintains 120 volts across its terminals. What is the smallest size of rubber-insulated copper wire to use for the line conductors connecting the generator to the lamp load, if a potential drop of $2\frac{1}{2}$ per cent is allowed along the line?

Clearly, the resistance of the *line* is to be found; this may be done by evaluating the potential drop across it and the current in it. A $2\frac{1}{2}$-per cent potential drop amounts to 0.025×120 or 3 volts across the two line wires of total length 400 ft., leaving 117 volts available for illuminating the lamps. The resistance of the line should be such as to give a 3-volt drop with a current of 30 amperes; this resistance value is given by Ohm's Law as $R = \dfrac{V}{I} = \dfrac{3}{30} = 0.10$ ohm. Hence the cross-section of the line conductors is $A = \rho \dfrac{l}{R} = \dfrac{10.4 \times 400}{0.10} = 41,600$ C.M., from equation (150). Referring to the table of copper wire sizes, the next larger standard size is found to be 41,700 C.M. = No. 4 A.w.g.; this is the wire size as determined by potential-drop considerations. Before adopting it, the allowable current-carrying capacity should be found. Referring again to the table, it is seen that a rubber-insulated wire of this size is rated at 70 amp. Since the line current is less than this value, a No. 4 wire will be adequate for use as line conductor in this installation.

226. Series and Parallel Connections. — In Fig. 226 are shown two simple forms of electric circuit.   In part I, a battery B supplies current to the two resistors R_1 and R_2 connected in *series*.   In part II, a generator G supplies current to the two lamps L_1 and L_2 connected in *parallel* or *multiple*.

In the series arrangement the current has the same value throughout the circuit; that is, the current is the same in the

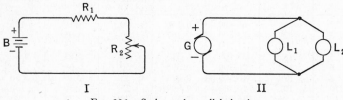

I   II

FIG. 226.   Series and parallel circuits

battery, in the fixed resistance R_1, and in the adjustable resistance R_2.   If the resistance of the circuit is altered, say by changing the value of R_2, the current through the entire circuit will automatically change to a new value.   The sum of the potential drops across the several resistances will be equal to the applied e.m.f. [§ 218]. Summarizing, in a series circuit the current is the same throughout and the potential drops add up to the value of the e.m.f. acting in the circuit.

In the parallel arrangement the current supplied by the generator will divide between the two lamps L_1 and L_2, and the current in each will be determined by the resistance of the particular lamp.   The potential difference between the terminals of lamp L_1 will be the same as that for lamp L_2.   In a parallel circuit the potential drop is the same across all branches and the currents in the branches add up to the value of the main current.

The resistance within the source, whether battery or generator, is usually small but may not be negligible.   It is in series with the external circuit and carries the same current.   Taking the internal resistance of the source as r, and the current as I, the potential drop within the source is Ir, by equation (148).   Upon tracing a path through the source from the — to the + terminal, there will be encountered a rise of potential equal to the e.m.f. E, and also a drop of potential amounting to Ir. Hence, the potential difference across the terminals of the source will be

$$V_t = E - Ir \qquad (151)$$

227. Equivalent Resistances. — Electric circuits are often composed of resistances which are connected in series or in parallel, and it may be desired to find the effect of such grouping upon the resistance of the circuit. Imagine several resistances, R_1, R_2, R_3, $\cdots$, to be combined in any manner, and let I_1, I_2, I_3, $\cdots$, be the respective currents in them. Further, let V_1, V_2, V_3, $\cdots$, be the respective potential drops across them, so that $R_1 = \dfrac{V_1}{I_1}$, $R_2 = \dfrac{V_2}{I_2}$, $R_3 = \dfrac{V_3}{I_3}$, $\cdots$. The entire group may be replaced by an equivalent single resistance R if the current I supplied to it is the same as the current supplied to the entire group and if the potential drop V across R is the same as the potential

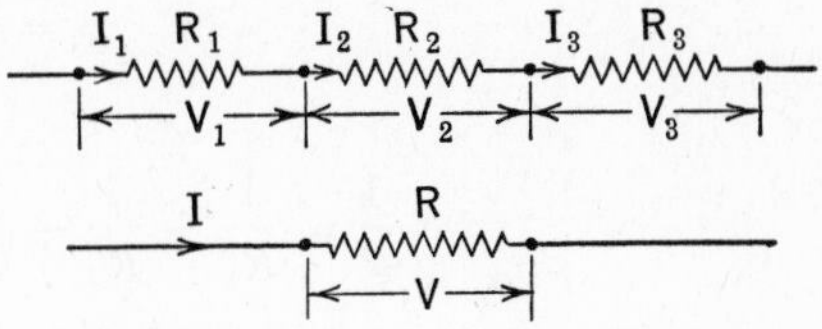

FIG. 227. Resistances connected in series

drop across the entire group. Some simple groupings will be considered in the following paragraphs.

Series Connection. — When the resistances are connected in series, as in Fig. 227, it follows from the properties of the series circuit that

$$I = I_1 = I_2 = I_3 = \cdots$$

and

$$V = V_1 + V_2 + V_3 + \cdots$$

Using Ohm's Law,

$$R = \frac{V}{I} = \frac{V_1 + V_2 + V_3 + \cdots}{I} = \frac{V_1}{I} + \frac{V_2}{I} + \frac{V_3}{I} + \cdots$$

$$= \frac{V_1}{I_1} + \frac{V_2}{I_2} + \frac{V_3}{I_3} + \cdots$$

or the total resistance of the group of resistances is

$$R = R_1 + R_2 + R_3 + \cdots \qquad (152)$$

This equation shows that the equivalent resistance of several devices connected in series is equal to the sum of their individual resistances.

Parallel Connection. — When the resistances are connected in parallel as in Fig. 228, the properties of the parallel circuit show that

$$I = I_1 + I_2 + I_3 + \cdots$$

and

$$V = V_1 = V_2 = V_3 = \cdots$$

whence

$$R = \frac{V}{I} = \frac{V}{I_1 + I_2 + I_3 + \cdots}$$

and therefore

$$\frac{1}{R} = \frac{I_1 + I_2 + I_3 + \cdots}{V} = \frac{I_1}{V} + \frac{I_2}{V} + \frac{I_3}{V} + \cdots$$

$$= \frac{I_1}{V_1} + \frac{I_2}{V_2} + \frac{I_3}{V_3} + \cdots$$

or

$$\frac{1}{R} = \frac{1}{R_1} + \frac{1}{R_2} + \frac{1}{R_3} + \cdots \qquad (153)$$

which shows the relation between the individual resistances R_1, R_2, R_3, $\cdots$, and the equivalent resistance R when these are joined in parallel. It is an interesting fact that the group resistance is less than the lowest of the individual resistances.

Two Resistances in Parallel. — The connection of *only two* resistances in

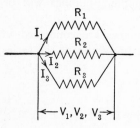

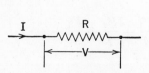

FIG. 228.   Resistances connected in parallel

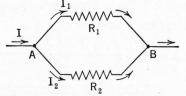

FIG. 229.   Two resistances connected in parallel

parallel, as in Fig. 229, is of frequent occurrence in electrical circuits. Under these conditions, equation (153) becomes

$$\frac{1}{R} = \frac{1}{R_1} + \frac{1}{R_2} = \frac{R_1 + R_2}{R_1 R_2}$$

from which the equivalent resistance is found to be

$$R = \frac{R_1 R_2}{R_1 + R_2}$$

that is, the product of the two resistances divided by their sum.

The division of current between *two* parallel branches is indicated in Fig. 229, where the main current I divides into I_1 and I_2. Since the potential drop between A and B is the same whether calculated for the upper or the lower branch, it follows that $I_1 R_1 = I_2 R_2$, or

$$\frac{I_1}{I_2} = \frac{R_2}{R_1}$$

showing that the branch currents are inversely proportional to the two branch resistances.

228. Network Calculations. — A circuit which includes a number of resistances arranged in series and parallel groupings

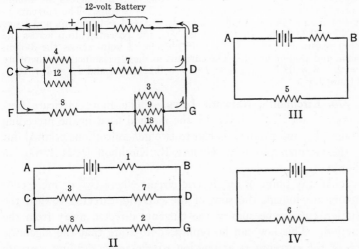

Fig. 230.   Simplifying an electric network

forms a *network*. In the circuit shown in part I of Fig. 230, a 12-volt battery of 1-ohm internal resistance delivers current to the resistance elements shown, the numbers on them indicating the values of the several resistances in ohms. In order to find the current in each of the resistances, the circuit is simplified step by step as shown in the successive diagrams in the figure, reducing it finally to a simple series circuit as in part IV. By repeated application of Ohm's Law, it is then possible to compute the current supplied by the battery, the current in each of the resistance elements, and the potential drop across each.

The solution for the circuit in the figure follows: The 4-ohm and 12-ohm parallel combination is equivalent to a single resistance of $\frac{4 \times 12}{4 + 12} = 3$ ohms; and the 3-ohm, 9-ohm, and 18-ohm parallel combination is equivalent to a single resistance of $1 \div (\frac{1}{3} + \frac{1}{9} + \frac{1}{18}) = 2$ ohms. Substituting these values, diagram II of the figure is obtained. Next, adding the series-connected resistances, the branches CD and FG become equivalent to single resistances of 10 ohms each. Combining these in parallel, an equivalent load resistance of 5 ohms is obtained, as in part III. Finally, the circuit reduces to that shown in part IV, where the total resistance of 6 ohms includes the 1-ohm internal resistance of the battery.

The current supplied by the battery is $I = E \div R = 12 \div 6 = 2$ amp. The potential drop across the 1-ohm battery resistance is $V = I \times r = 2 \times 1 = 2$ volts, leaving $12 - 2 = 10$ volts across AB. This same potential difference will be available to the two branches CD and FG, and since each of these has a resistance of 10 ohms, the current in each is 1 amp. In the branch CD, the potential difference across the 7-ohm resistance is $V = I \times R = 1 \times 7 = 7$ volts, and that across the 4-ohm, 12-ohm parallel combination is $V = 1 \times 3 = 3$ volts. The currents in the 4-ohm and 12-ohm resistances are $I_4 = 3 \div 4 = 0.75$ amp. and $I_{12} = 3 \div 12 = 0.25$ amp. In the branch FG, the potential drop across the 8-ohm resistance is $1 \times 8 = 8$ volts, leaving 2 volts across the 3-ohm, 9-ohm, and 18-ohm group. The currents in these resistances are therefore $I_3 = 2 \div 3 = 0.67$ amp., $I_9 = 2 \div 9 = 0.22$ amp., and $I_{18} = 2 \div 18 = 0.11$ amp.

229. Kirchhoff's Network Laws. — The more intricate networks are not easily solved by the method used in the preceding paragraphs, and recourse is had to two generalizations pointed out by the German physicist, Gustav R. Kirchhoff (1824–1887), as follows:

1. At any point in an electric circuit where two or more conductors are joined, the sum of the currents directed toward the junction equals the sum of the currents directed away from the junction. This law can be rephrased to state that the algebraic sum of the currents at a junction equals zero. Calling currents toward the junction positive and those away from the junction negative, then symbolically $\Sigma I = 0$.

2. Around any closed path in an electric circuit, the algebraic sum of the potential differences equals zero. Considering rise of potential positive and drop of potential negative, and remembering that a current I in a resistance R corresponds to a potential difference IR, this law may be stated $\Sigma E - \Sigma IR = 0$.

In applying these laws to the solution of a network, first assume some direction for the current in each branch and then express Kirchhoff's Laws in as many independent equations as there are unknown currents.   Solving these equations simultaneously will yield the currents in the several branches of the circuit. If the result gives a negative value for any current, this indicates that the direction originally assumed for that particular current should be reversed.

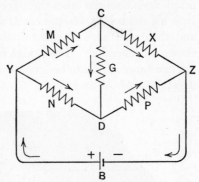

To illustrate the foregoing procedure, consider the network represented in Fig. 231 to be supplied by a battery of e.m.f. E and of negligible resistance. The directions assumed

FIG. 231.   Illustrating Kirchhoff's Laws

for the currents in the several branches are shown on the diagram. Applying the First Law,

At point C: $I_M = I_G + I_X$

At point D: $I_N + I_G = I_P$

Applying the Second Law,

Around path $BYDZB$: $+E - I_N N - I_P P = 0$

Around path $BYCZB$: $+E - I_M M - I_X X = 0$

Around path $YCDY$: $- I_M M - I_G G + I_N N = 0$

In solving the equations simultaneously, care must be exercised to eliminate an unknown current each time the number of equations is reduced.   Proceeding in this manner, the current in branch G of the network is found to be

$$I_G = E \cdot \frac{NX - MP}{(M + X)(GN + NP + PG) + MX(N + P)}$$

The currents in other branches may be determined in the same way.

230. The Wheatstone Bridge. — The network represented in Fig. 231 is used as a *bridge circuit* for finding the value of an unknown resistance by comparing it with a known standard. This method, devised in 1833 by S. H. Christie, was brought to public attention by the English physicist, Sir Charles Wheatstone (1802-1875), and has remained associated with his name.

In the Wheatstone Bridge, four resistances, M, N, P, and X, are connected to a battery B as shown in Fig. 231, and a sensitive current-measuring device called a galvanometer is connected where the resistance G appears in that figure. One of the resistances, X, is unknown, and the other three are known and adjustable in value. In using the bridge, resistances M and N are given suitable values, and then resistance P is manipulated until the galvanometer G shows no deflection. The bridge is then said to be balanced, and the resistance of X can be found from a knowledge of the values of resistances M, N, and P.

FIG. 232.   Wheatstone Bridge and its internal arrangement
(*Courtesy of Leeds & Northrup Company*)

To derive the equation of the balanced bridge, it should be observed that since there is no current in the galvanometer, the current in M must be the same as that in X; call this current in the upper branch of the bridge I_C. Similarly, the current in N is the same as that in P; call this current in the lower branch I_D. The fact that there is no current in the galvanometer also shows that the potential at point C must be the same as that at point D. Hence the potential drop across M must be the same as that across N; also the potential drop across X must be the same as that across P. Expressed mathematically:

$$I_C M = I_D N$$

$$I_C X = I_D P$$

Dividing one expression by the other, term by term, there results $\frac{M}{X} = \frac{N}{P}$; whence the resistance of the unknown is

$$X = \frac{M}{N} P \tag{154}$$

which is the equation of the balanced bridge. The resistances M and N which appear as a ratio in the equation are called the *ratio arms* of the bridge, and resistance P is called the *rheostat arm*.

Commercial bridges are made in various designs. In the form illustrated in Fig. 232, the resistances M, N, and P are included within the case, and binding posts are provided for external connections to the battery and galvanometer and to the resistance being measured. Both ratio arms are controlled by a single dial, and the rheostat arm is arranged with four dials by which it can be adjusted in steps of 1 ohm from 0 to 9999 ohms. Switches known as keys are provided in the battery and galvanometer circuits, since in the use of the bridge these circuits are closed only while a balance is being obtained.

231. Influence of Temperature upon Resistance. — The resistance of a metallic conductor usually increases as the temperature is raised. The law governing this change has the same form as that which applies to the expansion of a rod [§ 139], but the variation of resistance with temperature is usually much greater than the corresponding change of dimensions. Calling R_1 the resistance at some reference temperature, the resistance at a second temperature is expressed by

$$R_2 = R_1(1 + \alpha t) \tag{155}$$

where α is a constant called the *temperature coefficient of resistance*, and t is the elevation of the second temperature above the reference temperature. The physical meaning of α is the increase of resistance of a 1-ohm resistance when subjected to a temperature increase of 1 degree above the reference temperature.

The temperature coefficient is positive for metallic conductors, and for all pure metals the values have the same order of magnitude. Certain alloys have been developed in which α is very small; these materials are useful for the resistance elements in Wheatstone Bridges, resistance boxes, and other measuring instruments in which constancy of resistance is desired. For practical purposes, where the temperature change involved is small, the temperature coefficient is usually considered as remaining constant at the value which it has at the reference temperature; actually it varies somewhat with the temperature and for accurate calculations the average value for the given temperature range should be used. For non-metallic substances, including carbon, liquids, and insulating materials, the temperature coefficient is usually negative.

The following table lists the values of the temperature coefficient for a number of materials commonly used. Unless otherwise specified, these values apply to reference temperatures around 20° C.

Temperature Coefficients of Resistance

Material	α per centigrade degree
Aluminum	0.0038
Carbon (0 to 1850° C.)	−0.00025
Constantan	−0.00004 to +0.00001
Copper (at 20° C.)	0.00393
Iron	0.0062
Lead	0.0043
Manganin	0.000002 to 0.00005
Mercury	0.00090
Nichrome	0.00017
Platinum	0.0038
Silver	0.0040
Tungsten	0.0045
Zinc	0.0037

The Resistance Thermometer. — The fact that the resistance of a metallic conductor changes with temperature is utilized in the so-called *resistance thermometer.* This device consists of a calibrated coil of wire, which is placed in the location where the temperature is to be determined, together with suitable instruments for measuring its resistance. This type of thermometer is useful over a wide temperature range [§ 143], is very precise, follows temperature changes without appreciable lag, and can be read from a remote point.

To illustrate the measurement of temperature by this device, consider the resistance of a coil of platinum wire to be 10.0 ohms at 20° C. and 15.0 ohms when placed in a certain oven. Taking α as 0.0038 over the temperature range involved, the temperature elevation t of the oven above 20° C. is given by equation (155) as

$$ t = \frac{R_2 - R_1}{\alpha R_1} = \frac{15.0 - 10.0}{0.0038 \times 10.0} = 132 \text{ centigrade degrees,} $$

and the desired temperature is 132 + 20 = 152° C.

232. Super-conductivity. — Certain metals are found to exhibit a remarkable drop in resistance at very low temperatures, this effect being known as *super-conductivity*. As the temperature is lowered, the resistance of the specimen is observed to decrease in the manner to be expected from equation (155), but at a certain temperature, which seems to have a characteristic value for each material, and which is only a few degrees above absolute zero ($-273°$ C. or $0°$ K.), the resistance drops abruptly to an extremely low value. The resistance of a lead ring, for instance, becomes less than 10^{-12} of its value at $0°$ C.

Professor Onnes discovered this effect at the University of Leyden. As early as 1914, he reported a test of 1-hr. duration, in which current was produced in a lead ring at a very low temperature and the source of electromotive force was removed, nevertheless the current in the closed ring persisted without appreciable reduction throughout the test. Super-conductivity has been observed in seventeen metallic elements, including tin at $3.69°$ K., mercury at $4.12°$ K., and lead at $7.26°$ K., as well as in a large number of alloys.

PROBLEMS

1. How much work is done in moving a charge of 2 coulombs along an electric circuit between two points which have a potential difference of 20 volts?

2. A neon electric sign takes 4.8 watts per foot of tubing and has a total tube length of 135 feet. What is the weekly cost of operating the sign for 10 hours a day at a 5 cent per kw-hr. rate?

3. A 12-in. electric fan takes 0.8 amp. on 120-volt service mains. How much does it cost to operate it for 8 hr. if energy costs 7 cents per kw-hr.?

4. A 20-hp. motor operating at full load takes a current of 74 amp. from 230-volt supply mains. Compute the efficiency of the motor.

5. An electric household refrigerator is equipped with a ⅓-hp. motor which operates at full load 25 per cent of the time. The efficiency of the motor is 60 per cent. What is the energy cost to operate the refrigerator 30 days at 5 cents per kw-hr.?

6. (*a*) The field coils of an electric motor take 1.8 amp. at 220 volts. Determine the resistance of these coils. (*b*) How much current will a 30-ohm electric iron take when operated on 115-volt service mains?

7. (*a*) What is the resistance of a heating coil that draws a current of 5.8 amp. when connected across 115-volt service mains? (*b*) What is the potential difference across a lamp bank having a resistance of 30.2 ohms in which the current is 4 amp.?

8. A slidewire resistance has 250 turns wound on an insulating cylinder. A current of 2.3 amp. traverses the entire length of the wire, which has a resistance of 40 ohms. What is the potential difference between adjacent turns of the winding?

9. An electric heater of 38 ohms resistance is placed in 590 gm. of water contained in a brass calorimeter having a mass of 87 gm. A current of 3.3 amp. is passed through the heater for 4.6 min. What will be the temperature elevation of the calorimeter and its contents? Take the specific heat of brass as 0.090. Neglect the water equivalent of the heater itself, as well as radiation.

10. When electrical energy costs 6 cents per kw-hr., how much will it cost to heat 4.5 kilograms of water from 20° C. to the boiling point, if no energy is wasted?

11. The current in a lamp of 300 ohms resistance is 0.4 amp. At what rate in watts is electrical energy converted into heat?

12. A 120-volt electric heater consists of a coil of wire having a resistance of 27.8 ohms. Find the time required to produce 15,000 cal. with this heater.

13. How much would it cost to heat electrically the water in a pool 50 ft. long and 20 ft. wide, the water having an average depth of 6 ft.? The cost of electrical energy is 1.3 cents per kw-hr. The water is supplied at 45° F. and is to be heated to 68° F. Assume that 25 per cent of the heat supplied is wasted.

14. A concern pays for electrical energy and for maximum power demand in accordance with the following monthly schedule:

Energy			Power		
First 1,000 kw-hr.	5¢	per kw-hr.	First 50 kw.	$2.40	per kw.
Next 4,000 "	3	"	Next 750 "	2.00	"
" 50,000 "	1.3	"	Above this total	1.50	"
Above this total	1	"			

What will the concern be charged for 75,000 kw-hr. of energy during a month when the maximum power demand was 300 kw.?

15. The American Society for Testing Materials specifies a minimum of 891.58 lb. per mile-ohm for soft or annealed copper wire at 20° C. Taking the specific gravity as 8.89, find the corresponding resistivity in ohm-circular mils per foot.

16. A resistance coil is to be wound with manganin wire 0.5 mm. in diameter. What length of wire will be needed for a 20-ohm coil?

17. A tungsten wire used as a lamp filament is 56 cm. long and has a resistance of 20 ohms at room temperature. Find its diameter.

18. Compute the diameter of a copper wire 800 ft. long in order that the resistance of the wire may be 0.20 ohm.

19. Find the resistance of 1000 ft. of copper wire 0.15 in. in diameter.

20. A resistance coil is to be constructed of manganin wire having a diameter of 0.01 in. What length of wire in feet will be required if the resistance is to dissipate 250 watts when connected across 120-volt supply mains?

21. A cable of 1,000,000-C.M. cross-section is to be made of 127 equal strands. Find the diameter of each strand.

22. What is the resistance of 500 ft. of stranded copper wire, made of 17 strands each 0.032 in. in diameter?

23. A farm-lighting plant includes a storage battery having 32 volts across its terminals. From the battery a pair of No. 12 A.w.g. copper line wires extend to a point 60 ft. away, where a load drawing a current of 11 amp. is connected. Compute the potential difference across the load.

24. A lamp load which takes a current of 40 amp. is located at a distance of 250 ft. from a generator which maintains 120 volts across its terminals. What gage rubber-insulated copper wires are needed for the line connecting the lamps to the generator, if the allowable potential drop is 3 per cent?

25. A dry cell has 1.476 volts across its terminals when on open circuit; this is lowered to 1.435 volts when the cell delivers current to an external circuit of 2.5 ohms resistance. Calculate the internal resistance of the cell.

26. A battery having an e.m.f. of 6.4 volts and an internal resistance of 0.25 ohm supplies a current of 2 amp. to a lamp load. Find the potential difference across the terminals of the battery and also the resistance of the load.

27. A 60-watt, 120-volt lamp is connected in parallel with a 40-watt, 120-volt lamp. Find their combined resistance.

28. Derive an equation for the combined resistance of n equal resistances, all connected in parallel.

29. The field coil of a motor is found to take a current of 0.42 amp. when connected across a 112-volt line. (a) Compute the resistance of the field coil. (b) If an additional resistance of 500 ohms is joined in series with the coil under test, and the combination is connected across the same line, find the current in the coil and the potential drop across it.

30. The series-parallel circuit of diagram I can be reduced to the simple series circuit of diagram II. Show that the current in the load

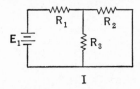

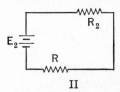

I   II

resistance R_2 is the same in both circuits when the ratio of voltages is $\dfrac{E_2}{E_1} = \dfrac{R_3}{R_1 + R_3}$ and when the resistance $R = \dfrac{R_1 R_3}{R_1 + R_3}$.

31. Suppose that two resistances of 2 ohms and 4 ohms are connected in parallel and this combination is joined in series with a 5-ohm resistance and a battery having an e.m.f. of 3 volts and an internal resistance of 0.8 ohm. Find the current in the 4-ohm resistance.

32. Seven resistances, of 200 ohms each, are arranged in two groups, the first group comprising 4 resistances in parallel and the second group comprising 3 resistances in parallel. If the groups are connected in series across a 220-volt line, find the potential drop across each group. Assume each resistance to remain unchanged.

33. Find the current in each resistance of the network shown in the accompanying diagram, and the potential drop across each. The e.m.f. E of the battery is 12 volts and its internal resistance is 1 ohm, as shown beside the e.m.f. symbol. The numbers of the resistances indicate also their resistance values in ohms.

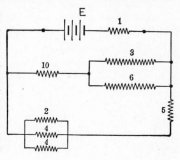

34. Show that in the circuit illustrated, the insertion of a battery in any branch resistance will cause the current to be zero in the branch bearing the corresponding letter when $AA' = BB' = CC'$.

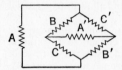

35. A field winding on a motor consists of a copper coil having a resistance of 270 ohms at 20° C. What will be its resistance if the temperature rises 40 centigrade degrees?

36. A copper wire is used as a resistance thermometer for measuring temperatures around 20° C., its resistance being 40 ohms at this temperature. How much will its resistance increase for a temperature rise of 1 centigrade degree?

37. A coil of platinum wire used as a resistance thermometer is connected as arm X of a Wheatstone Bridge, Fig. 231. At 18° C., the bridge balances when $M = 1$ ohm, $N = 10$ ohms, and $P = 272$ ohms. With the resistance thermometer placed in a freezing mixture, a new balance is obtained when $M = 1$ ohm, $N = 10$ ohms, and $P = 240$ ohms. Find the temperature of the freezing mixture.

38. A typical filament is of tungsten 0.0019 in. in diameter and 20 in. in length. Find the power supplied to it when connected across 118-volt supply mains, assuming the filament to operate at 2700° C. and taking its temperature coefficient of resistance to be 0.0039 per centigrade degree over the temperature range involved.

CHAPTER XXIII

ELECTRIC CELLS

233. Electrolytic and Voltaic Cells. — It is generally known that the electric current can be used to produce hydrogen and oxygen from dilute acid by electrolysis, or to deposit a metal coating on an electrode in a plating bath. The apparatus used in either process is called an *electrolytic cell*. In such a cell, electrical energy supplied from an outside source serves to produce the chemical changes involved, a small part being wasted as heat. Electrolytic cells are used not only for gas manufacture and electroplating, but also for the refining of metals and in industrial chemical processes.

Other forms of cells, such as the dry cell and storage cell, are used to supply electrical energy; these are called *voltaic cells*. In this type, chemical energy is liberated within the cell and transformed into electrical energy, part being converted to heat. Voltaic cells are called *primary* cells if the elements must be replaced after use, and *secondary* or *storage* cells if they can be restored to their initial condition by charging from an electric supply circuit.

234. Electrolytic Action. — The conduction of electricity in liquids is attributed to the presence of positive and negative ions [§ 196] in solutions of acids, bases or salts, and to the motion of these charges between the electrodes when a potential difference is applied across them. Such solutions are termed *electrolytes*, and the process of conduction through them is called *electrolysis*. Except for chemical actions which may occur, the behavior of any electrolytic cell is based entirely upon the attraction of unlike charges and the repulsion of like charges.

A solution of hydrochloric acid, for example, presents evidence of containing H atoms, each of which has lost an electron and is therefore positively charged, and Cl atoms, each with a surplus electron and therefore negatively charged. The charged particles or ions are represented with appropriate + or − signs. The foregoing action is described by saying that the acid *dissociates* into

389

positive hydrogen ions and negative chloride ions, or symbolically,

$$HCl \rightleftarrows H^+ + Cl^-$$

While in the ionic state, the substances do not have the properties of the corresponding atoms; thus H^+ is essentially different from H_2. For example, a solution of H^+ ions affects indicators such as litmus; a solution of hydrogen gas does not. A change of properties would, indeed, be expected from the modifications in atomic structure.

Evidence indicates that bare H^+ ions are practically non-existent in aqueous solutions; instead they are believed to occur in a hydrated form as *hydronium* ions, H_3O^+, each being a combination of H^+ and H_2O. To avoid complexity, however, the hydrogen ion will be represented in this book by the simpler notation H^+.

The mechanism of electrical conduction through liquids will be illustrated by specific examples.

Electrolysis of Hydrochloric Acid. — Suppose two platinum plates A and C, connected to a battery as shown in Fig. 233, to be dipped

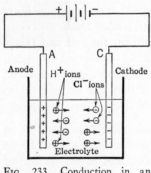

FIG. 233. Conduction in an electrolytic cell

into a dilute solution of hydrochloric acid. The H^+ ions will be attracted by the negative plate C and repelled by the positive plate A, and the Cl^- ions will be attracted by the positive and repelled by the negative plate. The result will be a drifting or migration of ions in both directions through the liquid (this motion being in addition to the unordered motion of the particles corresponding to the temperature). Each H^+ ion upon reaching plate C combines with an electron there, forming a hydrogen atom:

$$H^+ + e \rightarrow H$$

From these atoms hydrogen molecules are produced and pass off as gas. The Cl^- ions upon reaching plate A give up their electrons and become chlorine atoms:

$$Cl^- - e \rightarrow Cl$$

the atoms combining to form molecules of chlorine which will be liberated at this plate.

Decomposition of Water. — As a typical illustration of the decomposition of water, consider the effect of passing electricity through a dilute sulfuric acid solution (H_2SO_4), using insoluble electrodes of platinum or carbon. The H^+ ions of the acid will be attracted by the negative plate and repelled by the positive plate, and the $SO_4^=$ ions will be attracted by the positive and repelled by the negative plate. The result will again be a drifting of ions in both directions through the liquid. Each H^+ ion upon reaching the cathode combines with an electron there, forming a hydrogen atom. These atoms combine into molecules and escape as gas, that is:

$$2H^+ + 2e \rightarrow H_2 \uparrow$$

The $SO_4^=$ ions upon reaching the anode give up their electrons and combine with the water present to form more sulfuric acid, liberating oxygen as a gas, that is:

$$2SO_4^= - 4e + 2H_2O \rightarrow \underbrace{4H^+ + 2SO_4^=}_{2H_2SO_4} + O_2 \uparrow$$

Electroplating. — Consider next an electrolytic cell in which the electrolyte is a dilute copper sulfate solution, and suppose at first that non-corrosive electrodes of platinum are used. The following equations represent the formation of the ions and the reactions which are believed to occur at the electrodes:

$$CuSO_4 \rightleftarrows Cu^{++} + SO_4^=$$

At cathode $\quad Cu^{++} + 2e \rightarrow Cu \downarrow$

At anode $\quad SO_4^= - 2e + H_2O \rightarrow \underbrace{2H^+ + SO_4^=}_{H_2SO_4} + O$

These show that copper is plated upon the cathode, and that the $CuSO_4$ electrolyte gradually changes its composition. By substituting copper for platinum as the material of the anode, this defect is overcome, the anode reaction being:

$$SO_4^= - 2e + Cu \rightarrow CuSO_4$$

while the cathode reaction remains unchanged. In this process copper is dissolved from the anode and plated on the cathode, and the electrolyte remains unchanged.

Many metals may be electroplated under the general conditions just described, the anode being made of the metal to be electroplated and the electrolyte being a solution of one of its salts. Silver may be deposited from silver nitrate using a silver anode.

Chromium plating presents more difficulty in practice than the plating of other metals, but is very popular on account of the hardness of the deposit and its resistance to corrosion. Chromium is usually deposited from a chromic acid bath, the anode material being lead or iron. The chromium content of the electrolyte is restored from time to time as the process continues.

Under certain conditions two substances can be deposited simultaneously in an electrolytic cell. For example, the use of a cyanide solution in which both zinc and copper are present makes it possible to obtain a simultaneous deposit of zinc and copper, that is, of brass.

It is also possible to deposit rubber electrolytically from rubber latex (the milky juice of rubber trees), although the process probably differs from electroplating as this term is ordinarily used. The latex is in suspension and the particles have negative charges, a frequent occurrence among colloids. Upon applying a high potential difference to the electrodes, the latex particles move to the anode, to which they become affixed.

Electrolytic Corrosion. — Electrolysis sometimes produces unexpected and destructive effects. An example illustrating electro-

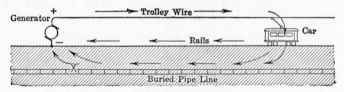

Fig. 234.   Illustrating electrolytic corrosion

lytic corrosion of an underground pipe from the leakage currents of an electric railway line is indicated in Fig. 234. This diagram represents a generator at a power station supplying current through a trolley wire (or third rail) to the motor on an electric car. The current is returned to the generator partly by way of the rails and partly along the grounded pipe line. The pipe is likely to become corroded at the region marked X, for here the moist earth around the pipe serves as the electrolyte, and the pipe itself acts as the anode of an electrolytic cell. Continued current through this "cell" will wear away the anode, as previously described. To eliminate this corrosion, the point X and the negative terminal of the generator should be bonded together by a wire, thus providing a metallic path for the current leaving the pipe.

235. Faraday's Laws of Electrolysis. It will be observed that whenever *hydrogen or any metal is liberated in an electrolytic cell*, this action, with rare exceptions, occurs *at the cathode*, and that when other substances are liberated this action takes place at the anode. It will also be observed that, if electrolysis is to continue, the external circuit must continuously supply electrons to the cathode and remove them from the anode; in other words, a current is necessary in the circuit containing the cell. It appears further that in forming a hydrogen or other univalent atom at the cathode one electron is required, while for a bivalent atom two electrons are required, and so on. Similarly, at the anode one electron is released in forming a univalent atom, and two electrons in forming a bivalent atom. Since a flow of 6.25×10^{18} electrons per second constitute a current of one ampere [§ 217], it follows that in an electrolytic cell a current of 1 amp. maintained for 1 sec. (that is, a quantity of electricity of 1 coulomb) is capable of liberating at the cathode 6.25×10^{18} hydrogen or other univalent atoms, or half this number of bivalent atoms, and so on. A corresponding liberation of atoms will also occur at the anode of the cell.

Quantitative measurements in electrolytic cells are based on two laws due to Faraday, as follows:

1. *The mass of a substance liberated in an electrolytic cell is proportional to the quantity of electricity passing through the cell.*

2. *When the same quantity of electricity is passed through different electrolytic cells, the masses of the substances liberated are proportional to their chemical equivalents.* The chemical equivalent of an element is the ratio of its atomic weight w in grams to its valence number z; in the case of radicals the chemical equivalent is the sum of the atomic weights of the component elements divided by the valence number of the radical.

The atomic weights and usual valence numbers of several elements are given in the accompanying table.

Atomic Weights and Valence Numbers

Element	Atomic weight	Valence number
Chlorine	35.46	-1
Copper	63.57	$+2$
Hydrogen	1.008	$+1$
Oxygen	16.00	-2
Silver	107.88	$+1$
Zinc	65.38	$+2$

In applying Faraday's Laws of electrolysis, it is first desirable to find what quantity of electricity will liberate 1 chemical equivalent of a substance. Consider silver, for example, which has a chemical equivalent of 107.88 gm. Since this element is univalent, 1 coulomb of electricity will deposit 6.25×10^{18} atoms. But Avogadro's constant, 6.02×10^{23}, is the number of atoms in a gram-atom of a substance; hence there are 6.02×10^{23} atoms in 107.88 gm. of silver. To deposit this amount of silver will therefore require $(6.02 \times 10^{23}) \div (6.25 \times 10^{18}) = 96,500$ coulombs. This quantity of electricity, which is also known as 1 *faraday*, will liberate 1 chemical equivalent of any substance.

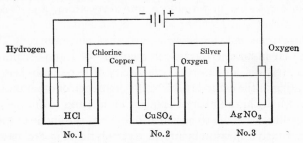

Fig. 235. Electrolytic cells in series

As further examples, consider the three cells represented in Fig. 235, which are connected in series with a battery and, therefore, carry the same current. Upon passing 96,500 coulombs around the circuit there will be liberated w/z grams of the substances designated in the various cells as follows:

Cell No. 1 $\dfrac{1.008}{1} = 1.008$ gm. of hydrogen and $\dfrac{35.46}{1} = 35.46$ gm. of chlorine.

Cell No. 2 $\dfrac{63.57}{2} = 31.8$ gm. of copper and $\dfrac{16}{2} = 8.0$ gm. of oxygen.

Cell No. 3 $\dfrac{107.88}{1} = 107.88$ gm. of silver and $\dfrac{16}{2} = 8.0$ gm. of oxygen.

The mass of a substance liberated in electrolysis can be found by simple proportion, knowing that 96,500 coulombs will liberate 1 chemical equivalent. Thus, to determine how much copper would be plated from a solution of a cupric salt by a current of 10 amp. maintained for 1 hr. (that is, by 36,000 coulombs), let m represent the desired mass, and write:

$$m : \frac{63.57}{2} = 36,000 : 96,500$$

from which $m = 11.86$ gm.

The preceding proportion can also be written as an equation

$$m = \frac{I t}{96,500} \times \frac{w}{z} \qquad (156)$$

wherein the quantity of electricity is expressed as the product of the current I in amperes and the time t in seconds.

The electrolytic action of the current is used as the basis of the legal definition of the ampere. The so-called *international ampere* is specified by act of the U. S. Legislature as "the unvarying current, which, when passed through a solution of nitrate of silver in water in accordance with standard specifications, deposits silver at the rate of 0.001118 gm. per sec." The student can readily show that this definition is in agreement with the foregoing data.

236. Osmotic and Solution Pressures.—The investigations of osmotic pressure described in § 117 showed that for non-conducting solutions the osmotic pressure is proportional to the concentration; that is, to the number of molecules of solute per unit of volume. For solutions of electrolytes, the osmotic pressures are found to be larger than this proportion would predict. This result led to the theory that in electrolytes, the molecules dissociate into a larger number of parts (ions), thus accounting for the increased osmotic pressure. For dilute electrolytic solutions, the osmotic pressure is approximately proportional to the concentration of the ions.

When a metal plate is dipped into a solution of one of its salts, a contact is established between the metallic *atoms* of the plate and the positive metallic *ions* of the solution. Two tendencies exist, either of which may determine the action that results; first, *metallic ions tend to acquire electrons and deposit themselves on the plate as atoms*, and second, *the atoms of the plate tend to lose electrons and go into solution as ions*. The tendency for metal to deposit on the plate is proportional to the concentration of the ions, and thus varies directly as the osmotic pressure. For this reason it is usual to say that the osmotic pressure tends to drive the metal out of solution, and deposit it in the atomic form. Theoretically, with sufficiently high concentration of ions, the osmotic pressure could be made large enough to cause deposition in all cases. On the other hand, if the ionic concentration is low, the osmotic pressure will be small, and the tendency of the plate to dissolve will predominate. At some intermediate concentration value, neither deposition nor dissolution will occur; it is supposed under this condition that the osmotic pressure is exactly neutralized by a so-called *solution pressure*. Although the real significance of this term is in doubt, it is usual to think of the solution pressure of a metal as an agency which tends to throw the metal into solution in the form of positive ions.

Osmotic pressure varies with the concentration of the ions in a dilute solution; solution pressure has a characteristic value for each metal. For a copper plate dipped in a copper sulfate solution of ordinary concentration, the osmotic pressure is larger than the solution pressure, and a few Cu^{++} ions will take electrons from the plate, forming atoms of copper which deposit upon the plate. The action will stop almost immediately, however, because the plate becomes positive and repels the advance of further positive ions. In contrast, consider a zinc plate dipped in a zinc sulfate solution. The solution pressure of the zinc is larger than the osmotic pressure of the ions in solution, and a few atoms of the plate dissolve, leaving their electrons behind, and go into solution as Zn^{++} ions. This effect is also of very slight magnitude because the plate becomes negative, and the throwing off of further positive ions is prevented by electrostatic attraction between plate and ions. The mass of metal deposited or dissolved in these cases is very minute. The processes could be made continuous, however, by removing the charges from the plates as fast as they are formed.

237. Single-electrode Potentials. — The analysis given in the preceding section shows that a copper plate placed in a solution

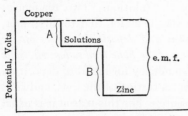

FIG. 236. Potentials in voltaic cell

of a copper salt assumes a higher potential than the solution, and that a zinc plate placed in a solution of a zinc salt assumes a lower potential than the solution. Calling these single-electrode potentials A and B respectively, the effect of putting the two solutions in contact is illustrated in Fig. 236, in which the potentials are offset for clearness. The combination forms a voltaic cell with the copper positive and the zinc negative. Neglecting any small potential difference at the junction of the solutions, the e.m.f. of the cell would be the sum of the single-electrode potentials A and

B. The materials referred to are used in the Daniell cell, which is described in § 242.

The potential of a given metal with respect to a solution of one of its salts under specified conditions can be expressed precisely. Its value is called the *normal electrode potential* if the solution is "normal"; that is, if 1 liter at 25° C. contains an effective concentration of 1 chemical equivalent of the metallic ions. The normal electrode potential of copper is +0.3448 volt and that of zinc is −0.7581 volt. Potential values for a number of substances are tabulated in § 239.

It is interesting to note how such potentials are measured. If a voltmeter were connected between the electrode and the solution, the immersed wire from the voltmeter would itself form an electrode, and the voltmeter would read the total potential of the voltaic cell so formed. It seems impossible to avoid the use of a second electrode in making such a potential measurement, and consequently an electrode is used for this purpose that has a constant and reproducible potential. The *hydrogen electrode* is commonly used as such a reference electrode, its potential with respect to a solution of normal hydrogen-ion content being arbitrarily taken as zero.

Fig. 237 illustrates the apparatus utilized in measuring the normal electrode potential of the metal *X* by reference to the

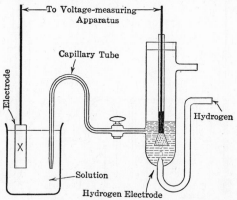

FIG. 237.   Hydrogen electrode used in measuring normal electrode potential

hydrogen electrode shown at the right. Hydrogen, which is non-conducting as a gas, is passed over a plate of platinum which is covered with platinum black. Here the gas is *adsorbed*, that is, condensed and held upon the surface; in this condition, hydrogen is conducting like a metal electrode. The hydrogen electrode, immersed in a solution of normal hydrogen-ion content, forms a half cell, and this is connected by a "liquid bridge" within a capillary tube to the other half cell, composed of the metal under test in a normal solution of one of its salts. The normal electrode potential of the metal is found by measuring the potential difference between the electrodes, a potentiometer [§ 248] being generally used for this purpose.

Another reference electrode in common use is composed of mercury and calomel (mercurous chloride) in a solution of potassium chloride (KCl). The potential of this so-called *calomel electrode* with reference to the normal hydrogen electrode varies from 0.24 to 0.34 volt, depending upon the concentration of the potassium chloride solution and the temperature.

*238. Hydrogen Ion Measurements. — The degree of acidity or alkalinity of a solution is determined by placing a hydrogen electrode in it to form a half cell, combining this with another half cell having a different reference electrode, and measuring the potential difference of the combination. The apparatus using hydrogen and calomel electrodes is indicated in Fig. 238.

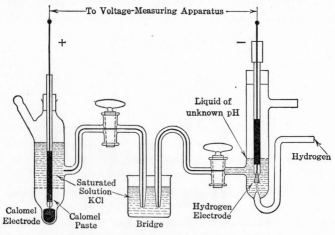

FIG. 238.   Measuring pH value of a solution

All acids yield hydrogen ions when dissolved in water, and the degree of acidity of a solution depends upon the quantity of hydrogen ions per liter of solution. Pure water, which represents a state of true neutrality, dissociates into H^+ and OH^- ions, but so feebly that at ordinary temperatures it contains only 10^{-7} gm. of H^+ ion per liter. In acid solutions, the hydrogen ion concentration is greater than this value, and in alkaline solutions it is less. Suppose that in a certain HCl solution, each liter contains 0.001 gm. of hydrogen ions, that is, the hydrogen ion concentration in grams per liter is $0.001 = 10^{-3}$. The numerical value of the exponent is called the *pH value*; for the solution considered the *p*H value is 3. Any *p*H number between 0 and 7 indicates an acid solution, the acidity decreasing as the numbers increase. For *p*H numbers larger than 7 the solution is alkaline, the alkalinity increasing as the numbers increase.

With the arrangement shown in the figure, the potential of the hydrogen electrode is directly proportional to the *p*H value of the surrounding solution; hence this *p*H value can be found from the measured potential difference by subtracting the potential of the calomel electrode and multiplying the result by a constant. This method of measurement is particularly useful with solutions in which the acidity or alkalinity is so feeble as to escape detection by other means.

239. Electromotive Series of the Metals. — The relative chemical activities of the metals can be indicated by arranging them in tabular form with the most active one at the top of the series. Each metal in the list displaces those below it from chemically equivalent solutions of their simple salts, and is itself displaced by those above it, under ordinary conditions. The result is attributed to differences in solution pressure.

The accompanying table indicates the more important metals and gives their normal electrode potentials. Each of these values represents the e.m.f. of a cell having a hydrogen electrode and an electrode of the metal referred to. The e.m.f. of a cell having any two metals for its electrodes in a uniform electrolyte can be predicted from the individual potential values. Consider, for example, a copper-zinc cell. On the potential scale, copper is +0.34 volt and zinc is −0.76 volt, each with respect to hydrogen, consequently the potential of copper is 0.34 + 0.76 or 1.10 volts higher than that of zinc. The copper-zinc cell has an e.m.f. of this value, and its positive terminal is the one attached to the copper electrode. The e.m.f. of a voltaic cell depends upon the materials used and not upon size.

Electromotive Series of the Metals

Element	Symbol	Normal electrode potential (referred to hydrogen electrode) volts	
Potassium................	K	−2.92	high solution pressure
Sodium..................	Na	−2.71	
Magnesium..............	Mg	−1.55	
Zinc.....................	Zn	−0.76	
Iron.....................	Fe	−0.44	
Tin......................	Sn	−0.13	
Lead.....................	Pb	−0.12	
Hydrogen..............	**H**	**0.00**	
Bismuth.................	Bi	+0.20	
Copper..................	Cu	+0.34	
Mercury.................	Hg	+0.80	
Silver...................	Ag	+0.80	low solution pressure

240. The Voltaic Cell; Polarization. — A primary cell of elementary type may be constructed by placing electrodes of copper and zinc in a dilute sulfuric acid solution, as indicated in Fig. 239. Such a cell will set up a current from copper to zinc in an external circuit of resistance R. The action of the cell is explained by supposing the sulfuric acid to dissociate principally in the following manner:

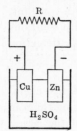

FIG. 239. Diagram of a voltaic cell

$$H_2SO_4 \rightleftarrows 2H^+ + SO_4^=$$

At the copper plate, the osmotic pressure of the H^+ ions in solution is greater than the solution pressure of the copper, and these ions deposit themselves upon the copper plate, thereby giving it a positive charge.

At the zinc plate, the solution pressure of the zinc is much greater than the osmotic pressure of the H^+ ions in the solution; therefore, zinc atoms dissolve, throwing Zn^{++} ions into solution and leaving electrons on the plate, a process which makes the zinc plate negative.

The electrons on the zinc plate repel one another along the wire, this action being assisted by the attraction of the positively charged copper plate; thus, a current of electricity is established through the external circuit R. The Zn^{++} and $SO_4^=$ ions remain in the solution, unless the latter is evaporated, when they unite to form zinc sulfate, as represented by the equation:

$$Zn^{++} + SO_4^= \rightarrow ZnSO_4$$

Impurities in the electrodes act like tiny short-circuited cells, and the electrodes are consumed wastefully. This so-called *local action* can be reduced by amalgamating the surface of the zinc.

The current supplied by the simple voltaic cell is quickly reduced in value during even a short period of use because of the accumulation of hydrogen on the positive plate. This action not only introduces a high resistance into the circuit, but alters the material of the electrode and sets up an opposing e.m.f. which must be overcome before the cell can supply current to the external circuit. This effect, called *polarization*, is present in many types of cells. Polarization of a voltaic cell is due primarily to the formation of hydrogen on its positive plate and to changes in concentration of its electrolyte. In voltaic cells which are subject to polarization some substance is usually added to combine chemically with the hydrogen gas as it forms. This substance is called a *depolarizer*.

In the operation of an electrolytic cell having like electrodes, it frequently happens that the electrodes become coated with dissimilar materials. Such a cell then acts like a voltaic cell opposing the applied e.m.f., and its own e.m.f. must be overcome before current can be set up in it. Thus, a cell with platinum electrodes in a solution of hydrochloric acid may cease to conduct current because hydrogen and chlorine accumulate on the electrodes and set up an e.m.f. of polarization opposing the outside source. So long as both electrodes of an electrolytic cell remain of the same substance, whatever electrode potential is developed at one of them will be neutralized by an equal and opposite potential at the other, supposing the electrolyte to be uniform throughout. The smallest potential difference applied to the cell will then set up a current in it.

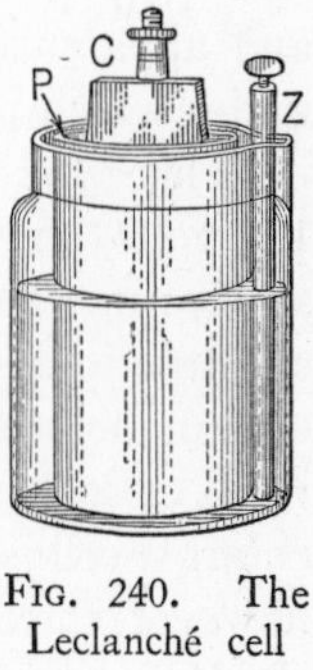

FIG. 240. The Leclanché cell

241. Leclanché and Dry Cells. — In the cell devised by Georges Leclanché, Fig. 240, a positive electrode C of carbon and a negative plate or rod Z of zinc are immersed in a solution of ammonium chloride (NH_4Cl). A porous cup P around the carbon electrode contains manganese dioxide as a depolarizer. The familiar dry cell employs the same materials, but the construction is different; a section of this cell is shown in Fig. 241. These are primary cells, either of which may be represented diagrammatically as in Fig. 242.

When the cell delivers current, the zinc dissolves, leaving electrons behind, which repel one another along the external circuit to the carbon plate. The Cl^- ions in the electrolyte migrate toward the Zn^{++} ions near the zinc electrode, and the NH_4^+ ions migrate toward the carbon electrode. The formation of hydrogen gas at this electrode is prevented to a considerable extent through the agency of manganese dioxide. The initial cell reactions are probably as follows:

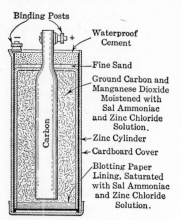

FIG. 241. Sectional view of dry cell

Binding Posts

Waterproof Cement

Fine Sand

Ground Carbon and Manganese Dioxide Moistened with Sal Ammoniac and Zinc Chloride Solution.

Zinc Cylinder

Cardboard Cover

Blotting Paper Lining, Saturated with Sal Ammoniac and Zinc Chloride Solution.

Carbon

Dissociation of electrolyte:

$$NH_4Cl \rightleftarrows NH_4^+ + Cl^-$$

Near negative electrode:

$$Zn^{++} + 2Cl^- \rightarrow ZnCl_2$$

Near positive electrode:

$$2NH_4^+ + 2e + MnO_2 + H_2O \rightarrow$$

$$2NH_4OH + MnO$$

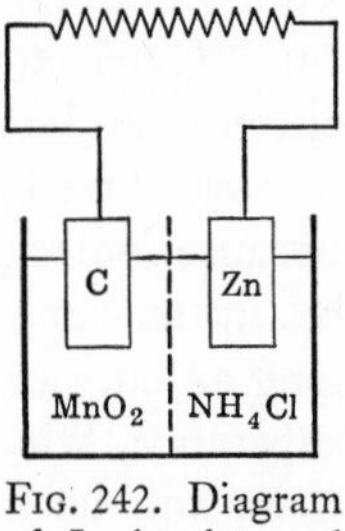

FIG. 242. Diagram of Leclanché and dry cells

The complete reactions within the cell are obscure, and apparently are influenced by the conditions under which the cell is used.

This type of primary cell has an electromotive force of about 1.5 volts and is best adapted to "open-circuit" work, that is, service in which the cell is called upon to deliver current only for short periods, its circuit at other times being open. The operation of annunciators, door bells, and flash lamps are typical illustrations of such service. The depolarizing action in the ammonium chloride cell is imperfect and the e.m.f. falls off with continued use; however, the cell recuperates during periods of open circuit because the layer of gas which may have been formed has an opportunity to disappear. In a typical test, a dry cell was caused to deliver current to a 3-ohm load continuously for 1 hr., and during this period its e.m.f. was observed to fall from 1.53 to 1.43 volts, but upon standing on open circuit for 30 min., the e.m.f. increased again to 1.49 volts.

*242. Daniell and Gravity Cells. — A cell invented by J. F. Daniell, Fig. 243, comprises a copper electrode C in a saturated copper sulfate solution and a zinc electrode Z in a dilute zinc sulfate solution, containing a little sulfuric acid. The solutions are separated by a cup P of unglazed earthenware, which allows the passage of ions but prevents the solutions from diffusing. The so-called gravity cell employs the same materials, but they

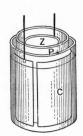

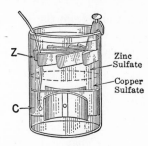

FIG. 243. The Daniell cell   FIG. 244. The gravity cell

are differently arranged; a section of this cell, Fig. 244, shows the denser copper sulfate solution at the bottom of a jar and the lighter zinc sulfate solution above it. The electrodes are in their respective solutions and the wire leading to the copper electrode is insulated to prevent contact with the zinc sulfate solution. A diagram representing the cells is given in Fig. 245.

In either type, the copper electrode is positive and the zinc electrode is negative, and the copper sulfate solution surrounding the copper serves as a depolarizer. The zinc dissolves because of its high solution pressure, displacing hydrogen from the sulfuric acid and leaving the electrode negative; while the copper, on account of its low solution pressure, receives a copper

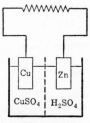

FIG. 245. Diagram of Daniell and gravity cells

deposit and becomes positive. When the electrodes are connected by an external circuit, a current is established, discharging the electrodes and allowing the process to continue. The following cell reactions are believed to occur:

The zinc in dissolving leaves electrons on the plate and throws off Zn^{++} ions; these combine with $SO_4^=$ ions to form zinc sulfate:

$$Zn \rightarrow Zn^{++} + 2e$$
$$H_2SO_4 \rightleftarrows 2H^+ + SO_4^=$$
$$Zn^{++} + SO_4^= \rightarrow ZnSO_4$$

The Cu^{++} ions of the depolarizer take electrons from the copper plate, depositing metallic copper:

$$CuSO_4 \rightleftarrows Cu^{++} + SO_4^=$$
$$Cu^{++} + 2e \rightarrow Cu \downarrow$$

Hydrogen ions from the sulfuric acid pass through the porous partition and combine with the $SO_4^=$ ions of the depolarizer, yielding sulfuric acid:

$$2H^+ + SO_4^= \rightarrow H_2SO_4$$

As the cell operates, the zinc electrode wears away and the copper electrode gains weight, while the concentration of the zinc sulfate solution increases and that of the copper sulfate solution diminishes. The changes in concentration alter the osmotic pressures and affect the e.m.f. of the cell somewhat, but not enough to interfere with its practical use.

This type of primary cell is best adapted to closed-circuit work, in which it continually delivers a small current, because this action helps to prevent the solutions from mixing by diffusion. It is used principally in the operation of railway signal circuits.

243. Standard Cells. — Voltaic cells of special form are used as standards of e.m.f. for measuring potential differences. These measurements are made with a potentiometer as described in § 248, under conditions such that the standard cell delivers only very small currents for brief periods of time.

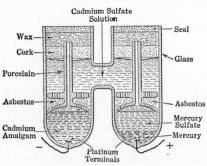

Fig. 246. Weston standard cell

In the Weston standard cell, Fig. 246, the electrodes are placed in the opposite sides of an H-shaped glass vessel which serves as a container for the electrolyte. The positive electrode is a paste of mercurous sulfate and the negative electrode is composed of cadmium amalgam. The electrolyte is a solution of cadmium sulfate, which may be kept saturated by having crystals of cadmium sulfate present.

The e.m.f. of the saturated cell is 1.01830 volts at 20° C., and varies slightly but definitely with temperature changes. These cause slight variations in the amount of cadmium sulfate which dissolves in the solution, thus altering the concentration, and consequently affecting the e.m.f. of the cell to some extent. In the unsaturated cell, temperature changes do not affect the concentration of the electrolyte, and their effect on the e.m.f. is so small that it is usually neglected. Each unsaturated cell made must have its e.m.f. determined by comparison with an e.m.f. of known value.

244. The Lead Storage Cell. — For purposes requiring steady currents larger than can be supplied by primary cells, *storage batteries* are used. Typical applications include: stand-by service in power substations to supply the load for short periods in the event of temporary interruptions of the main circuits, propulsion of submarines and trucks, and automobile starting and lighting.

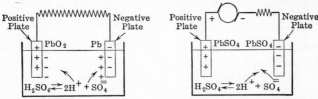

FIG. 247.   Discharge of lead storage cell   FIG. 248.   Charge of lead storage cell

When a storage battery is delivering current, it is said to be on *discharge*. After a period of discharge the battery may be restored to its original condition by supplying current to it in the opposite direction from an outside source; this action is called *charging*. The energy supplied to a battery during the charging process is not all delivered on discharge, usually 30 to 40 per cent being wasted in heat. The efficiency depends upon the size and construction of the battery.

The lead storage cell when charged consists essentially of a positive plate of lead dioxide and a negative plate of spongy lead, immersed in sulfuric acid as an electrolyte. As the cell discharges,

Fig. 247, both plates become coated with lead sulfate and the electrolyte becomes less dense. The principal cell reactions are believed to be as follows:

On Discharge

At negative plate $\qquad Pb \rightarrow Pb^{++} + 2e$

$$Pb^{++} + SO_4^= \rightarrow PbSO_4$$

At positive plate $\qquad PbO_2 + 2H^+ \rightarrow PbO + H_2O - 2e$

Lead dioxide (PbO_2) is inactive in the presence of sulfuric acid, but lead monoxide (PbO), which is formed on the reduction of PbO_2, reacts readily with sulfuric acid, thus:

$$PbO + H_2SO_4 \rightarrow PbSO_4 + H_2O$$

During discharge both plates become coated with lead sulfate ($PbSO_4$) and the sulfuric acid is partly converted into water, thus lowering the specific gravity of the electrolyte.

Upon charging the cell, Fig. 248, the lead sulfate on the positive plate is restored to lead dioxide and that on the negative plate to lead; the electrolyte returns to its original density. Thus:

On Charge

At negative plate $\quad PbSO_4 + 2H^+ + 2e \rightarrow Pb + H_2SO_4$

At positive plate $\quad PbSO_4 + SO_4^= - 2e \rightarrow Pb(SO_4)_2$

Plumbic sulfate, $Pb(SO_4)_2$, is unstable in the presence of water, consequently:

$$Pb(SO_4)_2 + 2H_2O \rightarrow PbO_2 + 2H_2SO_4$$

This action restores the cell to its original condition. If the cell is overcharged, hydrogen and oxygen are liberated as in the decomposition of water in an electrolytic cell. This effect is known as "gassing" and indicates the completion of charge.

During discharge of the lead storage cell, the e.m.f. falls quickly from an initial value of approximately 2.1 volts and remains nearly constant at 2.0 volts throughout most of the discharge period. At the approach of complete discharge the e.m.f. falls rapidly from this value. The state of charge of the cell is tested by measuring the specific gravity of the electrolyte with a hydrometer. For an automobile battery, the specific gravity of the electrolyte is 1.285 when the battery is fully charged, and when discharged it may be as low as 1.150.

A storage battery is charged for 8 hr. from 110-volt direct-current mains, the current being maintained at 10 amp. by a rheostat connected in series in the circuit. If the average e.m.f. of the battery during the charging period is 24 volts, find the total energy supplied from the mains, the amount transformed into chemical energy, and the amount wasted in heat.

The total energy supplied from the mains is found by equation (144) to be $110 \times 10 \times 8 = 8800$ watt-hr. and the amount transformed into chemical energy, by equation (143), is $24 \times 10 \times 8 = 1920$ watt-hr. Since the battery is connected in opposition to the supply mains, the net e.m.f. in the circuit is $110 - 24 = 86$ volts and the resistance of the circuit is found by Ohm's Law to be $86 \div 10$ or 8.6 ohms. The energy wasted in heat is accordingly given by equation (149) as $8.6 \times (10)^2 \times 8 = 6880$ watt-hr.

245. The Edison Storage Cell. — The storage cell devised by Thomas A. Edison (1847–1931) employs nickel oxide for the positive electrode and finely divided iron for the negative electrode, these materials being packed into pockets carried by steel grids. The electrolyte is a solution of potassium hydroxide. As the cell discharges, the nickel oxide becomes reduced and the iron becomes oxidized, but the electrolyte remains unchanged. The chemical reactions are complex and not fully understood.

This cell, which was designed for vehicle operation, is lighter than the lead storage cell, is less subject to mechanical derangement, and is not injured by freezing. Moreover, cells of this type can be discharged and left in that condition without injury. The e.m.f. is lower than that of the lead storage cell and drops somewhat during discharge, having an average value of about 1.2 volts.

246. Cells in Series and in Parallel. — Cells are frequently connected in series in order to obtain an increased e.m.f. They are sometimes connected in parallel in order that jointly they may supply a large current to a low-resistance load without demanding an excessive current from any single cell.

When a number of cells are connected in series, their combined e.m.f. is the sum of the e.m.f.'s of the individual cells.

When a number of cells having equal e.m.f.'s are connected in parallel, the e.m.f. of the combination is the same as that of any individual cell. Cells having appreciably different e.m.f.'s would not be connected in parallel in practice, because wasteful circulating currents would be set up in the cells themselves, even if the external circuit were open.

247. Measurement of Cell Resistance. — The ammeter-volt-meter method described in § 220 can be used to determine the

internal resistance of a voltaic cell, using connections as shown in
Fig. 249, in which F and G represent the terminals of a cell having
an internal resistance r.   Across these terminals there is connected

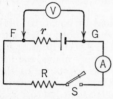

a high-resistance voltmeter V, and also a
low-resistance load R in series with a switch
S and an ammeter A. With the switch
open, the current in the cell will be very
small, and the voltmeter reading, V_1, may
be taken as practically equal to the e.m.f.

FIG. 249. Measuring in-
ternal resistance of cell

of the cell. With the switch closed, the
ammeter will indicate the current I in the
cell, and the voltmeter reading V_2 will be
lower than the former value V_1 because of the potential drop Ir
in the cell. Consequently

$$r = \frac{V_1 - V_2}{I} \qquad (157)$$

is the internal resistance of the cell.

248. The Potentiometer. — The e.m.f. of a cell is not given
exactly by the reading of a voltmeter connected across the cell
terminals, because even a high-resistance voltmeter takes some
current. Such e.m.f.'s can be compared accurately with the
known e.m.f. of a standard cell by means of a potentiometer.
An advantage of the potentiometer method is that the measurement is made when the cell is not supplying any current, and since
there is *no potential drop* in
the cell and *no polarization*,
the value measured is truly
the e.m.f.

The apparatus used in a
potentiometer measurement is
indicated in Fig. 250. A storage
battery B maintains a steady
current in the slidewire MN,

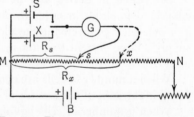

FIG. 250. Elementary potentiometer circuit

to one end of which connec-
tions are made to a standard cell S or to the cell X under test.
By means of a double-throw switch, either of these cells may be
connected through the galvanometer G to a slider which can be
touched at different points along the wire MN. The battery B
should have a constant e.m.f. and naturally it should be larger than
that of either S or X.

The current I from the battery B establishes a uniform potential drop along the slidewire MN, the potential being higher at M than at N. The cells S and X both have their positive terminals connected to M, and these terminals, therefore, have the same potential as M. When the double-throw switch is closed either way, the slider, if free from the slidewire, will have a potential which is lower than that of M by an amount equal to the e.m.f. of the cell which the switch has placed into the circuit. There will be some point along MN which will have the same potential as the slider; this point can be found by touching the slider to different points until one is found for which the galvanometer shows no deflection. Under these conditions there will be no current in the circuit branch containing the cell and galvanometer, and the potential drop along the wire to the point of contact will then be equal to the e.m.f. of the cell which is in circuit. Thus, with the double-throw switch connected to the standard cell of e.m.f. E_s, a balance will be obtained at some point s such that $E_s = IR_s$, where R_s is the resistance of the slidewire from M to s. Then with the double-throw switch connected to X, another balance will be obtained at some other point x, such that $E_x = IR_x$, where E_x is the e.m.f. being measured and R_x is the resistance of the slidewire from M to x. From these relations,

$$\frac{E_x}{E_s} = \frac{IR_x}{IR_s}$$

whence

$$E_x = E_s \frac{R_x}{R_s} \tag{158}$$

giving the unknown e.m.f. in terms of that of the standard cell and the known resistances.

This result may be verified by applying Kirchhoff's Second Law [§ 229] around a path from M along the slidewire to the contact point, returning through the cell S or X. For balance at s with the standard cell there is obtained: $-IR_s + E_s = 0$; and for balance at x with the other cell: $-IR_x + E_x = 0$. These equations yield the same result as found previously.

Since the resistance of the slidewire is proportional to its length, the unknown e.m.f. may also be expressed as

$$E_x = E_s \frac{l_x}{l_s}$$

where l_x and l_s are the wire lengths from M to x and from M to s respectively.

In commercial potentiometers, the slidewire is usually replaced, at least in part, by resistance coils arranged with dial switches, and potential differences up to about 1.5 volts can be read directly from the setting of the instrument at balance. Higher values than this can be measured with the potentiometer when used with a "volt box"; this is an arrangement of resistances for dividing the total potential difference into two definite parts, one of which is less than 1.5 volts.

PROBLEMS

1. An ammeter was calibrated by connecting it in series with an electrolytic cell containing copper sulfate solution. During a 10-min. test the weight of the cathode increased by 2.023 gm., the instrument reading being constant at 10.00 amp. What correction should be applied to the ammeter at this scale reading?

2. A sheet of metal 10 cm. square is coated on both faces with silver in a plating bath containing silver nitrate solution, through which a current of 0.3 amp. is maintained for 30 min. Find the thickness of the plating. The specific gravity of silver is 10.45.

3. A current of 600 amp. is supplied to 30 electrolytic cells in series for a period of 8 hr., the cells containing acidulated water. How many kilograms of oxygen are liberated?

4. In copper refining, pure copper is deposited from copper sulfate solution in an electrolytic cell using impure copper as the anode. If the potential difference across the cell is 0.25 volt, how much energy is used in depositing 1 lb. of copper?

5. How many atoms of hydrogen will be liberated by the passage of 500 coulombs of electricity through an electrolytic cell containing acidulated water?

6. How much silver will be deposited from a silver nitrate solution in an electrolytic cell by the passage of 96,500 coulombs of electricity?

7. A steady current is maintained in an electrolytic cell containing silver nitrate for 1 hr. and deposits 2.145 gm. of silver on the platinum container. What is the value of the current?

8. The *electrochemical equivalent* of an ion is the mass in grams liberated in electrolysis by 1 amp. in 1 sec. Compute the electrochemical equivalents of copper, oxygen, and silver.

9. How much silver will be deposited from a silver nitrate solution in an electrolytic cell by a current of 10 amp. maintained for 30 min.?

10. What quantity of electricity must be passed through an electrolytic cell in order to decompose 1 gm. of water?

11. How long would it take a current of 2 amp. to liberate 3.54 gm. of silver from a solution of silver nitrate?

*12. For each ampere-hour delivered by a gravity cell, compute the amount of zinc dissolved and the amount of copper deposited within the cell.

13. A storage battery having an e.m.f. of 12 volts is being charged from a 110-volt generator, the total resistance of the circuit being 10 ohms.

What length of time will be needed to pass 60 amp-hr. of electricity through the battery?

14. A 32-volt storage battery is charged from 110-volt direct-current supply mains, a resistance being connected in series with the battery to limit the charging current to 8 amp. Compute the power wasted in heat.

15. A storage battery has an e.m.f. of 6 volts and an internal resistance of 0.1 ohm. Find the potential difference across the terminals of this battery (*a*) when it is delivering 8 amp., and (*b*) when it is being charged with 8 amp.

16. Two dry cells, each having an e.m.f. of 1.5 volts and an internal resistance of 0.6 ohm, are to be connected in such a manner as to supply as large a current as possible to an external circuit. Should the cells be connected in series or in parallel (*a*) if the external circuit has a resistance of 0.5 ohm, (*b*) if the external circuit has a resistance of 5.0 ohms?

17. Six voltaic cells, each having an e.m.f. of 1.0 volt and an internal resistance of 0.8 ohm are connected in two groups, each composed of three cells in series. The two groups are joined in parallel and supply current to an external circuit of 4 ohms resistance. Find the current in each cell.

18. Two batteries, each composed of 6 cells in series, are connected in parallel and jointly supply current to an external circuit of 8 ohms resistance. Each cell has an e.m.f. of 2.0 volts and an internal resistance of 0.16 ohm. Compute the current in the external circuit and the potential difference across the terminals of each cell.

19. Two storage cells connected in parallel supply jointly a current of 20 amp. to an external circuit. The cells have e.m.f.'s of 2.1 volts and 2.0 volts, and each has an internal resistance of 0.05 ohm. Find the current in each cell.

20. A voltaic cell, having an e.m.f. of 1.56 volts and an internal resistance of 0.4 ohm, is connected to an external circuit of 10 ohms resistance. Calculate (*a*) the current in the circuit, (*b*) the potential difference across the terminals of the cell, (*c*) the power supplied to the external circuit, and (*d*) the power wasted within the cell.

21. A Daniell cell is found to establish a current of 0.078 amp. in an external circuit of 10 ohms resistance. The current increases to 0.122 amp. when the resistance of the external circuit is reduced to 5 ohms. Compute the e.m.f. of the cell and also its internal resistance.

CHAPTER XXIV

ELECTROMAGNETISM

249. Magnetic Effect of the Current. — The discovery of electromagnetism was made by Oersted in 1820, through his observations that an electric current in a conductor is surrounded by a magnetic field. He also found that the direction of the field about a current-carrying wire is tangentially perpendicular to the wire and that the intensity of the field diminishes in receding from the wire. The lines of force about an isolated wire are concentric with it, as can be proved by arranging the wire vertically and moving a suspended magnet or compass around

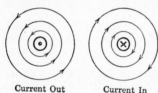

Current Out   Current In

Fig. 251. Diagrams of field around a current-carrying wire

it. Fig. 251 shows two diagrams of the magnetic field around a wire; the heavy circles indicate the wire in section and the light circles represent lines of force. When the current is directed toward the observer, as represented by a dot within the wire, the magnetic flux will be counterclockwise, as shown at the left. When the current is reversed in direction, the flux will also be reversed, as shown at the right. These directions indicate how an isolated N magnet pole would move about the wires if free to do so.

A simple rule for determining the relative directions of current and flux makes use of the *right hand*, the fingers being curved as though grasping the wire carrying the current, and the thumb being outstretched. *When the thumb points in the direction of the current the fingers will point along the lines of force.* Another popular rule applies the direction of advance of a right-handed screw.

The magnitude of the field due to an electric current can be computed by means of a fundamental expression due to Ampère. This relationship will be explained with the aid of Fig. 252, which depicts a curved wire *pq* in which there is an electric current. Each elementary length of the wire contributes something to the magnetic field intensity at all points around the wire. As expressed by

Ampère, the contribution of the element Δs to the field at any point P is

$$\Delta H = \frac{I \sin \theta \, \Delta s}{r^2}$$

where I is the current, r is the length of a line joining the wire element and the point in question, and θ is the angle between this line and the direction of the current. The total field intensity at the point P is, therefore

$$H = \Sigma \frac{I \sin \theta \, \Delta s}{r^2} = \int \frac{I \sin \theta \, ds}{r^2} \qquad (159)$$

the latter form being in calculus notation.

That the field intensity should vary inversely as the square of the distance from a wire might be expected by comparison with the field intensity due to a magnet pole or an electric charge. Further, it is reasonable to suppose that doubling the current or doubling the length of the element would double the field intensity. The fact that the flux is concentric about the wire suggests that the field intensity due to the element has its greatest value in the direction normal to the element and its least value along the direction of the element, but experimentation was required to prove that the intensity varies as the sine of the angle θ.

FIG. 252. Finding intensity of magnetic field around a wire

250. Circular Current; Electromagnetic Units. — The laws for determining the direction and magnitude of the field produced by

an electric current apply to all forms of circuits and will now be adapted to a few simple shapes. Suppose, first, that a wire is bent into the arc of a circle and that it is desired to compute the field intensity at the center of the arc.

FIG. 253. Illustrating the definition of unit current

Fig. 253 shows a wire forming an arc of radius r centered at P and carrying current in a clockwise direction, with the wires connecting the arc to the rest of the circuit arranged radially so that they will not affect the field at the center. Applying the right-hand rule, it is found that the magnetic field is directed into the page in the region toward the center of the arc and out of the page in the region away from the center. For all positions of the element ds the radius r is constant and perpendicular to the element, so that the angle θ of equation (159) is 90°. Hence, the field intensity at the center of the arc becomes

$$H = \frac{I}{r^2} \int ds$$

in which the integral $\int ds$ represents the full length of the arc.

The foregoing equation is used to define unit current on the basis of its magnetic effect, the current having unit value when each of the other quantities is unity. Thus, the *electromagnetic unit of current*, or *abampere*, is a current such that in an arc 1 cm. long and having 1 cm. radius, it will produce at the center of the arc a field intensity of 1 oersted. The ampere is one-tenth of an abampere.

If the arc in Fig. 253 is extended to form a complete circular loop having a radius of r cm., the integral becomes the circumference of the circle, $2\pi r$. Expressing the current in the loop in amperes, the field intensity at the center in oersteds becomes $H = I \times 2\pi r \div 10\,r^2$. A coil of N turns will have a field intensity N times as great, provided the turns are concentrated so that the entire coil has little axial length compared with its radius. The field intensity at the center of such a coil is consequently

$$H = \frac{2\pi N I}{10\,r} \tag{160}$$

From this expression the *ampere may be defined as the current which in a coil having 1 turn and a radius of 1 cm. will produce at the center a field of intensity* $\frac{2\pi}{10}$ *oersted.*

The study of Electricity and Magnetism involves three systems of units. The *electrostatic* system is based on electricity at rest, as described in Chapter XX. The *electromagnetic* system is based on the magnetic effect of the current. The *practical* system, referred to in Chapter XXII, is an adaptation of the electromagnetic system, each practical unit being some multiple or sub-multiple of ten times as large as the corresponding electromagnetic unit.

The relations among these systems will be illustrated by considering the entity of electric charge. In the electromagnetic system, the unit of charge, called the *abcoulomb*, is naturally the quantity of electricity transferred by a current of 1 abampere maintained for 1 sec. This quantity is entirely independent of the electrostatic unit of charge, which is defined [§ 200] on the basis of its force action upon a like charge. Careful tests have been made comparing the two systems, as a result of which it is found that 1 abcoulomb is equal to 3×10^{10} e.s.u. of charge. The coulomb is one-tenth of an abcoulomb, and consequently equals 3×10^9 e.s.u. of charge.

251. Magnetic Field about a Straight Conductor. — The general expression for field intensity given by equation (159) was verified experimentally by the French physicists Jean B. Biot (1774–1862) and Felix Savart (1791–1841), as applied to the magnetic field produced by current in a long straight conductor.

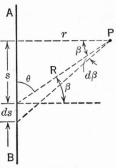

In Fig. 254 let AB represent a portion of such a wire extending indefinitely in both directions, and let it be required to determine the field intensity at a point P in space at a perpendicular distance r from it. The field at this point may be considered as made up of the contributions of successive elementary lengths, such as ds, comprising the whole wire. Using the symbols R, s, θ and β as in the figure, the field intensity at P due to a current of I amp. in the elementary length ds is found to be

Fig. 254. Field intensity near a straight wire

$$dH = \frac{I \sin \theta \, ds}{10 \, R^2} = \frac{I \cos \beta \, ds}{10 \, R^2}$$

where $\beta = 90° - \theta$.

The total field intensity at the point under consideration due to the entire wire is found by the summation of a series of terms like the foregoing. This is done by calculus, after first rewriting the equation in terms of the single variable β. Since $s = r \tan \beta$, $ds = r \, d\beta/\cos^2 \beta$, and $R = r \sec \beta$, it follows that

$$dH = \frac{I \cos \beta \, r \, d\beta}{10 \, r^2 \sec^2 \beta \cos^2 \beta} = \frac{I}{10 \, r} \cos \beta \, d\beta$$

The total field intensity at P is expressed as

$$H = \frac{I}{10 r} \int_{\beta = -\frac{\pi}{2}}^{\beta = \frac{\pi}{2}} \cos \beta \, d\beta$$

Integrating this expression, the field intensity in oersteds at a point r cm. from a long straight wire carrying a current of I amp. reduces to

$$H = \frac{2I}{10\,r} \qquad (161)$$

Thus, at a point 5 cm. from a long straight wire carrying a current of 8 amp., the field intensity has a magnitude of $(2 \times 8) \div (10 \times 5) = 0.32$ oersted.

252. Motion of Pole in ·Magnetic Field. — It is of interest to calculate the amount of work that must be done in moving an isolated magnet pole once around any closed path in opposition to a magnetic field. Consider first a long straight conductor, as represented in part I of Fig. 255, in which there is a current of I amp., and suppose that a pole of unit strength is moved along the dotted path of radius r cm. once around the wire. The force in dynes acting upon this pole will be numerically equal to the field strength given by the foregoing equation as $H = \dfrac{2I}{10\,r}$. To move the unit pole completely around the wire in a circular path of length $2\pi r$ cm. against this force would require

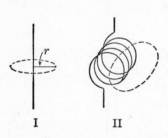

FIG. 255. Path of pole in magnetic field

$$W = 2\pi r \times \frac{2I}{10\,r} = \frac{4\pi I}{10}$$

ergs of work. Since the radius disappears from the result, the work required is found to be independent of the path, and would be the same for any closed path around the conductor, whether circular or not. The work remains the same if the wire is not straight, or even if it is bent into a closed coil. To move a unit pole through a coil of N turns, as in part II of the figure, would require $4\pi NI/10$ ergs to link its path with all of the turns.

⋆253. The Solenoid. — A coil of wire wound uniformly in a long helix is termed a *solenoid*. Solenoids have a wide application in magnetic apparatus, and it is important to be able to determine the field intensities within them. This can be done by considering the amount of work needed to move a unit magnet pole around a closed path in opposition to the field, as in the preceding section.

In a ring solenoid the helix is bent to form a toroid, as though the wire were wound around an automobile tire. For such a solenoid of N turns carrying a current of I amp., the work done in moving a unit pole once around the median line of the toroid would be $4\pi NI/10$ ergs, since its path would be linked with all of the turns. The work can also be expressed as Hl, where H is the field intensity in oersteds along the solenoid axis and l is the length of the median line in centimeters. Therefore, $4\pi NI/10 = Hl$, and the field intensity along the axis is

$$H = \frac{4\pi N I}{10\,l} = \frac{4\pi\,n\,I}{10} \tag{162}$$

where $n = N/l$ is the number of turns per unit of length. The same expression may be used for a straight solenoid, but applies only to its central portion.

254. Lines of Induction; Magnetic Flux. — The student is familiar with the use of lines to represent magnetic field intensity and need only be reminded that field intensity means force per unit pole to appreciate why these lines are called lines of force. In the preceding sections the presence of a magnetic field around an electric current has been explained, and values for field intensity have been found for a number of circuit shapes. A generalization might be drawn, using the idea of magnetic lines, to the effect that an electric current always establishes lines of force around it. One might naturally inquire whether the situation can be reversed, and thus produce a current in a circuit by placing a magnetic field near it. Experiment shows that such a result can be obtained, but only while the number of magnetic lines passing through the circuit is *changing* [§ 259]. The process is described by saying that when the number of magnetic lines changes an e.m.f. is set up, and this e.m.f. develops a current in the circuit. An e.m.f. set up in this manner is said to be *induced*, and the process is called *induction*.

The generation of such an e.m.f. can be demonstrated with two coils wound upon a wooden ring as illustrated in Fig. 256. The *primary coil P* is a ring solenoid which is connected to a battery through a switch *s*, and the *secondary coil S* is joined to a galvanometer *G* to indicate the e.m.f. induced in that coil. While the switch in the primary circuit is being closed or opened the galvanometer will show a momentary deflection each time, but there will be no steady deflection when the switch is left closed.

An increased deflection will be observed if the foregoing experiment is repeated with the coils wound upon a core of iron or other magnetic material. Under these circumstances the deflection produced upon closing or opening the primary circuit will be much larger than before. The presence of the magnetic core causes a large increase in the number of magnetic lines within the solenoid. This is not due to any increase in the field intensity H, which, as shown by equation (162), depends only upon the number of turns

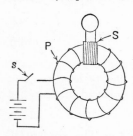

FIG. 256. Illustrating magnetic induction

per unit length and the current, and so is independent of the material within the solenoid. The result is due to additional lines produced by the magnetization of the iron; these lines together with the lines of force which represent H are all effective in inducing e.m.f. and are called *lines of induction*. The number of lines of induction passing perpendicularly through an area of 1 sq. m. is represented by the symbol B. In a vacuum, and practically also in air, the lines of force represented by H and the lines of induction represented by B are identical, but inside of a magnetic substance, B is larger than H, often many times as large.

The term *magnetic flux* refers to the total number of *lines of induction* extending through any specified region. If these lines are uniform through an area A sq. cm., with B lines extending normally through each square centimeter, the total flux Φ extending through the area will be

$$\Phi = BA \tag{163}$$

By rearranging terms in this equation, the magnetic induction may be expressed as $B = \Phi/A$, that is, the amount of flux per unit area. For this reason, the magnetic induction B is commonly called *flux density*.

The unit of magnetic flux is the *maxwell;* this unit is named after the English physicist, J. Clark Maxwell (1831–1879). *One maxwell is one line of magnetic flux.* The unit of flux density is called the *gauss*, after Karl F. Gauss (1777–1855), German mathematician and physicist. *A gauss is one maxwell per square centimeter.* It is represented by a single line of magnetic flux extending perpendicularly through an area of 1 sq. cm.

It has already been observed that within a magnetic material the flux density B is greater than the field intensity H; the ratio

$$\mu = \frac{B}{H} \tag{164}$$

is called the *permeability* of the material. The permeability of a magnetic material does not have a fixed value even for a particular specimen, but varies with the flux density in it and with its previous magnetic history. These variations are discussed in Chapter XXV. For a vacuum, and practically for air, the flux density and field strength are numerically equal, and the permeability is unity.

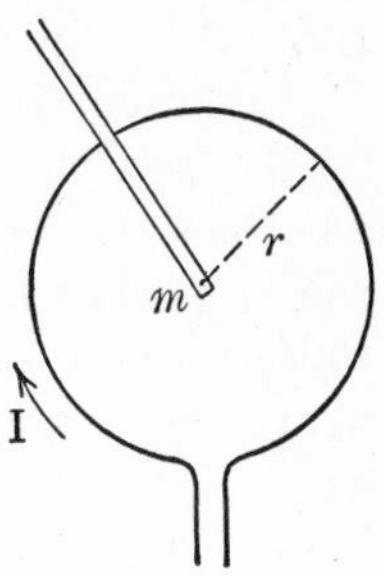

255. Force on Conductor in a Magnetic Field; Ampère's Law. — The analysis of the circular loop considered in § 250 can be extended to show that a current-carrying conductor experiences a force when located in a magnetic field. To determine this force, imagine an isolated N pole of strength m units to be placed at the center of the loop, Fig. 257, where the field is H. It will be acted upon by a force directed into the page and having a value in dynes

Fig. 257. Finding the force on a conductor

$$F = mH = m\,\frac{2\pi NI}{10\,r}$$

by equations (137) and (160), where I is the current in amperes in each of the N turns of the coil of radius r cm. Since the current-carrying coil acts with this force on the magnet pole, the pole must react upon the coil with an equal force, according to Newton's Third Law of Motion. The force on the coil is, therefore,

$$F = \left(\frac{m}{r^2}\right)\frac{I}{10}\,(2\pi\,rN)$$

which is exactly the same as the preceding equation except that both numerator and denominator have been multiplied by r.

This equation can be simplified by considering the significance of the term within each parenthesis. The first expresses the flux density of the radial magnetic field at a distance r cm. from a magnet pole of strength m in accordance with equations (138) and

(164), so that $\dfrac{m}{r^2} = \mu H = B$. Since every part of the wire is at this common distance r from the pole, B represents the flux density in gausses at the wire due to the pole. The second parenthesis is the total length of the wire in the coil and will be represented in centimeters by L. Consequently, the force on the wire in dynes will be

$$F = \frac{BIL}{10} \qquad (165)$$

and will be directed toward the reader in Fig. 257.

Equation (165) is a mathematical statement of Ampère's Law for the force on a conductor; it asserts that any conductor carrying a current and located in a magnetic field at right angles to the flux will be pushed by a force that is proportional to the flux density, to the current, and to the length of the wire. While the equation was derived for a particular shape of coil (that is, circular) by

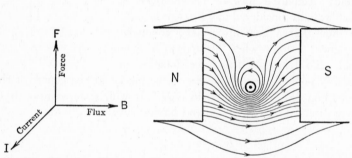

FIG. 258. Direction of force on a wire

FIG. 259. Composite magnetic field of magnets and conductor

consideration of the field intensity at a particular point (that is, the center of the coil), it is perfectly general and can be applied to all forms of circuits.

In applying Ampère's Law, it should be noted that for any straight piece of wire of length L the directions of F, B, and I are mutually perpendicular. Fig. 258 shows these directions along the three geometric axes. If the conductor is not at right angles to the flux, but makes an angle ϕ with it instead, then the effective length is the component $L \sin \phi$, and the force is expressed by

$$F = \frac{BIL}{10} \sin \phi \qquad (166)$$

The relative directions of the magnetic flux, conductor current, and force on the conductor shown in Fig. 258 can be visualized by the concept that magnetic lines tend to become as short as possible, and when in the same direction exert a sidewise thrust upon one another [§ 213]. Fig. 259 illustrates a wire located in a magnetic field produced by the poles N and S. The current is shown by the dot within the conductor to be directed toward the reader and, consequently, the magnetic flux which it produces will be counter-clockwise. Below the conductor the lines produced by the poles and those produced by the conductor are both to the right and the resultant field will be strong, but above the conductor the two fields are in opposition and therefore the resultant field will be weak. The fact that the wire will be pushed upward as a result of this flux distribution can be visualized by the tension along the lines of the field from N and S and by the repulsive action between them below the conductor where all the lines have the same direction.

256. The Galvanometer. — The instruments ordinarily used for measuring electric currents depend for their operation on the force action on conductors in magnetic fields. In the usual form of such instruments, a coil of wire is suspended in a magnetic field and a current is established in it; the forces thus produced on the coil deflect it from its position of rest and the amount of deflection serves as a measure of the current. This is the operating principle of the *d'Arsonval galvanometer* (named after the French physicist, Arsene d'Arsonval) that is employed for the measurement of small currents, as well as of most am-

meters and voltmeters used in electrical testing.

Fig. 260 shows the coil of a galvanometer between the poles of a strong permanent magnet. It carries a mirror M so that its deflections can be read with a telescope and scale. Assume that there are N turns on the coil, that it is located in a uniform field of flux density B gausses, and that a current of I amp. circulates around the coil in a clockwise direction. This current is conducted to

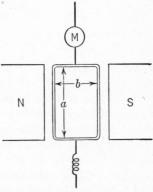

FIG. 260. A galvanometer coil

the coil by a flat metal ribbon which serves as the suspension and is led out by a helix of similar material below the coil. Applying

Ampère's Law to the left side of the coil of length a cm., the force upon this side in dynes is

$$F = \frac{BINa}{10}$$

and the force on the other side will be of like amount. These forces act in opposite directions but combine to produce a torque in a common direction, the right side of the coil moving forward out of the page and the left side moving backward into the page. When the coil lies in the plane of the magnet as shown, the torque in dyne-centimeters will be

$$T' = 2\frac{BINa}{10} \times \frac{b}{2} = \frac{BINA'}{10}$$

where $A' = ab$ is the area of the coil face. As the coil turns in response to this torque the lever arm becomes less than $b/2$, and ultimately the coil would come to rest in a position at right angles to that shown. However, the suspension exerts a restoring torque on the coil as it moves from the position shown, the value of which is proportional to the twist ϕ of the suspension, or

$$T'' = \tau\phi$$

where τ is a constant determined by the stiffness of the suspension. The coil will come to rest where $T' = T''$, and therefore

$$\frac{BINA'}{10} = \tau\phi$$

showing that the twist ϕ for a given instrument (that is B, N, A' and τ fixed) is proportional to the current I. With a parallel field, as assumed in Fig. 260, this expression would be true only for small deflections. In the galvanometer as actually constructed a stationary cylindrical core is mounted within the moving coil and the pole pieces are usually curved. A radial magnetic field is thus established, and the coil always swings perpendicularly to the flux. By this means the twist is made proportional to the current throughout the entire range of the instrument.

Another form of this galvanometer, called a *ballistic galvanometer*, has a coil of considerable width in order to give it a high moment of inertia; its purpose is to measure electric charge rather than current. A small quantity of electricity is discharged through such an instrument and a deflecting torque is set up for a brief interval. The coil continues to rotate after the discharge has been completed and the maximum *throw* of the instrument is read. This throw is proportional to the charge and the instrument can be calibrated to measure quantity of electricity directly.

257. Ammeters and Voltmeters. — Instruments for measuring current and potential difference in commercial testing are galvanometers of more substantial type in which the coil is pivoted and fitted with a pointer that moves over a suitably calibrated scale. Current is supplied to the coil through flat spiral springs which also serve to return the pointer to the zero position when the current ceases. There is no structural difference between an ammeter and a voltmeter, and both deflect in proportion to the current in the movable coil. The difference between them is one of electrical resistance; the instruments are designed in this respect so that their introduction into a circuit for purposes of measurement will not change the quantities they are intended to measure.

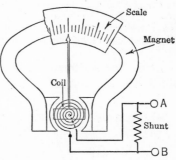

In the ammeter, Fig. 261, the coil is provided with a by-pass, called a *shunt*, connected directly across the terminals *A* and *B*, so that the current in the coil will be only a small but definite part of the entire current in the circuit.

FIG. 261. Construction of an ammeter

The ammeter has a very low resistance so that the potential drop across it will be small; naturally care must be taken to have enough resistance in the circuit associated with this meter so that the current will be limited to a value within its range. *Never connect an ammeter across service mains*, for it would burn out immediately.

In the voltmeter the movable coil is connected in series with a resistance, so that the instrument may be connected directly across a generator or service mains and yet take only a small current. A voltmeter has a high resistance so as to divert as little current as possible from the circuit to which it is connected. In a sense the voltmeter protects itself because of its high resistance, but care must be exercised not to apply potential differences exceeding the range of the instrument. The range of a voltmeter can be extended if desired by the use of an additional series resistance external to the instrument. Such an auxiliary resistance is called a *multiplier*.

The resistance of the shunt or series resistance for a particular instrument can be found by applying Ohm's Law, as the following examples will show:

Suppose an ammeter to have a moving coil of 5 ohms resistance, which deflects across the entire scale when carrying a current of 0.01 amp. Find the shunt resistance necessary to make this instrument a 10-amp. ammeter (that is, one which deflects full scale when the main-line current is 10 amp.). At full-scale deflection, the potential drop across its coil is $E = I \times R = 0.01 \times 5 = 0.05$ volt, and this must then also be the potential drop across the shunt. But the current in the shunt is $10 - 0.01 = 9.99$ amp., consequently, its resistance must be $R = E \div I = 0.05 \div 9.99 = 0.005005$ ohm.

Likewise, suppose a voltmeter to have a coil of 5 ohms resistance, which deflects full scale when carrying a current of 0.01 amp. Find what resistance must be connected in series with the coil if this instrument is to have a range of 150 volts (that is, the instrument is to deflect full scale when 150 volts are impressed across its terminals). Since the current is the same in the coil and series resistance, the resistance of the entire instrument is $R = E \div I = 150 \div 0.01 = 15,000$ ohms, and inasmuch as the coil has a resistance of 5 ohms, the series resistance must have the value of $15,000 - 5 = 14,995$ ohms.

258. The Wattmeter. — Since power is the product of potential difference and current [§ 219], an instrument to measure power

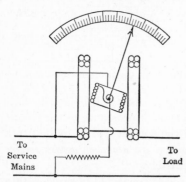

must be arranged so that the deflection of the coil will be proportional to the potential difference as well as to the current. The permanent magnet common to voltmeter and ammeter is replaced in the *wattmeter* by a heavy winding that is connected in series with the load circuit like an ammeter; in this way the flux density B within it is made proportional to the load current. The moving coil is connected in

To Service Mains

To Load

FIG. 262. Diagram of a wattmeter

series with a high resistance across the circuit under measurement, and the current I in the coil is thereby made proportional to the potential difference across the load. Since the force on the coil is proportional to $B \times I$ according to equation (165), it will be proportional to the product of the amperes in the load and the volts across it. Therefore, the instrument can be calibrated to read watts directly. The arrangement and connections of the wattmeter are shown in Fig. 262; the "current winding" is shown by the vertical coils in series with the load, and the "potential winding" is shown by the movable coil bridged across the lines.

The metering of electrical energy for determining the cost of electric service is not accomplished by wattmeters, for these instruments indicate merely the instantaneous rate at which the energy is used; the meter that is used for this purpose is called a *watt-hour meter*. It is similar electrically to the wattmeter but the coil is arranged to rotate continuously at a rate dependent upon the power expended in the load circuit, and the charge is based upon the number of revolutions made.

259. Induced Electromotive Force. — In 1831, Faraday discovered that an e.m.f. could be induced in an electric circuit by relative motion between the circuit and a magnet. This action was mentioned in § 254, and will be further illustrated by describing some fundamental experiments.

Fig. 263 shows a bar magnet NS and a coil of wire, the coil being in a vertical plane and having its circuit closed through a galvanometer G. Nothing happens as long as the apparatus remains stationary, but when the magnet is moved horizontally toward the coil, the galvanometer deflects, showing that an e.m.f. is being induced in the coil and sets up a current in its closed circuit. The faster the magnet is moved, the larger the deflection will be; if it is brought to rest, the deflection again becomes zero. Upon moving the magnet away from

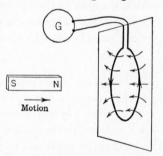

Fig. 263.   Inducing an e.m.f. in a coil

the coil, similar results are obtained, but the deflections are reversed, showing that the e.m.f. is now in the opposite direction. The same effects may be produced by moving the coil instead of the magnet, by using an electromagnet instead of a permanent magnet, or by turning the coil. These tests lead to the conclusion that *an e.m.f. will be induced in a coil of wire whenever there is a change in the magnetic flux linked with it.*

The magnitude of the induced e.m.f. can be found by considering the energy relations in a circuit so arranged that a portion of it moves through a magnetic field. Fig. 264 is a plan view of such a circuit with the moving part located in a uniform field directed into the page.   Two bare parallel rails MN and PQ are joined at the left by the stationary conductor MP.   A bare wire CD extends perpendicularly from one rail to the other and may be moved along them.   An e.m.f. is induced when the wire is moved and sets up a current in the loop $CMPD$.   To determine the value of this e.m.f., suppose that the wire CD has a length L between the rails and that a force F is exerted upon it.   If the force acts for a time interval dt, moving it uniformly a distance ds, the work done is

$dW = F\,ds$.   Taking the current in the loop, expressed in absolute units, as I, then the force acting upon the wire because of its presence in the field of flux density B is given by Ampère's Law [§ 255] as the product BIL, and the applied force F must have this same value in the opposite direction.   Hence the work can be

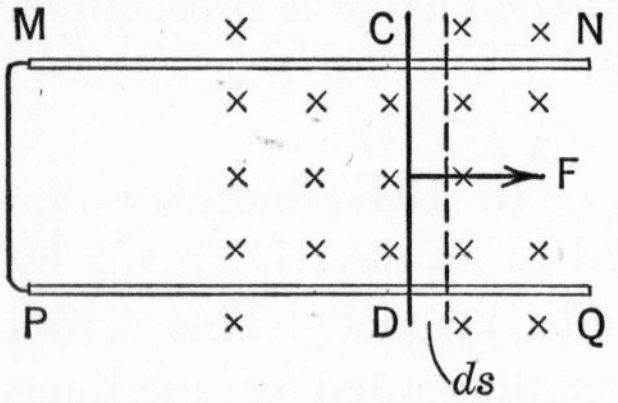

FIG. 264.   Calculating induced e.m.f.

expressed as $dW = BIL\,ds$.   But $L\,ds$ represents the amount by which the area of the circuit changes, and this area multiplied by the flux density B gives the change in the magnetic flux linking the circuit, namely $d\Phi$.   Consequently

$$dW = I\,d\Phi \qquad (167)$$

where the work dW is expressed in ergs, the current I in abamperes, and the change in flux $d\Phi$ in maxwells.

The work can also be expressed independently in terms of the e.m.f. induced in the circuit; if this is represented in absolute units by e_i, then, as explained in § 219

$$dW = Ie_i\,dt$$

The two expressions represent the same quantity of work and may be equated, yielding $I\,d\Phi = Ie_i\,dt$, from which $e_i = -\dfrac{d\Phi}{dt}$, the negative sign being introduced to take care of direction, as explained in the following section.

This equation serves to define the electromagnetic unit of e.m.f., or *abvolt*, as the e.m.f. induced in a circuit when the flux linked with it changes at the rate of 1 maxwell (1 line) per sec.   The volt is 100 million times as large as the abvolt, and therefore *the flux must change at the rate of 10^8 lines per sec. in order to induce an e.m.f. of 1 volt.*

The foregoing expression applies to any circuit; for example, to the coil shown in Fig. 263. For a coil wound with several turns close together, so that all are subject to the same variation of flux, equal e.m.f.'s would be induced in the several turns and these would be added to obtain the total induced e.m.f. Consequently, the e.m.f. induced in a coil of N turns when the flux through it changes at the rate of $\dfrac{d\Phi}{dt}$ lines per sec. is given in volts by the expression

$$e_i = -N\frac{d\Phi}{dt} \times 10^{-8} \qquad (168)$$

As a numerical problem, suppose a coil consisting of 6 turns wound close together to be arranged as shown in Fig. 263; find the e.m.f. induced in the coil when the magnet is moved away from it in such a manner that the flux through the coil changes uniformly from 10,000 lines to 6000 lines in 0.2 sec. In this case

$$\frac{d\Phi}{dt} = \frac{6000 - 10,000}{0.2} = -20,000 \text{ lines per sec.,}$$

and the induced e.m.f. is

$$e_i = 6 \times 20,000 \times 10^{-8} = 12 \times 10^{-4} \text{ volts} = 1.2 \text{ millivolts}$$

Another way of regarding the process of induction is to consider that *an e.m.f. is induced in a circuit whenever any of its conductors cuts magnetic flux.* By a rearrangement of the preceding equations expressing work done, it is seen that $BIL\,ds = Ie_i\,dt$, whence $e_i = BL\dfrac{ds}{dt}$. But $\dfrac{ds}{dt}$ is the velocity of the conductor CD in Fig. 264 and consequently the e.m.f. induced in a circuit in which a conductor of length L cm. cuts magnetic flux of density B gausses with a velocity v cm. per sec. may be expressed as BLv abvolts. Introducing a negative sign as before, and converting the result to volts, the induced e.m.f. is

$$e_i = -BLv \times 10^{-8} \qquad (169)$$

260. Direction of Induced E.m.f.; Lenz's Law. — Experiments on induced electromotive force conducted by the Russian physicist, H. F. Emil Lenz (1804–1865), led to the generalization called Lenz's Law. This law states, in effect, that whenever a current is set up by a change of flux through a circuit, *its direction will be such as to oppose the act which caused it.* The minus sign is used in the foregoing equations for induced e.m.f. to indicate that the e.m.f. is one of opposition. Under the conditions shown in Fig. 263 the act which induces the e.m.f. is the movement of the N pole of the magnet toward the coil. In order to oppose this .act, the adjacent face of the coil must also acquire N polarity, and lines of force must be established through the coil pointing toward the magnet. By the rule described in § 249 the current to produce this flux direction must have a counter-clockwise direction as viewed from the magnet.

Again, under the conditions represented in Fig. 264, the act which caused the induced e.m.f. was the motion of the conductor *CD* toward the right, a motion which increased the flux linking the circuit. To oppose this act, the induced e.m.f. must be directed so that it tends to set up a current that would *decrease* the flux linking the circuit. This direction is from *D* to *C* in the figure.

261. Action of Magnetic Field on Moving Charge. — It has been shown that a conductor carrying a current experiences a force when located transversely in a magnetic field; this force is given by equation (165) as $F = \dfrac{BIL}{10}$, where B is the flux density of the magnetic field, I is the current in the conductor, and L is its length. Since a moving charge constitutes a current, it follows that a force will also act upon a charge moving in a magnetic field. Its magnitude can be found by considering a charge Q to be transferred along a conductor of length L in the time t, the velocity of transfer being $v = \dfrac{L}{t}$ and the current being $I = \dfrac{Q}{t}.$ Eliminating t between these expressions, it follows that $IL = Qv$, and therefore the force acting upon the moving charge can be expressed as $\dfrac{BQv}{10}$ dynes when B is in gausses, Q is in coulombs, and v is in centimeters per second. If Q is stated in electrostatic units of charge, the force in dynes is given by

$$F = \frac{BQv}{3 \times 10^{10}} \qquad (170)$$

The direction of this force is at right angles to both the motion of the charge and the direction of the field.

The sidewise thrust upon such particles as electrons, protons, and alpha particles is utilized in the determination of electronic mass and in the acceleration of the heavier particles for bombarding atomic nuclei.

262. Electronic Measurements; Ratio of Charge to Mass. —
The principles of electromagnetism and electrostatics enabled the
English scientist, Joseph J. Thomson, to determine the ratio of the
charge of the electron to its mass.   He used an evacuated tube of
the form shown in Fig. 265, which contains a cathode *C* and an
anode *A* near one end, the anode being pierced by a small hole at
the center.   Near the middle of the tube a pair of charged plates
PP are arranged to establish an electric field vertically directed in
the view shown, and at the same region a pair of magnet poles,
represented in the figure by the dotted circle *M*, are arranged to set

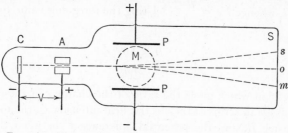

Fig. 265.   Thomson's apparatus for electronic measurements

up a magnetic field at right angles to the page.   The right-hand
end of the tube contains a fluorescent screen *S*.

Upon applying a potential difference *V* across the electrodes
C and *A*, electrons issue from *C*; while most of them fall upon
the anode, a number pass through the hole in it.   In the absence
of the electric and magnetic fields, these electrons would travel
undeviated with some velocity *v* to the screen, where they would
produce a bright spot at *o*.   Energizing the plates *PP* would subject
each electron passing between them to an upward force of $\mathscr{E}e$
dynes [§ 201], $\mathscr{E}$ being the electric field intensity between the plates
and *e* the charge of the electron.   In consequence the spot on the
screen would be displaced upward to some point *s*.   Energizing the
magnet *M* would cause each electron to experience a vertical force of
$\dfrac{Bev}{3 \times 10^{10}}$ dynes according to equation (170), where *B* is the
flux density of the magnetic field.   By properly arranging the
polarity of the magnet, this force can be made to act in a downward direction, so as to deflect the spot on the screen to some
point *m*.   Finally, by having the electric and magnetic fields
acting simultaneously and adjusting their strengths appropriately,
the upward force on the electrons due to the one can be made equal

to the downward force on them due to the other; under this condition the bright spot on the screen can be brought to the undeflected position o. Then $\mathscr{E}e = \dfrac{B\,e\,v}{3 \times 10^{10}}$, from which the electron velocity can be determined as

$$v = 3 \times 10^{10}\,\frac{\mathscr{E}}{B}$$

An electron of mass m in moving from C to A has an amount of work Ve done upon it, which appears as kinetic energy when it leaves A, whence $Ve = \dfrac{m\,v^2}{2}$. Using the foregoing value for v and solving,

$$\frac{e}{m} = \frac{9 \times 10^{20}\,\mathscr{E}^2}{2VB^2}$$

an expression which gives the ratio of the charge e of the electron to its mass m in terms of the electric field intensity $\mathscr{E}$, the magnetic flux density B, and the potential difference V between the electrodes C and A. The units used in the foregoing equations are: m = gm., v = cm. per sec., B = gauss, e = e.s.u. of charge, V = ergs per e.s.u. of charge, and $\mathscr{E}$ = dynes per e.s.u. of charge. Conversion to other units may be made by noting that a potential difference of 1 erg per e.s.u. of charge = 300 volts, and that an electric field intensity of 1 dyne per e.s.u. of charge = 300 volts per cm.

The numerical value of $\dfrac{e}{m}$, based on a number of recent measurements, is approximately 5.28×10^{17} e.s.u. per gm. Combining this result with the value of the electronic charge $e = 4.80 \times 10^{-10}$ e.s.u. as determined by Millikan's method [§ 204], the mass of the electron is found to be 9.11×10^{-28} gm.

It is customary to express the energy of such high speed particles in terms of the potential difference through which an electron must accelerate in order to acquire the particular energy value. *The energy represented by an electron accelerating through a difference of potential of one volt is called an electron-volt.* Since 1 erg of work per e.s.u. of charge is equivalent to 300 volts, and since the charge of the electron is 4.80×10^{-10} e.s.u. of charge, it follows that

$$1 \text{ electron-volt} = \frac{4.80 \times 10^{-10}}{300} = 1.60 \times 10^{-12} \text{ erg}$$

*263. The Cyclotron. — The application of electromagnetic principles to the problems of modern research is illustrated in a device developed by Professor Ernest O. Lawrence and called the *cyclotron.* The purpose of this apparatus is to give charged particles very high speeds and a large amount of energy, so that they may be used for the bombardment of atoms in the investigation of nuclear structure and artificial radioactivity [Chapter XL].

Essentially the cyclotron consists of a pair of hollow semi-circular segments X and Y, Fig. 266, like a large pill-box which has been cut in two, with the halves separated; one segment is charged positively and the other negatively, and then the polarity of the charges is reversed again and again in rapid succession by connection to a source of alternating current. The segments are placed in an evacuated space within a uniform magnetic field at right angles to the plane of the segments; that is, perpendicular to the page in the figure.

A positive ion, such as the nucleus of a helium atom, is released at A and is attracted into the segment X, supposing this to be negative at the moment. It is continuously deflected by the magnetic field and moves in a circular path, leaving segment X at B. Supposing the polarity of the segments to be reversed at this instant, the ion is accelerated by the difference of potential that exists between the segments, and enters Y at a higher speed, after which it travels again in a circular path until it emerges at C. By a repetition of these events the ion moves along the dotted path, traveling each half-

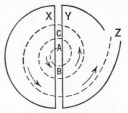

FIG. 266.   Path of particles in a cyclotron

revolution with higher speed, and finally leaves the apparatus at Z, where the material to be bombarded is located.

It is of interest to note that the ions travel around any semicircle of the path in the same time regardless of the radius. The force exerted by the magnetic field of flux density B upon a charge Q moving with a speed v is $F = \dfrac{B\,Q\,v}{3 \times 10^{10}}$, using the same units as in the preceding section; this force acts continuously at right angles to the direction of motion of the charge and becomes the centripetal force of its circular motion. It may be expressed as in earlier chapters, by $\dfrac{m\,v^2}{r}$, where m is the mass of the charged particle and r is the radius of its path; hence

$$\frac{B \, Q \, v}{3 \times 10^{10}} = \frac{m \, v^2}{r}$$

But the speed of a particle which moves around a semi-circular path of radius r in a time t is

$$v = \frac{\pi \, r}{t}$$

Substituting this value in the foregoing equation yields

$$t = \frac{3 \times 10^{10} \, \pi \, m}{B \, Q}$$

which is independent of r. Thus, as the ion moves, it completes each half-revolution in the same time interval. By properly regulating the magnetic field intensity B the time interval may be varied so as to coincide with that elapsing between the polarity reversals of the segments. The apparatus builds up extremely high ionic velocities without the use of unduly high potentials.

The energy possessed by a particle of mass m gm. as it leaves the cyclotron segments of radius r cm. is clearly

$$W = \tfrac{1}{2}m \, v^2 = \frac{m \, \pi^2 \, r^2}{2 \, t^2}$$

and will be expressed in ergs when the polarity reversal time is in seconds.

As an illustration, consider a cyclotron having segments of 40 cm. radius upon which the polarity reverses 30×10^6 times per sec., the apparatus being adjusted for the acceleration of hydrogen nuclei, and calculate the energy of the issuing proton beam. Each proton has a mass of 1.661×10^{-24} gm.; when at the edge of the segment the radius of its path is 40 cm.; and the time for $\tfrac{1}{2}$ revolution is $1 \div (30 \times 10^6)$ sec. Hence by the equation of the preceding paragraph its kinetic energy is

$$W = \frac{1.661 \times 10^{-24} \times \pi^2 \times (40)^2}{2 \left(\dfrac{1}{30 \times 10^6}\right)^2} = 1180 \times 10^{-8} \text{ ergs. This is equivalent}$$

to $1180 \times 10^{-8} \div (1.60 \times 10^{-12})$ or 7,470,000 electron-volts.

PROBLEMS

1. Compute the intensity of the magnetic field at the center of a circular coil of 40 turns, and having a radius of 8 cm., the current in the coil being 0.3 amp.

2. A magnet pole of 100 units strength is placed at the center of a flat coil of 10 turns having a radius of 8 cm. Compute the force acting on the pole when the current in the coil is 4 amp.

3. The field strength along the axis of a coil of radius r cm. at a distance d cm. from its plane can be shown to be $2\pi Nr^2I \div 10(r^2 + d^2)^{3/2}$, where I is the current in amperes in the N turns of the coil. When two such identical coils are mounted parallel to each other r cm. apart, the field intensity along their common axis is found to be fairly uniform when the current direction is the same in both. Such an arrangement is used to neutralize the earth's field over a small zone by aligning the coil axis with that field and directing the current properly. Using coils having 40 turns each and 32 cm. diameter, what current is needed to neutralize a field of 0.53 gauss midway between the coils?

4. A vertical coil of 20 turns of wire, 30 cm. in diameter, is turned to be in the plane of a compass needle mounted at its center. What current will produce a 25° deflection of the needle if the horizontal intensity of the earth's field is taken as 0.20 oersted?

5. A pair of long parallel wires 1 ft. apart carry 15 amp. in opposite directions. Find the intensity of the magnetic field at a point half way between them.

*6. A solenoid 1 meter in length and 3.5 cm. in diameter is completely wound with 12 turns per cm. length. Compute the field intensity at the center of this solenoid when 1 amp. is maintained in the winding.

7. A wire one meter long is stretched straight and held horizontally at right angles to the earth's magnetic field at a place where that field has horizontal and vertical components of 0.33 oersted each. What is the direction and value of the force acting on the wire when the current in it is 15 amp.?

8. Two parallel wires are 5 cm. apart and the currents in them are 20 amp. and 30 amp. respectively. Compute the force which either wire exerts upon the other per centimeter of length.

9. A particular galvanometer produces a deflection of one division on its scale when 1.8 microvolts are impressed upon it. The resistance of the instrument is 34 ohms. What deflection will the galvanometer produce when it is connected in series with a dry cell having an e.m.f. of 1.5 volts and a standard megohm resistance?

10. A galvanometer coil 3 cm. long and 1.5 cm. wide, wound with 200 turns, is supported as shown in Fig. 260. The magnetic field has an intensity of 800 oersteds and the suspension requires a torque of 0.2 dyne-cm. to twist it through 1 radian. Compute the angular deflection of the coil when a steady current of 0.2 microampere is maintained in it.

11. The moving coil of an ammeter has a resistance of 4.0 ohms and deflects full scale when the current in it is 0.0125 amp. Compute the resistance of the shunt needed to make this instrument a 5-amp. ammeter.

12. The moving coil of an instrument has a resistance of 10 ohms and produces a full-scale deflection when the current in it is 0.005 amp. (*a*) Find the shunt resistance necessary to make this coil serve for a 15-amp. ammeter. (*b*) Find the series resistance necessary to make this coil serve for a 3-volt voltmeter.

13. A millivoltmeter of 2 ohms resistance yields full-scale deflection when 50 millivolts are impressed across it. What must be the resistance of an external 20-amp. shunt for use with this millivoltmeter?

14. A wire 5 meters long is wound in a flat circular coil of 10 turns, and the ends of the wire are connected together, forming a closed circuit of 0.08 ohm resistance. The N pole of a magnet is brought toward the coil, increasing the flux through it from 1200 lines to 7500 lines in ¼ sec. Find the direction and the average values of the induced e.m.f. and the resulting current.

15. Compute the quantity of electricity which will flow through the coil of Problem 14 if the flux through it is changed from 1000 lines to 10,000 lines in 0.1 sec.; in 0.2 sec.

16. The coil of Problem 14 is suspended so that its plane lies in the magnetic meridian of the earth and is then turned through 90° about a vertical axis in $\frac{1}{80}$ sec. Compute the average e.m.f. induced in it if the horizontal intensity of the earth's field is 0.20 oersted.

17. A coil of wire pivoted to turn about a vertical axis and having its plane perpendicular to the horizontal component of the earth's field is suddenly turned through 180° while connected across a ballistic galvanometer. Compute the quantity of electricity discharged through the galvanometer from the following data: diameter of coil, 22.5 cm.; turns on coil, 1025; resistance of coil, 250 ohms; resistance of galvanometer, 2000 ohms; horizontal component of earth's field, 0.18 oersted.

18. A coil composed of 12 turns of wire is placed on a table top and the S pole of a magnet is brought downward toward it. If the flux through the coil changes from 1000 lines to 50,000 lines in 0.3 sec., what will be the magnitude and direction of the e.m.f. induced in it?

19. To find the intensity of the earth's magnetic field at a particular location, a coil, pivoted on a vertical axis, was turned in the field, and the e.m.f. induced in it thereby was measured. The coil has a diameter of 24 cm. and is composed of 30 turns of wire. Starting with the plane of the coil parallel to the earth's field, it was turned through one-quarter of a revolution in 0.012 sec.; this resulted in an average induced e.m.f. of 2 millivolts. What is the horizontal component of the earth's field?

20. The flux density in the air gap of a large electromagnet is to be measured with the aid of an exploring coil connected to a ballistic galvanometer. The coil consists of 50 turns of fine wire wound as a flat winding having an average diameter of 2.7 cm. It is placed perpendicular to the magnetic flux in the gap and then quickly pulled out of the field. As a result, a quantity of electricity of 0.0012 coulomb is observed to flow through the galvanometer circuit of which the total resistance is 34 ohms. What is the flux density in the air gap? The time of cutting the flux will not be involved in the result, but a symbol or any arbitrary number may be used for it in carrying through the solution.

21. Using Thomson's apparatus, Fig. 265, without the charged plates PP, it is found that a charged particle moving in a magnetic field at right angles to the flux travels in a circular arc because of the lateral force exerted upon it. Show that for a particle of mass m gm. charged with Q coulombs the radius of the arc in centimeters is

$$r = \frac{10^4}{B} \sqrt{\frac{20Vm}{Q}}$$

where V is the accelerating potential in volts and B is the flux density in gausses.

22. In determining the ratio of the charge of an electron to its mass, it was found necessary to have a magnetic field of 16.7 gausses in order to balance the effect of an electric field of 500 volts per cm., and the potential difference between anode and cathode was 2560 volts. Compute e/m and the velocity of the electron.

*23. In using a cyclotron to accelerate helium nuclei, what value of magnetic flux density should be used if the polarity of the cyclotron segments is reversed 30 million times per sec.?

CHAPTER XXV

INDUCTANCE AND CAPACITANCE

INDUCTANCE

264. Mutual Induction. — A change of current in an electric circuit produces an alteration in the magnetic field around it, and the accompanying change in flux sets up an e.m.f. in any circuit that may be located nearby. The current in a circuit may change under many conditions, such as closing and opening the circuit or varying the load; with alternating current even the maintenance of current without any alteration of the circuit involves changes of current value from moment to moment. The e.m.f.'s induced in neighboring circuits by these current changes are often desired and the circuits are designed in such cases to develop particular e.m.f.'s to suit the purposes intended; in other cases the e.m.f.'s induced disturb the normal operation of the neighboring circuits, and provisions are made to minimize these disturbances.

Consider two coils, 1 and 2, to be placed side by side and assume that a battery B is connected to coil 1 and a galvanometer G is connected to coil 2, as shown in Fig. 267. So long as the current in coil 1 remains steady, the magnetic flux extending through coil 2 will be steady also and the galvanometer will show no deflection. Now assume that the current is changed by moving the slider along

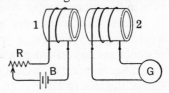

Fig. 267. Coils coupled magnetically to show mutual induction

the rheostat R; as a result the flux through coil 2 will change and the galvanometer will deflect. If, in a short interval dt, the current changes by the amount di, and meanwhile the flux linking coil 2 changes by the amount $d\Phi$, there will be induced in coil 2 an e.m.f. that is proportional to $\dfrac{d\Phi}{dt}$, as expressed by equation (168).

But the flux is proportional to the current that produces it and hence the time rate of change of flux is proportional to the rate of

435

change of current, or $\dfrac{d\Phi}{dt} \propto \dfrac{di_1}{dt}$. Therefore the induced e.m.f. in coil 2 will be proportional to the rate of current change in coil 1, or

$$e_2 = M\frac{di_1}{dt} \qquad (171)$$

where M is a factor depending upon the magnetic coupling of the two coils and called the *coefficient of mutual induction*.

The expression above indicates that the more rapidly the current changes the greater will be the e.m.f. induced; this can be shown experimentally by moving the rheostat slider at different speeds. Further, if the battery (with rheostat) and galvanometer are interchanged, it will be found that an e.m.f. is induced in coil 1 when the current is altered in coil 2. It develops that this e.m.f. will be

$$e_1 = M\frac{di_2}{dt}$$

where M has the same value as before and $\dfrac{di_2}{dt}$ is the time rate of change of current in coil 2.

The coefficient of mutual induction, also called the *mutual inductance*, is expressed in terms of a unit called the *henry*; it is named after the American physicist, Joseph Henry (1797–1878). Two coils are said to have a mutual inductance of 1 henry when a current *change* of 1 amp. per sec. in one coil causes an e.m.f. of 1 volt to be induced in the other.

The mutual inductance of the coils represented in Fig. 267 would be greatly increased by placing the coils on an iron rod, but it would not have a fixed value, because a given change in current would not in general cause a proportional change in the magnetic flux in the iron [§ 270].

The direction of the induced e.m.f. can be found by Lenz's Law. Thus, increasing the current in coil 1 is equivalent to moving this coil nearer to coil 2 mechanically; an action that causes the e.m.f. induced in coil 2 to be opposite in direction to the current in coil 1. Also, decreasing the current in coil 1 causes the e.m.f. induced in coil 2 to have the same direction as the current in coil 1.

265. Self-Induction. — When two circuits are close together, as illustrated by the coils in Fig. 267, a change of current in one of them produces an e.m.f. in the second because of the accompanying change in flux linking the second coil, as already explained. It

will be clear that the change of current in one of the coils will cause
a change of flux not only through the other coil but also through
the very coil in which the current is changing. Hence, by the process just described, a change in the current *in one coil alone* will
cause an e.m.f. to be induced in that coil. As before, the e.m.f.
will be proportional to the rate of current change, or

$$e_i = -L\frac{di}{dt} \qquad (172)$$

where L is a factor, like M in the preceding equations, which is
characteristic of the coil itself and its magnetic environment. The
direction of this e.m.f. is always such as to oppose the change of
current which caused it; for this reason a negative sign is used in
the equation and e_i is designated as the *counter e.m.f. of self-induction*. Similarly, L is called the *coefficient of self-induction*, or simply
inductance.

Inductance, like mutual inductance, is expressed in henries.
*A circuit has an inductance of 1 henry if a current change of 1 amp.
per sec. causes an e.m.f. of 1 volt to be induced in it.* A circuit in
which a large counter e.m.f. of self-induction is set up for a given
rate of current change is said to have a large inductance.

A coil of many turns of wire has more inductance than the
same wire when unwound so as to form only a single loop, because
the e.m.f. induced depends not only upon the rate of change of flux
but also upon the number of turns through which this change
occurs. The inductance would also be increased by winding the
coil upon an iron core.

The effect of inductance can be illustrated by the circuit shown
in Fig. 268, in which a coil of wire with many turns around an iron
core is shunted around a lamp
and joined to a direct-current
generator, some resistance being
included in the circuit. The
coil has vastly more inductance
than the lamp, but much less
resistance than the lamp. When
the switch is closed the lamp
will flash brightly for a brief

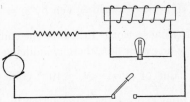

FIG. 268.   Experiment to illustrate effect
of inductance

interval and then become dim. This action is explained by the
fact that the magnetic field around the coil had first to be established and that during its formation the e.m.f. of self-induction

hindered the current growth in the coil, consequently the coil did not serve as an effective shunt on the lamp. Again, when the switch is opened quickly, the lamp will flash even more brightly, because the large e.m.f. induced in the coil by the rapidly decaying flux then establishes a strong pulse of current through the lamp.

For some purposes it is necessary to have coils of wire with very little or no appreciable inductance, and this means, of course, that there must be very little magnetic flux around them. Such so-called *non-inductive coils* are wound by arranging the wire in a long "hair-pin" loop and winding the two conductors so formed side by side until the coil has the desired resistance; in this way the flux due to current in one conductor neutralizes that of the other. The resistance coils of Wheatstone Bridges and other apparatus for electrical measurements are usually wound non-inductively.

It is possible to state the mutual inductance of two neighboring coils in terms of their individual inductances L_1 and L_2 by means of the expression

$$M = k \sqrt{L_1 L_2}$$

where k is a constant that expresses the *closeness of coupling*. If all the flux produced by the current in one coil links all the turns of the other coil, then there is no magnetic leakage and $k = 1$; this represents the tightest possible coupling.

*266. Inductance of a Solenoid. — The inductance of a coil of wire depends upon the number of magnetic lines that one ampere in the coil can produce. This fact can be verified by considering the current in a coil of inductance L to change from one value to another, thereby inducing in its winding an e.m.f. having an instantaneous value given by $e_i = -L\dfrac{di}{dt}$ volts, as given in the preceding section. In reality the coil of N turns is cut by its own lines of magnetic flux, thereby inducing an e.m.f. having an instantaneous value of $e_i = -N\dfrac{d\Phi}{dt} 10^{-8}$ volts [§ 259]. Obviously, these equations express the same action in different ways, and therefore

$$L\frac{di}{dt} = N\frac{d\Phi}{dt} 10^{-8}$$

From this expression, $L = N\dfrac{d\Phi}{di} \times 10^{-8}$. Assuming the flux to grow uniformly with the current and that a value of flux Φ will be reached when the current is I, the inductance of the coil becomes

$$L = \frac{N\Phi}{I} 10^{-8} \qquad (173)$$

where the product of the number of turns N and the number of flux loops Φ linked with them is spoken of as *flux-linkages.*

This result provides a useful definition of unit inductance, as follows: *The henry is the inductance of a circuit which produces 100 million flux-linkages per ampere of current in that circuit.*

Applying equation (173) to a solenoid, the magnetic flux in the core of length l, area A, and permeability μ, becomes $\Phi = \mu H A$, where H is the field intensity. This intensity is given in § 253 by $H = \frac{4\pi NI}{10\,l}$, and consequently the inductance, in henries, becomes

$$L = \frac{N}{I} A\mu \frac{4\pi NI}{10\,l} 10^{-8} = \frac{4\pi N^2 A\mu}{l} 10^{-9}$$

showing that the inductance of a solenoid varies directly with the square of its number of turns, and depends upon the dimensions A and l of the flux path as well as the permeability of that path.

267. Growth and Decay of Current in Inductive Circuits. — To illustrate the application of equation (172), consider a solenoid of 10 ohms resistance and 2 henries inductance to be connected to a 120-volt unidirectional source. There would be a current of 12 amp. in this circuit according to Ohm's Law, but this value will not be attained instantly because of the counter e.m.f. of self-induction. The current rises rapidly at first and then builds up more and more slowly as it approaches its final value.

At an instant when the rate of current growth is 50 amp. per sec., the counter e.m.f. will have a momentary value of $e_i = L\frac{di}{dt}$ = 2 × 50 = 100 volts, and the current in the solenoid at that instant will be (120 − 100) ÷ 10 = 2 amp. When the rate of current growth has fallen to 10 amp. per sec., the counter e.m.f. will be momentarily 2 × 10 = 20 volts, and the current value at that instant will be (120 − 20) ÷ 10 = 10 amp. This example shows that the current in an inductive circuit will not at once reach its steady value upon applying a difference of potential, but will rise gradually to its ultimate value.

The foregoing illustration also indicates that Ohm's Law in its simple form applies only to steady currents. A broader statement of the circuit conditions includes the counter e.m.f. of self-induction as well as the difference of potential V impressed upon the circuit, as follows:

$$V = L\frac{di}{dt} + R\,i \tag{174}$$

This equation may be regarded as a generalization of Ohm's Law or as an application of Kirchhoff's Second Law [§ 229] to the circuit being studied; it merely expresses symbolically the statements of the foregoing paragraph. At the instant when an inductive circuit is connected to an electrical source, all of the potential difference causes the current to grow, for then the current i is zero and $V = L\frac{di}{dt}$; in contrast, when the current has reached its final value I, $\frac{di}{dt}$ is zero and $V = RI$. Equation (174) is a differential equation, and its solution for the current at any instant involves exponential functions. It will suffice to give the result, namely

$$i = \frac{E}{R}\left(1 - \epsilon^{-\frac{Rt}{L}}\right)$$

where i is the current t seconds after impressing E volts upon a circuit having a resistance of R ohms and an inductance of L

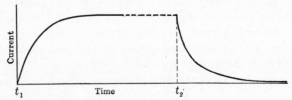

FIG. 269. Growth and decay of current in an inductive circuit

henries, and where ϵ is the base of natural logarithms, namely 2.7183.

When the applied difference of potential is withdrawn from the circuit by short-circuiting the source, the current falls to zero gradually. The current values during this period are given by that part of the foregoing equation which is subtracted from E/R.

Fig. 269 shows a graph of current in an inductive circuit from the instant it is connected to a constant source of supply until the current subsequently falls to zero after short-circuiting the source. At instant t_1 a constant difference of potential is applied to the circuit and at instant t_2 the source is short-circuited.

*268. Energy of a Magnetic Field. — In establishing current in an inductive circuit, work must be done against the e.m.f. of self-induction in creating the magnetic field around the circuit. The power involved in neutralizing this e.m.f. at any instant during the period of current growth is the product of the current i already established and the instantaneous counter e.m.f. $e_i = L\dfrac{di}{dt}$. In establishing the ultimate current I in the circuit the total energy expended in the magnetic field is determined by the method of integration in calculus as

$$W = \int_{t=0}^{t=t} i\, e_i\, dt = \int_{i=0}^{i=I} iL\frac{di}{dt}\, dt = \left|\frac{L i^2}{2}\right|_0^I$$

or
$$W = \tfrac{1}{2}L I^2 \qquad (175)$$

The energy of the magnetic field will be expressed in joules when the current is in amperes and the inductance is in henries.

Equation (175) is analogous to the expressions for the kinetic energy of a moving mass [§ 72], and affords an energy concept of the unit of inductance. A circuit of 1 henry inductance and carrying a current of 1 amp. will have 1/2 joule of energy stored in its magnetic field.

269. The Induction Coil. — The development of e.m.f. in one winding by a change of current in another as described in § 264 is the operating principle of the induction coil. Fig. 270 shows the two windings surrounding a straight core composed of soft-iron wire. The primary winding, represented by the heavy wavy line, is connected in series with a battery, a switch S, and an interrupter; the secondary winding, repre-

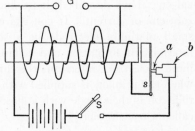

Fig. 270.   Circuit of an induction coil

sented by the light wavy line, is a coil of many turns connected across a spark gap G. The interrupter is an armature mounted on a flat spring s which carries a hard metal contact a; this periodically touches a similar but stationary contact b when the spring is set into vibration.

When the switch is closed, the current through the primary winding establishes magnetism in the core, inducing an e.m.f. in the secondary winding. The armature is soon attracted to the core and the contact between a and b is broken. Current in the primary winding is thus interrupted and the magnetism in the core falls to a low value (the residual magnetism), again inducing an e.m.f. in the secondary winding. The armature is then released from the core and springs back, closing contact between a and b. This cycle is repeated as long as the switch is closed at a rate determined by the stiffness of the spring and the mass of its armature. The e.m.f.'s induced in the secondary produce a succession of sparks across the gap.

Every time the contacts a and b separate, the energy of the magnetic field is converted partially into heat in a spark that is formed between these contacts. To secure as high an induced e.m.f. as possible, a condenser, not shown in the figure, is bridged across the contacts so as to eliminate the spark and quicken the absorption of the magnetic energy. This energy is converted into electric energy in the condenser, and the charge so built up is released a moment later when the contacts come together. The rate of current change in the primary, and consequently the induced e.m.f. in the secondary, is much greater when the contacts separate than when they close; as a result the discharge across the gap is practically unidirectional. The spark shows a short bright section near the negative terminal.

An electrolytic interrupter may be used instead of the mechanical one above described; it produces very rapid and sharp interruptions of current. It consists of a large lead electrode and a small platinum electrode in a solution of sulfuric acid. The intermittent formation and collapse of gas bubbles on the platinum $+$electrode interrupts the current. No interrupter is needed when the primary is supplied with alternating current; the induction coil is then made with a closed core of laminated iron and is called a transformer [§ 297].

270. Magnetic Substances. — The inductance of a circuit and the energy that can be stored in the magnetic field around it depend a great deal upon the properties of the region in which this field is built up. The permeability of this region to magnetic flux and the work involved in changing the flux from one value to another are both important.

Substances are classed into three groups according to their permeabilities. For *diamagnetic* substances the permeability μ is less than unity, for *paramagnetic* substances it is greater than unity, and for *ferromagnetic* substances it is very much larger. The values of μ for all known diamagnetic substances are but slightly less than unity; the most diamagnetic substance, bismuth, has a permeability of 0.99998. The values of μ for paramagnetic substances are but slightly greater than unity; for example, platinum has a permeability of 1.00002. Iron, nickel and cobalt are the ferromagnetic elements, and certain alloys are also ferromagnetic. Naturally, magnets are made of ferromagnetic substances.

To determine whether a substance is diamagnetic or paramagnetic, a rod of it is suspended between the poles of a powerful magnet. If the rod aligns itself so that its longer dimension lies in the direction of the field the substance is paramagnetic (or ferromagnetic); if it assumes a position crosswise to the direction of the field the substance is diamagnetic.

The permeability of any ferromagnetic substance is not a constant quantity but depends greatly upon the field intensity; this dependence of μ upon H is usually shown indirectly by curves, called magnetization curves, which coordinate the flux density B with the field intensity H.

Such a curve may be obtained for a sample of iron or other material by arranging the specimen in the form of a ring, equipped as shown in Fig. 256 with a primary winding connected to a battery and a secondary winding closed through a ballistic galvanometer. A rheostat, not shown, is connected in series with the primary coil for adjusting the current. In conducting the test, the primary circuit is closed and the corresponding throw of the galvanometer is observed, and this procedure is repeated with constantly increasing values of primary current, starting each time with the specimen demagnetized. For each observation the field intensity H inside the specimen is proportional to the primary current [§ 253] and the flux density B can be shown to be proportional to the galvanometer throw.

Fig. 271 shows a typical magnetization curve for silicon steel, a material that is widely used in electrical apparatus and machinery. It will be observed that for low field intensities, the flux density B increases in direct proportion to H, but that for large field intensities the specimen becomes "saturated" with flux, and a large increase of H causes only a slight increase of B. To find the permeability for a given field intensity, the corresponding value of the flux density is read from the curve, and these values are substituted in equation (164). Thus, silicon steel at 20 oersteds has a

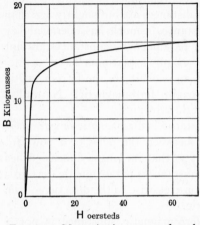

flux density of 14,500 gausses, and the corresponding permeability is $\mu = B \div H = 14,500 \div 20 = 725$.

The table that appears below lists a number of ferromagnetic materials with their maximum permeability values and the corresponding flux densities. The values are only approximate inasmuch as definite figures depend on the purity of the substance, the method of preparation, and the thermal treatment.

FIG. 271.   Magnetization curve of steel

The Heusler alloys (only one of which is tabulated) were discovered by F. Heusler, a German physicist, and are interesting in that the ingredients are non-magnetic substances. On the other hand, there are steels which by proper thermal treatment are rendered practically non-magnetic. Iron ceases to be ferromagnetic at 770° C.

Permeabilities of Magnetic Materials

	μ_{max}	B, gausses
Cobalt....................................	170	3000
Iron-cobalt alloy (Co 34%).................	13,000	8000
Heusler alloy (Cu 60%, Mn 24%, Al 16%)...	200	2000
Iron, purest commercial annealed............	6000 to 8000	6000
Nickel.....................................	400 to 1000	1000 to 3000
Permalloy (Ni 78.5%, Fe 21.5%)............	over 80,000	5000
Perminvar (Ni 45%, Fe 30%, Co 25%)......	2000	4
Silicon steel (Si 4%)......................	5000 to 10,000	6000 to 8000
Steel, cast................................	1500	7000
Steel, open-hearth.........................	3000 to 7000	6000

An interesting application of paramagnetic substances occurs in the measurement of temperatures near the absolute zero. It is found that the factor $(\mu - 1)$ for such substances is inversely proportional to the absolute temperature, and the variation of this factor serves to specify a scale for these low temperatures. Measurements are made by placing a paramagnetic salt, like chromic alum or various gadolinium compounds, in the region under test within a pair of coils that are connected in the manner described for the measurement of flux density and field intensity. Readings of the associated ballistic galvanometer permit the evaluation of μ for the salt and from this the temperature is derived.

*271. Hysteresis. — In magnetizing a piece of iron, work must be done upon its molecular magnets in order to align them in any definite direction, and when they are aligned first one way and then the other many times per second, as in an alternating-current electromagnet, the work is considerable and produces appreciable heating. This waste of energy in the iron due to cyclic magnetization is called *hysteresis loss*.

The process of magnetization and demagnetization can be studied with an iron ring arranged as described in the foregoing section. By varying the primary current the field intensity within the iron can be altered, and each variation of current causes a throw of the galvanometer from which the corresponding change in flux density can be determined. As the current is increased from zero to some desired maximum value, the field intensity H and the flux density B will increase as previously described, their relationship being indicated by a magnetization curve such as shown in Fig. 271.

If the current is now decreased step by step the magnetization curve is not retraced but will have higher values as shown by curve CD in Fig. 272. When the current has been reduced to zero there will still be some flux in the ring, and the ordinate OD corresponding to this condition repre-

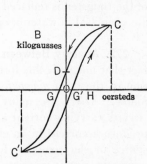

FIG. 272. Hysteresis loop

sents the residual magnetism. It would be necessary to reverse the direction of current and increase its value so as to produce a field intensity OG in order to demagnetize the ring completely.

Next, the magnetization is increased in the reverse direction until the current has reached the same maximum value as before, causing the curve to continue from D to C' in the figure. By reducing the current to zero, reversing its polarity, and increasing it again to the initial maximum value, the rest of the magnetization cycle will be obtained as indicated from C' through G' to C. The closed curve CC' is called a *hysteresis loop* for the sample under test, and its area can be shown to represent energy loss. If the sample were magnetized by an alternating current, then the loss represented by one loop would occur for each individual cycle of current values. Had the magnetization in both directions been carried to a lesser maximum value, the hysteresis loop would have been smaller and less loss would have been represented by its area. Charles P. Steinmetz (1865–1923), American electrical engineer, showed that the hysteresis loss is proportional to the 1.6 power of the maximum flux density attained during the current cycle.

For the iron parts of electrical machinery, it is necessary to use soft iron because it has a low hysteresis loss and a high permeability under the conditions applying to such apparatus. On the other hand, permanent magnets are made of tungsten steel or more frequently of chromium steel, because in these materials the residual magnetism is high (about 10,000 gausses) and because a large demagnetizing field is necessary to destroy the magnetism. A typical composition of tungsten steel is: tungsten 3 to 6, carbon 0.7, manganese and silicon 0.7 per cent, and the rest iron. The composition of chromium steel is the same except that all or most of the tungsten is replaced by 2 per cent of chromium. These steels are quenched in water or oil at temperatures from 750 to 850° C.

272. Analogy Between Electric and Magnetic Circuits. — The fact that magnetic flux forms closed loops accounts for the application of the term *magnetic circuit* to the path that the flux loops follow. There are many points of similarity between electric circuits carrying current and magnetic circuits carrying flux. To produce a current in an electric circuit requires that it contain a source of electromotive force. Likewise, to produce a flux the magnetic circuit requires an agency called *magnetomotive force* (abbreviated m.m.f.). Furthermore, resistance in the electric circuit has a counterpart called *reluctance* in the magnetic circuit; its value depends upon the dimensions and material of the magnetic circuit. The unit of reluctance, to which no name is assigned, is the reluctance offered by a portion of a magnetic circuit 1 cm. long, 1 sq. cm. in cross-section, and of unit permeability.

The unit of magnetomotive force, the *gilbert*, is that magneto-motive force that would establish a flux of 1 maxwell in a magnetic circuit having a reluctance of 1 unit.

Fig. 273 illustrates the parallelism between electric and mag-netic circuits. At the left is shown an electric circuit of resistance R, in which a battery of e.m.f. E sets up a current I. At the right is shown a toroidal core of reluctance $\mathscr{R}$ and surrounded by a coil of wire carrying a current; this magnetizing agency sets up a magnetomotive force $\mathscr{F}$ to establish a flux Φ

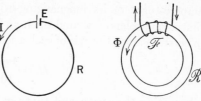

Fig. 273. Electric and magnetic circuits compared

through the toroid. The equations and units for the two circuits are given below in parallel columns:

ELECTRIC	MAGNETIC
$\text{current} = \dfrac{\text{e.m.f.}}{\text{resistance}}$	$\text{flux} = \dfrac{\text{m.m.f.}}{\text{reluctance}}$
$I = \dfrac{E}{R}$	$\Phi = \dfrac{\mathscr{F}}{\mathscr{R}}$
$\text{amperes} = \dfrac{\text{volts}}{\text{ohms}}$	$\text{maxwells} = \dfrac{\text{gilberts}}{\text{reluctance units}}$
Resistance of a wire of length l, of sectional area A, and of resistivity ρ is	Reluctance of a flux path of length l, of sectional area A, and of permeability μ is
$R = \dfrac{\rho\, l}{A}$ (150)	$\mathscr{R} = \dfrac{l}{\mu A}$ (176)

While the parallelism between the two circuits is seemingly exact, there are important differences which make the calculation of magnetic circuits less direct. In the electric circuit, the resistance does not depend upon the current, except insofar as it is influenced by heating. In the magnetic circuit, on the other hand, the reluctance depends upon the magnetic flux, because the perme-ability is not constant. Also, in the electric circuit, the current is practically confined to the conductors, whereas in the magnetic circuit there is usually more or less magnetic leakage through the surrounding medium, because no material serves as an insulator for magnetic flux.

273. Magnetic Circuit Calculations. — The amount of flux in a magnetic circuit can be computed, neglecting leakage, when the dimensions and permeability of the circuit are given and when the ampere-turns of its magnetizing winding are known. Consider first a ring solenoid wound upon an iron core. The field intensity in oersteds along the axis of such a solenoid was shown in § 253 to be

$$H = \frac{4\pi NI}{10\,l} \tag{162}$$

where N is the number of turns in the magnetizing coil, l is the length of the coil in centimeters, and I is the current in it in amperes. It has been found that the field intensity is practically uniform throughout the cross-section of the coil, and hence the flux established in the core is given in maxwells by

$$\Phi = \mu HA = \mu\,\frac{4\pi NI}{10\,l}\,A$$

where A is the cross-section of the core in square centimeters, and μ is its permeability. Rearranging terms, the foregoing equation can be put in the form

$$\Phi = \frac{\dfrac{4\pi NI}{10}}{\dfrac{l}{\mu A}} = \frac{\mathscr{F}}{\mathscr{R}} \tag{177}$$

where the numerator represents the m.m.f. of the winding and the denominator represents the reluctance of the core. The product NI is called the ampere-turns of the winding.

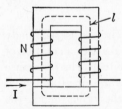

Equation (177) is not limited to the ring solenoid but applies to magnetic circuits in general. The term l should be interpreted as the length of the entire core in case the winding does not cover it completely.

Consider an inverted U-shaped magnet with its contacting member or armature, Fig. 274,

Fig. 274. Calculation of an electromagnet core

to have a core length indicated by the dotted line of 34 cm., and a core cross-section of 8 sq. cm. The winding consists of 500 turns and the current in it is 1.5 amp. Assume the permeability of the iron core to be 540 under the stated magnetization, and compute the flux established in the core.

The m.m.f. of the winding is $\dfrac{4\pi NI}{10} = \dfrac{4\pi\,500 \times 1.5}{10} = 942$ gilberts,

and the reluctance of the core is $\dfrac{l}{\mu A} = \dfrac{34}{540 \times 8} = 0.0079$ reluctance units;

hence the magnetic flux is $\mathscr{F} \div \mathscr{R} = 942 \div 0.0079 = 119{,}000$ maxwells.

The customary method of procedure when iron is present is to make use of the *B-H* curve rather than to specify the permeability. For the magnet just considered the field intensity is $H = \dfrac{4\pi nI}{10} = \dfrac{4\pi}{10} \times \dfrac{500}{34} \times 1.5 =$ 27.7 oersteds. Assuming Fig. 271 to apply to the iron, this field intensity yields a flux density of $B = 14{,}900$ gausses (making the permeability at this magnetization $14{,}900 \div 27.7 = 540$); consequently the total flux is $\Phi = BA = 14{,}900 \times 8 = 119{,}000$ maxwells.

CAPACITANCE

274. The Condenser. — Two conductors separated from each other by some insulating medium form a condenser; the conductors are often called the plates of the condenser and the insulation is called the *dielectric*. Condensers are used to reduce arcing at contact points, to neutralize the effects of inductance, and to obtain pulses of current for various purposes. In an automobile ignition circuit the condenser is ordinarily composed of two long strips of tinfoil separated by treated paper. The condenser commonly used in radio reception consists of two sets of aluminum plates separated by air, the effective area of the plates being varied by turning one set with respect to the other.

A condenser can be charged by connecting its plates to the terminals of a battery or other source of direct current. Electrons will be removed from one plate and flow to the other until a state of equilibrium is reached in which the plates have a potential difference equal to the e.m.f. of the battery. Assume that each plate has a definite charge, one being positive and the other negative, when connected across a particular battery. If a battery of higher e.m.f. were used the charges would also be larger, but the ratio of the charge on either plate to the potential difference between the plates would remain the same. This ratio of condenser charge Q to potential difference V is defined as the capacitance of the condenser; it is given by

$$C = \frac{Q}{V} \tag{134}$$

In this expression, if Q is in electrostatic units of charge and V is in ergs per electrostatic unit of charge, C will be in electrostatic units of capacitance. Usually, however, the expression is used with the practical system of units, Q being in coulombs and V in volts; in this case C is expressed in a unit derived from the name of Faraday, the *farad*. *A condenser has a capacitance of 1 farad when a potential difference of 1 volt will charge it with 1 coulomb of electricity.* The farad is an enormously large unit of capacitance, and for convenience a smaller unit, the microfarad (abbreviated mf.) is generally used. A farad = 10^6 microfarads = 9×10^{11} e.s.u. of capacitance.

Oceanic cables act as condensers of very large capacitance. The conductor at the center serves as one plate of the condenser, and the sheathing together with sea water forms the other plate, the gutta percha and other insulating layers between them being the dielectric. Such a cable 2000 miles long has a capacitance around 0.001 farad; when this amount is written as 1000 mf. it gives a better picture of the large value of this capacitance.

*275. Energy of a Charged Condenser. — When a condenser is connected across a battery, it charges very quickly and the current falls from an initially high value to zero within a fraction of a second. Its value at any instant during this brief period is

$$i = \frac{dQ}{dt}$$

dQ being the small amount of charge that was transferred in the time interval dt, when this interval is vanishingly small. Using equation (134), this current can be written as

$$i = C\frac{dv}{dt} \tag{178}$$

showing that the momentary value of the charging current is proportional to the time rate of change of potential difference $\frac{dv}{dt}$ across the condenser. Compare with equation (172).

The energy that is supplied to a condenser in charging it can be determined by evaluating the work dW done in transferring a small charge dQ from one condenser plate to the other when the potential difference between them is v; this is found to be $dW = v\,dQ$ according to equation (133). Summing up amounts like this, or its equivalent $v\,i\,dt$, during the entire charging period t in which a potential difference V is established across the condenser, the result is given by

$$W = \int_{t=0}^{t=t} v\,i\,dt = \int_{v=0}^{v=V} v\,C\frac{dv}{dt}\,dt = \left|\frac{Cv^2}{2}\right|_0^V$$

or
$$W = \tfrac{1}{2}CV^2 \qquad (179)$$

an expression which shows the amount of electrical energy that is stored in the condenser to set up an electric field in the dielectric. When the capacitance C of the condenser is expressed in farads and the potential difference V is in volts, the energy W will be in joules.

276. The Parallel-plate Condenser. — The capacitance of a parallel-plate condenser is determined entirely by the dimensions and properties of the dielectric, and is not affected, for instance, by the materials used for the plates, provided only that these are electrical conductors. Consider a condenser, Fig. 275, which consists of a pair of conducting plates separated by a dielectric layer of thickness s,

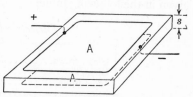

Fig. 275. Computing the capacitance of a condenser

of effective area A, and of dielectric constant K. Assume that the plates have charges of $+Q$ and $-Q$ and that the potential difference between them is V. The charges will be confined to the interior surfaces of the plates by mutual attraction, and will establish a uniform electric field in the region between them, the intensity of which is given by equation (135) as $\mathscr{E} = \dfrac{V}{s}$. Using the convention of dielectric flux described in § 201, there will be $4\pi Q$ flux lines extending from the positive plate to the negative plate, making the number per unit area of dielectric $\dfrac{4\pi Q}{A}$. The flux per unit area is also represented by the product $K\mathscr{E}$.

The electric field established between the plates can then be expressed not only by $\mathscr{E} = \dfrac{V}{s}$ but also by $\mathscr{E} = \dfrac{4\pi Q}{KA}$, consequently

$$\frac{V}{s} = \frac{4\pi Q}{KA}$$

Finally, since the capacitance of a condenser is the ratio of the charge on one of the plates to the difference of potential between them, that is $C = Q/V$, it follows that

$$C = \frac{KA}{4\pi s} \qquad (180)$$

If the dimensions are given in centimeters, the result will be in electrostatic units of capacitance; this may be converted to microfarads by dividing by 9×10^5.

Since the capacitance of a condenser is directly proportional to the dielectric constant, it is possible to define the dielectric constant of a material as the ratio of the capacitance of a condenser with that material as dielectric to its capacitance when the dielectric is a vacuum. Some typical values of dielectric constant are given in the following table:

Dielectric Constants

Glass, crown.................	5 to 7
Glass, flint....................	7 to 10
India rubber.................	2.1 to 2.3
Mica.........................	5.7 to 7
Paper, dry...................	2 to 2.5
Paraffin wax................	2 to 2.3
Water (pure)................	81

Find the capacitance of a condenser formed of 21 square metal plates measuring 10 cm. along each edge, separated by sheets of mica 0.01 cm. thick and having a dielectric constant of 6. Alternate plates are connected to one terminal of the condenser and the remaining plates are connected to the other terminal. Regarding the 20 dielectric sheets as equivalent to a single one having an area of $20 \times 10 \times 10 = 2000$ sq. cm., the capacitance is $\dfrac{6 \times 2000}{4\pi \times 0.01 \times 9 \times 10^5} = 0.106$ mf.

The capacitance of a condenser may be measured experimentally by comparison with a standard condenser, using a ballistic galvanometer [§ 256]. The condensers are charged separately from the same battery and each is discharged in turn through the instrument, the maximum throw being noted in each case. The deflections being proportional to the charges, and these in turn being proportional to the capacitances, it follows that the capacitances are in the same proportion as the deflections.

277. Condensers in Parallel and in Series. — Condensers are often connected in parallel in a circuit in order to increase the capacitance of that circuit. Let C_1, C_2, and C_3 be the capacitances of three condensers that are connected in parallel as in Fig. 276, to form a condenser of equivalent capacitance C. The potential differences across the condensers will be represented by V_1, V_2, and V_3, and the charges on them by Q_1, Q_2, and Q_3. The corresponding potential difference and charge for the equivalent condenser will be taken as V and Q.

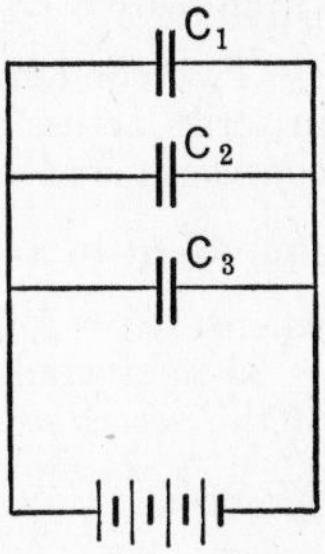

For the parallel connection, each condenser has the same potential difference as the source, or

$$V = V_1 = V_2 = V_3 = \cdots$$

and the total charge is distributed among them, or

$$Q = Q_1 + Q_2 + Q_3 + \cdots$$

FIG. 276. Condensers in parallel

Applying equation (134), namely, $C = \dfrac{Q}{V}$, $C_1 = \dfrac{Q_1}{V_1}$, and so on,

$$C = \frac{Q}{V} = \frac{Q_1 + Q_2 + Q_3 + \cdots}{V} = \frac{Q_1}{V_1} + \frac{Q_2}{V_2} + \frac{Q_3}{V_3} + \cdots$$

or

$$C = C_1 + C_2 + C_3 + \cdots \qquad (181)$$

showing that the combined capacitance of several condensers connected in parallel is equal to the sum of the individual capacitances.

Condensers are sometimes connected in series in order to lessen the potential difference across them; the capacitance will be reduced

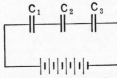

FIG. 277. Condensers in series

by this arrangement. In the series connection of Fig. 277, the same momentary flow of electrons occurs in all of the condensers, thus giving each an equal charge, or $Q = Q_1 = Q_2 = Q_3 = \cdots$; and the applied potential difference is divided among the individual condensers, or

$$V = V_1 + V_2 + V_3 + \cdots$$

Then

$$\frac{1}{C} = \frac{V}{Q} = \frac{V_1 + V_2 + V_3 + \cdots}{Q} = \frac{V_1}{Q_1} + \frac{V_2}{Q_2} + \frac{V_3}{Q_3} + \cdots$$

or

$$\frac{1}{C} = \frac{1}{C_1} + \frac{1}{C_2} + \frac{1}{C_3} + \cdots \qquad (182)$$

an expression which shows the relation between the capacitances C_1, C_2, C_3, . . ., of the individual condensers and the equivalent capacitance C when these are connected in series.

Two condensers having capacitances of 3 mf. and 6 mf. are connected in series across a 12-volt direct-current source. Find the charge of each condenser and the potential difference across each. The combination is equivalent to a single condenser of capacitance C such that $\frac{1}{C} = \frac{1}{3} + \frac{1}{6}$, whence $C = 2$ mf. The charge of this condenser would be $Q = 2 \times 12 = 24$ microcoulombs, and this is the charge of each individual condenser in the series connection. The potential difference across the 3-mf. condenser is $\frac{24 \text{ microcoulombs}}{3 \text{ microfarads}} = 8$ volts, and that across the 6-mf. condenser is obtained similarly as 4 volts.

In verifying experimentally the potential distribution in circuits containing condensers in series, it is necessary to use voltmeters that do not require current for their operation; a useful instrument for this purpose is the so-called *electrostatic voltmeter* in which the deflection depends upon the force action between charged plates.

PROBLEMS

1. It is found that a current of 1.3 amp. in a coil of 50 turns establishes a magnetic flux of 6500 lines through it. Find the inductance of the coil.

2. What is the total inductance of the field winding of a bipolar generator that has 3570 turns per spool and has a total flux of 2.4×10^6 maxwells when the exciting current is 2.1 amp.?

*3. A spool with a wooden core wound full of wire has an inductance of 100 millihenries. This wire is removed and the spool is rewound with wire having twice the diameter of the first, the new winding again filling the spool. How much inductance will the new winding have?

*4. Calculate the inductance of the air-core solenoid mentioned in Problem 6 of Chapter XXIV.

5. A coil of wire has an inductance of 0.15 henry and a resistance of 5 ohms. What e.m.f.'s will be induced in this coil when the current changes at the rates of 40 and 12 amp. per sec.?

6. How fast will the current grow in the coil of the preceding problem: first, at the instant it is connected to a 10-volt storage battery, and second, when the current has reached three-quarters of its ultimate value?

7. Calculate the current in the coil of Problem 5 at an instant 0.06 sec. after connecting it to a 24-volt storage battery.

*8. A certain dynamo field coil has an inductance of 3.7 henries when carrying a current of 1.26 amp. Determine how much energy resides in the magnetic field about this coil.

9. By heat treating iron in hydrogen it has been possible to produce a permeability of 340,000 in a field of 0.02 oersted intensity. Compute the flux in such a specimen having a cross-section of 0.40 sq. cm.

*10. The hysteresis loss in a core of sheet steel is 100 watts when a 25-cycle current (that is, one that reverses $25 \times 2 = 50$ times each second) circulates around it and produces a maximum flux density of 8000 gausses.

What loss will occur in this core when energized by a 60-cycle current of sufficient value to produce a maximum density of 10,000 gausses?

11. A cylindrical iron rod is 20 cm. long and 2.5 cm. in diameter, Ascertain the reluctances of this rod between opposite ends (*a*) when its permeability is 700 and (*b*) when its permeability is 300.

12. An iron toroid having a ring diameter of 6 in. and a sectional diameter of 1 in. is completely wound with 960 turns of wire. If a current of 0.71 amp. in the winding establishes a flux of 72,800 maxwells in the ring, compute (*a*) the reluctance of the ring, and (*b*) the permeability of the iron of which it is made. (The dimensions should be converted to centimeter units.)

13. The magnet and armature described in § 273 are arranged to have an air gap between them of 2 mm. at each side. Neglecting the change that this adjustment makes in the permeability of the iron, compute the magnetic flux density in the core.

14. An iron rod 50 cm. long and 3 cm. in diameter is bent and welded to form a closed ring. Upon this core is wound a coil of 2800 turns. What current is needed in the winding to establish a flux density of 15,000 lines per sq. cm. within the core, if the permeability of the iron under these conditions is 200?

15. Find the capacitance of the condenser formed by the circular plates described in Problem 11 of Chapter XX.

16. Find the dielectric constant of amber, if a large plate of this material 0.15 cm. thick when placed between metal sheets measuring 10 × 24 cm. provides a condenser of 0.00040 mf. capacitance.

17. A condenser consists of two brass plates each 20 cm. long and 8 cm. wide, separated by a layer of air 0.2 cm. thick. The condenser is permanently connected across a 40-volt battery. Find (*a*) the charge of the condenser and (*b*) the energy stored in it. A large sheet of glass 0.2 cm. thick and having a dielectric constant of 8 is next inserted between the plates, completely filling the space between them. (*c*) How much additional charge will the condenser now take from the battery, and (*d*) what will be the total energy stored in it?

18. A condenser is made up of 15 sheets of tinfoil each 10 cm. long and 6 cm. wide, which are separated by sheets of waxed paper of dielectric constant 2.25 and having a thickness of 0.008 cm. Alternate sheets of tinfoil are connected to one terminal of the condenser, and the remaining sheets of tinfoil are connected to the other terminal. Find the capacitance of the condenser in microfarads.

19. Two condensers of 5 mf. and 7 mf. capacitance are connected in parallel and this combination is connected in series with a third condenser of 8 mf. capacitance, across 120-volt direct-current supply mains. Find the charge of each condenser and the potential difference across each.

20. A condenser of 1 mf. capacitance is charged by a 12-volt battery, which is then removed. This condenser is next connected across another condenser which is identical with the first, except that it is initially uncharged. Precautions are taken to prevent loss of charge by leakage during the experiment. Compare the initial and final states of the two condensers with regard to charge, potential difference, and stored energy. How is the change in the total energy accounted for?

21. Two condensers having capacitances of 2 mf. and 4 mf. respectively are connected in parallel, and this combination is joined in series with a condenser of 5 mf. capacitance across a 48-volt battery. Compute the charge in the 4-mf. condenser.

CHAPTER XXVI

ALTERNATING CURRENTS

278. Generation of Alternating Electromotive Force. — The production of an electromotive force in a conductor by the cutting of magnetic flux, as explained in § 259, is the basic principle of operation of all types of electric generators. Most generators used at present are of the alternating type, and set up currents which traverse the circuit first in one direction and then the other, reversing their directions many times a second. An alternating e.m.f. is produced when a conductor repeatedly cuts flux first in one direction and then in the other. The simplest way to accomplish this result is to place a coil of wire in a magnetic field between the two poles of an electromagnet, and rotate the coil about an axis in the plane of the coil and at right angles to the flux. Fig. 278 shows a simple *alternator* wherein the coil *ABCD* rotates between the magnet poles N and S of the field structure. The ends of the coil are joined to *slip rings*, and *brushes* X and Y press against them, so that the coil while rotating may remain connected to the external circuit R.

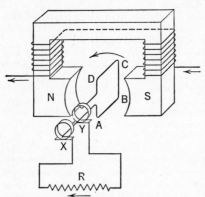

FIG. 278. Elementary alternating-current generator

At an instant during rotation when the coil is in the position shown, no e.m.f. will be generated, since at this instant neither coil-side *AB* nor *CD* is moving across the magnetic flux. As the coil rotates in a counter-clockwise direction from this position, *AB* moves upward and *CD* moves downward through the flux, setting up small e.m.f.'s directed from *A* to *B* and from *C* to *D*; these add together and make brush Y positive and brush X negative, and a current is produced in circuit R having the direction shown. The current keeps increasing in magnitude until the coil is horizontal, at which instant the conductors have their greatest velocity at right angles to the flux. As the coil turns further, the e.m.f. becomes smaller, finally reaching zero again when the coil-sides AB and CD have interchanged places. During the second half-revolution the same effect is produced, but the e.m.f. is in the opposite direction because AB is then moving downward and CD upward through the flux; as a result the current in R is reversed.

To investigate how the e.m.f. or current varies from moment to moment, consider the coil in cross-section, Fig. 279, with the ends A and D of its two conductors facing the reader, and suppose it to revolve at constant speed v in a uniform magnetic field. As already stated, the e.m.f. induced will be zero when the coil passes position AD, and will have a maximum value, say E_m, as it passes the axis of the poles NS, for there the conductors forming the sides of the coil move at right angles to the flux. At some intermediate coil position such as $A'D'$,

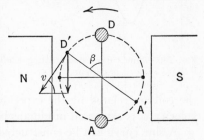

FIG. 279.   Coil rotating in a uniform magnetic field

making an angle β with the initial position AD, the induced e.m.f. will have a value between these extremes of 0 and E_m; it can be found by resolving the linear velocity v of the conductor into two components. The effective component is the one that is perpendicular to the flux, namely $v \sin \beta$ as shown; hence the e.m.f. at that position becomes $e = E_m \sin \beta$. Taking t as the time in which the coil turns through the angle β, its angular velocity is $\omega = \beta/t$; consequently, the instantaneous e.m.f. generated in it may be written as

$$e = E_m \sin \omega t \qquad (183)$$

This equation shows that the e.m.f. generated by a coil rotating at constant speed in a uniform field can be represented by a sine curve with respect to time.

When such an alternating e.m.f. is generated in a circuit, the current established will undergo similar variations, and the instantaneous current i will be related to the maximum value I_m in the same way, that is

$$i = I_m \sin \omega t \qquad (184)$$

Hence a sine curve, as shown at the left in Fig. 280, may be used to represent either the alternating e.m.f. of the generator or the alternating current in the circuit.

During the time that the coil rotates through 360°, a complete *cycle* of e.m.f. or current values will be produced, and the curve will have a positive lobe from 0 to 180° and a negative lobe from 180° to 360°. The time required to complete 1 cycle is known

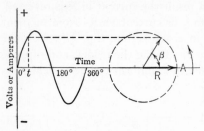

as the *period*, and the number of cycles completed per second is called the *frequency*. For a coil rotating in a bipolar field and driven at 3600 rev. per min. (60 rev. per sec.), the period will be $T = \frac{1}{60}$ sec., and the frequency will be $f = 1/T = 60$ cycles per sec. The frequency and the angular velocity of the coil are related by the expression $\omega = 2\pi f$, where the angular velocity ω is expressed in radians per second.

FIG. 280.   Sine curve of alternating e.m.f. or current

A sine curve can be constructed by considering a point which rotates uniformly around a circle, and projecting its successive positions upon the vertical diameter of the circle [§ 85]; the projections determine the corresponding ordinates of the curve. It is usual to represent an alternating e.m.f. or an alternating current with the aid of a radius extending to such a rotating point. The radius is a vector having a length equal to the maximum value of the sine curve, and is assumed to turn counter-clockwise, making one revolution per cycle. The rotating vector R in Fig. 280 represents the sine curve shown at the left; its vertical projection after a rotation of β from the zero position at A gives the value of the e.m.f. or current at instant t, as shown.

279. Effective Values. — One might well inquire how a definite numerical value can be given to an alternating current, when it actually has all values from zero up to the maximum value corresponding to the highest point on the sine curve. Such an evaluation is made possible through the heating effect of the current. Suppose that a direct current of 1 amp. is passed through a coil immersed in water, and that the heat produced in a given time is measured. Upon repeating the test with alternating currents of different magnitudes in the coil, a value will eventually be found for which the same amount of heat is produced in the same time. This alternating current is then said to have an *effective value* of 1 amp. Thus, in a particular conductor, *one ampere of alternating current will produce the same amount of heat in a given time as one ampere of direct current.*

Since the heating effect is known to be proportional to the square of the current, the effective value of an alternating current can be calculated from the sine curve by squaring all of the ordinates, taking the average of these values, and extracting the square root. The effective value, being the root of the mean square of the instantaneous currents, is also called the root-mean-square or r-m-s. value of the current. This process is indicated in Fig. 281, wherein the instantaneous values of current i are plotted as a sine wave at the top, and the corresponding values of current squared i^2 are plotted below; the latter curve is observed to be a sine curve

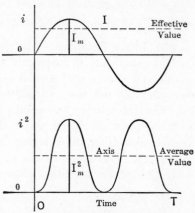

Fig. 281. Determination of the effective value of current

also, but one having doubled frequency and having its axis displaced by an amount equal to the amplitude. The ordinate of this axis is clearly the average of the i^2 values, and the square root of this ordinate gives the effective current I.

A definite relation exists between the effective value of a sinusoidal alternating current and its maximum or *peak* value I_m; it can be determined easily from the procedure represented in Fig. 281. Since the average of the current squared values is $\frac{1}{2}I_m{}^2$, the effective current is the square root of this amount, namely $I_m/\sqrt{2}$; whence the effective value is

$$I = 0.707 \ I_m \qquad (185)$$

Alternating e.m.f.'s are expressed in the same manner. Representing the maximum value of a sinusoidal e.m.f. by E_m, the effective value is

$$E = 0.707 \ E_m \qquad (186)$$

Whenever alternating quantities are expressed it is understood that effective values are meant; thus, an alternating current of 10 amperes means an effective current of 10 amperes (its maximum or peak value is 14.1 amp. if sinusoidal). Alternating-current ammeters and voltmeters are calibrated to indicate effective values.

A 25-cycle alternating current of sinusoidal wave shape has a maximum value of 30 amp. Find the effective value of this current, and also its momentary value at an instant 0.002 sec. after passing in a positive direction through the zero value. The effective value is 0.707 × 30 = 21.2 amp. Since the angular velocity $\omega = 2\pi \times 25$, the instantaneous current value for $t = 0.002$ is given by equation (184) as $i = 30 \sin (2\pi 25 \times 0.002)$

$$= 30 \sin \frac{\pi}{10} = 30 \sin 18° = 9.27 \text{ amp.}$$

280. Phase Relations. — In circuits connected to alternating-current generators it frequently happens that the e.m.f. of the source and the current established by it, although of the same frequency, do not rise and fall together. As a result there is a time interval between any point on the e.m.f. cycle and the corresponding point on the current cycle. This interval represents an angular separation, called a *phase difference*, that may be expressed in degrees. The term phase is also applied in referring to two or more like quantities, either alternating currents or e.m.f.'s.

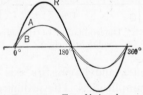

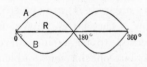

Fig. 282.   E.m.f.'s in phase   Fig. 283.   E.m.f.'s in opposition

Phase difference will be explained by supposing two alternating-current generators to be connected in series, the machines generating the same e.m.f. at the same frequency. If the e.m.f.'s pass through the zero value at the same instant, rise together, pass through the maximum value together, and so on, they are said to be *in phase*. The total e.m.f. available is the sum of the two individual e.m.f.'s. The e.m.f. curves coincide as illustrated in Fig. 282 in which the individual curves A and B are slightly displaced from each other to reveal their separate identities. The resultant e.m.f. curve R is obtained by adding the ordinates of curves A and B point by point.

Unless the two e.m.f.'s rise and fall together, they are *out of phase* with respect to each other. Fig. 283 represents the condition when one machine is generating its maximum positive e.m.f. at the instant that the other has its maximum negative value. The curves A and B are displaced from each other by 180°, indicating that the two e.m.f.'s are in opposition and annul each other; thus the resultant e.m.f. is zero. In Fig. 284 the e.m.f. A of one generator reaches each e.m.f. value somewhat before B, the phase difference shown being 60° with A *leading B*, or *B lagging A*. The resultant e.m.f. R is shown in each of the figures.

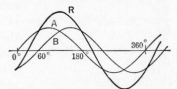

FIG. 284.   Two alternating e.m.f.'s displaced by 60°

The phase relations shown above can be represented more simply by replacing the sine curves by appropriate vectors. In constructing these, the effective values of the alternating quantities are customarily represented by the vectors instead of the maximum values. The vector diagrams in Fig. 285 correspond respectively to the phase relations shown in Figs. 282 to 284. The vectors A and B represent two individual e.m.f.'s of equal value and R represents the resultant.

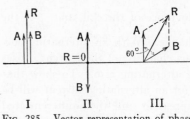

I   II   III

FIG. 285.   Vector representation of phase differences

Assuming A and B to be in phase, the resultant R will be their numerical sum. This condition is represented by drawing A and B along the same line, and adding them; part I of the figure shows this addition but the vectors are shown apart for clearness. When the individual e.m.f.'s are in opposition, as shown in part II, their resultant is zero. When they are out of phase as in part III, the resultant may be obtained by the Parallelogram Method; its magnitude and phase are correctly represented by R in the figure.

281. Circuits Containing Resistance Only. — The current in a circuit containing only resistance when an alternating e.m.f. acts in it is determined by Ohm's Law [§ 220]. At an instant when the e.m.f. is zero, the current will also be zero; when the e.m.f. has had its maximum positive value, the current will also have its maximum positive value, and so on. Thus, *the current will be in phase with the e.m.f.*, as represented in Fig. 286 by the curves I and

E. Also, if a part of any alternating-current circuit contains resistance only, the potential difference across that part of the circuit will be in phase with the current in that part.

At high frequencies, and particularly with conductors of large cross-section, it is found that a conductor presents more resistance to an alternating current than to a direct current. The increase is due to e.m.f.'s which are set up by variations of flux within the conductor itself; these crowd the current toward the surface, giving rise to the so-called *skin effect*, and thereby render the inner portion of the conductor less effective than the outer layers.

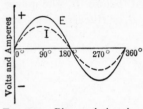

Fig. 286. Phase relations in a circuit having only resistance

282. Inductive Circuits. — It was pointed out in § 265 that whenever the current is changing in an inductive coil, an e.m.f. is induced in it which depends upon the inductance of the coil and upon the rate of change of current. This e.m.f., called the e.m.f. of self-induction, has a value at any instant given by the expression $e_i = - L \dfrac{di}{dt}$, where L is the inductance of the coil, and $\dfrac{di}{dt}$ is the instantaneous rate of current change. With an alternating current in such a coil, the continuous changing of the current causes the e.m.f. of self-induction to be alternating also. To show that such is the case, the expression for an alternating current will be substituted in the foregoing expression and then differentiated with respect to time. Since, from equation (184), the instantaneous current is $i = I_m \sin \omega t$, it follows that $\dfrac{di}{dt} = I_m \omega \cos \omega t$, and consequently the e.m.f. of self-induction becomes

$$e_i = - \omega L I_m \cos \omega t$$

This equation represents a cosine curve, which has the same shape as the sine curve of current, but is displaced 90° from it. To verify this fact, observe that any value of time t which would make sin ωt a maximum in the equation for current, would make cos ωt zero in the equation for e_i, and vice versa. By Lenz's Law, the e.m.f. of self-induction is directed in such a way as to oppose the change of current which produces it; thus, when the current is increasing, this e.m.f. is opposite in direction to the current, and when the current is decreasing, this e.m.f. has the same direction as the current. Therefore, the e.m.f. of self-induction, shown in Fig. 287 by the dot-dash curve, lags the current i by 90°.

The opposing e.m.f. of self-induction can be compared to the opposing e.m.f. of a storage battery while being charged. The difference of potential provided by the charging source may be regarded as composed of two parts, one of which must be equal and opposite to the e.m.f. of the battery, and the other part sets up the current through the resistance of the battery. In an alternating-current circuit having both inductance and resistance, the e.m.f. of the source may be looked upon as having two components, one of which is equal and opposite to the e.m.f. of self-induction, while the other establishes the current through the resistance of the circuit. If this resistance be disregarded, the e.m.f. E of the source will be equal and opposite to the e.m.f. of self-induction, and the current will lag E by 90°, as indicated in Fig. 287.

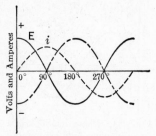

Fig. 287. Phase relations in a circuit having only inductance

Inductance in a circuit not only makes the current lag the e.m.f. but *chokes it down to a smaller value* than if the inductance were not present. The choking effect will be computed by imagining a circuit to contain inductance only (resistance being neglected), in which case the e.m.f. of the source will be $e = -e_i = \omega L I_m \cos \omega t$. This e.m.f. will have its maximum value E_m when $\cos \omega t = 1$, whence $E_m = \omega L I_m$. A similar relation will be true for the effective values of e.m.f. E and current I, or $E = \omega L I$. Since $\omega = 2\pi f$ [§ 278], it follows that the current in amperes established in an inductance of L henries by an e.m.f. of E volts of frequency f cycles per sec. is

$$I = \frac{E}{2\pi f L}$$

The quantity $2\pi f L$ is called the *inductive reactance* of the circuit; it is symbolized as X_L and is expressed in ohms when the inductance L is in henries. Thus

$$X_L = 2\pi f L \qquad (187)$$

283. Capacitive Circuits. — A condenser that is connected across a source of alternating e.m.f. becomes charged alternately in opposite directions, and electrons surge to and fro in the connecting wires. This means that there is an alternating current in them and for this reason alternating current is said to "flow through" a condenser, even supposing the condenser to have a perfectly insulating dielectric. An alternating-current ammeter placed in such a circuit will show a steady deflection. The condenser presents a certain reactance to an alternating current which is somewhat similar to the reactance of an inductance coil; it is called *capacitive reactance.* The value of this reactance can be derived

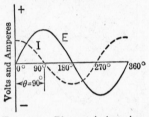

in a manner similar to that followed in the preceding section using equations (178) and (183); the result is

$$X_C = \frac{1}{2\pi f C} \qquad (188)$$

and is expressed in ohms when the capacitance C is in farads and the frequency f is in cycles per second.

Fig. 288. Phase relations in a circuit having only capacitance

Supposing the circuit to have negligible resistance, the current I in the condenser leads the e.m.f. E of the source by $\theta = 90°$, for when this e.m.f. starts to decrease from its maximum value the condenser will begin to discharge in the opposite direction. These relations are shown in Fig. 288, the current changing from $+$ to $-$ at the instant the e.m.f. recedes from its maximum $+$ value.

284. The Alternating-current Series Circuit. — It has been shown that the alternating current in a circuit containing only resistance is in phase with the e.m.f. of the source, that the current in a circuit containing only inductance lags that e.m.f. by 90°, and that the current in a circuit containing only capacitance leads that e.m.f. by 90°. Where all three of these elements of a circuit are combined in series, the current will be the same throughout and the potential drops across the several parts of the circuit will add up vectorially to the e.m.f. of the source. The relations of the potential differences in such a circuit are shown in the vector diagram of Fig. 289, wherein the datum represents the phase of current. The potential difference across the resistance R is

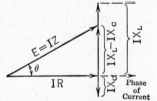

Fig. 289. Vector diagram for a series circuit

in phase with the current and is shown as IR, that across the inductance L *leads* the current by 90° and is shown as IX_L, and that across the capacitance C *lags* the current by 90° and is shown as IX_C. The net reactive drop in potential is the difference between the capacitive drop and the inductive drop, and will be either $IX_C - IX_L$ or $IX_L - IX_C$, depending on which is the greater. This reactive drop added at right angles to the resistance drop will equal the e.m.f. E of the source. The total opposition presented by the circuit may be expressed in a manner similar to Ohm's Law as

$$Z = \frac{E}{I}$$

where Z is called the *impedance* of the circuit, and is expressed in ohms. Its value is indicated by the figure as

$$Z = \sqrt{R^2 + (X_L - X_C)^2}$$

The current in such a circuit is given by the general equation

$$I = \frac{E}{\sqrt{R^2 + (X_L - X_C)^2}} \qquad (189)$$

and lags the e.m.f. by an angle

$$\theta = \tan^{-1} \frac{X_L - X_C}{R} \qquad (190)$$

It is interesting to note that in circuits having large values of L, X_L is large and the current is small, but that in circuits having large values of C, X_C is small and the current is correspondingly large.

To illustrate the solution of a circuit problem, consider a 20-volt, 1000-cycle source of alternating e.m.f. acting in a series circuit having a resistor of 200-ohms resistance, an inductive coil of 20-millihenries inductance and negligible resistance, and a condenser of 0.36-mf. capacitance. The inductive reactance will be $X_L = 2\pi \times 1000 \times 0.020 = 125.6$ ohms by equation (187), and the capacitive reactance will be $X_C = 1 \div (2\pi \times 1000 \times 0.36 \times 10^{-6}) = 442.3$ ohms by equation (188); consequently the net reactance will be $442.3 - 125.6 = 316.7$ ohms. The impedance of the circuit will be $Z = \sqrt{(200)^2 + (316.7)^2} = 374.6$ ohms. The application of 20 volts to this circuit will establish a current of $20 \div 374.6 = 0.0534$ amp., or 53.4 milliamperes. It leads the e.m.f. by the angle $\theta = \tan^{-1} \frac{316.7}{200} = 57.7°$.

If the condenser were removed from the circuit, the current would be $20 \div \sqrt{(200)^2 + (125.6)^2} = 0.0846$ amp.; and if, instead, the inductive coil were removed, the current would be $20 \div \sqrt{(200)^2 + (442.3)^2} = 0.0412$ amp.

An inspection of equation (189) shows that when the quantity within the parenthesis is zero, that is, when

$$2\pi f L = \frac{1}{2\pi f C}$$

the current in the circuit will have its greatest value $I = E/R$ and will be in phase with the supply e.m.f. Such a condition is called *resonance*. The frequency at which resonance occurs is evidently

$$f = \frac{1}{2\pi \sqrt{LC}} \tag{191}$$

and is called the *natural frequency* of the circuit.

285. Power and Power Factor. — The power expended at any instant in an alternating-current circuit is the product of the instantaneous e.m.f. and the instantaneous current. Consider first a condenser circuit, in which the current I leads the e.m.f. E by 90°, as shown in Fig. 290. From a to b, the e.m.f. and cur-

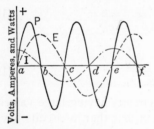

Fig. 290. Curves of e.m.f., current, and power in a capacitive circuit

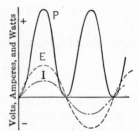

Fig. 291. Power expended in a resistive circuit

rent are both positive, and upon multiplying their instantaneous values point by point in moving along the time axis, a positive lobe of the power curve is obtained; it is marked P and its area represents energy stored in the condenser. From b to c, the e.m.f. is positive but the current is negative, giving a negative lobe in the power curve, the area of which represents energy being returned to the circuit as the condenser discharges. During the second half of the e.m.f. cycle from c to e, the situation is the same; consequently, the power curve is alternately positive and negative, and since the lobes have the same area, the net energy expended in the circuit is zero. A similar result is obtained in an inductive coil of negligible resistance; in this case the current lags the e.m.f. by

90°. Evidently, a current that is 90° out of phase with the e.m.f. represents no power expenditure.

A different condition exists in a circuit containing only resistance. The current and e.m.f. in such a circuit are in phase, as shown in Fig. 291, and whether both instantaneous values are positive or both negative their product will have a positive value. The power curve is similar to that shown in Fig. 290 but is entirely above the axis and the area under it represents power expended in the circuit as heat.

For circuits in which the current is neither in phase nor 90° out of phase with the e.m.f., the power curve will have positive lobes that are larger than the negative lobes; the difference between their areas represents the amount of power expended. This power can be determined most readily by representing the effective e.m.f. and current as vectors and computing the component of current that is in phase with the e.m.f. Thus in Fig. 292, the current I lags the e.m.f. E by the angle θ, and the current component in phase with E is $I \cos \theta$. Therefore, the power expended in the circuit is

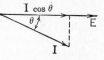

Fig. 292. Phase relations in computing power

$$P = E I \cos \theta \qquad (192)$$

Since $\cos \theta$ is a factor by which the product EI must be multiplied in order to give power, it is known as the *power factor* (abbreviated p.f.) of the circuit. Equation (192) may be written

$$\text{p.f.} = \frac{P}{E I} \qquad (193)$$

and the power factor of a circuit defined as the ratio of the power expended in a circuit to the product of the e.m.f. acting in the circuit and the current in it; that is, the ratio of the watts to the volt-amperes. Reference to Fig. 289 shows that the power factor of a circuit can be expressed also as the ratio of its resistance R to its impedance Z. For a circuit containing resistance only, the phase angle is 0, so that $P = EI$, as for direct currents, and the power factor has its maximum value of unity. A highly inductive circuit has a low power factor, the current lagging the e.m.f. considerably; a highly capacitive circuit also has a low power factor, in this case the current leading the e.m.f. by a large angle. Low power factor is a disadvantage, because on the ordinary constant-potential circuit it necessitates a relatively large current in order to supply a given amount of power. Electrical machinery for alternating currents is always rated in kilovolt-amperes (abbreviated kva.).

An inductive load takes 8 amp. when connected to 2200-volt, 60-cycle supply mains. The power factor has the low value of 0.75, and improvement is sought by connecting a 2-mf. condenser in parallel with the load. Find the resulting power factor of the combination. To help in visualizing the problem, the student is advised to construct a vector diagram. Use the applied potential difference V as a basis of reference, and show the current in the inductive load lagging this potential difference by an angle $\theta = \cos^{-1} 0.75 = 41.4°$. Resolve this current into a component of 8 cos 41.4° = 6.00 amp. in phase with V and a component of 8 sin 41.4° = 5.29 amp. lagging V by 90°. The condenser has a reactance of $X_C = 1 \div (2\pi \times 60 \times 2 \times 10^{-6}) = 1327$ ohms and takes a current of $2200 \div 1327 = 1.66$ amp. which should be shown leading V by 90°. The resultant current has two components. One of these is 6.00 amp. in phase with V. The other is found by subtracting the condenser current from the lagging component of the inductive load current; it equals $5.29 - 1.66 = 3.63$ amp. and lags V by 90°. The resultant current thus lags V by the angle $\tan^{-1} (3.63 \div 6.00) = 31.2°$, giving as the improved power factor the value cos 31.2° = 0.855.

★286. Alternating-current Measurements.

— The usual measurements in alternating-current circuits involve the determination of current, difference of potential, and power. In particular applications and in research there is also need for measurements of frequency and wave form, and for experimental knowledge of the variation of the circuit elements with changes in frequency.

In practical measurements, the effective value of an alternating current or e.m.f. is desired and such values are indicated directly by instruments of suitable design and calibration. In the *hot-wire* ammeter, the current passes through a resistance wire which elongates upon heating, and this action is magnified mechanically to deflect a pointer across a scale.

The *iron-vane* instrument makes use of the fact that iron is attracted by a coil carrying current regardless of the direction of current, and hence will be attracted if the current is alternating. In an ammeter of this type the current in a stationary coil causes the attraction of a soft-iron vane, which, as it moves, swings a pointer over a scale. An instrument of similar construction is used as a voltmeter, the coil having a high resistance in series with it to permit direct connection across a supply circuit.

The *dynamometer* type of ammeter has two current coils in series, one of which is stationary. The other coil carries a pointer and is pivoted at right angles to the field of the first, being normally held in this zero position by a coiled spring. An alternating current through the instrument reverses simultaneously in both coils, and the resulting torque on the moving coil is, therefore, always in the same direction. When a high resistance is connected in series with the coils, this type of instrument can be used as a voltmeter.

The power expended in a device connected in an alternating-current circuit cannot be measured with a voltmeter and an ammeter; for this purpose a wattmeter is used. This type of instrument is described in § 258 and operates with alternating as well as with direct currents. The deflecting torque set up within the instrument is affected not only by the product of the current and the potential difference but also by the phase angle between

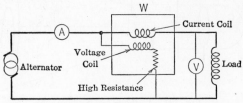

Fɪɢ. 293.   Connections for measuring power factor

them, and the instrument is so designed that its deflection is proportional to the power expended.

The power factor of a load circuit can be determined by measuring the power with a wattmeter *W*, the current with an ammeter *A*, and the potential difference with a voltmeter *V*, connected as shown in Fig. 293; and dividing the watts by the volt-ampere product.

The d'Arsonval type of galvanometer described in § 256 will not deflect when an alternating current is passed through it, because the coil tends to turn first one way and then the other, and its moment of inertia is too great to allow it to follow the rapid reversals of the deflecting torque. By a suitable redesign of this instrument, an *oscillograph* is obtained which will respond to the variations of an alternating current and will follow its wave form. The moving element of this instrument is a single loop of fine wire, on which a tiny mirror is mounted; its moment of inertia is so small that it can respond to alternating currents of thousands of cycles per second. A beam of light reflected from the mirror permits the vibrations of the loop to be photographed on a moving film.

Another form of oscillograph makes use of the *cathode-ray tube*, which is somewhat similar to the evacuated tube used in Thomson's experiment for determining the charge-to-mass ratio of the electron, as discussed in § 262. The appearance of the cathode-ray tube is shown in Fig. 294 wherein the cathode C is a filament [§ 302], the anode A is a disk pierced by a hole, and the pairs of plates P_1 and P_2 are arranged in planes at right angles to each other. Upon heating the filament and maintaining a difference of potential between it and the anode, an electron stream or cathode ray passes through the hole, travels straight ahead, and impinges upon a

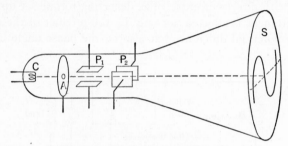

Fig. 294. Cathode-ray oscillograph

fluorescent screen S, producing a tiny luminous spot. When the plates P_1 are charged, the electric field established between them acts on the electron stream and deflects it upward or downward, and when a field is established between plates P_2 the electron stream is deflected toward or away from the reader. If the potential differences on the deflecting plates vary, the electron stream will be deflected accordingly, and the spot on the screen will move about, tracing a luminous line that reveals the character of these potential differences.

When used as an oscillograph to show the wave form of an alternating e.m.f., one pair of plates, P_2 in the figure, is periodically charged at a uniform rate from a condenser and then suddenly discharged, each time sweeping the luminous spot across the screen along the dotted line and making it hop back to the starting point again. The alternating e.m.f. is applied to the other pair of plates, thereby producing vertical displacements of the spot; the combination of the two displacements gives a picture showing the wave shape. The rapidity of the sweep motion is adjusted to the frequency of the alternating e.m.f. in order to produce a steady image of its wave shape on the screen.

PROBLEMS

1. A 60-cycle alternator generates an e.m.f. represented by a sine curve having a maximum value of 155 volts. (*a*) What is the value of the e.m.f. at an instant 1/360 sec. after passing through zero in a positive direction? (*b*) What would an alternating-current voltmeter read if connected across the alternator?

2. A certain immersion heater consists of a 10-ohm resistance wire encased in a metal shell. The heater is placed in 5.24 liters of water and an alternating current of 11 amp. is passed through it for 10 min. Assuming that all of the heat produced is used in heating the water, compute the resulting temperature rise. Disregard the water equivalent of heater and container.

3. It is commonly specified that a motor shall be able to withstand, between current-carrying parts and frame, the application of a sinusoidal potential difference having an effective value of twice rated value plus 1000 volts. What is the maximum or peak potential difference to which a 220-volt motor would be subjected in this test?

4. Find the resultant e.m.f. produced by two alternators connected in series. One generates an e.m.f. of 110 volts and the other an e.m.f. of 40 volts, the smaller e.m.f. lagging the other by 90°.

5. A solenoid has an inductance of 0.32 henry. What is its reactance to an alternating current having a frequency of 1000 cycles per sec.?

6. A coil of 0.1 henry inductance and 18 ohms resistance is connected across a 220-volt, 60-cycle line. Find (*a*) the reactance of the coil, (*b*) its impedance, (*c*) the current in it, and (*d*) the angle by which this current will lag the applied potential difference.

7. A certain inductive coil of negligible resistance takes a current of 10 amp. when connected across a 110-volt, 60-cycle line. Find the reactance and the inductance of the coil.

8. A length of copper wire, having a sectional area of 2055 C.M., is wound to form a helix of 900 turns each 11.5 in. in diameter. It has an inductance of 0.404 henry. Determine the current in this coil when it is connected across 120-volt, 25-cycle service mains.

9. Find the reactance of a 2-mf. condenser to an alternating current having a frequency of 1000 cycles per sec. What potential difference across the condenser will produce a current of 1 milliampere?

10. Derive the expression for the capacitive reactance of a condenser given in equation (188).

11. A 60-cycle, 110-volt potential difference is impressed across a condenser of 4 mf. capacitance. Compute the reactance of the condenser and the current in the circuit.

12. A cable splicer's tone set supplies a current of 800 cycles per sec. at 10 volts to a series circuit composed of a telephone receiver and a "retardation coil." The receiver has a resistance of 1400 ohms and a reactance of 1400 ohms at this frequency, while the coil has corresponding values of 600 and 1500 ohms. What is the current in the circuit?

13. What inductance in millihenries should be connected in series with a 0.0015-mf. condenser in order to produce a current of 6 milliamperes when connected to a 6-volt, 40,000-cycle source of electricity? Neglect resistance.

14. Across a 220-volt, 60-cycle line there are connected in series a resistance of 100 ohms, a coil having a resistance of 40 ohms and an inductance of 0.25 henry, and a condenser of 150 ohms reactance. Find the

potential differences across the resistance, the inductive coil, and the condenser.

15. If the resistance, the inductive coil, and the condenser referred to in Problem 14 are disconnected and then connected in parallel across a 12-volt, 60-cycle line, find the current in each branch. Combine these currents vectorially to find the main current supplying the three branches.

16. Across a 110-volt, 25-cycle line there are connected in series a resistance of 200 ohms, an inductance coil having a reactance of 100 ohms and a resistance of 40 ohms, and a condenser of 25 microfarads capacitance. Find (*a*) the impedance of the circuit, (*b*) the current, and (*c*) the angle by which the current leads or lags the applied potential difference.

17. A condenser is connected in series with a 50-ohm resistance across a 100-volt alternating-current line, the reactance of the condenser being 80 ohms. Calculate the current in the circuit, and the phase angle by which this current will lead the applied potential difference.

18. What inductance connected in series with a 20-mf. condenser will produce resonance at a frequency of 60 cycles per sec.?

19. Find the power consumed in a coil having a resistance of 100 ohms and an inductance of 0.40 henry when connected across a 110-volt, 60-cycle supply line.

20. Find the power factor of the coil described in Problem 6, and of the capacitive circuit described in Problem 17.

21. A manufacturing company purchases electrical energy for its factory in accordance with the following contract for monthly billing:

Demand charge (based on 15-min. periods)

$1.20 per kva. for first 300 kva. of maximum demand
0.75 per kva. for next 1700 kva. of maximum demand
0.50 per kva. for excess kva. of maximum demand

Energy charge

0.91 cent per kw-hr. for first 90,000 kw-hr. in month
0.70 cent per kw-hr. for excess kw-hr. in month

What is the amount of the bill for a month in which the maximum demand is 1000 kw. at a power factor of 67 per cent and the energy is 400,000 kw-hr.?

CHAPTER XXVII

ELEMENTS OF ELECTRICAL MACHINERY

287. Generators and Motors. — The electric *generator* is a machine that is driven mechanically, usually by an engine or turbine, and which is capable of producing an electric current in a circuit connected to it. This machine converts mechanical energy into electrical energy. The electric *motor*, on the other hand, is supplied with current from an electrical source and is able to exert a torque upon a shaft; that is, it can do mechanical work. The term dynamo is applied to either generator or motor.

The direct-current dynamo has the same physical construction for use as a generator or as a motor, except for minor differences of design and, adjustment. Such a machine, if driven mechanically, will act as a generator and deliver unidirectional current to a circuit, or, if supplied with unidirectional current from a suitable electrical source, will run as a motor to operate a machine coupled to it.

288. The Direct-current Generator. — The simplest type of generator is the alternating-current machine described in § 278, consisting essentially of a coil rotated in a magnetic field and provided with slip rings for connection to the external circuit. To convert this machine into a direct-current generator of rudimentary form requires only that the slip rings be replaced by a split metal tube or *commutator*, as in Fig. 295.

The purpose of the commutator is to reverse the connections of the coil with respect to the external circuit at the instants when the e.m.f. reverses in the coil. Starting with the coil in the position shown, the performance during the first half-revolution, represented between 0 and 1 in Fig. 296, is the same as that of the alternator; this produces the positive lobe shown in the figure. During this time, conductor AB has been connected to brush Y and conductor CD to brush X. Then the commutator interchanges these connections, joining AB to X and CD to Y; consequently during the second half-revolution, from 1 to 2 in the figure, another positive lobe is produced with the direct-current generator, instead of the negative lobe produced by the alternator. Thus, as the coil is rotated, it supplies a pulsating but unidirectional current to the external circuit R.

289. Direct-current Generator Construction. — The modern generator used for furnishing large currents at constant potential is

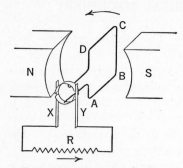

Fig. 295.   Generator with two-segment commutator

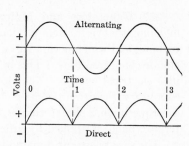

Fig. 296.   Illustrating commutator action

a development of the simple machine illustrated in Fig. 295.   It consists essentially of a stationary *field* structure composed of electromagnets, and a rotating *armature* carrying a number of coils, together with a multi-segment commutator and brushes.

The field structure may have one or more pairs of poles.   A bipolar field, with one N and one S pole, is shown in Figs. 278

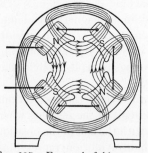

Fig. 297.   Four-pole field structure

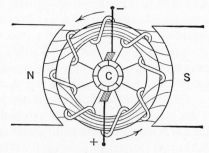

Fig. 298.   Ring armature

and 295.   A typical 4-pole construction is illustrated in Fig. 297; the poles are alternately N and S, and there are four flux paths as shown by the four groups of flux loops.

An early form of armature for a bipolar machine is shown in Fig. 298.   The coils form a continuous closed winding upon an iron ring, and are connected as shown to the segments of the commutator C. Brushes press against the commutator at points midway between the pole pieces N and S, and constitute the positive and negative terminals of the machine.   The magnetic lines follow the iron ring because of its low reluctance, leaving the space inside of the ring practically free from flux.   When the armature is rotated, the conductors on the outer cylindrical surface of the ring cut the flux as they sweep past the poles.   Those moving downward at the left will have e.m.f.'s induced in them toward the observer, while those moving upward at the right will have e.m.f.'s induced in them away from the observer.   The conductors moving across the top and bottom are not cutting flux and no e.m.f.'s are induced in them.   As the armature moves from the position shown, the actions described recur continuously, each conductor as it advances through the field being replaced by the one next to it.

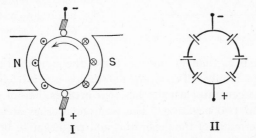

FIG. 299.   Representing induced e.m.f.'s in armature

Tracing the winding by starting at the top brush, two paths will be found leading to the bottom brush, each path containing the same number of active conductors with e.m.f.'s so directed as to make the bottom brush positive and the other negative.   These paths are in parallel and the total e.m.f. generated by the armature is the sum of the e.m.f.'s of the conductors on one side.   This is illustrated in part I of Fig. 299, wherein the forward and backward e.m.f.'s are represented respectively by dots and crosses in the conductors, or better still in part II, wherein the e.m.f.'s are represented by equivalent voltaic cells.   Incidentally, the armature coils as they reach positions at the top and bottom are momentarily short-circuited by the brushes, but this does no harm since e.m.f.'s are not being induced in them at those positions.

A considerable part of the winding on a ring armature is ineffective because the conductors on the inside do not cut flux.   In modern machines the ring is replaced by a drum-shaped iron core with the conductors laid in slots along the cylindrical surface, each conductor being joined to one nearly opposite it by an end connection. With this construction all of the conductors are active in cutting flux. The drum armature is similar in operation to the ring armature, and can also be illustrated by diagrams like those in Fig. 299.

The generator in practical use has a large number of armature coils and a correspondingly large number of commutator segments. The advantage of this construction will appear from Fig. 300, which shows the effect of connecting in series two coils which are so located that when either coil has its maximum e.m.f., the e.m.f. in the other coil is zero. The instantaneous values of these e.m.f.'s are added and their resultant is represented by the heavy line in the figure. It will be seen that the fluctuation is less in the resultant e.m.f. than in the e.m.f.'s of the individual coils. By using a large number of coils, the fluctuation is nearly eliminated.

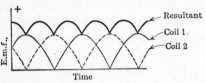

Fig. 300. Reduction of e.m.f. fluctuations

A 4-pole generator usually has four brushes, two of which are positive and two negative. The positive brushes are joined to form one terminal of the generator, and the negative brushes are joined similarly to form the other terminal. With this construction, there are four parallel current paths through the armature. In any generator, the e.m.f. will be the same as that generated in one of the parallel paths through its armature, and the total current will be the sum of the currents in these paths.

The iron structure which supports the armature coils is made of thin sheets or *laminations*, in order that the motion of the armature through the flux may not induce currents to any great extent in the iron itself. Currents induced by flux changes in metal masses are called *eddy currents*. They waste energy in heat, and thus reduce the efficiency of a dynamo.

290. Electromotive Force of a Generator. — The e.m.f. of any direct-current generator can be computed by finding the average e.m.f. induced in each armature conductor and multiplying this value by the number of conductors in series in each path through the armature. When the machine is driven at n rev. per sec., it will complete 1 rev. in $\dfrac{1}{n}$ sec., and if it has P poles the entire flux Φ

extending from each pole will be cut in $\dfrac{1}{P}$ of this time, or $\dfrac{1}{Pn}$ sec.

The average rate of cutting flux is therefore $\Phi \div \dfrac{1}{Pn}$ lines per sec.,

and hence the average e.m.f. induced in each armature conductor is

$\dfrac{\Phi P n}{10^8}$ volts. Calling Z the total number of conductors and p the

number of paths in parallel through the armature, there will be $\dfrac{Z}{p}$

conductors in series in each path, and hence the e.m.f. of the generator in volts will have an average value of

$$E = \frac{\Phi P n Z}{p 10^8} \tag{194}$$

For example, compute the e.m.f. of a 4-pole generator driven at 1200 rev. per min., supposing that the machine has 120 armature conductors arranged in four parallel paths, and that 4,800,000 lines of flux extend from each magnet pole. Rather than solve the problem by substituting in equation (194), it will be more valuable to follow the steps in its derivation. For this generator, each conductor makes 1 rev. in 1/20 sec. and cuts the flux of 4,800,000 lines in one-fourth of this time or 1/80 sec. The average e.m.f. per conductor is $48 \times 10^5 \div \left(\dfrac{1}{80} \times 10^8\right) = 3.84$ volts, and since there are $120 \div 4 = 30$ conductors in series in each armature path, the average e.m.f. of the generator is $3.84 \times 30 = 115.2$ volts.

Expressions such as equation (194) are of value in analyzing the action of a machine. Thus, for a given generator, the quantities P, Z, and p in this equation are fixed, showing that the e.m.f. is determined by the speed and flux, or

$$E \propto n \times \Phi$$

The e.m.f. induced in the armature conductors can be raised or lowered by driving them faster or slower, or by increasing or decreasing the flux which they cut. In practice, the speed of a generator is determined by that of the driving engine or other prime mover, and the e.m.f. of the machine is adjusted by changing the flux. This is accomplished by varying the current in the field coils with a rheostat. To show the effect of field-current variation in a generator driven at constant speed, consider first the field circuit to be open; under this condition only a small e.m.f. is generated by the armature conductors in cutting the residual magnetic flux. When a current is set up in the field, the e.m.f. becomes greater, and as the field current is increased step by step the flux, and hence the e.m.f., will increase in proportion. Finally, however, a value of field current will be reached for which the iron approaches saturation (see Fig. 271). Beyond this, an increase of field current will increase the flux density but little, and this limits the e.m.f.

*291. The Shunt Generator. — The field winding of a direct-current generator is usually supplied with current from the armature of the machine itself. This is done in the *shunt-wound* generator by shunting the field coils across the armature terminals B and D as shown in part I of Fig. 301, and in the simplified diagram,

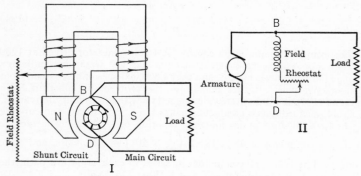

Fig. 301.   Shunt generator connections

part II. With these connections, a small part of the current supplied by the generator is used to excite its own field.

Suppose that such a generator is producing an e.m.f. E, and that its armature, of resistance R_a, is supplying a current I_a. A small drop in potential, $I_a R_a$, occurs in the armature itself. Consequently, the potential difference V_t across the machine terminals will be smaller than the e.m.f. generated by this amount, or

$$V_t = E - I_a R_a \qquad (195)$$

This equation shows that as the load on the generator increases, thereby increasing the armature current I_a, the potential difference across its terminals V_t must fall off. It is also lowered by the reduction in the field current and by the magnetizing action of the current in the armature conductors, an effect which is treated in electrical engineering texts.

292. The Direct-current Motor. — The fundamental principle upon which every electric motor operates is stated in § 255; briefly it is that a conductor carrying a current and appropriately placed in a magnetic field experiences a sidewise thrust. The magnitude of this force on a conductor of length L cm., carrying a current of I amp., and placed at right angles to a magnetic flux of density B lines per sq. cm. is given by equation (165) as $F = \dfrac{BIL}{10}$ dynes. The direction of the force can be determined by reference to Fig. 258. If the current in the wire is directed toward the observer, and the magnetic flux is directed from left to right, the wire will be forced upward. This is explained by the action of the magnetic lines of force in contracting to their shortest length and pushing sidewise upon each other.

Fig. 302 illustrates the armature conductors within the field of a bipolar motor. A commutator (not shown) keeps the current in the right-hand belt of conduc-

tors flowing toward the observer and that in the left-hand belt flowing away from him. It will be seen that the conductors at the right are forced upward and those at the left are forced downward. Each conductor experiences a torque determined by the force acting upon it and the lever arm of this force about the axis of rota-tion. These torques all have the

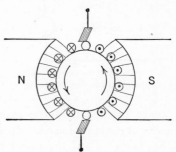

Fig. 302. Direction of torque in armature

same direction, counter-clockwise in the present instance, and may be added to give the total torque developed by the armature which enables it to turn a shaft and drive a mechanical load.

For a given motor, the torque will depend upon two factors: first, the current in the armature conductors; and second, the density of the flux in which they are located, or, just as truly, the total flux extending from a pole face. Calling these quantities I_a and Φ respectively, it follows that

$$T \propto I_a \times \Phi$$

The torque can be measured experimentally by a band brake placed around a pulley, and from the result the horsepower output of the motor can be calculated as described in § 77.

293. The Shunt Motor. — A direct-current motor in which the field coils are connected in parallel with the armature, as shown in Fig. 303, is called a *shunt motor.* Current is supplied through a starting device which first connects the field winding across the mains and then joins the armature to them through starting resistances that are gradually cut out of circuit. The field current can be computed directly by Ohm's Law, by dividing the potential difference V_t across the field by the field resistance R_f; that is, $I_f = V_t/R_f$. The current in the armature involves further consideration.

As the armature rotates, even though it turns by virtue of its own motor action, its conductors cut magnetic flux and an e.m.f. is induced in them, just exactly as in the armature of a generator. To determine the direction of this e.m.f., suppose the currents in the armature conductors to be directed as shown in Fig. 302, driving the armature in a counter-clockwise direction. From

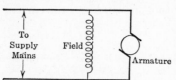

FIG. 303.   Connections of shunt motor in running position

Lenz's Law, explained in § 260, it will be found that the e.m.f. induced in each conductor is opposite to the direction of the current. As a motor rotates, therefore, a counter e.m.f. is induced in its armature that depends primarily upon its speed; its value can be calculated in the same way as for a generator. If the motor is connected across supply mains which provide a difference of potential V_t at the motor terminals, and if E_c is the counter e.m.f., the net potential difference acting to produce current in the armature will be $V_t - E_c$, and the current through the armature of resistance R_a will be

$$I_a = \frac{V_t - E_c}{R_a} \tag{196}$$

If the mechanical load on a motor is increased, the machine automatically develops a larger torque. This action may be explained as follows: The increased load exerts an increased backward torque on the armature, causing it to slow down somewhat, and thereby reducing the counter e.m.f. induced in it. As a result, the net potential difference becomes greater, causing the armature current to increase, and thereby a larger torque is developed. The motor, therefore, takes more armature current and drives the greater load at a slightly reduced speed.

As a typical example, suppose a shunt motor operating on a 230-volt line to have a field resistance of 100 ohms and an armature resistance of 0.15 ohm, and to be rotating at a speed such that its counter e.m.f. is 228 volts. The field current will be $I_f = \dfrac{230}{100} = 2.30$ amp. and the armature current will be $I_a = \dfrac{230 - 228}{0.15} = 13.3$ amp. If the load is increased so that the counter e.m.f. falls to 223 volts, the armature current will become 46.7 amp. Thus, a drop from 228 to 223 volts increases the current from 13.3 to 46.7 amp.

Just as a motor when turning develops a counter e.m.f., so also a generator which is delivering current sets up an opposing torque. This fact can be verified easily by noting that in a generator under load, the armature conductors carry current and are located in a magnetic field; a study of the distribution of flux will show that the torque set up is opposite to the direction of rotation. This torque must be overcome by the driving engine, and the engine must do more work as the electrical load on the generator is increased.

Shunt motors are applied to wood-working machinery, lathes, drills, printing presses, and the like, where fairly constant speed is desired, and where heavy mechanical loads are not applied until the motor is running. There are other types of direct-current motors having different operating characteristics; their description and fields of application are to be found in texts on electrical engineering.

294. The Alternating-current Generator. — The simple alternating-current generator, or alternator, was described in § 278 and consists essentially of a coil rotated in a magnetic field and provided with slip rings for connection to the external circuit. The modern alternator is a development of this simple machine, but usually the field coils rotate and the armature is stationary. The desired e.m.f. is obtained by having a sufficient number of armature coils connected in series, these coils being placed in slots along the inner surface of a laminated iron structure called the *stator*. Fundamentally, the operation is the same whether the field or the armature constitutes the rotating element or *rotor*.

The *synchronous speed* of an alternator is the speed at which it will generate its rated frequency. In a 2-pole machine a cycle, representing 360 *electrical degrees*, will be produced once in each revolution of the rotor. In a 4-pole machine a cycle will be produced twice in one revolution, and in general, in a machine having

P poles there will be $P \div 2$ cycles generated per revolution. If the machine is driven at a speed of n rev. per sec., the frequency in cycles per second will be

$$f = \frac{Pn}{2} \qquad (197)$$

In this country the standard frequencies are 25 and 60 cycles per sec. Alternators that are to be driven at slow speeds must be designed with many pairs of poles in order that they may have standard frequency.

The alternator described in § 278 generates a single alternating e.m.f. and is called a *single-phase* machine to distinguish it from the more usual type of alternator which generates two or three alternating e.m.f.'s at the same time, and is called a *polyphase alternator*. These e.m.f.'s have the same magnitude and have definite phase relations with each other.

The two-phase alternator consists of two independent sets of

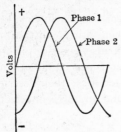

Fig. 304. E.m.f. curves of two-phase alternator

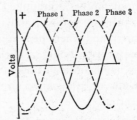

Fig. 305. E.m.f. curves of three-phase alternator

coils mounted 90 electrical degrees apart, so that in a bipolar field, they would be at right angles to each other. Upon driving such a machine, each set of coils generates an alternating e.m.f., and because of the relative positions of the coils, the e.m.f.'s are 90° apart in phase. These e.m.f.'s are plotted with respect to time in Fig. 304. The machine has four terminals so that it may supply a four-wire circuit, the potential difference across one pair of wires being displaced from that across the other pair as indicated. Sometimes one wire is common to the two phases.

The three-phase alternator consists of three like sets of coils, symmetrically placed on the armature so as to produce three equal e.m.f.'s that are 120 electrical degrees apart in phase as shown in Fig. 305. Such a machine has three and sometimes four terminals, rather than six, because the armature coils are interconnected.

*295. Polyphase Connections. — There are two ways in which the windings of a three-phase machine are usually connected.   In one of these, called the Y-*connection*, one end of each winding is joined to a common point, and the three line wires are connected to their other ends, as in Fig. 306.   With this connection the current in any line *A*, *B*, or *C*, is the same as that in the corresponding phase winding 1, 2, or 3; and the e.m.f. acting between any two lines is $\sqrt{3}$ times the e.m.f. in one of the phase windings.   For instance, the e.m.f. between *A* and *B* is found by combining the e.m.f.'s in *oa* and *ob;* these differ in phase by 120° but one is reversed with respect to the other and so must be subtracted from it.

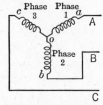

Fig. 306.   Y-connection of three-phase alternator

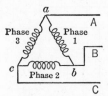

Fig. 307.   Delta connection of three-phase alternator

The other method of connecting the armature windings of a three-phase alternator is to arrange them in a closed delta or triangle, from the corners of which the line wires are brought out. This so-called *delta connection* is shown in Fig. 307.   The e.m.f. acting between any two lines *AB*, *BC*, or *CA*, is the same as the e.m.f. in one of the phase windings 1, 2, or 3, and the line currents are $\sqrt{3}$ times the currents in the phase windings.

The system supplied by a three-phase generator can be loaded across any pair of wires, but a balanced condition should be sought by dividing the load equally across the three pairs of wires.   Many loads, such as the three-phase induction motor, contain three equal parts joined either in delta or in Y, as in the phase windings of an alternator.   Such a machine is connected to all three wires of the system and forms a balanced load.

The total power developed in a three-phase alternator is the sum of the amounts of power developed in its phase windings. Expressed in terms of the line values, which can be directly measured, the power developed in a three-phase generator supplying a balanced load is

$$P = \sqrt{3}\, E I \cos \theta \qquad (198)$$

where E represents the e.m.f. acting between any pair of lines, I is the line current, and θ is the phase angle between E and I. This equation for the power developed in a generator can also be applied to the power absorbed in a balanced three-phase load.

*296. The Induction Motor. — The most widely used alternating-current motor is the *polyphase induction motor*. It consists essentially of a stationary field structure and a rotating element as shown pictorially in Fig. 308. The rotor usually consists of heavy copper bars welded to end rings and embedded in iron laminations; the latter are not shown in the figure. The resemblance of the rotor to a squirrel cage accounts for naming the

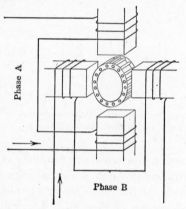

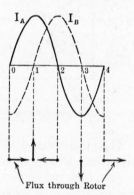

FIG. 308.   Diagram of two-phase induction motor

FIG. 309.   Current and flux relations in two-phase motor

machine a "squirrel-cage" motor. The windings on alternate poles are connected to one phase, and the windings on the others are connected to the other phase, of a two-phase supply circuit, the currents through these coils being designated I_A and I_B in Fig. 309, and their positive directions by the arrows in Fig. 308.

At the instant indicated by 0 on the curves, $I_A = 0$ and I_B has its maximum negative value, and the flux through the rotors will be horizontally directed toward the right. After $\frac{1}{4}$ cycle, $I_B = 0$ and I_A has its maximum positive value as indicated by 1 on the curves; the flux will now be directed upward. At the instant corresponding to 2 on the curves, $I_A = 0$ again and I_B is positive, directing the flux horizontally toward the left, and so on. In this manner, the same effect is produced upon the rotor as if the flux through it were rotating mechanically. The result is to induce currents in the rotor bars in such directions as to make the rotor follow the rotating field.

The rotor will not rotate as fast as the field, for if it did no magnetic flux would be cut by the rotor bars and no current would be set up in them. The difference between the actual rotor speed and the synchronous speed of the rotating field is called the *slip* of the motor. As the load on the motor is increased, the machine slows down somewhat, thereby increasing the slip and causing larger currents to be induced in the rotor; these larger currents set up a greater torque, enabling the motor to drive the increased load. The polyphase induction motor has similar characteristics to those of the direct-current shunt motor, but it operates without sliding electrical contacts of any kind.

The induction motor, if once running near synchronous speed, would continue to run if one phase were disconnected, for the alternations of flux produced by the other phase current would be properly timed to give unidirectional torque. Such a machine would not start on a single-phase circuit. There are single-phase induction motors, however, that utilize a built-in starting device which is automatically cut out of circuit when the motor comes up to speed.

The three-phase induction motor is similar in construction and performance to the two-phase machine but has three sets of windings for connection to a three-phase supply circuit; it is the type most frequently used.

297. Transformers. — In transmitting electrical power over long distances, it is of advantage to use large potential differences, because the same amount of power can be transmitted with a correspondingly small current, thus reducing heating loss in the transmitting lines, and permitting the use of smaller line wires. Transformers are used to change the potential difference from one value to another; in power transmission they step it up to a high value at the alternator end of a line and step it down at the other end to a suitable value for the apparatus in the consumer's premises.

The transformer consists essentially of two coils of wire, entirely separate electrically but wound upon the same core of laminated iron, as represented in the diagram, Fig. 310. The coil which is connected across the supply mains is called the primary coil, and the other is called the secondary coil. The alternations of the primary current set up an alternating flux in the core, and the continual building up and collapsing of this flux induces an e.m.f. in the secondary coil. The value of this e.m.f. depends upon the number of turns N_2 and upon the rate of change of flux $\dfrac{d\Phi}{dt}$ through them, in accordance with equation (168), which gives

$$e_2 = -N_2\frac{d\Phi}{dt} \times 10^{-8} \text{ volts.}$$

The variations of flux which produce the secondary e.m.f. also affect the primary coil of N_1 turns and induce in it an e.m.f.

$$e_1 = -N_1\frac{d\Phi}{dt} \times 10^{-8} \text{ volts.}$$ This e.m.f., by Lenz's Law, opposes

the potential difference impressed upon the primary coil, somewhat

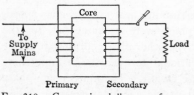

FIG. 310.   Conventional diagram of transformer

as in the counter e.m.f. of a motor. This explains the fact that a transformer under no load takes very little current from the supply circuit, for the e.m.f. induced in the primary coil is very nearly equal to the potential difference of the supply; for practical purposes they may be taken equal. Combining the foregoing expressions and changing to effective values of e.m.f.,

$$\frac{E_1}{E_2} = \frac{N_1}{N_2} \tag{199}$$

showing that the e.m.f.'s in the transformer coils are directly proportional to the numbers of turns on their windings.

Upon connecting a load across the secondary winding, the e.m.f. induced in that coil will set up a current. This current will oppose the magnetizing effect of the primary current, and will reduce the flux in the transformer core slightly. As a result, the counter e.m.f. induced in the primary winding is lessened, and more current is taken from the supply mains. In this manner the input to a transformer automatically accommodates itself to the output.

The efficiency of transformers is very high, as might be expected from the absence of moving parts, and values from 95 to 99 per cent are usual. Most transformers have but little effect upon the power factor of a circuit. Therefore, disregarding losses, the input volt-amperes will equal the output volt-amperes, or $I_1E_1 = I_2E_2$, whence from equation (199)

$$\frac{I_1}{I_2} = \frac{N_2}{N_1} \qquad (200)$$

showing that the primary and secondary currents, I_1 and I_2, are inversely proportional to the numbers of turns on their respective coils. The rating of transformers in kilovolt-amperes may be taken for practical purposes to represent either the input or the output.

As an example, suppose that a 10-kva. transformer with 900 primary turns and 90 secondary turns is connected across 2200-volt alternating-current supply mains and that it is delivering its rated load. By equation (199), $2200 \div E_2 = 900 \div 90$, whence the secondary e.m.f. is $E_2 = 220$ volts. At full load, $I_1E_1 = I_2E_2 = 10,000$ volt-amperes; hence the primary and secondary currents are respectively 4.55 amp. and 45.5 amp.

Transformers used in electric welding have massive secondary windings of one or only a few turns in order to produce large currents, and the parts to be welded form a part of the secondary circuit.

PROBLEMS

1. A generator has 4 square pole pieces measuring 8 in. on each edge, and has a flux density in the air gap of 40,000 lines per sq. in. The machine has 360 conductors arranged in four parallel paths through the armature. Compute the e.m.f. of the generator when driven at 750 rev. per min.

2. A bipolar shunt generator has square pole pieces measuring 20 cm. on each edge, and has a flux density in the air gap of 8000 lines per sq. cm. The armature has 160 conductors; it has a resistance of 0.15 ohm and is delivering a full-load current of 20 amp. The field coils have a total resistance of 100 ohms. How fast must this machine be driven in order to generate an e.m.f. of 120 volts?

3. The field structure of the generator in Problem 2 is equivalent to a U-shaped iron bar 80 cm. long and 400 sq. cm. in cross-section, and the armature core is equivalent to an iron cube measuring 20 cm. along the edges and separated from the pole faces by an air gap 0.5 cm. at each side. How many ampere-turns must the field coils provide in order to establish the stated flux density? Assume the permeability of the iron to be 110.

4. A bipolar generator has square pole pieces measuring 20 cm. on each edge and an armature 20 cm. in diameter which is driven at 1200 rev. per min. If the flux density in the air gap is 12,000 lines per sq. cm., compute (a) the average e.m.f. induced in one of the armature conductors during the half-revolution in which it sweeps past one pole face, and (b) the instantaneous e.m.f. induced at an instant when the conductor is moving perpendicularly to the flux.

5. How many armature conductors must be provided in the generator of Problem 4 if this machine is to generate an e.m.f. of 115 volts?

*6. For the machine described in Problem 2, find (a) the potential difference across the terminals, and (b) the field current.

*7. A generator which develops a continuous e.m.f. of 120 volts has an armature with two paths in parallel, the resistance of each path being 0.08 ohm. When the total armature current is 60 amp., compute (*a*) the potential difference across the generator terminals, and (*b*) the power wasted as heat in the armature.

*8. A large shunt generator is delivering 400 amp. to an external load, the potential difference across its terminals being 230 volts. The resistance of the armature is 0.018 ohm and that of the field is 15 ohms, and the losses in other parts of the machine are 2200 watts. Find the efficiency of the generator at this load.

9. The armature of a bipolar shunt motor is 25 cm. in diameter and supports 100 conductors each carrying 15 amp. It revolves at 1200 rev. per min. between square pole faces measuring 25 cm. on each edge, in a field of flux density 8500 lines per sq. cm. Assuming that each conductor moves at right angles to the flux, compute the torque and the horsepower developed by the armature.

10. If the machine described in Problem 4 is run as a motor, what torque will be produced by one of the armature conductors, assuming that the conductor carries a current of 25 amp. and moves at right angles to the flux?

11. A shunt motor having a field resistance of 200 ohms and an armature resistance of 0.16 ohm takes a current of 20 amp. when connected across 120-volt mains. Compute (*a*) the field current, (*b*) the armature current, (*c*) the counter e.m.f., (*d*) the power wasted in heat in the field circuit, and (*e*) the power wasted in heat in the armature circuit.

12. If the motor described in Problem 11 delivers an output of 2.75 hp., compute its efficiency.

13. A shunt motor connected to 115-volt supply mains has an armature resistance of 0.20 ohm and a field resistance of 140 ohms, and is generating a counter e.m.f. of 109 volts. Compute (*a*) the armature current, (*b*) the field current, and (*c*) the total current taken by the motor.

14. Compute the counter e.m.f. of the motor described in Problem 9.

15. A shunt motor is connected directly across 110-volt supply mains. The field has a resistance of 180 ohms and the armature has a resistance of 0.9 ohm. How much current is the motor taking if it is turning fast enough to develop a counter e.m.f. of 100 volts?

16. Find the synchronous speed of a 12-pole, 60-cycle generator.

17. (*a*) What is the frequency of the e.m.f. generated by a 6-pole alternator driven at 1200 rev. per min.? (*b*) How many poles must an alternator have in order to generate 25 cycles per sec. while driven at 150 rev. per min.?

*18. What are the possible synchronous speeds for 60-cycle induction motors above 350 rev. per min.?

*19. A three-phase, delta-connected induction motor operating on 440-volt supply mains has a power factor (lagging) of 0.80 and an efficiency of 0.85 when delivering 20 hp. What is the line current?

20. A 100-kva. transformer designed to step up the potential difference up from 2200 to 16,500 volts has 880 turns on its primary winding. Find the number of secondary turns, and also the primary and secondary currents when the transformer is fully loaded.

21. Power is transmitted from Boulder Dam to the Pacific Coast over three-phase lines with 287,000 volts between conductors. Find the current in each conductor when 120,000 kva. are transmitted.

CHAPTER XXVIII

THERMOELECTRICITY AND THERMIONICS

298. Contact Potential. — It is known that two different metals placed in contact with each other assume slightly different potentials. This effect, discovered by Volta, is now explained as a transfer of the free electrons that are present in all metals. These electrons in their rapid and haphazard motion cross the boundary between the metals and they pass more readily in one direction than the other, thereby making one metal negative and leaving the other positive. The difference of potential between the metals, spoken of as *contact potential*, depends upon the metals used, and is also influenced by the temperature of the junction.

The *copper-oxide rectifier* depends upon the contact potential at the surfaces of copper and cuprous oxide when firmly pressed together. Under this condition, electrons pass easily from the copper to the oxide but not in the reverse direction. This type of rectifier usually consists of copper disks or plates that are oxidized on one side by heating to a high temperature. It is used principally for charging storage batteries, for low-potential electrochemical processes, and for low-current control circuits.

299. The Seebeck Effect. — When a circuit is formed of two wires of different metals and one of their junctions is at a higher temperature than the other an e.m.f. is produced in the circuit; this *thermoelectric effect* is attributed largely to the contact potentials at the junctions. The discovery of thermoelectricity was made by the German physicist, Thomas J. Seebeck (1770–1831).

Fig. 311 shows an iron wire and a copper wire joined to form a thermocouple, with the circuit completed through a galvanometer to indicate the e.m.f. produced. Assume the low-temperature junction to be kept at 0° C, while the temperature of the other junction is raised. Because of the thermo e.m.f. a current will be

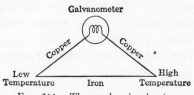

Fig. 311. Thermoelectric circuit

observed which has a clockwise direction for the circuit shown in the figure. As the high-temperature junction is heated more and more, the thermo e.m.f. increases to a maximum value, then diminishes to zero, and increases again in the opposite direction. Fig. 312 shows these values as computed from data given in the International Critical Tables. For a given pair of metals, the thermo e.m.f. depends upon the temperatures of the two junctions; it is also affected by structural changes in the metals such as are produced by heat treatment, rolling, drawing, and pressure.

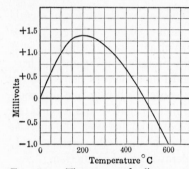

FIG. 312. Thermo e.m.f. diagram of iron-copper couple

it is also affected by structural changes in the metals such as are produced by heat treatment, rolling, drawing, and pressure.

The temperature at which the thermo e.m.f. of a couple has a maximum (or minimum) value is called the *neutral point*, and the temperature at which this e.m.f. reverses is called the *inversion point*. For the iron-copper couple these temperatures are approximately 205 and 480° C. respectively. Other pairs of metals behave similarly and have their own characteristic neutral and inversion temperatures.

The slope of the thermo e.m.f. curve at any temperature is called the *thermoelectric power* of the couple; it is the e.m.f. produced at that temperature by a 1-degree temperature difference between the two junctions of the couple. Thus, for the iron-copper couple the thermoelectric power is 13.7 microvolts per degree at 0° C. and 3.7 microvolts per degree at 150° C.

Electromotive forces that are produced by couples formed of any two metals can be ascertained from a knowledge of their thermoelectric powers with respect to some metal chosen as a standard, such as lead or platinum. For this purpose graphs of thermoelectric power against temperature are useful. Fig. 313 shows such graphs for a few metals against lead; they are straight lines over the temperature range shown. An example will clarify the procedure.

Consider an iron-copper couple over the range from 0 to 150° C. For iron the thermoelectric power falls from a value of 16.5 microvolts per degree at 0° to 8.1 at 150° C.; and for copper the thermoelectric power rises from a value of 2.8 microvolts per degree at 0° C. to 4.4 at 150° C.

It follows that the total e.m.f. generated by an iron-lead couple over this temperature range is the average of 16.5 and 8.1 microvolts per degree multiplied by 150 degrees, or 12.3 × 150 = 1845 microvolts; similarly the total e.m.f. of a copper-lead couple over the same range is 3.6 × 150 = 540 microvolts. Consequently, the e.m.f. of an iron-copper couple would be 1845 − 540 = 1305 microvolts; see also Fig. 312. The same result is obtained by computing the area between the graphs for iron and copper in Fig. 313 over the temperature range from 0 to 150° C. and observing that each square represents 5 microvolts.

Measurements of radiant heat energy are made with a multiplicity of couples formed of two metals and placed close together;

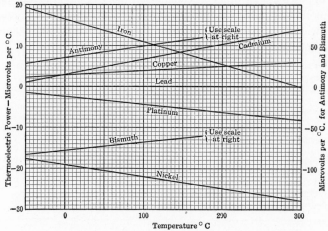

FIG. 313. Thermoelectric powers of some metals against lead

such compact groups are called *thermopiles*. These are often constructed of short lengths of bismuth and antimony connected in series alternately, and put together in zig-zag fashion so that every other junction can be exposed to the radiation while the intermediate ones are shielded from it.

The *thermo-ammeter*, which utilizes a thermo-junction in contact with a hot wire, is used in radio and research work for measuring small alternating currents. Heat is evolved in the wire by the current being measured and causes the thermocouple to generate an e.m.f., thereby producing a deflection in a calibrated instrument connected across the couple. Increased sensitivity is secured by placing the wire and couple in a vacuum.

300. Thermocouples in Pyrometry. — The e.m.f. of a thermocouple varies in a known manner with the temperature difference between its junctions. Consequently, by keeping one junction at constant temperature, the temperature of the other junction can be measured by observing the e.m.f. produced. When so used, a thermocouple is called a *thermoelectric pyrometer*, the latter word indicating its particular applicability to measurements at high temperatures. A number of couples are used for this purpose. One of the most satisfactory for a wide temperature range has one metal of platinum and the other of an alloy of 90% platinum and 10% rhodium; a less expensive couple that is serviceable for ranges between 400° C. and the lowest temperatures has one metal of copper and the other of constantan (copper 60%, nickel 40%). The following table shows the e.m.f.'s available with these couples at various standard temperatures (melting and boiling points of substances), the cold junction being at 0° C.

Millivolts Produced by Thermocouples

Standard point	Temperature, °C.	Platinum- Plat. Rhod.	Copper- Constantan
Water b.p....................	100	0.643	4.276
Naphthalene b.p.............	217.9	1.585	10.248
Cadmium m.p...............	320.9	2.503	16.083
Aluminum m.p.............	657	5.827	
Silver m.p..................	960.5	9.111	
Nickel m.p.................	1452.6	14.973	
Palladium m.p.............	1549.5	16.144	

Temperatures of furnaces and of molten metals can be measured with the thermoelectric pyrometer, but the thermal junction must be protected from furnace gases and from direct contact with the molten substances.

301. Peltier and Thomson Effects. — Besides the Seebeck Effect described in § 299, there are two other thermoelectric effects: the Peltier Effect, discovered by the French physicist, Jean C. A. Peltier (1785–1845), and the Thomson Effect discovered by William Thomson, who later became Lord Kelvin.

The Peltier Effect is an inversion of the Seebeck Effect. When two dissimilar metals are connected in series with a source of e.m.f. which establishes a current in the circuit, one junction will become heated and the other cooled. This effect is distinct from the heating of both metals by the current due to their resistance. The extent to which the junctions are heated or cooled by a given current depends solely upon the metals used. For an iron-copper junction at room temperatures about 4 calories are developed per hour per ampere of current. At ordinary temperatures when a current traverses the circuit of Fig. 311 in a clockwise direction, the left junction will become heated and the right junction will become cooled. Thus, comparing the two effects, the hot and cold junctions are interchanged for the same direction of current.

An analysis of the foregoing effects prompted Lord Kelvin to predict on theoretical grounds that an e.m.f. must exist between different parts of the same metal if they are at different temperatures. He demonstrated that if a uniform metal bar is heated at the middle and a current is sent through it from end to end from an external source, the heat would be conducted unequally along the two halves. In a copper bar, for example, the region where current is directed from a colder to a hotter part will be cooler than if there were no current, and the region where current is directed from a hotter to a colder part will be warmer. The same is true for cadmium, silver and zinc, but the effect is reversed in iron and nickel, to mention but a few metals. This effect and the e.m.f. involved are named after Thomson. Lead shows no appreciable Thomson Effect, and this accounts for its frequent use as a reference metal [see Fig. 313].

The evolution or absorption of heat at the junctions of a thermoelectric circuit demonstrates that there must be a difference of potential at places where two dissimilar metals are in contact. If both junctions are at the same temperature the thermo e.m.f.'s at the two junctions are in opposite directions and annul each other; but if there is a temperature difference these two e.m.f.'s do not balance, and their resultant, together with the Thomson e.m.f.'s, establish a current in the circuit.

302. Thermionic Emission. — In 1883, Edison experimented with an evacuated tube containing a heated filament and a separate electrode, and discovered that a current would be set up between them if the electrode were positive with respect to the filament but not if it were negative. In the light of present knowledge this current is explained by the passage of electrons from the interior of the filament into the space surrounding it and the attraction of these emitted electrons to the nearby electrode. The escape of electrons through the surface of a metal is comparable in many respects to the escape of molecules from a liquid during the process of evaporation. The situation is a little different, however, because an electron about to pass out of the metal induces a positive charge on the surface behind it and is pulled back.   This action gives rise to a so-called *potential barrier*, somewhat like surface tension, which must be overcome before the electron can escape.   Upon heating the metal, the electrons in it are given more kinetic energy, thus assisting them in passing the potential barrier at the surface.

The emission of electrons by a hot body, called thermionic emission, is the operating principle of the modern two-element electron tube.   This device consists of a bulb or tube having a filament like that of an incandescent lamp and a separate metal plate, as shown in Fig. 314.   The tube is evacuated and the filament is heated to incandescence by battery *A*.   Electrons from the filament will be attracted to the plate when it is maintained positive by battery *B* as indicated, and the galvanometer will show a deflection.   If the plate were made negative by reversing battery *B*, the electrons evaporated from the filament would be repelled by the plate and, since no electrons are emitted from the cold plate, the galvanometer would not show a deflection.   Thus, the electrons can flow only from filament to plate, or what corresponds to the same thing, current can be directed only from plate to filament. Consequently this electron tube, containing the plate as anode and the heated filament as cathode, acts as a rectifier.

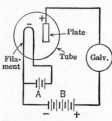

FIG. 314.   Two-element electron tube

The number of electrons emitted per unit of time increases with the temperature of the filament and depends upon the substance of which it is made.   The rate of electron emission is generally expressed as the current per unit of surface area of the hot body, an equation for this current being:

$$I = A T^2 \epsilon^{-\frac{b}{T}} \qquad (201)$$

as given by the English physicist, Owen W. Richardson.   Herein I is the current in amperes per square centimeter, T is the absolute temperature in degrees K, and A and b are constants.   The value of A is 60.2 for pure metals that may serve as the hot body; the values of b for three of the usual filament materials as found experimentally are: molybdenum 50,900, thorium 38,900, and tungsten 52,400.

303. Rectifier Tubes. — The current from plate to filament of an electron tube as expressed by the foregoing equation is the steady value that results when the plate potential is high enough to sweep all the electrons from the region around the filament as fast as they are liberated. At lower potential differences between the two electrodes of the tube the current will be less because some of the evaporated electrons will fall back into the filament, being repelled by a negative charge that builds up in the space around that electrode and called the *space charge*. The currents at these lower potential differences are indicated by curves such as Fig. 315.

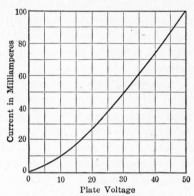

FIG. 315.   Characteristic curve of thermionic rectifier

In most types of electron tubes it is not expedient to measure the maximum emission or saturation current because its value is so large as to change the emitting conditions or to damage the tube.

The figure shows the lower portion of the current-potential characteristic curve of a Type 80 thermionic rectifier tube used in radio receiving sets for supplying direct currents to their other tubes. The filament is supplied with 5.0 volts and takes a current of 2.0 amp. This rectifier has two anodes and one filament so as to pass current during both halves of the alternating-current cycle.

The circuit of the full-wave rectifier is shown in Fig. 316. The upper secondary winding of the iron-core transformer T supplies the current to heat the filament F, and the lower secondary winding 1–2 connects with the two anodes P_1 and P_2. Mid-taps 3 and 4 on these windings lead to the load circuit. Assuming an instant when terminal 1 of the lower secondary winding is positive, the current is directed from P_1 to F, to 4, through the load, to 3 and

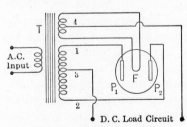

FIG. 316.   Full-wave rectifier

back to 1. When terminal 2 is positive, the path of the current will be from P_2 to F, to 4, through the load, to 3 and back to 2. Consequently the load current will be unidirectional. Since this current would pulsate between zero and a maximum value, a *filter* is used to make the current steady. It usually consists of inductive coils connected in series with the load and condensers connected in parallel with the load. High alternating voltages can be rectified similarly, the tube for this purpose being often termed a *kenotron*.

Gases and vapors are used in some types of rectifier tubes in order to obtain large currents through ionic conduction rather than by electronic conduction alone. The Tungar rectifier and the mercury-vapor rectifier are examples.

The *Tungar rectifier* tube contains argon or other inert gas at low pressure, a cathode of tungsten coiled into a closely wound spiral, and an anode of graphite having a relatively large area. The gas atoms are bombarded by the electrons emitted from the cathode and become ionized when electrons are knocked out of them. These gas ions are positively charged and serve as the principal means of conducting electricity through the tube. Tungar rectifiers are available for half-wave as well as for full-wave rectification, and are often used for charging small storage batteries from alternating-current service mains.

The *mercury-arc rectifier* contains an electrode of mercury and one of graphite, in an evacuated container of glass or steel. In starting the action, an auxiliary electrode is touched for a moment to the mercury pool and then withdrawn, striking an arc. Thereupon mercury vapor is formed which becomes ionized by electrons proceeding from the mercury surface, and causes conduction between the electrodes. When the rectifier is connected to alternating-current mains, there will be a current only during those intervals when the mercury electrode is negative, thus accounting for the rectifying action of the device. Two anodes are used for full-wave rectification from a single-phase supply; more are used when converting from polyphase systems. Steel-tank rectifiers are designed for currents up to several thousand amperes, and are used in supplying power for traction systems.

304. Three-element Electron Tubes.

— An American inventor, Lee De Forest, conceived the idea of adding another electrode to the two-element electron tube described in the preceding section in order to control the number of electrons passing from filament to plate. The introduction of this so-called *grid* electrode has rendered the tube exceedingly useful as a sensitive detector of radio waves, as an amplifier of electrical signals and as a generator of high-frequency alternating currents.

The effect of the grid is like that of a shutter which, opening and closing, controls the flow of electrons going through it from filament to plate. This control is accomplished by changing the potential of the grid. When the grid is positively charged, it attracts elec-trons and increases their flow from the filament to the plate. When nega-tively charged it repels the electrons so that they will not go to the plate. Consequently, when the grid G of a tube is made alternately positive and negative by joining its terminals TT' in Fig. 317 to a source of alter-

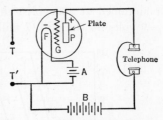

FIG. 317. Three-element electron tube

nating current, the electron flow from F to P will be increased and decreased accordingly, thereby varying the direct current in the plate circuit; this variation can be detected by the telephone receivers shown. In this way the grid can serve as a gate-valve in controlling the plate current while taking practically no power itself.

The behavior of a three-element tube or *triode* is best portrayed by curves of plate current plotted against plate potential. Such a family of curves is shown in Fig. 318 for a Type 27 tube used in radio sets as a detector, an oscillator, or an amplifier, for a number of grid potentials ranging from $E_c = 0$ to $E_c = -45$ volts. The cathode of this tube is a thin metal sleeve coated with thorium or other active material, and a heating coil of tungsten wire, which is mounted within but separated from the sleeve. This construc-tion makes it possible to heat the cathode with alternating current without introducing disturbing effects. The heater takes 1.75 amp. at a potential difference $E_f = 2.5$ volts.

The *voltage amplification* of a tube is defined as the ratio of a change in plate potential to a change in grid potential in the opposite direction such that the plate current will remain un-changed. An illustration will make the meaning of this factor clear.

For the triode having the characteristics shown in Fig. 318, assume -13.5 volts on the grid and $+180$ volts on the plate, both with respect to the filament terminal; for these conditions the plate current will be 5.0 milliamp. Again, with −9 volts on the grid and +140 volts on the plate, the plate current will also be 5.0 milliamp. Thus, an increase of 4.5 volts on the grid yields the same output with a decrease of 40 volts on the plate. The ratio of 40 to 4.5 shows the voltage amplification to be 40 ÷ 4.5 or 9.

As previously mentioned, the space between cathode and plate has a negative charge because of the presence of electrons. Making the grid negative assists this space charge in limiting the electron flow. The curves show, for example, that with the plate potential maintained at 200 volts, the plate current is 12 milliamp. with −9 volts on the grid, 7 milliamp. with −13.5 volts on the grid,

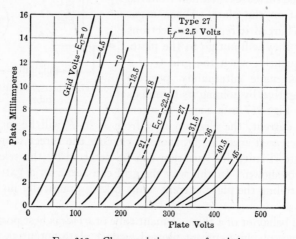

FIG. 318.   Characteristic curves of a triode

and 2.8 milliamp. with −18 volts on the grid. This illustrates the large variation in plate current that can be obtained by relatively small changes of grid potential.

*305. Thyratron and Ignitron Tubes. — A three-electrode electron tube containing mercury vapor, called a *thyratron*, is used for controlling currents of the order of amperes by varying the conditions of its grid potential. With some definite potential difference between filament and plate, ionization of the vapor begins at some particular grid potential. With the grid more negative than this critical value, no ionization will occur, but above this value a current will be established provided the plate is positive with respect to the heated cathode. After the plate current is once started, the grid cannot stop or control it. However, if the current stops sufficiently long for the vapor to deionize, the grid will resume control.

With alternating potentials on both plate and grid, the latter electrode can regain control once each cycle and delay establishment of current in the plate circuit as long as the grid is sufficiently negative. Therefore, the phase relation between these two potentials fixes the point in each cycle when current is established and thereby determines the average amount of current in the plate circuit. Fig. 319 shows the effect of shifting the phase between the plate potential P and the grid potential G. The dotted curves show the critical grid potentials and the shaded areas indicate the relative currents in the plate circuit; note that the shaded area

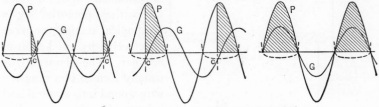

FIG. 319. Thyratron control through phase shift

begins when the dotted curve has a particular ordinate c. The thyratron is useful chiefly in controlling contactors, solenoids, magnetic brakes, and rectifiers.

The *ignitron* resembles a mercury-arc rectifier but utilizes an auxiliary electrode of silicon carbide or other high-resistance material for initiating ionization during each positive half-cycle. The tube current is controlled by changing the point in the cycle when "ignition" occurs (that is, when ionization begins); this is done by connecting a thyratron to the auxiliary electrode and shifting the phase of grid potential on the latter tube. Ignitrons are used for controlling large currents such as are necessary in electric welding.

306. The X-ray Tube. — In 1895 the German physicist, Wilhelm K. Röntgen (1845–1923), discovered that an invisible radiation which had great penetrating power and was capable of affecting photographic plates could be produced by a beam of cathode rays [§ 196] when it impinged upon heavy metals. He called these radiations *x-rays*, but they are now also spoken of as *Röntgen rays*.

It has been determined by experiment that x-rays are produced upon the bombardment of metals by electrons going at high speeds (from one-tenth to one-half the speed of light, which is 186,000 miles per second). These negatively charged particles are produced by a hot cathode and projected upon an anode, or target, and are given a high velocity by maintaining a large difference of potential between these electrodes. The bombardment of the target gives rise to a radiation similar to visible light but having much higher frequencies of vibration.

The general shape of an x-ray tube is depicted in Fig. 320. The anode A and cathode C are connected to a source of high-potential direct current that is obtained from a high alternating potential by a mechanical rectifier or more effectively by a kenotron rectifier. The filament C is usually formed of a tungsten wire wound into a spiral and is heated by current supplied through a transformer as shown. The target of wrought tungsten is attached to a molybdenum rod and supported by an iron sleeve which helps to radiate the heat evolved.

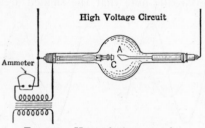

FIG. 320.   Hot-cathode x-ray tube

When different substances are interposed between a protected photographic plate or film and a source of x-rays, the radiation penetrates them to different extents, according to their densities, so that the plate or film, upon development, shows the shadows of the objects interposed. When the hand is so placed near an x-ray tube, the plate is much less affected directly behind the bones than behind the flesh, because the bones are relatively opaque to the radiations. A print made from such a plate gives shadows of the bones and a faint outline of the flesh. Broken bones and foreign objects in the body can be located accurately in this manner. Powerful equipments have been developed for inspecting welds in thick steel plates and locating defects by means of x-ray photographs.

X-rays may be used for the direct examination of objects by the use of a fluoroscopic screen. This screen consists of a piece of cardboard coated with certain crystals, as platinobarium cyanide, or tungstate of calcium, which fluoresce under the action of x-rays.

If the hand be interposed between such a screen and the tube, the shadow of the bones can be plainly seen.

Physicians use x-rays not only in making examinations but also for their curative action. Animal tissue undergoes a change in structure when exposed to x-rays and is destroyed by prolonged exposure. In x-ray therapy, the rays are concentrated upon abnormal or diseased tissue that is to be destroyed.

When a gas is exposed to x-rays it becomes ionized, and the amount of ionization produced serves as a measure of the intensity of the rays. Such a measurement is carried out with an ionization chamber and an electroscope. The chamber consists of a closed metal box, having a window of thin celluloid or aluminum, and containing an insulated metal electrode to which the electroscope is connected. When the rays are admitted through the window, and a difference of potential is maintained between the electrode and the box, the ions produced by the x-rays separate; those of one sign gather on the electrode while those of the other sign collect upon the chamber. The rate at which the electroscope becomes charged is an accurate measure of the intensity of the x-rays.

The radiation from an x-ray tube covers a wide range of frequencies, the range extending to higher frequencies as the potential difference between the target and cathode is increased. It has been shown that there is an upper limiting frequency f_m determined by the potential difference V, the relation being

$$Ve = hf_m$$

where the product Ve represents the energy in ergs with which the electrons strike the target, and h is Planck's constant [§ 190]. In this expression e is the charge of the electron, namely 4.80×10^{-10} e.s.u., and V is the potential difference in ergs per unit charge. Reducing to volts [§ 222], the maximum frequency becomes $f_m = 2.41 \times 10^{14}\, V$.

307. The Photoelectric Cell. — Experiments made around 1888 showed that freshly polished zinc would lose a charge of electricity when illuminated by ultra-violet light, but only when the charge was negative. This expulsion of electrons is now known to occur from many substances as soon as they are illuminated by ordinary or ultraviolet light. This effect is called *photoelectric emission*, and the negative charges emitted are sometimes called *photoelectrons* to indicate their origin. It is found that with light of a given frequency of vibration (color) a variation of light intensity does not cause a change of velocity of the electrons emitted, but does change the number expelled per unit of time. On the other hand, an increase in the frequency of the incident light increases the velocity of expulsion, and a decrease in frequency decreases the velocity of expulsion down to a limiting frequency, characteristic of the metal used, at which the photoelectric effect disappears. These facts are expressed quantitatively by the Einstein photoelectric equation, which states that the maximum kinetic energy of the electrons expelled from the alkali metals is

$$\tfrac{1}{2}m\,v_m^2 = hf - w$$

Herein m is the mass of the electron, v_m is the maximum velocity of the electrons, h is Planck's constant, f is the frequency of the incident light, and w is the energy required to pull an electron out of the metal. The low-frequency limit, or threshold value of f, is obtained when $hf = w$; this limit for such materials as caesium, sodium and potassium is in the infra-red, and therefore photoelectric emission occurs throughout the visible light range. Others show emission only for ultra-violet light. The foregoing facts have an important bearing upon the theory of light and radiation [§ 429]. It is of interest here to observe that the number of electrons which are emitted per second is proportional to the intensity of light which causes the action.

The photoelectric cell is an electron tube that consists of a light-sensitive surface, most often of caesium, constituting the cathode, and a small wire or plate constituting the anode, both within a

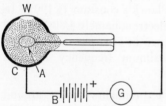

FIG. 321.   Photoelectric cell circuit

glass tube. The diagram of such a cell appears in Fig. 321, the battery B being connected to the anode A and cathode C through a galvanometer G. When light enters at the window W it falls upon the cathode film on the inside surface of the glass, and the electrons emitted are drawn to the anode, thus constituting current in the circuit and producing a deflection of the galvanometer. Experiment shows that over considerable ranges the current is directly proportional to the illumination at the cell. Photoelectric cells are of the vacuum type and of the gas-filled type; in the latter helium or argon is used at a pressure of a few millimeters. Much greater currents can be obtained in the gas-filled type than in the other because of the ionization of the gas molecules by collision with electrons and other molecules. The currents are of the order of microamperes, for the usual range of illumination; three-electrode electron tubes are generally used with photoelectric cells to amplify their currents.

Photoelectric cells are used particularly for color analysis and comparison, control of street lights and electric signs, counting operations, and for talking motion pictures.

PROBLEMS

1. A potentiometer is used with an iron-constantan thermocouple to determine the melting point of silver. With one thermal junction at 0° C. and with the other in the silver at its temperature of solidification, the potentiometer reads 54.6 divisions on its scale. With the Weston standard cell connected to the potentiometer, the reading was initially adjusted to be exactly 1000 divisions. What is the e.m.f. generated by the couple at the melting point of silver and what is the average e.m.f. per degree developed over the temperature range involved?

2. Compute the thermo e.m.f generated by an iron-nickel couple, the junctions of which are at 20° C. and 200° C.

3. Compute the thermo e.m.f. generated by a copper-nickel thermocouple when its junctions are at 0° C. and 250° C. respectively.

4. To measure the temperature at a concealed point within an electric motor, one junction of a nickel-iron thermocouple is placed at this point, the other junction being maintained at 0° C. If the couple produces an e.m.f. of 1.82 millivolts, compute the temperature at the concealed point.

5. A thermopile is composed of 49 antimony-bismuth junctions on one face and an equal number on the other. Radiation falls upon one face of the thermopile while the other is at the room temperature of 20° C., and the total e.m.f. generated is 0.130 volt. What is the temperature of the thermopile face that receives the radiation?

6. A thermopile being designed for use in fire detection is to have a certain number of antimony-bismuth junctions on one face and an equal number on the other. It is desired to generate a total e.m.f. of at least 50 millivolts when the exposed face of the thermopile reaches 100° C., the other face remaining at the room temperature of 20° C. What is the smallest number of junctions that may be used on the exposed face?

7. Calculate the emission current per square centimeter from a tungsten filament when its temperature is 2000° K.

8. Theoretical analysis shows that the constant A of Richardson's equation is given by $A = \dfrac{2\pi emk^2}{h^3}$ amp. per cm.^{2} per deg. K^2, where e and m are respectively the charge in coulombs and the mass in grams of the electron, k is the gas constant per molecule, and h is Planck's constant. Refer to the values given in this book for these quantities and calculate the magnitude of A.

9. Referring to the rectifier tube having the characteristic shown in Fig. 315, determine the average value of the rectified current when a sinusoidal e.m.f. having a peak value of 40 volts is applied to the rectifier arranged for full-wave rectification.

10. A mercury-arc rectifier for changing alternating to direct current has a rating of 750 kw. at 625 volts. What current is delivered at the rated output?

11. Calculate the voltage amplification constant of the triode having the characteristic curves shown in Fig. 318 when the grid potential is varied from −4.5 to −9.0 volts and the plate current is maintained at 6 milliamp.

12. The so-called plate resistance of an electron tube is the ratio of a small change in plate potential to the corresponding change in plate current. Determine the plate resistance of the triode mentioned in the preceding problem for the following condition: plate potential = 180, grid potential = −13.5.

13. The ratio of a small change in plate current to the corresponding small change in grid potential which produced it (all other potentials remaining unchanged) is called the mutual conductance of the tube and is usually expressed in microamperes per volt. What is this constant for the triode of the two preceding problems at 150 volts when the grid potential is varied from −4.5 to −9.0 volts?

14. Find the voltage amplification of the electron tube referred to in Fig. 318 when the grid potential is varied from −13.5 to −18 volts and the plate current is maintained at 2 milliamp.

15. A surface of 1 sq. in. at a distance of 15 in. from a 60-watt frosted lamp receives about 0.2 lumen of light flux. About this much reaches the gate of the "sound-track" of a motion picture film. If the photoelectric cell passes 6 microamp. with this amount of light flux, what will be the change of photoelectric current when the film is inserted and varies the flux from 0.01 to 0.04 lumen?

16. Taking 3×10^{14} cycles per sec. as the photoelectric threshold for potassium, compute the work required to draw one of the least firmly bound electrons from its surface. What potential difference would be needed to remove such an electron?

CHAPTER XXIX

FUNDAMENTALS OF ELECTRICAL COMMUNICATION

308. Single Morse Telegraph. — Communication by electrical means was not accomplished practically until the discovery of electromagnetism. The system of telegraphy devised in 1837 by the American artist and inventor, Samuel F. B. Morse (1791–1872), provides one channel of communication over an electric circuit, and is called accordingly the *single Morse telegraph*. The basic principle is the actuation of an electromagnet by current controlled remotely. The circuit consists of a line wire, a ground return path of negligible resistance, two or more switches called keys for opening and closing the circuit, and two or more electro-mechanical instruments called sounders. Signals are transmitted by manipulating a key in accordance with a code, and are received by listening to the clicks produced by the armature of the sounder as it is attracted and released by its electromagnet.

On long telegraph lines the current received is small and consequently sensitive relays are used in the line circuits in place

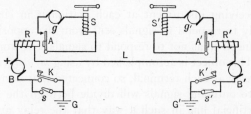

Fig. 322. Single Morse circuit with relays

of the sounders. A relay has a light armature and functions merely to open and close a local circuit which includes a sounder, rather than to produce an audible response itself.

Fig. 322 shows the circuit of a Morse telegraph between two widely separated stations. When the line is idle, the circuit is kept closed by means of the by-passes s and s' associated with the keys K and K', and the current path includes generators B and B', relays R and R', line L, and ground from G to G'. Assuming the operator at the left-hand station to send messages, he interrupts the circuit by opening *s* (as shown in the figure) and then establishes current pulses by depressing his key for long and short intervals to produce the so-called dashes and dots of the telegraph code. These current pulses through the relay windings cause the armatures *A* and *A'* to be attracted intermittently, thereby closing and opening the local circuits which include the generators *g* and *g'*, and the sounders *S* and *S'*. When through sending, he again completes the circuit by closing *s*, thereby enabling the other operator to respond.

The points of support of overhead telegraph lines offer leakage paths to ground and, consequently, not all of the current that starts out on a line reaches the receiving instrument. In order to assure sufficient current on long lines under all weather contitions, instruments called telegraph repeaters are introduced every few hundred miles to retransmit the signals automatically from one section of the line to the next; these operate in either direction.

309. Duplex Signaling. — Two messages may be transmitted simultaneously in opposite directions over a single-line circuit in *duplex telegraphy* without interference. A sending and a receiving operator are required at each station. As the message capacity of a duplexed line is twice that of the same line when operated as a single Morse circuit, considerable economy is effected in line equipment.

The receiving instrument at each station is in circuit at all times ready to respond to signals sent from the opposite station, but is arranged so as not to respond to signals sent from its home station. This object is accomplished by using an *artificial line* and a *neutral relay* at each terminal, so connected that currents corresponding to outgoing signals will divide between the actual line and the artificial line in such a way that the relay at the home station will not operate but the relay at the other station will. The artificial line is an assembly of resistances and condensers which together simulate the actual line.

The simplest type of duplex telegraph is illustrated in Fig. 323. Each relay *R* and *R'* has two windings, identical as to number of turns and resistance, that are distributed evenly over the core. Each artificial line *A* and *A'* is adjusted experimentally so that the current from the generator, with only one key depressed, will divide equally between the two coils of the home relay.

The transmission of two messages in opposite directions over this duplex telegraph will be described by considering various positions of the keys.   If neither key is depressed, the generators *B* and *B'* are disconnected and therefore neither relay is actuated. The depression of one key, say *K'*, provides two paths for current from generator *B'*; the current divides equally between them and

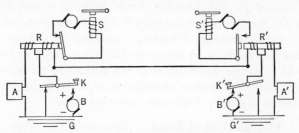

FIG. 323.   Single-current duplex telegraph using neutral relays

the two parts circulate around the iron core of relay *R'* in opposite directions; consequently their magnetomotive forces will neutralize each other and leave the core unmagnetized.   The current in the line and relay *R* at the other station magnetizes the core of that relay, causing the armature to be attracted and the sounder *S* to be actuated.   Similarly, the depression of key *K* causes sounder *S'* to be actuated.   The depression of both keys connects the two generators in opposition and, since under this condition there can be no current in the line wire or in the line coils of the relays, both of these instruments will be actuated by the currents supplied by the home generators through the artificial line coils. The transmission of signals in both directions simultaneously is merely a succession of the four combinations of key positions mentioned, and since a relay at one station is energized whenever the key at the other station is depressed regardless of the position of the home key, it is clear that such duplex transmission is accomplished without interference.

Another type of relay may be used in the duplex circuit; it is a *polarized relay* and has a permanent magnet and an electromagnet, as illustrated in Fig. 324.

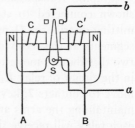

FIG. 324.   Polarized relay

The permanent magnet has a N pole at each end and a S pole of double strength, called a consequent pole, in the center.   Soft-iron pole pieces attached to the ends of this magnet carry the coils C and C', and the armature T is pivoted between them. With current in the windings from A to B, the magnetism produced by coil C opposes that of the permanent magnet and the magnetism produced by coil C' aids that of the permanent magnet; consequently the armature is drawn to the stronger right-hand pole and closes contact for the sounder circuit between a and b. The contact will then remain closed even if the current in the windings were to vanish entirely; however, a reversal of current would cause the armature to be drawn to the idle contact at the left. Thus, the armature will move from one contact to the other only when the current direction changes, regardless of the intensity of current above some minimum operating value.

*310. **Multiple Use of Lines.** — Systems of telegraphy have been devised which provide more than two channels of communi-

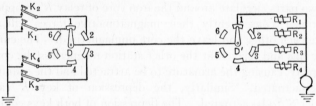

Fig. 325.   Scheme of multiplex telegraph transmission

cation over a single wire line. In the modern *multiplex system*, distributors are used for assigning the line periodically to corresponding transmitting and receiving devices, the connections at the two stations being made simultaneously by synchronously rotating contact arms. The principle is illustrated in Fig. 325 for telegraphic transmission in one direction only. Four keys are shown connected to stationary contact segments at the transmitting distributor D, and four relays are shown joined to similar segments at the receiving distributor D'. When the arms of the two distributors move to contacts 1, key K_1 will be momentarily in the circuit of relay R_1 and control its operation; when the arms move to contacts 2, key K_2 will control relay R_2, and so on. By maintaining the arms at the two stations in step with each other, each relay will receive signals only from the key marked with the same subscript, and there will be no confusion of signals. The speed of these synchronously revolving arms is made sufficiently great so that they will make contact with any one pair of instruments, say K_1R_1, one or more times during the short time required to form a dot signal. By assigning the line in this way to the four sets of instruments, each set repeatedly having exclusive use of the line for only brief moments, four channels of communication are afforded by a single line. In this system the relays are of the polarized type and the keys include a feature not shown in the figure, whereby the current is reversed at the end of each dot or dash signal. This action releases the relay so that it may respond to the next signal. Synchronous rotation of the distributors is secured by the use of small motors having magnetic fields controlled by reeds that vibrate at their natural frequencies, the synchronizing devices being connected to contacts 5 and 6.

311. The Telephone. — The transmission of speech by telephone was first accomplished in 1876 by Alexander G. Bell (1847–1922), American inventor and physicist. The elements of telephonic communication consist of a transmitter for producing a variable current having the same characteristics as the incident sound waves [§ 333], and a receiver for converting this variable current into sound waves to reproduce the original sounds.

The transmitter consists of carbon granules confined between two electrodes, one being rigid and the other flexibly mounted on the diaphragm against which the voice is directed. Variations of air pressure on the diaphragm cause changes of resistance of the granules because their contacting areas are altered. The receiver comprises a small electromagnet combined with a permanent magnet, and a thin diaphragm to complete the magnetic circuit. Variations of current in the electromagnet cause variations in the attraction of the diaphragm, thereby setting it into vibration to produce sound.

The simplest connection for demonstrating the transmission of speech is a series circuit including a transmitter, a receiver, and a battery. A sound impressed upon the transmitter causes its diaphragm to be moved with varying amplitudes and frequencies. Each push against the diaphragm lowers the resistance of the transmitter, causes a larger current in the circuit, and produces in the receiver an increased pull upon its diaphragm. Without the permanent magnet, the receiver diaphragm would produce sounds of double pitch. The reason for this will be evident when an alternating current is assumed in the receiver winding, for then the diaphragm would be attracted once for the positive lobe of the cycle and once for the negative, thereby producing two complete vibrations of the diaphragm for each current cycle.

Fig. 326 shows a sectional view of a modern telephone handset, with the transmitter at the left and the receiver at the right mounted together in a shell of molded insulation. The trans-

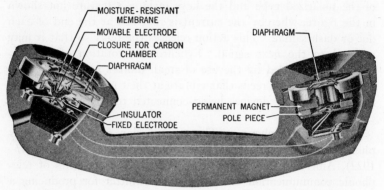

FIG. 326. Handset developed by the Bell Telephone Laboratories

mitter diaphragm is a shallow cone of thin aluminum alloy fastened at its rim just back of the mouthpiece. Carbon granules fill the enclosure between the movable electrode carried on the diaphragm and the fixed electrode. The receiver has a bipolar

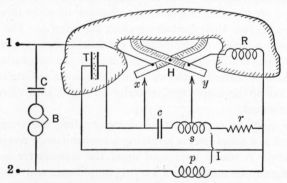

FIG. 327. Connections of a subscriber's telephone set

electromagnet on pole pieces of permalloy, together with two straight bar magnets and a diaphragm of magnetic alloy. The connections of this set are given in Fig. 327, in which the principal elements are the transmitter T, the receiver R, the switch H, the bell B, and the induction coil I.

The bell serves in calling the subscriber to the telephone and is actuated by alternating current of about 16 cycles per sec. supplied from the central office. The path of this current between line wires 1 and 2 includes only the condenser C and the polarized ringer B, the latter being constructed like a polarized relay with one end of its armature designed to strike alternately against two gongs. When the user lifts the handset from its support to engage in conversation, the switch H makes contacts at x and y, closing the transmitter and receiver circuits respectively. These circuits are coupled magnetically by the primary and secondary windings p and s of the induction coil, and include a resistance r and a condenser c to match the average line constants.

In talking, the vibration of the transmitter diaphragm varies the resistance in the circuit 1, x, T, p, 2 and produces corresponding variations of current in another telephone set to which the line wires lead. In listening to speech originating at the other set, the current variations produced by it occasion corresponding variations in the circuit just mentioned, as a result of which e.m.f.'s are developed in the secondary winding of the induction coil. These produce corresponding current variations in the circuit s, y, R, r and operate the receiver accordingly. The connections are so designed that the receiver will respond very little to variations of current produced by its companion transmitter, thereby making it unresponsive to extraneous noises picked up at the home station and hence more effective as a receiver of incoming speech signals.

312. Telephone Repeaters. — The three-element electron tube [§304] is used with an appropriate circuit on long telephone lines for amplifying the voice currents. The electrical energy to be amplified is applied to the input or grid circuit of the tube, and the amplified energy is made available in its output or plate circuit. The tube circuits thus constitute a *repeater element* which permits of telephone transmission in one direction.

The connection diagram of such a repeater element is given in Fig. 328. A high resistance is connected across the secondary winding of the input transformer T so that a portion of the e.m.f. induced in this winding may be impressed between the filament F and the grid G. The battery A provides current to heat the filament, and the battery E_c maintains the grid negative to prevent current in the grid circuit. The circuit from the plate P of the tube includes the battery B and the reactance coil L; the latter confines the voice currents to the output circuit indicated by the terminals at the right. Small variations in the voice currents in

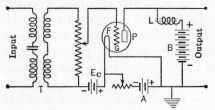

FIG. 328.   Telephone repeater element

the input transformer cause proportional variations in grid potential, and these in turn produce similar but amplified variations in the output circuit. For the usual two-way telephonic transmission over a single line circuit either one or two such repeater elements are needed, depending upon the manner of connection.

The gain in power produced by a repeater is expressed in terms of a unit called the *decibel* (abbreviated db.). One decibel represents a ratio between two power values of $10^{0.1}$. When the gain of a repeater is N db., the ratio of the output power P_2 to the input power P_1 is $10^{0.1N}$, or

$$\frac{P_2}{P_1} = 10^{0.1N}$$

Herefrom, the gain in decibels becomes

$$N = 10 \log_{10} \frac{P_2}{P_1} \tag{202}$$

As an illustration of the decibel scale in expressing amplification, suppose the input to an amplifier is 5 microwatts. A gain of 10 db. would give a power ratio $P_2/P_1 = 10^{0.1 \times 10} = 10$; consequently there would be a 10-fold increase and the output would be 50 microwatts. Similarly, a gain of 60 db. would signify a 10^6-fold power increase to 5 watts. Again, if the input is 5 microwatts and the output is 300 microwatts, then the gain in decibels from equation (202) would be $N = 10 \log_{10} 300/5 = 10 \log_{10} 60 = 10 \times 1.778 = 17.8$ db.

313. Electromagnetic Radiation. — In circuits having capacitance and inductance distributed over zones of appropriate areas, the production of alternating currents of high frequencies causes some of the energy to leave the circuits in the form of radiation. The discovery of this propagation of electromagnetic radiation through space was made about 1887 by the German physicist, Heinrich R. Hertz (1857–1894), who also showed that the disturbances have measurable velocity and wave lengths. The Italian scientist, Guglielmo Marconi (1874–1937), applied this discovery to the transmission of intelligence, and brought about radio communication. The systems involve the production of electromagnetic waves in space at transmitting stations and their detection at receiving stations.

When a wire is extended into the air and an alternator is joined between it and ground, the alternating e.m.f. forces electrons up and down the wire, causing its upper end to be charged alternately + and −. The wire, or so-called *antenna*, together with the ground, act like the plates of a condenser and the region between is under electrostatic stress. At a certain instant the top of the antenna is negatively charged while the ground is positive, as shown at the left in Fig. 329; the broken lines at the antenna show the electrostatic lines of force. When the e.m.f. in the antenna reverses, its upper end becomes positively charged and comes positively charged and

Fig. 329. Propagation of electromagnetic waves

the ground becomes negative, and the strained region falls away from the antenna. As the e.m.f. reversals continue, lobes of electrostatic fields are set up as illustrated in the figure, and these, together with the magnetic fields which accompany the electron surges in the antenna, travel outward as electromagnetic waves. Their velocity of propagation is 300,000 km. per sec.

*314. The Electron-tube Oscillator. — The rapid oscillation of the electrons in a radio antenna can be produced by high-frequency alternators, electric arcs, and electron tubes; the latter method is now the most common. The three-element tube is generally used for this purpose with the plate and grid circuits so coupled that some energy in the plate circuit is fed back to the grid circuit. Fig. 330 shows a simple form of such an oscillator.

To explain the operation of this circuit, consider the instant when the filament and plate circuits are closed. The filament F, heated by current from the battery A, will emit electrons which pass to the plate P, establishing a current in the plate circuit and developing a magnetic field in the right-hand portion of the inductive coil L. This growing field about L_2 cuts the turns of L_1, inducing an e.m.f. in the left-hand portion of the coil, exactly as in a transformer.   The momentary direction of the counter e.m.f. in L_2 is such as to make the intermediate point O positive with respect to b.   Similarly the e.m.f. induced in L_1 will be such as to make point a positive with respect to O, and therefore positive to b also.   Thus, as the current in the plate circuit grows, it is aided by the positive potential pulse imparted to the grid G by L_1 (see § 304). However, as the plate current ceases to rise in value, that is, as the plate-circuit current approaches saturation, the e.m.f. induced in L_1 diminishes to zero.   Under these conditions the plate-circuit current must decrease because the positive potential which was available at the grid is now lacking.   As the plate current falls in value, the e.m.f. induced in L_1 is reversed in direction and increased in magnitude.   This reversal of the potential difference across L_1 aids the reduction of the plate current until it reaches zero.   When

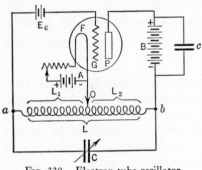

FIG. 330.   Electron-tube oscillator

this value is attained the e.m.f. induced in L_1 is again zero and the plate current begins to rise because the negative grid potential necessary to maintain zero plate current no longer exists. Once more the current rises in the plate circuit and produces an e.m.f. in L_1 directed to make G positive; thus aiding the current to grow, which growth continues until saturation is reached.   Thereafter this cycle of events is repeated, and continuous oscillations are established.

Condenser c is a by-pass around the battery B for the high-frequency pulses to the plate.   The battery E_c is added to the circuit to permit selection of the most efficient operating condition, that is, one which results in a minimum loss in both grid and plate circuits.

The frequency of the oscillations generated by the electron-tube oscillator is determined largely by the constants of the alternating-current circuit, consisting in this case of the inductive coil ab and the variable condenser C.   The natural frequency of this circuit in cycles per second is given by equation (191).

To illustrate the computation, consider a simple series circuit to have a coil of 0.06 millihenry inductance and a condenser of 0.001 microfarad capacitance. The natural frequency of this circuit is

$$f = \frac{1}{2\pi\sqrt{0.06 \times 10^{-3} \times 0.001 \times 10^{-6}}} =$$

$$\frac{1}{2\pi\sqrt{6 \times 10^{-14}}} = \frac{10^7}{2\pi\sqrt{6}} = 649{,}000 \text{ cycles per sec.}$$

If a condenser of like capacitance were connected in series with the other, the combined capacitance would be half the former value and the natural frequency of the circuit would be $\sqrt{2}$ times as great as before, namely 918,000 cycles per sec.

*315. The Radio Transmitter. — The oscillations produced by the electron-tube oscillator are transferred to the antenna of a *radio telephone transmitter* through a coupling device, as shown in Fig. 331 by the coil L'. The inductance of this coupler together with the capacitance and in-ductance of the aerial with respect to ground constitute the elements of an alternat-ing-current circuit that has a definite but adjustable natural frequency. A condenser is shunted across the secondary winding of the transformer to by-pass the high-frequency currents.

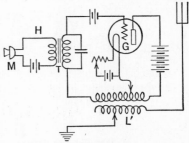

Fig. 331.   Radio telephone transmitter

The electromagnetic waves set up by the antenna may be used for radio telephony by modulating the generated wave to conform to an envelope which has the characteristics of the sound to be transmitted. The sound waves correspond in length to the frequency of the vibrating source, and these frequencies range from about 16 to upward of 10,000 cycles per second. The process of modulation may be considered as a superposition of such audio-frequency waves on the radio waves generated by the oscillator. This is somewhat analogous to the superposition of the speech waves on the direct current used in the wire telephone.

Modulation may be accomplished by inserting a microphone and a transformer in the grid circuit of the electron-tube oscil-lator, as shown. This arrangement, known as *grid modulation*, is very simple and effective in low-power circuits. The sound waves impinging upon the microphone M are converted into corresponding electrical current variations in the local circuit H, and these voice currents impress suitably varying potentials upon

the grid *G* by means of transformer *T*. Thus, the grid is subjected
to two sets of potential variations, one being the very rapid radio-
frequency oscillations or carrier wave as shown at the right in
Fig. 332, and the other being the relatively slow voice or sound
frequency variations as shown at the top in the figure. As a
result the oscillations generated by the tube, which are constant
in frequency, are varied in amplitude in accordance with the
sound wave so that a curve passing through the successive maxima

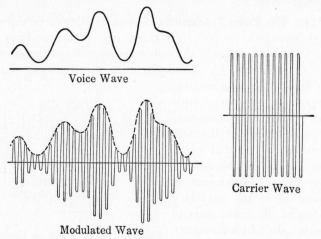

Voice Wave

Carrier Wave

Modulated Wave

FIG. 332.   Modulating high-frequency currents for radio telephony

of the radio-frequency waves represents the sound wave. The
lower diagram represents the modulated wave formed by super-
posing the voice current on the carrier wave. This procedure is
also used in carrier-current transmission over wires [§ 317].

Various types of microphones are used at present, but only two
will be mentioned. The *electrodynamic transmitter* carries on its
diaphragm a tiny coil located in the field of a stationary magnet,
and e.m.f.'s are generated in the coil when the pressure on the
diaphragm changes. The *velocity microphone* has a light corrugated metallic ribbon between the pole pieces of an electromagnet,
and e.m.f.'s are induced in the ribbon when incident sound waves
set it into vibration, the velocity of the ribbon being in phase with
the velocity of the air particles.

The frequency of a radio transmitter can be controlled by
utilizing crystals, like quartz, which exhibit the *piezoelectric effect*.
If a plate is cut in a particular way from a quartz crystal, it is found

that compressing the plate causes its faces to become charged and then stretching it causes this charge to be reversed. Conversely, if the plate is located in an alternating electric field, it will contract and expand periodically and set up mechanical vibrations of constant frequency. The vibration rate will vary inversely with the thickness of the plate, its value for 1 mm. thickness of quartz being about 3×10^6 cycles per sec. By placing a quartz plate of appropriate thickness between two electrodes that are connected to the grid circuit of an electron tube transmitter tuned to the frequency of the plate, the frequency of the tube may be kept constant regardless of load changes.

316. The Radio Receiver. — The function of the *radio receiving set* is to absorb energy from the electromagnetic waves available in its vicinity which are emitted from a selected transmitting or broadcasting station, to transform these weak high-frequency oscillations into amplified currents of lower and audible fre-

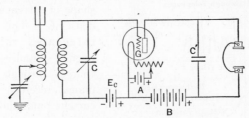

Fig. 333. Simple electron-tube receiver

quency, and to convert these currents into sounds having minimum distortion and sufficient volume. To receive waves from a particular station, the radio set is tuned to it by adjusting the capacitance or inductance of its antenna circuit, and the high-frequency currents induced in that circuit are rectified by a detector, usually an electron tube.

Fig. 333 shows the circuit of a simple electron-tube detector used in a receiver, in which the batteries A and B provide the power for the filament and plate circuits respectively. The variations of potential difference across the variable condenser C act upon the grid G of the tube through the battery E_c. The number of cells in this battery is adjusted to select the point on the characteristic curve of the tube for proper operation. Variations of grid potential produce amplified variations of current through the telephone receivers in the plate circuit, as explained in § 304.

The plate-current grid-potential characteristic of the tube is illustrated in Fig. 334, showing the extent to which rectification is carried out. The greatest rectification will result when the e.m.f. E_c of the grid battery conforms to the bend of the characteristic curve. No rectification would be produced at the straight portion of the curve because equal positive and negative swings of the grid potential yield equal increases and decreases of plate current.

The wavy line at the bottom of the figure indicates the potential variation produced by an incoming signal on the condenser C of the tuned circuit. By projecting the successive points up to the tube characteristic and from there across to the right, there is obtained the corresponding wavy line which represents the wave shape of current in the condenser C'. This condenser integrates the high-frequency impulses and discharges through the telephone receiver, giving a current pulse shown by the median line of this curve.

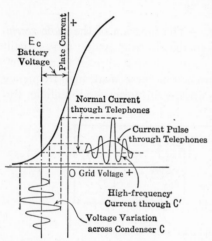

FIG. 334.   Action of a simple electron-tube detector

In another detector circuit the battery E_c is replaced by a condenser and a very high resistance connected in parallel, and called respectively a *grid condenser* and a *grid leak*.

In order that an electron-tube detector may operate to the best advantage, it is necessary that the potentials upon its grid be reasonably large. Since the energy ordinarily received in antennas is insufficient to develop such potentials, it is almost always desirable to build up the received radio-frequency impulses before applying them to the detector. The process of increasing these radio-frequency potentials is termed *radio-frequency amplification*. This is accomplished by one or more electron tubes connected somewhat like that in Fig. 328. The detector tube converts the radio-frequency oscillations into waves of audible frequencies and passes them to the telephones.

With one or more stages of radio-frequency amplification applied ahead of the detector tube of a receiver, the output of the detector may still be too weak to actuate the sound-reproducing devices. The output may then be increased by means of *audio-frequency amplifiers* which usually have two stages of amplification. The second stage often employs a tube of larger capacity, a so-called *power tube*, in order to yield large volumes of sound in a loud speaker.

*317. Carrier-current Transmission. — The modulation of high-frequency waves at the radio transmitter and their rectification at the radio receiver have been applied with success to telegraphy and telephony over line wires in order to increase the number of channels of communication afforded by a single circuit. This method is termed *carrier-current* communication, since alternating currents of different and relatively high frequencies are employed to "carry" the signal or speech waves. With this system a single circuit could furnish a number of telephone and telegraph channels. While the system is essentially the same for both telegraph and telephone transmission, the following description will be confined to telegraphy for the sake of simplicity.

The carrier currents are usually generated by electron-tube oscillators which have their frequencies determined by the inductance and capacitance of their associated circuits. Modulation in the present carrier telegraph system is accomplished by merely starting and stopping the carrier current with a key or relay contact in accordance with the telegraph signals. The several carrier currents are separated by selective circuits or filters. Rectification is accomplished by an electron-tube detector or rectifier with a shunt condenser, the resulting direct current being passed through the receiving relay. Thus, each key serves to produce variations of intensity of only one carrier current, and these variations are made intelligible by only one of the receiving relays connected to the line.

318. Television. — The problem of vision at a distance by electrical means has received much attention in recent years and several television systems are in experimental operation. The fundamental principles involve: 1, scanning the scene to be transmitted spot by spot in an orderly fashion; 2, establishing a current that varies with the light intensities of these spots; 3, amplifying these current variations and transmitting them over wire lines or by radio waves; 4, converting the electrical pulsations into corresponding light fluctuations at a receiving station; and 5, arranging these light patches upon a screen to form an image of the original scene. Further, the entire scene must be scanned repeatedly about 15 times or more per second in order that its successive images may merge to produce a steady result like that of motion pictures.

In the television system devised by Vladimir K. Zworykin, a narrow electron beam is used to scan an image of the scene in a photoelectric tube of special design called an *iconoscope*. This is an evacuated glass tube arranged as illustrated in Fig. 335. The electrons are emitted by a heated cathode C, are controlled and

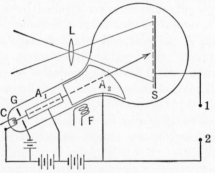

Fig. 335.   Iconoscope for converting light image into varying current

focused by passing them through the grid G and the anodes A_1 and A_2, and are directed upon the screen S. This screen consists of a thin sheet of mica having a metal film on one side and a tremendous number of tiny photosensitive particles resembling a mosaic on the other. The scene to be transmitted is imaged upon the mosaic by a lens system L as shown, and as a result its particles are illuminated to various intensities. Each particle may be regarded as a tiny photoelectric cell that also forms a condenser with the metal film on the other side of the mica sheet, and therefore each one acquires a charge by photoelectric emission that depends upon the intensity of light upon it. The electron beam is deflected from one side to the other along a line, and then similarly from line to line by means of a magnetic field that is symbolized by F in the figure. In this way the entire image is scanned and the charges on the particles of the mosaic are released in succession, thereby establishing a current in the output circuit 1, 2 that fluctuates in accordance with the light elements of the screen image. This current is amplified by electron tubes and transmitted to the distant station by methods already described in this chapter.

The television receiver comprises electrical receiving and amplifying tube circuits, together with a large vacuum tube resembling the cathode-ray oscillograph described in § 286. The intensity of the electron beam in the tube is controlled by the fluctuating current that represents the incoming picture signals. This beam is moved from side to side and from line to line by applying appropriate potentials to its deflecting plates as previously explained or by using a magnetic field for its deflection. With proper synchronization of the scanning operation to that at the transmitter, an image of the original scene will be produced upon the fluorescent screen of the receiving tube.

PROBLEMS

1. How far would it be possible to telegraph over a single Morse line having 8.4 ohms resistance per mile of length and having a 120-volt generator at each end? Assume that there are two 150-ohm relays in this series circuit, each requiring 0.05 amp. for actuation, and that there is no leakage of current from the line to ground.

2. Compute the signal current in a single Morse telegraph circuit 300 mi. long, which has at each end a 120-volt generator and a 200-ohm relay. Assume the line resistance to be 10.6 ohms per mile and neglect leakage.

3. A 400-mile telegraph line (single wire with earth return), having a resistance from end to end of 3200 ohms, shows an insulation resistance to ground of 1 megohm per mile in wet weather. A 120-volt generator, a key and a 250-ohm relay are connected in series at each terminal of this single Morse line. Assume the leakage to be concentrated at the middle point of the line, and calculate the currents through a relay when only the key at the home station is closed, and when both keys are closed.

4. A duplex telegraph circuit has a line of 1800 ohms resistance, two artificial lines of 1900 ohms each, and two relays of 200 ohms each (100 ohms for each winding). A generator of 150 volts is connected at each station as indicated in Fig. 323. Compute the current in each relay winding when one key is closed, and when both keys are closed.

5. A simple telephone subscriber's loop consists of a 60-ohm transmitter, two miles of No. 19 gage conductor having a resistance of 44 ohms per mile, and a 24-volt battery. This series circuit also includes two windings of a "repeating coil" having 21 ohms each, two "heat coils" (or fuses) of 3 ohms each, a "supervisory relay" of 9 ohms, and one winding of an induction coil having 14 ohms. (*a*) Determine the steady current in the circuit. (*b*) What percentage current change will be produced by a 10 per cent change in the resistance of the transmitter?

6. A particular transmitter generates 10^{-11} watt when placed 1 ft. from a person speaking in a moderate tone of voice. Assuming that 20 watts are required to operate a loud-speaker system in a typical audi-

torium, calculate the gain of an amplifier connected between transmitter and loud speakers to meet this requirement.

7. An amplifier increases the power received in the ratio of 300 to 1. Express the result in decibels.

8. The input to a telephone repeater is 10 microwatts and its output is 3.5 watts. Calculate the gain of the repeater in decibels.

9. A telephone repeater which is supplied with 8 microwatts produces a gain of 40 db. What output does it deliver?

10. An antenna has a capacitance to ground of 0.00072 mf. and its circuit includes an inductance of 0.043 millihenry. What is the natural frequency of the antenna circuit?

11. A condenser of 0.0012 mf. is inserted in series with the antenna circuit of Problem 10. Determine the natural frequency under this condition.

12. An antenna circuit has an inductance of 0.080 millihenry and a capacitance to ground of 0.001 mf. Determine the resonant frequency of this circuit.

13. What capacitance connected in series with the circuit of Problem 12 will increase the natural frequency to 660 kilocycles per sec.?

*14. How much inductance should be used with a 0.02-mf. condenser in order that the circuit so formed shall be tuned to a 30,000-cycle carrier current?

SOUND

CHAPTER XXX

WAVE MOTION

319. Some Types of Waves. — In the study of wave motion it will become apparent that waves are of many kinds and of common occurrence. Water waves sweep across the surface of the ocean; distortional waves surge to and fro within vibrating bodies; sound waves carry tones and noises through the air; and electromagnetic waves transmit radio programs, light, and x-rays.

Probably everyone has thrown a stone into quiet water and watched an ever-widening circular wave spread over the surface from the point of impact. The water does not move as a whole, but some particular configuration of the surface does. To set up such a configuration the individual particles of water must move in transmitting the wave, but their motion takes place over rather short paths. Another example of wave propagation is the motion of a disturbance along a rope stretched horizontally. If the rope is pulled by the hand and the hand is moved up suddenly and then back again, a wave will start along the rope. When launched in this way, the wave consists practically of only one crest, and is called a *single-pulse* wave. If the hand is moved up and down repeatedly, going through the same motion each time, a *train* of waves will be set up in the rope. These waves all have the same configuration and are called *periodic* waves. Unless specially mentioned, all of the waves to be studied herein are of this kind.

The motion of the diaphragm of a telephone receiver sets up periodic waves in the surrounding air. Each outward movement of the diaphragm compresses the air in front of it, and each backward movement rarefies the air. These conditions are transmitted outward from the receiver as a wave disturbance comprising so-called *condensations* and *rarefactions*. Upon entering the ear, these waves produce the sensation of sound, and the waves themselves are called *sound waves*.

523

Waves can be produced by vibrations other than those of material particles. The current in the antenna circuit of a radio station sets up a magnetic field and an electric field in the region around it. As the current oscillates, these fields continually build up and collapse, and in so doing set up electromagnetic waves which spread outward from the antenna. These waves are not transmitted by motion of air particles but by changes in the magnetic and electrical conditions of space.

Most waves can be classified as either longitudinal or transverse. A *longitudinal* wave is one in which the vibrating particles move forward and backward parallel to the direction in which the wave is propagated. The sound wave produced by the vibrating diaphragm alluded to ahead is longitudinal. In a *transverse* wave, the particles vibrate at right angles to the direction of propagation. The wave moving along the rope previously mentioned is transverse. Electromagnetic waves of all types act as transverse waves.

The progress of any wave involves two distinct motions. The wave itself moves forward with constant speed, which means that the configuration advances equal amounts in equal periods of time. Meanwhile, the particles of the medium that conveys the wave vibrate to and fro in harmonic fashion. Their locations at successive moments depend upon the period, amplitude, and phase of the vibration. These terms have been used in the study of harmonic motion; for convenience they are restated below, together with some others commonly used in wave motion.

The *period* of a vibrating particle is the time in which it completes one vibration, and the *frequency* is the number of vibrations completed per second. The *amplitude* of vibration is the maximum displacement from the undisturbed position. Two particles vibrating with the same frequency have definite *phase relations*. They are *in phase* when they continually pass through corresponding points of their paths at the same times. Otherwise, they are *out of phase*; for the particular condition where they reach their maximum displacements in opposite directions at the same instant, they are in *phase opposition*. The *wave length* is the distance, measured along the direction of propagation, between two points which are in phase on adjacent waves.

320. The Mechanism of Wave Propagation. — The process by which a wave advances will be explained by reference to a mechanical model, Fig. 336, in which a long coiled spring with dis-

tributed small masses represents the medium and the small masses
$A, B, C \ldots$ represent the vibrating particles. The spring is fastened
at the distant end, and A is given harmonic motion along the path
0–1–2–0.

During the time that the end A is moving up to position 1, B
is pulled upward by the spring tension, and proceeds in that direction, as shown in part I of the figure.   Because of its inertia, B continues to move upward when A reverses its direction.   As A moves

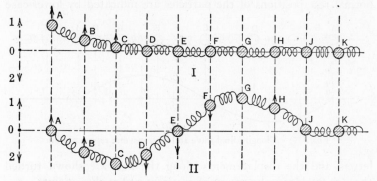

FIG. 336.   Mechanical wave model illustrating a transverse wave

to 2, a downward force acts on B which soon arrests its upward
motion and causes it to move down.   The same behavior is repeated
at the lower end of the path, and it follows that B will have the
same kind of motion as A, but will reach a corresponding point of
the path a little later than A will.   As a consequence of the inertia
of the weights and the elasticity of the spring, similar motion will
be imparted successively to all parts of the spring, and the weights
will reach their maximum displacements in the sequence A, B, C
and so on, causing the wave to advance toward the right.   At the
instant represented in part II of the figure, A has been given a
complete vibration and the wave has advanced to J; the wave has
a crest at G and a trough at C.

The same model will also serve to illustrate the motion of a
longitudinal wave, as represented in Fig. 337.   Motion of A toward
the right compresses the spring and motion toward the left extends
it, giving B the same kind of motion as A, except for a slight lag in
phase.   Similarly, B produces a corresponding motion of C, and so
on.   There results a series of condensations, in which the weights are
close together, separated by rarefactions in which they are further
apart, both of which move to the right and constitute the advancing

wave. In the condensations, the weights are moving in the same direction as the wave, while in the rarefactions they are moving in the opposite direction. At the instant shown in the figure, the wave has advanced to *J*.

In a longitudinal wave, the wave form is not apparent, but may be made so by laying off the displacements of the particles at right angles to the direction in which they actually occur. Such a construction is shown at the bottom of the figure. In this diagram the normal rest positions of the particles are indicated by lower-case

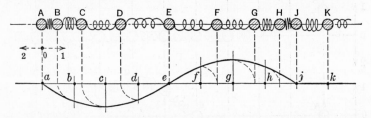

Fig. 337. A longitudinal wave and its transverse representation

letters and the displacements along the axis are shown turned through 90 degrees by means of arcs centered at these points.

From the waves produced with the mechanical wave model, some general inferences may be made. Wave motion evidently is not due to bodily transfer of the medium through which the wave advances. It is caused by vibrations of individual particles over short ranges about normal rest positions, all the particles having the same kind of motion, but with a progressive change of phase along the direction of propagation. Moreover, mechanical wave motion requires that the transmitting medium possess inertia and elasticity; for electromagnetic waves these properties are replaced by their electrical equivalents, inductance and capacitance.

321. Energy Transmission by Waves. — Waves transmit energy along the direction of propagation. This fact can be illustrated by the mechanical model of Figs. 336 and 337 which shows waves progressing to the right. For either type of wave, each section of the spring exerts a force on the weights at its ends, and the weights at the right move in the direction of this force, but those at the left are constrained to move in opposition to it. Each spring section thus *does work on* the weight at the *right* and *has work done upon it* by the weight at the *left* [§ 69], and each weight, in turn, performs a similar action on the adjoining spring sections.

Thus, a continuous transfer of energy takes place toward the right, in the direction of wave travel. In the model described, assuming no energy to be wasted as the wave advances, the amplitude of vibration would be the same for all of the weights. On the other hand, in a wave which spreads out as it advances, such as a circular wave on the surface of water, the amplitude of vibration would diminish as the wave progresses, since the energy is distributed over a larger and larger surface. The energy of a wave may be transformed in various ways; for example, that of a sound wave may be converted into mechanical energy in setting the ear drum into vibration.

When an advancing wave encounters a medium of a different character, some of its energy will be *reflected* back into the initial medium, some will be *transmitted* in the second medium, and the rest will be *absorbed*. For a light wave which impinges upon a sheet of glass, most of the energy is transmitted to the region behind the glass, part being returned by reflection at the surfaces and a small portion being absorbed within the glass itself. Complete absorption occurs when a light wave strikes black velvet, no light being reflected from it or transmitted through it. Usually when the energy of a wave is absorbed it is converted into heat.

322. Equations of Wave Motion. — A relation exists between the frequency of vibration of the source, the velocity of propagation of the wave, and the wave length, that is applicable to wave motion within any medium.

Assume a body which is vibrating at a definite rate, the disturbance thus produced moving away as a wave in the surrounding medium. In the periodic time T, the vibrating body completes one vibration, and the wave meanwhile advances uniformly a distance equal to its wave length λ, whence the velocity of the wave is $V = \lambda/T$. Remembering that the period T is the reciprocal of the frequency f, it follows that the wave velocity is

$$V = f\lambda \tag{203}$$

In this expression, the wave velocity V is determined completely by the properties of the transmitting medium and does not depend upon either the frequency of the source or the wave length. It follows that whenever f changes there must be a corresponding change in λ to satisfy the equation.

To consider the relation between wave propagation and the motion of the particles in the transmitting medium, suppose that a source vibrating with frequency f sets up a wave of amplitude r which moves with velocity V, the particles of the medium executing harmonic motion at right angles to the direction of wave propagation. The displacement of any particle is given at any instant by

$$y = r \sin 2 \pi f\left(t - \frac{x}{V}\right) \qquad (204)$$

In this expression, t is the time reckoned from the instant that the vibrating particle passes through the midposition of its path in a positive direction, and x is the distance of the particular particle from the source along the direction of propagation. By selecting a particular value for t and plotting the values of y for different values of x, a sine wave is obtained which represents a snap shot of the wave in space; if this process is repeated for a slightly greater value of t, it will be found that the whole wave profile has moved away from the source.

To learn how the displacement of a particle of the medium varies from moment to moment, a particular value for x is selected to represent the distance of the particle from the source and y is plotted against t. This also yields a sine curve and represents the harmonic vibration of the particle in the medium with respect to time, the displacement of the particle being given by an equation of the form

$$y = r \sin 2 \pi f t \qquad (205)$$

323. Wave in a Stretched Rope.

— The velocity of a transverse wave in a stretched rope is determined by the mass of the rope per

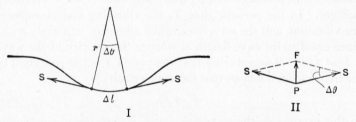

Fig. 338.   Transverse wave in stretched rope

unit length and the force or tension with which the rope is stretched. To show how these quantities are related, suppose a rope stretched horizontally to receive an impulsive blow at one place giving it there a dent having the shape shown in Fig. 338. The displacement will produce a distortional wave which will travel along the rope with some velocity V, substantially retaining the shape of the dent in its forward motion. To keep this dent stationary in space, imagine the rope to be of infinite length and to be carried with the same speed V in the opposite direction. Perhaps the reader will have observed the maintenance of such shapes in the movement of a belt around two pulleys. With this artifice, sections of the rope move continuously around the curve, and the forces acting upon them can be evaluated. This becomes simple if the dent, or a small part of it, is regarded as circular, for the force then becomes the centripetal force of circular motion.

In part I of the figure, the short central section of the dent Δl is considered as a circular arc of radius r subtending an angle $\Delta\theta$ at the center. If this section has a mass Δm, the centripetal force acting upon it is $F = \dfrac{\Delta m V^2}{r}$, and is provided jointly by the forces S,S, each representing the stretching force in the rope. Laying off these forces from a common point P, as in part II of the figure, and noting that $\Delta\theta$ is very small, it follows as a close approximation that $F : S = \Delta l : r$, whence

$$\frac{\Delta m V^2}{r\,S} = \frac{\Delta l}{r} \quad \text{or} \quad S = \frac{\Delta m}{\Delta l}\,V^2$$

Calling the mass per unit length of the rope $\dfrac{\Delta m}{\Delta l} = m_1$, and re-arranging terms, the velocity of the rope, and its equivalent, the velocity of the distortional wave along the rope, will be

$$V = \sqrt{\frac{S}{m_1}} \tag{206}$$

In metric units, S is usually expressed in dynes and m_1 in grams per centimeter; with these units V will be given in centimeters per second.

In British units, it is convenient to use the weight per unit length of the rope $w_1 = m_1 g$, rather than the mass per unit length. The wave velocity in feet per second then becomes

$$V = \sqrt{\frac{S\,g}{w_1}}$$

where the tension S is in pounds, the acceleration due to gravity g is in feet per second per second, and w_1 is in pounds per foot.

As an illustration, suppose a wave to be established in a 40-ft. rope which weighs 5 lb. and which is stretched with a force of 50 lb. The wave velocity will be

$$V = \sqrt{\frac{50 \text{ lb.} \times 32 \text{ ft./sec.}^2}{5 \text{ lb./40 ft.}}} = 113.1 \frac{\text{ft.}}{\text{sec.}}$$

and the time required to travel the length of the rope will be 40 ft. $\div$ 113.1 ft./sec. = 0.354 sec.

324. Electromagnetic Waves. — The velocity of an electromagnetic wave in any medium can be shown to be

$$V = \frac{c}{\sqrt{K\mu}} \tag{207}$$

In this expression K is the dielectric constant of the medium and μ is its permeability. The constant c represents the ratio of the electromagnetic unit of charge (based on electricity in motion) to the electrostatic unit of charge (based on electricity at rest); its value is 3×10^{10} cm. per sec. An electromagnetic wave in a vacuum, for which K and μ are each equal to unity, would thus have the same numerical value for its velocity. It has been found by direct measurement that this figure expresses almost perfectly the velocity of light, which fact led Maxwell to conclude that light consists of electromagnetic waves. It should be mentioned that although $K = 1$ for a vacuum, its value for other media depends upon wave length.

The velocity of light, radio, and other electromagnetic waves is approximately the same in air under normal conditions as in a vacuum. The value 3×10^{10} cm. per sec. or 186,000 mi. per sec. may be used for either air or vacuum without appreciable error for present purposes.

Many kinds of radiations are propagated by electromagnetic waves, their wave length ranges being of the order listed in the accompanying table. These waves are all of the same character and differ only in frequency and wave length.

The Electromagnetic Spectrum

Type of wave	Wave length
Radio............................	above 1000 km. to 10 meters
Short-wave......................	10 meters to 1 meter
Ultra short-wave.................	1 meter to 0.1 cm.
Infra-red........................	0.030 to 0.000076 cm.
Visible light.....................	0.000076 to 0.000040 cm.
Ultra-violet......................	0.000040 to 0.0000013 cm.
X-rays...........................	10^{-6} to 10^{-9} cm.
γ-rays...........................	10^{-8} to 5×10^{-11} cm.

★325. Propagation of Sound. — The longitudinal waves transmitting sound do not pass through a vacuum. This fact can be
demonstrated by operating an electric bell within the chamber of an
air pump and then withdrawing the air; the hammer can be seen
striking the bell but no sound will be heard. The physical medium
required for the propagation of sound may be in the state of a solid,
liquid or gas. Consideration will first be given to propagation
within a liquid, and the analysis will show that the velocity is
determined by the elasticity and density of the medium. The
expression for this velocity is found by comparing the pressure and
velocity of the particles within a condensation with these characteristics of the particles in the undisturbed medium, and evaluating
the force which produces the change of motion.

Fig. 339 pictures a longitudinal wave, represented by vertical
lines, advancing toward the left with a speed V through a liquid

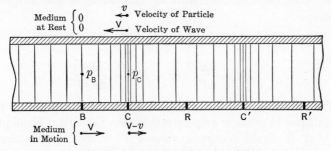

FIG. 339. Longitudinal wave in a fluid

medium. The liquid is assumed to have a constant cross-section.
Rarefactions are shown at R and R', and condensations at C and
C'; at point B just ahead of the foremost condensation the medium
is as yet undisturbed by the wave. Restricting attention to two of
these points, it is evident that the pressure at C is greater than that
at B, since C is at a condensation; the difference between these
pressures may be expressed as $p_C - p_B$. Also, remembering that
in a condensation the vibrating particles are moving in the same
direction as the wave, the medium at C will have some velocity v
toward the left when that at B is at rest.

Imagine now that the liquid as a whole is moving with the same
speed V as the wave but in the opposite direction, so that the rarefactions and condensations remain stationary with respect to the
surroundings. Let t be the time required for the liquid stream
to flow from B to C; in this time interval a certain mass m of liquid

passes B at a speed V and an equal mass passes C at a reduced speed, namely $V-v$, as indicated at the bottom of the figure. Calling the reduction of speed ΔV, it is seen that in time t a mass of liquid m undergoes a speed reduction ΔV; that is, it has a negative acceleration equal to $\Delta V/t$. The reduction in speed may be attributed to the fact that the pressure acting backward upon the liquid at C is greater than the pressure urging it forward at B. Let Δp represent the unbalanced pressure $p_C - p_B$, and A the sectional area of the liquid; then applying equation (31), $F = m\,a$,

$$A\,\Delta p = m\,\frac{\Delta V}{t}$$

The mass m may be evaluated by reference to point B. The volume of liquid passing this point in time t is AVt by equation (92), and hence its mass is $m = AVt\,d$, where d is the density of the undisturbed medium. Substituting this value in the foregoing equation:

$$A\,\Delta p = AVt\,d\,\frac{\Delta V}{t}$$

whence

$$Vd = \frac{\Delta p}{\Delta V} \quad \text{or} \quad V^2 d = \frac{\Delta p}{\Delta V/V}$$

The equation will be modified further by expressing the denominator in terms of volume rather than velocity. The liquid which at B would occupy a volume $V' = AVt$ is compressed by an amount $\Delta V' = A\,t\,\Delta V$ upon reaching C. In consequence $\frac{\Delta V'}{V'} = \frac{A\,t\,\Delta V}{AVt} = \frac{\Delta V}{V}$, and

$$V^2 d = \frac{\Delta p}{\Delta V'/V'} = E$$

where E is the bulk modulus of elasticity of the liquid [§ 97]. Rearranging terms, the speed of the liquid, and consequently that of the wave, is

$$V = \sqrt{\frac{E}{d}} \tag{208}$$

In metric units, E is expressed in dynes per square centimeter and d in grams per cubic centimeter; then V will be in centimeters per second.

The foregoing treatment may also be applied to the transmission of sound along a solid rod. The result will be the same as that just obtained, except that E is Young's modulus of the medium rather than its bulk modulus.

326. Velocity of Sound in Gases. — The method used in the preceding section for finding the velocity of a sound wave in a liquid which resulted in the equation $V = \sqrt{\dfrac{E}{d}}$ can also be used when the medium is gaseous. In order to interpret the elastic modulus E, it becomes necessary to inquire how the volume V' of the gas is affected by changes in the pressure p. If the temperature remained constant during compression and expansion, then in accordance with Boyle's Law [§ 128], a change of pressure Δp would cause a change of volume $\Delta V'$ such that

$$pV' = (p + \Delta p)(V' - \Delta V')$$

Neglecting the small $\Delta p \, \Delta V'$ product, it would follow that $p \, \Delta V' = V' \Delta p$, or $p = \dfrac{\Delta p}{\Delta V'/V'} = E$. Hence if the compressions and expansions were isothermal the velocity of the wave would be $V = \sqrt{p/d}$.

In the passage of a sound wave, the medium undergoes compression and expansion at a rapid rate, usually several hundreds of times each second. For gaseous media, it has been found that the heat generated during compression does not escape quickly enough to maintain uniform temperature, and that the compressions and expansions should be considered adiabatic rather than isothermal. In an adiabatic process, the pressure change Δp corresponding to a given volume change $\Delta V'$ is γ times as great as for an isothermal process, γ representing the ratio c_p/c_v. [§ 168]. Hence, for such a process

$$\frac{\Delta p}{p} = \gamma \frac{\Delta V'}{V'}$$

and the modulus of elasticity E in equation (208) should be replaced by $\gamma \, p$. Consequently the velocity of a sound wave in gases is

$$V = \sqrt{\frac{\gamma \, p}{d}} \tag{209}$$

the units being the same as in equation (208). In air under normal pressure and at a temperature of $0°$ C., using γ as 1.40 and the other values as given in Chapter XIII, sound is found to travel at a velocity

$$V = \sqrt{1.40 \times 1{,}013{,}000 \frac{\text{dynes}}{\text{cm.}^2} \div 0.001293 \frac{\text{gm.}}{\text{cm.}^3}} = 33{,}130 \text{ cm./sec.}$$

The velocity of sound in the atmosphere is unaffected by changes in the barometric pressure because the density is changed in the same proportion, thereby leaving the ratio p/d unchanged. Changes in the temperature of the atmosphere, however, affect the density without influencing the pressure, and hence cause a change in the velocity of the wave. An inspection of the General Gas Law, equation (110), shows that the density of a gas varies inversely with its absolute temperature T. From this fact, and from equation (209), it follows that $V \propto \sqrt{T}$. Consequently, for two conditions 1 and 2, the ratio of the velocities of sound becomes

$$\frac{V_1}{V_2} = \sqrt{\frac{T_1}{T_2}} \qquad (210)$$

Some values of sound velocity in various media are given in the following table:

Velocity of Sound

	Tempera- ture ° C.	Velocity	
		meters per sec.	ft. per sec.
Air, normal pressure........	0	331.3	1,087
Aluminum...............	—	5100	16,700
Copper..................	—	3970	13,000
Hydrogen, normal pressure	0	1286	4,220
Iron and steel............	—	4900 to 5100	16,000 to 16,700
Lead...................	—	1230	4,040
Water..................	15	1450	4,760

For calculations in which the effect of temperature is of no interest, the velocity of sound in air may be taken in round numbers as 1100 ft. per sec.

★327. Water Waves. — In surface waves, like those observed on water, the particles transmitting the disturbance move longitudinally as well as transversely. The velocity of propagation depends upon the gravitational force on the liquid and upon its surface tension; it can be shown by extended analysis that the equation for the wave velocity when the liquid is deep is

$$V = \sqrt{\frac{g\lambda}{2\pi} + \frac{2\pi T}{\lambda d}}$$

where g is the acceleration due to gravity, T is the surface tension, d is the density of the liquid, and λ is the wave length. In shallow liquids the wave velocity is found to depend upon the depth h rather than the wave length λ, and is expressed by the equation

$$V = \sqrt{gh}$$

328. Wave-front Construction; Huygens' Principle. — A wave front is a surface of which all points are vibrating in phase. Fig. 340 illustrates a wave spreading outward from a source S, and the line W represents a wave front connecting particles of the medium which are momentarily at their greatest distances in a positive direction from the undisturbed positions. In a homogeneous medium the wave front from a point disturbance is spherical; however, at considerable distances from the source, small portions of such a wave front may be regarded as plane.

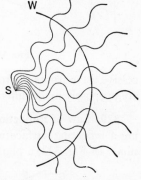

Fig. 340. Illustrating a wave front

By studying the changes in wave front which occur as a wave advances, it is possible to predict the effects that will be produced when a wave encounters an obstruction or when it is reflected or refracted. This study is greatly assisted by use of a principle accredited to the Dutch scientist, Christian Huygens (1629–1695).

Huygens' Principle states that every point on a wave front acts as though it were itself a center of disturbance, sending out little wavelets of its own, always away from the source, the collective effect of which constitutes a new wave front. Starting with a wave front in any given position, these wavelets may be represented by arcs of equal radius drawn from various points on the wave front as centers, the radius representing the distance the wavelets would advance in some specified time. A line or surface tangent to these arcs on the side toward which the wave is advancing shows the new shape and location of the wave front at the end of the time interval selected.

This construction is applied in part I of Fig. 341 to a plane wave front P and to a spherical wave front S, both advancing toward the right to new positions at P_1 and S_1 respectively.   The progression of a wave around an obstruction is illustrated in part II of the figure.   The same procedure is followed in constructing the suc-

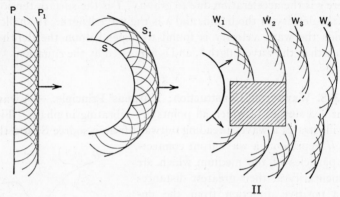

FIG. 341.   Huygens' construction

cessive wave fronts W_1 to W_4, but the time intervals between them are purposely made different.

329. Law of Reflection. — The behavior of a wave upon striking a reflecting surface will be determined by Huygens' construction.   In Fig. 342, a plane wave front represented in cross-section

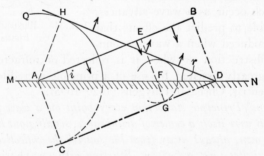

FIG. 342.   Reflection of plane wave at plane surface

by the line AB is shown impinging upon the surface MN, through which it cannot penetrate. If this surface had been absent, the wave would have advanced without change in direction, and in a certain time interval would have reached the position CD.   The presence of the reflecting surface, however, causes a change in the direction of the wave front. In the particular time interval, different points on the wave front move as follows: B advances directly to D; A cannot move to C and travels an equal distance above the surface to some point on the arc CQ of radius AC; and any other point E advances without obstruction to F and, being unable to continue to G, travels an equal distance to some point on the arc of radius FG. The line DH tangent to the arcs is a cross-section of the wave front at the end of the specified time, the wave being reflected back into the region above the surface MN.

The line AB represents the *incident* wave front and DH represents the *reflected* wave front. The angles i and r that these wave fronts make with the reflecting surface are called the angles of incidence and of reflection respectively. To show the relation between these angles, draw the radius AH to the point of tangency H. Since $BD = AC = AH$, the right triangles ADH and DAB are equal, and consequently the angles i and r are equal. These angles are also coplanar, since the points A, B, D, and H lie in the same plane. These facts are embodied in the *law of reflection*, which states that *when a wave incident upon a plane surface is reflected, the angles of incidence and of reflection are equal, and lie in the same plane.*

330. Law of Refraction. — A wave which enters another medium obliquely will undergo an abrupt change in direction if the velocity of the wave in the second medium is different from that in

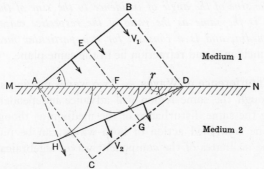

FIG. 343. Refraction of plane wave at plane surface

the first. This phenomenon is called *refraction*. In Fig. 343, the incident wave front AB, moving with velocity V_1 in medium 1, encounters the interface MN at an angle of incidence i. Here it is partly reflected back into medium 1 and partly transmitted

through medium 2. Consider the transmitted portion and suppose
its velocity to be V_2. In the time required for B on the wave front
to advance a distance BD to the interface at D in the first medium,
point A does not move an equal distance AC, but moves a distance
$(V_2/V_1) \times AC = AH$ in the second medium to some point on the
arc centered at A. Any other point E advances to F in the first
medium and then moves a distance $(V_2/V_1) \times FG$ in the second
medium to some point on the arc centered at F. The line DH
drawn tangent to these arcs represents the refracted wave front
at the end of this time interval, and the angle r which it makes with
the interface is called the *angle of refraction*.

It was discovered by Willebrod Snell (1591–1626), Dutch
astronomer and mathematician, that the ratio $\sin i / \sin r$ is constant for given media. To find the relation between these angles
draw the radius AH to the point of tangency H, and note that
$\sin i = BD/AD$ and $\sin r = AH/AD$. Consequently

$$\frac{\sin i}{\sin r} = \frac{BD}{AH} = \frac{BD}{(V_2/V_1)BD}$$

or

$$\frac{\sin i}{\sin r} = \frac{V_1}{V_2} \tag{211}$$

This relation expresses the *law of refraction*, which states that
*when a wave travels obliquely from one medium into another, the
ratio of the sine of the angle of incidence to the sine of the angle of
refraction is the same as the ratio of the respective wave velocities
in these media, and is a constant for two particular media.* The
angles of incidence and refraction lie in the same plane.

331. Interference of Waves. — Two waves moving simultaneously through the same region will advance independently, each
producing the same disturbance of the medium as though it were
alone. The combined action of both waves can be pictured by
adding the ordinates of the component waves algebraically, point
by point.

Two waves of the *same frequency, in phase with each other,*
and moving in the *same direction,* produce *reenforcement.* This
result is shown in part I of Fig. 344, in which the individual waves
are represented by A and B. The resultant wave R is in phase
with the component waves and has an amplitude equal to the sum
of their amplitudes.

Two waves of the *same frequency*, *in phase opposition*, and moving in the *same direction*, produce *destructive interference*; if further they have *equal amplitudes*, the result is a complete *annulment*. An annulment is represented in part II of Fig. 344, the

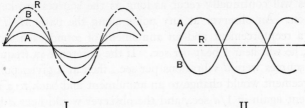

I   II

Fig. 344.   Reenforcement and annulment of waves

resultant R of the individual waves A and B being zero at all points.   In the wave-front constructions in Figs. 342 and 343 the multiplicity of wavelets, typified by the two arcs in each diagram, also interfere with each other, and it can be shown that these wavelets annul one another except at the outermost points where the envelope representing the new position of the wave front is located.

Two waves of *slightly different frequency* produce a type of *pulsating interference* which is particularly noticeable with sound

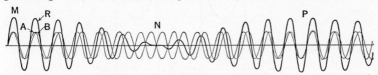

Fig. 345.   Interference producing beats

waves.   The resulting sound is alternately loud and soft, giving pulses or throbs which are spoken of as *beats*.   The effect is most pronounced when the individual waves have equal amplitude. Suppose two such waves A and B to originate from vibrating sources at M in Fig. 345, and let the frequency of the source generating A be 1 vibration per sec. greater than that of B.   Each source sets up a train of waves; these are indicated in the figure at a particular instant by their transverse representations and their resultant is represented by the wave R.   At the instant shown, the sources are vibrating in phase, and the waves produce reenforcement at M and P and an annulment at N.   At an instant $\frac{1}{2}$ sec. later, the sources will be in phase opposition, and the waves A and B will be displaced with respect to each other by one-half wave length from the positions shown, producing annulments at M and P and a reenforcement at N. At another instant $\frac{1}{2}$ sec. later still, the sources will once more vibrate in phase, and the relative positions of the waves will again be as shown in the figure. These changes will continually recur as long as the sources are kept in vibration. An observer at any point along the path MNP will notice a reenforcement and an annulment of sound each second, that is, he will hear 1 beat per sec. If the difference in frequency of the sources were d vibrations per sec., then at a given point, a reenforcement would change to an annulment and back to a reen-forcement again in $1/d$ sec., and the observer would hear d beats per sec.

332. Stationary Waves. — Two waves of *equal frequency and amplitude*, moving in *opposite directions* through the same medium, produce a *stationary* or *standing* wave. Such a wave has stationary

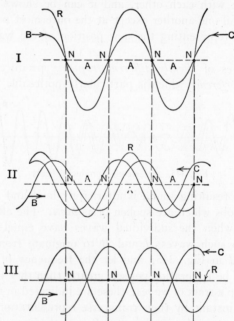

Fig. 346.   Location of fixed nodes in stationary wave

nodes, or points of zero displacement, with intermediate *antinodes* at which the displacement varies between its widest limits. In Fig. 346, B and C represent two such waves and R is their resultant.

In part I of the figure, the component waves coincide, yielding a resultant of double amplitude. In part II, representing the situation $\frac{1}{8}$ of a period later, both B and C have advanced $\frac{1}{8}$ wave length in their respective directions; and in part III, for an instant $\frac{1}{8}$ period later still, a similar advance has occurred, bringing the component waves into opposition. As the waves progress, the nodes N of the resultant remain fixed in space $\frac{1}{2}$ wave length apart, and the intervening antinodes A undergo a maximum variation of displacement.

The production of stationary waves can be demonstrated with a rope that is fastened to a wall at one end and moved transversely with appropriate frequency at the other end. The

FIG. 347.   Stationary wave in rope

outgoing waves are reflected at the wall with little reduction of amplitude, and consequently the two wave trains set up a stationary wave in the rope. Fig. 347 illustrates the appearance when the rope vibrates in three segments with nodes at N, the rope whipping back and forth at the antinodes A.

In an experiment devised by Melde a string is fastened to one end of a tuning fork that is kept vibrating electrically, say at 26.4 vibrations per sec. Assuming that the string is 90 cm. long and has a mass of 0.1 gm., find the stretching force that should be applied to the string when it extends along the direction of the prong so that the string will form 3 segments. The length of each segment is 30 cm., the wave length is 60 cm., and consequently the velocity of propagation is $264 \times 60 = 15{,}840$ cm. per sec. The required stretching force is found by equation (206) to be

$$S = m_1 V^2 = \frac{0.1 \text{ gm.}}{90 \text{ cm.}} \times \left(15{,}840 \frac{\text{cm.}}{\text{sec.}}\right)^2 = 279{,}000 \text{ dynes} = 285 \text{ gm.}$$

Another interesting way in which the production of stationary waves can be illustrated makes use of a flat dish with mercury and a tuning fork with a stylus on each prong. When the fork is set into vibration and the prongs are brought in contact with the surface, waves will proceed from these points of contact, as represented by the concentric circles about them at the black dots in Fig. 348, the full lines representing the crests and the dotted ones representing the troughs, at some particular instant. At points where full lines intersect or dotted lines intersect, the waves from the two sources meet in phase, and the disturbance of the surface by one source is reenforced by that of the other. Between these points, however, are intersections of full lines with dotted lines; these represent the meeting of a crest from one source with a trough from the other and are, therefore, points where destructive interference occurs. The surface of the mercury is thus divided

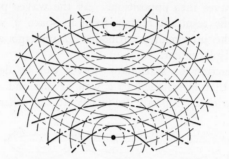

FIG. 348.   Interference pattern on mercury surface

into regions of maximum disturbance (shown by the heavy lines), separated by lanes where the surface remains almost perfectly at rest.

PROBLEMS

The numerical values of the moduli of elasticity and of densities of materials will be found in §§ 98, 111, and 131.

1. A tuning fork vibrates 200 times a second, and sets up a wave which travels outward with a speed of 1100 ft. per sec. Find the period and wave length of the wave.
2. A steel wire 50 cm. long, having a total mass of 0.1 gm., is stretched with a force of 12,000,000 dynes. The wire is struck a sudden blow near one end. Compute the velocity of the resulting transverse wave in the wire.
3. A string 150 yd. long weighs 2.5 oz. Determine the velocity of a transverse wave in this string when it is stretched with a force of 2 lb.
4. A stretching force of 20 lb. is applied to a long wire which weighs 0.003 lb. per foot of length. With what frequency should the wire be vibrated in order to set up a traveling wave in it having a wave length of 4 ft.?
5. If a wire 3 ft. long which weighs 0.0014 lb. is stretched between two points, with what force must the wire be pulled in order that a transverse wave set up in it may travel from one end to the other in 0.004 sec.?
6. The dielectric constant of paraffin is 2.10 for electromagnetic waves of great wave length. Find the velocity of such waves in paraffin, taking the permeability of this material as unity.
7. Compute the length of wave used in broadcasting a radio program at a frequency of 660 kilocycles per sec.

*8. A longitudinal wave sent by a ship to the bottom of the ocean returns after a lapse of 2.64 sec. Considering the elasticity of sea water to be the same as for pure water, calculate the depth of the ocean at this point.

*9. Compute the velocity of propagation of a sound wave in water.

*10. What time will be required for the transmission of a sound wave from end to end of a brass rod 1 meter long? Take 8.5 as the specific gravity of brass.

11. Compute the velocity of sound in hydrogen under normal conditions of temperature and pressure.

12. The velocity of sound in air at 1000° C. was found by measurement to be 700 meters per sec. How much does this result differ from the computed value?

*13. A steel pipe 100 yd. long is struck at one end, and sound waves travel to an observer at the other end both along the pipe and through the air. What is the time interval between the two sounds heard by the observer? Take the specific gravity of steel to be 7.8.

14. A road runs north 1 mi. from A to B and 1.5 mi. northeast from B to C. Clocks at B and C strike the hour of one at the same instant. What time interval will elapse between the two sounds as heard by an observer at A?

15. Researches are being made on acoustic altimeters for determining the altitude of an airplane from measurements of the time taken for sound to travel from the plane to earth and back. Suppose that in effecting a landing in a fog, such a time interval is 0.12 sec., how high is the airplane at the time?

16. Find the increase in velocity of sound in the atmosphere corresponding to a temperature rise from 0° to 20° C.

17. A V-shaped wave front is established by the bow of a boat when moving through the water. If the two portions of the wave front are 20° apart when the boat is traveling at 15 mi. per hr., compute the speed of the water waves.

18. A light wave traveling in air falls upon a glass plate, making an angle of incidence of 45°. If the angle of refraction is 29°, find the velocity of light in the glass.

19. A light wave traveling in air impinges on an amber plate making an angle of incidence of 50°. If the angle of refraction is 30°, find the velocity of light in the amber.

20. A rope weighing 2 oz. per ft. is fastened to a support at one end, and to the other end is tied another rope weighing 0.5 oz. per ft. The ropes are subjected to a tension of 625 lb. and the lighter one is set into vibration with a frequency of 5 vibrations per sec. There will be three distinct waves: one which advances toward the knot, another which is reflected back at the knot into the lighter rope, and the third which is transmitted onward into the heavier rope. Find the frequency, velocity, and wave length of each.

21. Three tuning forks, A, B and C, produce beats when sounded as follows: B and C make 7 beats per sec., and A and C make 8 beats per sec. It can be observed that fork B gives a sound a half tone higher than A, which means that the frequency of B is 5.9 per cent higher than that of A. Find the frequencies of the three forks on the basis that vibration rates lower than 20 are inaudible.

22. Two waves, produced by bodies making 4 vibrations per sec., travel in opposite directions in a rope weighing 0.005 lb. per ft., which

544 WAVE MOTION

is subjected to a stretching force of 5.6 lb. How far apart are the nodes in the resulting stationary wave?

23. Two waves of equal amplitude and set up by pulses with a frequency of 1000 per sec. are moving in opposite directions in a string which has a length of 5 meters and a mass of 2.5 gm. With what force must the string be stretched in order that the nodes in the resulting stationary wave shall be 3.5 cm. apart?

24. A specially constructed incandescent lamp has a U-shaped tungsten filament, each side of the U being 15 cm. long. When operated on a 60-cycle circuit, each side was observed to vibrate in two loops. (a) What is the frequency of vibration? (b) What is the stretching force on the filament if its diameter is 0.0044 cm.? The specific gravity of tungsten is 19.

CHAPTER XXXI

SOUND PRODUCTION

333. Characteristics of Sound. — The term sound is used in two senses: subjectively, it signifies the auditory sensation experienced by the ear, and objectively, it signifies the vibratory motion which gives rise to that sensation. It is used in the latter sense in Acoustics. This subject deals with the motion of vibrating bodies, the production and propagation of sound waves in different media, and the effect of discontinuities in the media. Some of these topics which are common to sound, light, and other wave disturbances are considered in the preceding chapter on Wave Motion; others, together with some of their applications, are discussed in the present and in the following chapter.

A variety of terms is employed in ordinary language to convey impressions of sounds; these include howl, whistle, squeal, rustle, rumble, and hum. Most of these would be classed as *noises*, in contrast with those that are spoken of as musical *tones*. The distinction is based largely upon the regularity of vibration of the source and the degree of damping, as well as the ability of the ear to recognize components that have a musical sequence. A stick when dropped upon a table top merely makes a noise, but when a number of sticks of appropriate lengths are dropped upon the table in suitable order the effect of musical tones may be produced. The complicated sounds of speech are formed by grouping the more or less sustained tones of vowels and the impulsive launching and quenching of these tones by the consonants.

The ear can distinguish tones that differ in *pitch*, in *loudness*, and in *quality*. Each of these characteristics is associated with one of the properties of the sounding body or of the waves which it produces. Thus, *pitch is determined by the frequency of vibration, loudness by the intensity of the sound, and quality by the nature of the vibrations as revealed by the wave shape*. Fig. 349 shows several curves depicting both the shapes of sound waves and the characteristics of the vibrations which produce them. The sine curves *A* and *B* differ in frequency, *B* producing the tone of higher pitch.

Curves A and C differ only in amplitude, A producing the louder sound; with the amplitude of A twice as great as C, the sound will have 4 times the intensity of the latter, although the loudness sensation will not increase in the same proportion. Curves A and D differ in shape, D having some components of higher frequency that are not present in A; the curves represent sounds of different quality.

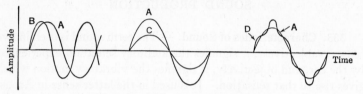

Fig. 349. Differences in sound waves

The pitch of a tone is directly proportional to the number of condensations and rarefactions received per second, which in turn is determined by the vibration frequency of the sounding source. This relationship can be shown experimentally by means of a siren consisting of a disk with regularly-spaced holes through which air is blown gently. As the disk revolves the air stream is interrupted, and the resulting puffs set up condensations and rarefactions in the medium, which are received by the ear. The rise in pitch with increased speed of the disk can be exhibited strikingly in this manner.

334. Intensity of Sound. — *The intensity of a sound is the time rate of transfer of vibratory energy per unit of sectional area of the sound wave.* To show that this intensity is dependent upon the amplitude and frequency of vibration of the sound, consider a plane wave in which the vibrating particles have harmonic motion, and ascertain the energy of a layer of the medium that is thin enough so that all of the particles in it may be assumed to have equal displacements. Assume a layer of thickness x and of unit area, and let the density of the medium be d; then the mass of this volume of the medium will be $m = xd$. Taking f to be the frequency of the vibrating particles and v to be their greatest velocity [§ 86], it follows that the maximum kinetic energy of the portion of the medium under consideration is

$$KE = \tfrac{1}{2}\, m\, v^2 = \frac{x\, d}{2}\, (2\pi f r)^2$$

The energy of the layer will all be of kinetic form as the particles sweep through their equilibrium positions and all of potential form when they have their maximum displacements r; at other times they will have some of each kind of energy, but the total will always be as just expressed if losses are neglected. In consequence, the total energy per unit volume of the medium is

$$\frac{KE}{x \times 1} = 2\pi^2 f^2 r^2 d \tag{212}$$

and may be termed the *energy density* of the wave. When metric units are employed this equation will give the energy in ergs per cubic centimeter. Taking the velocity of wave propagation as V cm. per sec., the time rate of transmission of energy per unit of area of the wave front will be V times the foregoing energy density, and this product is a measure of the physical intensity of the sound wave. Therefore, the *intensity* of the sound in ergs per second per square centimeter is

$$I = 2\pi^2 V f^2 r^2 d \tag{213}$$

This result shows that the intensity of a sound in a given medium is proportional to the square of the frequency of vibration as well as the square of the amplitude.

Equation (212) for energy density applies to a plane wave or to a spherical wave at a great distance from its source. At any distance from a point source, the energy density in the wave will vary inversely as the square of that distance [§ 189], consequently it may be concluded that the amplitude of vibration r will vary inversely as the distance from that source.

As a sound wave advances, variations in pressure occur at all points in the transmitting medium. The greater the pressure variations, the more intense the sound wave will be, and it can be shown that the intensity is proportional to the square of the pressure variation regardless of the frequency. Thus, by measuring pressure changes, the intensities of sounds having different frequencies may be compared directly, and instruments which make such measurements are preferred to those that measure amplitude.

335. Quality of Sound. — The tones produced by tuning forks have wave shapes approximating the sine waves A, B and C in Fig. 349 and are often referred to as pure tones. The tones produced by most sources can be represented by composite waves, in which the sound of lowest pitch, the fundamental, is accompanied by several overtones having frequencies 2, 3, 4, $\cdots$ n times that of the fundamental. Hermann L. F. Helmholtz (1821–1894),

German physiologist and physicist, showed that *the quality of a tone depends upon the number of overtones present, and upon their frequencies and intensities relative to the fundamental.* It is this characteristic that distinguishes tones of like pitch and loudness when sounded on different types of musical instruments.

It is possible to produce a tone of any desired quality by combining pure tones in suitable proportions. For example, the various vowel sounds, which are known to have complicated wave forms, have been duplicated by Professor D. C. Miller by combining the pure tones of particular organ pipes that were sounded together. Fig. 350 represents the compounding of three sine curves having frequencies of 100, 300 and 500 per sec., the resultant curve at the bottom being obtained by adding the ordinates point by point along the time axis. The resultant can also be expressed as the sum of three terms, each having the form given by equation (205); that is:

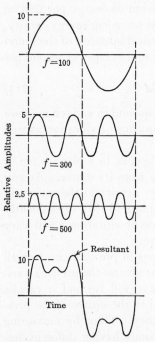

FIG. 350. Synthesis of wave shapes

$$y = 10 \sin (2\pi100\,t) + 5 \sin (2\pi300\,t) + 2.5 \sin (2\pi500\,t)$$

in which the coefficients 10, 5, and 2.5 represent the relative amplitudes of the component waves, and y is the instantaneous displacement of the resultant at any time t reckoned from the origin.

The reverse process, namely that of resolving a sound wave into its components, can also be carried out. Curves of sound wave shapes are obtained experimentally in several ways [§ 346] and measured. A mathematical analysis for determining the relative amplitudes and phases of the component pure tones is based upon a general principle stated by Jean B. J. Fourier (1768–1830), a French mathematician, to the effect that any periodic function can be represented by a trigonometric series, the terms of which involve frequencies that are integrally related to that of the original function. By Fourier's analysis, any periodic wave form can be resolved mathematically into component sine curves, of various amplitudes and phases, and having frequencies in the proportion 1, 2, 3, $\cdots$ n. There are several types of machines patterned after the planimeter that enable one to determine the sinusoidal components of complicated wave shapes; these are called *harmonic analyzers*.

336. Vibrating Strings. — The bowing of a string that is under tension sets up disturbances which travel to the ends of the string and are there reflected back again. At either end the incident and reflected waves have the same frequency and essentially the same amplitude and, since they move in opposite directions, establish a stationary wave in that portion of the string, forming nodes at intervals of one-half wave length from that end. The same effect is produced at the other end of the string. Since the reflected waves travel from end to end of the string repeatedly, the nodes produced by reflection from both ends will coincide only for definite wave lengths. If the string were set vibrating with a multitude of frequencies at the same time, most of these vibrations would annul one another, and only a few would persist. These are called *free vibrations;* they are the ones for which the length of the string is an integral number of half wave lengths.

The free vibrations of a string are transverse and set up condensations and rarefactions in the surrounding air which proceed away from the string as a longitudinal sound wave. The pitch of the resulting tone is the same as the frequency of vibration of the string.

The simplest mode of vibration of a string is that for which the ends of the string are the only nodal points, and the center is the

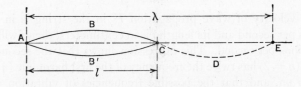

FIG. 351.   Relation between string length and wave length

only antinode. This condition, producing the *fundamental* tone of the string, is depicted in Fig. 351. Herein $ABCDE$ represents a sine wave of length λ, and AC represents the string of length l. During its vibration, the string travels periodically from its extreme upper position ABC to its extreme lower position $AB'C$, and forms a single loop which can be observed easily as a shadowy zone. Thus, for the fundamental mode of vibration the string forms one loop and its length is a half wave length.

The string may also vibrate at particular higher frequencies, depending upon the number of nodes between its ends. Fig. 352 illustrates the simpler modes of vibration, the string vibrating in one, two and three loops respectively. The corresponding tones are called *harmonics*; for the conditions shown they are known as the first, second and third harmonics. In general, if the string of

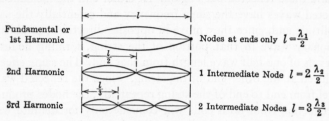

FIG. 352.   Harmonic vibrations of a string

length l vibrates in n loops, it will sound its nth harmonic and the wave length of that harmonic will be

$$\lambda = \frac{2l}{n} \qquad (214)$$

The frequency of vibration of the string is obtained by combining this expression with equation (203) for the velocity of wave propagation, namely $V = f\lambda$, where f is the frequency of vibration. Thus, the frequency of a vibrating string is

$$f = \frac{V}{\lambda} = \frac{nV}{2l} \qquad (215)$$

If the velocity of wave propagation V in the string is in centimeters per second and its length l is in centimeters, then f will be in vibrations per second. This expression shows that the second harmonic ($n = 2$) has twice the frequency of the first harmonic ($n = 1$), and so on, and that the possible frequencies of vibration of the string are proportional to the integers 1, 2, 3, 4, and so on.

To express the vibration rate of a string in terms of its physical constants, the foregoing equation may be combined with equation (206). Thus, the frequency in vibrations per second becomes

$$f = \frac{n}{2l}\sqrt{\frac{S}{m_1}} \qquad (216)$$

where n is the number of the harmonic (also the number of loops in the string of length l cm.), S is the stretching force of the string in dynes, and m_1 is the mass of the string per unit of length in grams per centimeter.

To illustrate the application of the foregoing expression, determine the proper tension of the A-string of a violin to give it a fundamental vibration rate of 440 per sec. The string is 32.7 cm. in length, 0.0523 cm. in diameter, and its density (aluminum-covered steel) is 3.5 gm./cm.³. Putting $m_1 = \pi r^2 d$ in equation (216), the stretching force becomes $S = 4\pi d(l r f)^2 = 12.57 \times 3.5(32.7 \times 0.02615 \times 440)^2 = 62.3 \times 10^5$ dynes $= 6.36$ kg.

Experimental verification of equation (216) can be carried out with a sonometer, which consists of a string mounted over a sounding board and rigidly fastened at one end. The other end of the string passes over a pulley and carries a weight to put the string in tension. By bowing the string at chosen places and by touching it lightly at appropriate points, the string can be set into vibration in a number of ways as illustrated by Fig. 352. The stretching force can be varied by altering the weight, and the length can be varied by shifting the movable bridges on which the string rests.

337. Vibration of Rods and Plates. — In order to set up a *longitudinal* vibration in a solid rod, it is stroked lengthwise with a small rosined pad. As a result, free vibrations will be produced, the possible modes of vibration depending upon the manner in which the rod is supported.

When the rod is supported at one end, it will vibrate in its fundamental mode with a node at that end and an antinode at the other. This longitudinal vibration is shown at the top of Fig. 353 in the usual transverse fashion. In this case the rod forms a half loop and the wave length extends over four rod lengths or $4l$. To obtain the second harmonic, the support of the rod must be changed

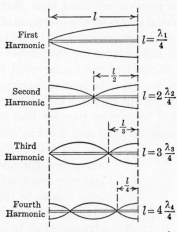

FIG. 353. Longitudinal vibration of a rod

to the midpoint, as shown in the second diagram of the figure. The rod then forms two half loops and the wave length is equal to two full loops or $2l$.   The remaining diagrams show the rod supported still differently, so as to form three half loops and four half loops, yielding the third and fourth harmonics respectively.   In general, if there are n loops, the wave length of the vibration is $\lambda = \dfrac{2l}{n}$. Theory shows that this result is true only when the wave length is large in comparison with the thickness or width of the rod.   The frequency of longitudinal vibrations in the rod will be given with the aid of equation (208) as

$$f = \frac{V}{\lambda} = \frac{n}{2l}\sqrt{\frac{E}{d}} \tag{217}$$

where E is Young's modulus of elasticity of the rod in dynes per square centimeter and d is its density in grams per cubic centimeter.   This equation applies to a rod fixed at both ends as well as to one which is fixed at one end only.   A rod fixed at both ends will have nodes at those points, while a rod fixed at one end only will have a node there and an antinode at the free end; in both cases they will vibrate in their fundamental modes.   Either rod may vibrate with one or more additional nodes to produce overtones. A rod fixed at one end can give forth only the odd harmonics.

Consideration of *transverse* vibrations in a straight rod or bar is more complicated than that of longitudinal vibrations.   The nodal points for the overtones of the fundamental transverse vibration are not so regularly located as in the lower diagram of Fig. 353, in consequence the frequencies of these overtones are not integral multiples of the fundamental tone.   Assume a rod to have two nodes and to be bent at the center.   As the bending progresses, the nodes will approach each other, and in the final U-shape the nodes will be so close together that the rod vibrates practically as two separate bars, each fixed at one end.   Fig. 354 illustrates such a

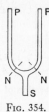

bent bar with a stem attached to the center to form a *tuning fork*, the nodal points being indicated by NN. Transverse motions of the prongs PP cause an up-and-down motion in the stem S, and this motion can be arranged to impart vibration to a sounding board or to a column of air to intensify the sound produced by the fork.   Tuning forks are usually made of steel or of magnesium.

Fig. 354.
Tuning fork

The vibrations of plates can be investigated experimentally by supporting them horizontally at the center or edge, sprinkling fine sand upon them, and setting them into vibration by mechanical or electrical means. The sand particles will hop about and accumulate in places of least motion, thus indicating a series of nodal lines. Fig. 355 shows photographs of some patterns of such lines formed on plates clamped at the center. A great many modes of vibration are possible, depending upon the manner of supporting the plate and of setting it into vibration. The diaphragms of telephone transmitters and receivers can be tested similarly.

A bell may be regarded as a combination of a plate and a cylinder, with relatively more metal near the center. Several overtones

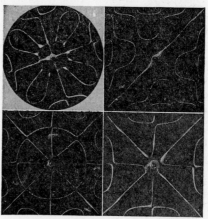

FIG. 355. Nodal lines of plates

accompany the fundamental tone of a bell when it is struck, and it is the aim of bell-founders to attain certain relationships between the frequencies of the principal overtones.

338. Vibrations of Air Columns. — Disturbances in air or other gaseous media are propagated as condensations and rarefactions in all directions in open space. When the medium has the form of a column within a rigid tube, a disturbance produced at one end travels to the other end, is there reflected, travels back to the initial end, is reflected again, and so on. Stationary waves are set up in the gaseous column and one or more nodal points are established within the tube. Fig. 356 illustrates how an air column can be placed in vibration by a jet of air impinging against one side of the tube at (*a*). The condensation so produced travels down the tube, is reflected, and reaches the upper end again; there it pushes the air jet aside as shown at (*b*),

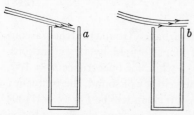

FIG. 356. Setting an air column into vibration

and as a consequence, a rarefaction starts down the tube. This is reflected at the bottom and retraces its path; upon arrival of the rarefaction at the top of the tube, the condition represented at (a) is restored. This process is repeated over and over again. The closed end of the tube becomes a node, the open end becomes an antinode, and the tube length constitutes a quarter wave length for the fundamental mode of vibration. A somewhat similar behavior is observed for a tube open at both ends; in this case a condensation is reflected as a rarefaction and both open ends become antinodes. With one nodal point between these ends, the air column will vibrate in its fundamental manner, and the tube length constitutes a half wave length.

Some overtones produced by air columns and the relation between the wave length λ and the length l of the column are indi-

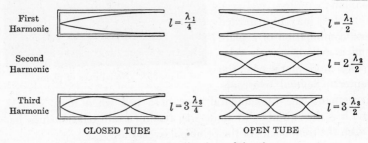

CLOSED TUBE   OPEN TUBE

FIG. 357. Harmonic vibrations of air columns

cated in Fig. 357. The frequencies of the various harmonics are given by the following expression:

$$f = \frac{V}{\lambda} = \frac{nV}{2l} \qquad (218)$$

where V is the velocity of the disturbance (sound) in the gaseous medium and n is the number of loops formed by the vibrations. For closed tubes $n = \frac{1}{2}, \frac{3}{2}, \frac{5}{2}, \cdots$, while for open tubes $n = 1, 2, 3, \cdots$ Taking 1100 ft./sec. as the velocity of sound, the frequency of the fundamental tone of a tube 8 ft. long will be $f = (\frac{1}{2} \times 1100) \div (2 \times 8) = 34.4$ vibrations per sec. when closed and $f = (1 \times 1100) \div (2 \times 8) = 68.8$ vibrations per sec. when open.

Equation (218) is not quite correct owing to the fact that reflection does not occur exactly in the plane of the open end but somewhat beyond it; with cylindrical tubes the plane of reflection may be taken as lying outside the tube by about 0.6 times the radius of the tube, assuming this radius to be small in comparison with the wave length. If the tube of the foregoing example is 4 in. in diameter, the actual tube lengths to produce notes of the frequencies computed would be 7 ft., 10.8 in. for the closed tube and 7 ft., 9.6 in. for the open tube.

339. Resonance. — The production of sound by some vibrating systems, such as strings, rods and air columns, has been considered in the three preceding sections. These systems were assumed to be set into vibration without constraint to produce free vibrations, that is, vibrations having frequencies determined entirely by the constants and properties of the vibrating bodies themselves. Such bodies may also be set in motion by periodic impulses imparted by outside agents; in this case the bodies are said to execute *forced vibrations*. When conditions are so adjusted that the frequency of forced vibrations is the same as the natural frequency of the body upon which they are impressed, the free vibrations reinforce the received ones; an effect which is known as *resonance*. When the impressed vibration has a different frequency from that of the free vibrations of a body, the received impulses sometimes help and sometimes hinder the free vibrations, and will not affect the free vibrations appreciably.

To illustrate the phenomenon of resonance, consider a tuning fork to be held over an air column, as shown in Fig. 358. The level of the water in the cylindrical tube *T* can be varied by raising or lowering the communicating vessel *V*. Upon sounding the fork and altering the height of the air column, resonance is established when the audible response is a maximum. This experiment affords a simple means of determining the velocity of sound in air; in such a test it is necessary to use a tuning fork of known frequency, to measure the length of the column at resonance, and to apply equation (218).

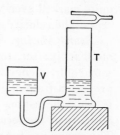

Fig. 358. Resonance of an air column

For example, a tuning fork vibrating 440 times per sec. is observed to produce resonance when held above an air column 18 cm. long. To compute the velocity of sound, the wave length is taken as $4 \times 18 = 72$ cm., whence by equation (203) the velocity is $\dfrac{440}{\text{sec.}} \times 72$ cm. $= 31{,}700$ cm. per sec., according to the data provided. The result is low because the end correction was neglected; the error might be avoided by using an air column sufficiently long to resonate at two lengths, their difference being $\frac{1}{2}$ wave length.

There are many applications of the phenomenon of resonance. Tuning forks are often mounted on top of wooden boxes closed at one end and open at the other; the length of such boxes is about one-quarter wave length of the sound emitted by the fork so as to produce a loud response. Resonance is utilized in the tuning of a radio receiver by adjusting the inductance or capacitance of its circuits for the same frequency as that of the radiation from the desired broadcasting station, as described in § 316. There are instances where resonance may build up free vibrations of such amplitude in structures as to produce dangerous effects in them. Soldiers break step in marching across bridges, for example, in order to eliminate the possibility of setting up destructive vibrations in the various members of such structures.

340. Doppler's Principle. — A person standing near a railroad track can observe a distinct lowering of pitch in the whistle of a train as it rolls past him. This observation illustrates a principle applicable to all wave motion; it was developed by the Austrian physicist, Christian Doppler (1803–1853). Applied to sound, this principle states that the pitch of the sound heard differs from the frequency of the vibrating source from which it originates whenever the observer or the source moves. This difference is quite marked even when the velocity of motion is only a few per cent of the velocity of sound, 1100 ft. per sec. in air.

Source Moving. — Suppose a whistle to be moving with a speed of 50 ft. per sec. toward a stationary observer, while emitting a sound of frequency 300 vibrations per sec. In 1 sec., the whistle will produce a train of 300 waves, the first of which will advance 1100 ft. while the last one is just being emitted from the source at a point 50 ft. from the location it had when the first wave was emitted. This train of waves occupies a length of $1100 - 50$ ft.; therefore, the wave length of the sound in air is $[(1100 - 50) \div 300]$ ft. The pitch heard by the observer is obtained by dividing the velocity with which the waves pass him by their wave length; in this example the observed pitch is $1100 \div \dfrac{1100 - 50}{300} = 300 \times \dfrac{1100}{1100 - 50}$

$= 314.3$ vibrations per sec. If the source had been stationary, the observed pitch would have been 300 vibrations per sec.; the difference between these results is due to motion of the source.

Using symbols, call f the frequency of the source, S its velocity, and V the velocity of wave propagation. The pitch observed when the source of sound moves toward the stationary observer will be

$$p = f\left(\frac{V}{V - S}\right) \qquad (219)$$

Similarly, when the source moves away from the observer, the observed pitch will be

$$p = f\left(\frac{V}{V + S}\right)$$

Observer Moving. — Suppose that the 300-cycle whistle is stationary, and that the observer is approaching it with a speed of 50 ft. per sec. The velocity with which the waves pass him is (1100 + 50) ft. per sec., and since the wave length of the sound in air is (1100/300) ft., the pitch heard by the observer becomes

$$(1100 + 50) \div \frac{1100}{300} = 300 \times \frac{1100 + 50}{1100} = 313.6 \text{ vibrations per}$$

sec. It is interesting to note that the increase in pitch in this case is different from that obtained with the source approaching the observer at the same speed.

To express the result in symbols, let O represent the velocity of the observer, the other symbols having the same significance as previously. The pitch of the sound heard by the observer when he approaches the stationary source will be

$$p = f\left(\frac{V + O}{V}\right) \qquad (220)$$

Source and Observer Moving. — When both the source of sound and the observer are moving, the pitch heard will be changed in the proportion $\frac{V}{V \mp S}$ by motion of the source, and in the proportion $\frac{V \pm O}{V}$ by motion of the observer. The pitch heard by the observer is, therefore

$$p = f \times \frac{V}{V \mp S} \times \frac{V \pm O}{V} = f\frac{V \pm O}{V \mp S} \qquad (221)$$

the signs in numerator and denominator being chosen to yield an increase in the observed pitch p when the source and the observer approach each other, and a decrease when they recede.

*341. Musical Scales. — The charm of music is based upon the blending and the succession of sounds to give pleasing auditory sensations. The characteristics of the ear impose certain physical restrictions on the frequencies of the sounds to be combined to secure harmonious effects. The ear would interpret quite differently a frequency increase of 50 vibrations per sec. in an initial sound having a pitch of 200 vibrations per sec. than a like increase in a sound having a pitch of 400 vibrations per sec., but would give the same interpretation to an increase of 100 vibrations per sec. in the sound of higher pitch. Thus, the ear recognizes two sounds to have the same tonal interval as two others, if the frequency ratios, rather than the frequency differences, are the same for the two pairs.

Further, two simultaneous sounds that have nearly the same frequency produce disagreeable pulsations in sound intensity. Two tuning forks that execute 200 and 205 vibrations per sec. would set up 5 beats per sec. if sounded together [§ 331], and produce an unpleasant musical effect. But if the frequency difference of two sounds is large, the beat frequency will be perceived as a new tone, called a *combination tone.* Two sounds are said to produce *consonance* when their combined effect is pleasant, otherwise they produce *dissonance;* the corresponding conditions are called concord and discord. The tones of a melody are chosen primarily to establish concord in the successive groupings of tones. The complete sequence of tones used for such selection constitutes a musical scale, and the tones are designated as notes of the scale.

Experience shows that tones having frequency ratios of 2 to 1, 3 to 2, 4 to 3, 5 to 3, 5 to 4, and 6 to 5 produce consonance; musical scales are based upon these ratios. The scales are formed by using three consonant combinations called *triads,* each of which is a chord formed of three tones. In such a chord, the octave of a tone may accompany or replace the fundamental without altering the nature of the chord.

The major scale of eight notes beginning with middle C as the basic note includes notes D, E, F, G, A and B of successively higher pitches in reaching the octave c. The frequencies of these notes are determined by the major triads CEG, FAc and GBd which notes have frequency ratios of $4 : 5 : 6$, and also by the pitch of some one note regarded as standard. Based upon the present standard concert pitch of 440 vibrations per sec. for A in the treble clef, the notes of the major scale have the following frequencies and intervals:

Major Scale

	C	D	E	F	G	A	B	c	d
Triads	4		5		6				
				4		5		6	
					4		5		6
Name	do	re	me	fa	sol	la	si	do	re
Frequency	264	297	330	352	396	440	495	528	594
Intervals		$\frac{9}{8}$	$\frac{10}{9}$	$\frac{16}{15}$	$\frac{9}{8}$	$\frac{10}{9}$	$\frac{9}{8}$	$\frac{16}{15}$	

The intervals $\frac{9}{8}$ and $\frac{10}{9}$ are called full tones, and the interval $\frac{16}{15}$ is called a half tone. A study of the frequencies tabulated reveals why a triad results in consonance, for the tones themselves as well as their harmonics will not produce disturbing beat notes. For example, the third harmonic of C coincides with the second of G, the fifth of C coincides with the fourth of E, the sixth of E coincides with the fifth of G, and so on.

The minor scale is built upon three minor triads for the same notes as the major scale, but having frequency ratios of $10 : 12 : 15$. The notes of this scale have the following frequencies and intervals over the range of values previously tabulated:

Minor Scale

	C	D	E	F	G	A	B	c	d
Triads	10		12		15				
				10		12		15	
					10		12		15
Frequency	264	297	316.8	352	396	422.4	475.2	528	594
Intervals		$\frac{9}{8}$	$\frac{16}{15}$	$\frac{10}{9}$	$\frac{9}{8}$	$\frac{16}{15}$	$\frac{9}{8}$	$\frac{10}{9}$	

The intervals have the same values as before, but have a different sequence. As a result, three additional notes are needed to produce the minor scale; these are below E, B and A of the major scale. Music rendered in the minor scale usually has a more plaintive character than that in the other scale.

To accommodate different instruments and voices, it is desirable to have sufficient tones to permit changing the tonic from C to some other keynote. If, for example, the successive notes were to be determined for the key of D, the same procedure followed above would indicate the successive frequencies for the major scale to be 297, 334, 371, 396, 445, 495, 557 and 594 vibrations per sec. These frequencies agree with those previously found for notes G and B as well as for the keynote, and approximate them for notes E and A; but two are quite distinct and these notes are designated as F sharp and c sharp.

Similar computations for other keys in both scales would reveal the necessity of having a large number of separate notes if it were desired to render a selection in any key. To avoid this situation and yet provide sufficient flexibility in musical instruments, like the piano and organ that produce sounds of fixed frequency, a scale has been developed which has 12 intervals and has the same frequency interval between consecutive notes. This so-called *tempered scale* has a frequency interval of the twelfth root of 2, namely 1.0595. The equal temperament scale is now universally used, and only those with well-trained ears can detect the slight errors of pitch from the natural scales.

*342. Musical Instruments. — Instruments for the production of music utilize various forms of vibrating bodies as the sound-generating elements, and some instruments have sounding boards or equivalents for the reinforcement of the tones produced. The following list gives some examples of the instruments that utilize the usual acoustic elements:

Air columns, conical	Bassoon, cornet, oboe, trombone
" " cylindrical	Clarinet, flute, organ, piccolo, saxophone
Plates and membranes	Cymbal, drum
Reeds and rods	Reed organ, xylophone
Strings, bowed	Violin, viola, violoncello, double bass
" plucked	Guitar, harp, mandolin, ukulele
" struck	Piano

The excitation of the air columns in some of the so-called wind instruments is accomplished by a thin stream of air or a reed which often has no definite frequency by itself, the air column responding by resonance. The column then vibrates at a constant rate as determined by its length, and reacts upon the exciter to keep its vibration rate unchanged. This method with reeds is utilized in the bassoon, clarinet, oboe, saxophone and some organ pipes, and with the human lips as reeds in the cornet and trombone. In other wind instruments, like the flute, piccolo and "flue" organ pipes, the air is set into vibration without reeds. The length of the air column is varied in the flute and clarinet by opening side holes in the tube, in the cornet by adding lengths of tubing by means of valves, and in the trombone by sliding one tube within another.

The stringed instruments have various numbers of strings that are constant or alterable in length. In the piano each string is of definite length; the string for the highest tone is usually from 5.0 to 5.5 cm. long, and the others are progressively longer. There are 88 notes extending over more than seven octaves from $27\frac{1}{2}$

to 4186 vibrations per sec. The strings of various diameters are set into vibration through key action by felt-nosed hammers at places approximately one-eighth the string length from one end. The lower tones have many harmonics while the high tones have few; the middle tones of the scale have at least ten harmonics of well proportioned intensities.

In the violin family of instruments there are four strings of equal length stretched over a resonant box of particular shape and construction. The G, D, A and e strings are tuned to fifths, that is, the relative frequencies of two neighboring strings are 3 : 2. Other tones are produced by varying the lengths of the strings by pressing them against the flat fingerboard with the fingers. The strings are set into vibration by drawing a bow strung with rosined horsehair across them, the vibration being a succession of alternate forced and free movements as the string adheres to the bow because of the pressure applied, and slips back again by virtue of its elasticity. The third, fourth and fifth harmonics are particularly prominent in the tones of the violin.

Within the past few years there has been an interesting development of electrically operated instruments designed to give the musical effects of the organ. The Everett Orgatron employs a series of metal reeds for each tone quality desired, the number of reeds in each series being the same as the number of keys on the instrument. One of the operating elements is shown in Fig. 359. The depression of a key lowers the pallet P, and allows a current of air to enter the chamber C and set the reed R into vibration. The reed and a metal "tone screw" S near it form the plates of a condenser, the capacitance of which varies periodically as the reed vibrates to and fro. The condenser is electrically charged, and the variations of its capacitance are accompanied by potential fluctuations.

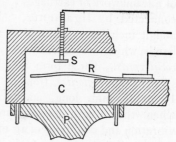

FIG. 359.   Operating parts of the Orgatron

These are applied to an electron-tube amplifier, resulting in the production of sound in a loud speaker. Desired qualities of tone are secured by shaping the reeds and using more tone screws.

In the Hammond electric organ a series of toothed disks is driven by a constant-speed motor, one disk being provided for the fundamental tone corresponding to each key on the instrument. The action will be explained by reference to Fig. 360, which repre-

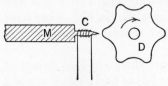

sents a disk D rotated near the tip of a permanent magnet M, on which there is a coil of wire C. The disk is made of steel, and as its teeth and slots move in succession past the magnet tip, variations of flux occur which induce an alternating e.m.f. in the coil.   An elec-

FIG. 360.   Inducing element of the Hammond organ

tron-tube circuit amplifies this e.m.f. and operates a loud speaker. The instrument provides for superimposing additional e.m.f.'s upon that of the fundamental to give desired tone qualities.

★343. Vocal Organs. — The organs of speech are composed of the vocal cords, through which the lungs force streams of air, and of the resonating chambers formed by the throat, mouth, and nasal cavities. Fig. 361 shows a sectional view of these parts of the neck and head. The larynx is the valve at the entrance of the windpipe consisting of a framework of cartilages connected by ligaments, and it includes two fibrous bands which are called the *vocal cords*. These form a straight slit (*glottis*) from 11 to 15 mm. long, and

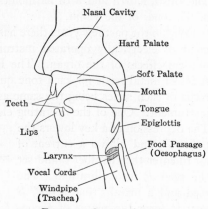

FIG. 361.   Organs of speech

when the breath passes through it the cords are set into vibration and send puffs of air to the chambers above it. The vibration rate is determined principally by the size of the glottis opening and to some extent by the tension of the vocal cords.   The lips, tongue and teeth modify the shape of the vocal passages; certain tonal characteristics are impressed by this action upon the air puffs and they emerge from the mouth as speech sounds.   When relaxed, the vocal cords are further apart and form a V-shaped aperture; in this condition the passage of air to and from the lungs occurs without the emission of sound, as in normal breathing.

The sounds of speech are complicated tones that have many harmonics. As with musical tones, the quality is determined by the relative intensities of these harmonics. Dr. Harvey Fletcher gives the following characteristic frequency regions of the vowel sounds in vibrations per second:

Speech sound	Low frequency	High frequency	Speech sound	Low frequency	High frequency
ū (pool)	400	800	a (tap)	750	1800
u (put)	475	1000	e (ten)	550	1900
ō (tone)	500	850	er (pert)	500	1500
a (talk)	600	950	ā (tape)	550	2100
o (ton)	700	1150	i (tip)	450	2200
a (father)	825	1200	ē (team)	375	2400

The numbers listed under low frequency are believed to be the approximate resonant frequencies of the mouth cavity, and those

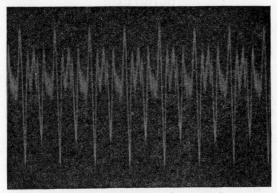

FIG. 362. Voice wave of vowel "o"

under high frequency of the throat cavity. These average values are departed from by different speakers and by the same speaker at different times. Fig. 362 illustrates the wave shape of the vowel "o" as in tone.

Measurements on the power of speech sounds show that the average power for conversational speech is about 10 microwatts. Talking as loudly as possible raises this average to about 1000 microwatts and talking as softly as possible without whispering lowers the average to about 0.1 microwatt.

The pitch of the voice in singing ranges generally from about 80 to 300 vibrations per sec. for bass voices, and from about 250 to 850 vibrations per sec. for soprano voices, but these ranges are extended considerably by many individuals.

Electrical production of voice sounds was demonstrated at the San Francisco Exposition and the New York World's Fair of 1939 by the Bell Telephone System. The apparatus used in this demonstration, called the "Voder," is equipped to produce and control two kinds of sound, one which simulates the passage of the breath through the mouth, teeth and lips to emit consonant sounds like "s," "th" and "f," and the other which imitates the vibration of the vocal cords to produce the various vowels. These sounds can be rendered in any desired sequence by the manipulation of thirteen keys, and the inflection is controlled by a pedal for changing the pitch. The apparatus contains vacuum-tube oscillators, amplifying equipment, and filters, such as are described in Chapters XXVIII and XXIX.

PROBLEMS

1. Calculate the intensity of a sound wave in air where the amplitude of the air particles is 10^{-5} cm. Take the wave length as 25 cm. and assume normal conditions of temperature and pressure.

2. Two sinusoidal sound waves A of 300 and B of 600 vibrations per sec. pass through the same medium, B having an amplitude one-half as great as A and being always in phase with A when A is at its positive peak values. Write an equation for the composite wave, reckoning t from an instant when wave A becomes positive; then verify the correctness of the equation.

3. Considering Fig. 350 to represent a sound wave in air, compute the intensities of the three component waves, taking each unit on the amplitude scale as equivalent to 0.0005 cm. Take the density of air as 0.001293 gm./cm.³

4. What are the pitches of the fundamental and first three overtones of a copper string 34 cm. long? Take the velocity of transverse waves in the string to be 160 meters per sec.

5. A section of a fishing line between two guides 10 in. apart on a rod was set in vibration by the wind and was observed to vibrate in two loops. The stretching force in the line was the weight of 40 ft. of it, which was found to be ¼ oz. Compute the frequency of vibration.

6. A phosphor bronze wire 0.0201 in. in diameter is stretched with a force of 10 lb. between two supports 24 in. apart on a sonometer board. Determine the pitch of the sound produced when the string is set into vibration in its fundamental mode. The specific gravity of phosphor bronze is 8.8.

7. The c' strings of a piano are of steel and have a length of 7.6 in. and a diameter of 0.035 in. What should be the stretching force to produce a fundamental tone of 1056 vibrations per sec.?

8. A copper rod 3.6 ft. long is clamped at the center and is stroked with rosined chamois to set up longitudinal vibrations. Taking the velocity of wave propagation in the rod as 13,000 ft./sec., compute the pitches of the two lowest tones produced.

9. An aluminum rod 2 ft. long is clamped at one end and is set into longitudinal vibration by stroking with rosined chamois. Compute the frequency of the fundamental vibration and that of the third harmonic.

10. The fundamental frequency of a tuning fork having prongs of rectangular section of thickness t and of length l is given by the equation: $f = 0.161tV/l^2$, where V is the velocity of sound in the material of the fork, and where all units involve centimeters. Calculate the frequency of a steel fork having prongs 10.9 cm. long and 0.77 cm. thick.

11. The fundamental frequency of a diaphragm clamped at the edge has been computed to be $f = 0.47hV/(a^2\sqrt{1 - \rho^2})$, where h is the thickness and a the radius of the diaphragm in centimeters, V is the velocity of sound in the material of which it is made in centimeters per second, and ρ is a constant of elasticity. Determine the frequency of a steel diaphragm 5.20 cm. in diameter and 0.0254 cm. thick, for which $\rho = 0.28$.

12. An organ pipe closed at one end is to produce a tone of 165 vibrations per sec. How long should it be?

13. A glass tube 15 in. long and 2 in. in diameter is thumped against the palm of the hand and withdrawn in rapid succession. The sound produced by this action is made up of two alternate tones, the lower is that for an air column closed at one end, and the higher is that for the column open at both ends. Compute the frequencies of these tones.

14. Compute the approximate pitch of the fundamental tone produced by blowing across the end of a tube 10 in. long, if the other end of the tube is open, and if it is closed. For a tube $\frac{1}{2}$ in. in diameter, what will the actual pitch be in each case if the end correction is taken into account?

15. Two organ pipes, each closed at one end, have lengths of 70 in. and 71 in. The pipes are sounded simultaneously, each producing its fundamental tone. Neglecting the end correction, determine the number of beats per minute.

16. The velocity of sound is measured by the method illustrated in Fig. 358, using an electrically operated tuning fork which vibrates 528 times per sec. held above a glass tube 30 in. long. As the water is lowered in the tube, two points of resonance are observed, the heights of the water column being 24.0 in. and 11.1 in. respectively. Compute the velocity of sound in air from these data.

17. A speed boat moving at 40 mi. per hr. sounds a signal on its horn, producing a tone of 280 vibrations per sec. Compute the pitch of the sound heard by an observer in another boat moving in the opposite direction and approaching the first at a speed of 30 mi. per hr.

18. An automobilist traveling at 50 mi. per hr. passes another who is traveling along the same road at half that speed in the opposite direction. He is sounding his horn steadily, and it produces a tone of 300 vibrations per sec. Determine the drop in pitch that will be observed by the other automobilist as the faster car passes him.

19. Compute the successive frequencies for the notes of the major scale, using $E = 330$ vibrations per sec. as the keynote.

CHAPTER XXXII

SOUND RECEPTION AND CONTROL

344. The Ear. — In the process of hearing sound, the acoustic waves enter the auditory canal of the outer ear and fall upon the eardrum; the vibration of this membrane is transmitted through the middle ear to the inner ear and received by nerve endings, which in turn send nervous impulses to the brain that cause the sensation of hearing. The principal parts of the ear are illustrated in Fig. 363, the inner ear being much enlarged with respect to the

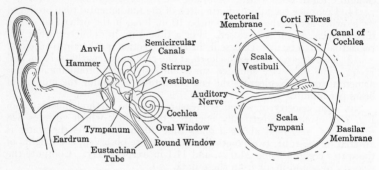

FIG. 363.   General view of ear and transverse section of cochlea

outer ear, and the sectional view of the end-organ (cochlea) being further magnified.   The cavity beyond the eardrum, called the *tympanum*, connects with the upper part of the throat through the *Eustachian tube* which opens when swallowing occurs, enabling an equalization of pressure with the outside air to be effected. The tympanum houses the three tiny bones of the middle ear, the *hammer*, *anvil* and *stirrup*, and the base of the latter bone is applied to a membrane which closes an oval window, called the *fenestra ovalis*.   There is also another membrane at that side of the tympanum which closes a round window, called the *fenestra rotunda*.   Both of these membranes transmit incoming vibrations to the inner ear. This part of the ear is encased in solid bone, and can be subdivided into three sections: the semicircular canals, which do not contribute to the process of hearing but serve as an organ of balance, the vestibule, and the *cochlea*. The latter has the form of a spiral of nearly three turns, and is the organ where the vibrations are translated into nerve impulses.

The cochlea is divided along its length into three parallel canals, as shown in the sectional view at the right, but the upper two, separated by a very thin flexible membrane, act mechanically as though they were one. The *scala vestibuli* and *scala tympani* have at their ends the oval and round windows respectively for communication with the tympanum, and are separated by a bony projection for about half their length and a flexible membrane, called the *basilar membrane*, for the other half. The terminal organs of hearing are the *Corti fibres* which are nerve terminals in the form of rods with small hairs that extend from one side of the basilar membrane into the canal of cochlea. Opposite them is a soft loose membrane called the *tectorial membrane*. In receiving sound, these two membranes move relatively to each other and stimulate the hair-like nerve endings, thereby causing the sound to be heard. That the cochlea is very small can be judged from the facts that the length is about 31 mm. when straightened out and that the greatest cross-section of any of its canals is less than 2 mm.[2] It is believed that the cochlea is responsive to different frequencies along the different parts of the length of its basilar membrane, so that its behavior may be likened somewhat to that of a harp. The reception of a complex sound on this basis would signify the agitation of certain of the resonating elements of the cochlea and the transmission of a corresponding pattern to the brain.

The range of sounds that can be heard varies with the individual, but the average range extends from about 20 to 20,000 vibrations per sec. If the ear is tested with tones of any one frequency and the intensity is changed, it will be found that the auditory sensation ceases when the intensity has been reduced to a sufficiently low level which is called the *threshold of audibility*, and that the sound produces the sensation of feeling and begins to be painful when the intensity has been increased to an appropriately high level which is called the *threshold of feeling*. Carrying out such a procedure over a wide frequency range results in data from which a pair of curves can be plotted, one for the lower limit of audibility and the other for the maximum auditory response, as shown in Fig. 364. These curves represent tests made on a number of persons with normal hearing and may be extrapolated to meet and thereby enclose a region termed the auditory sensation area.

The width of such an area would indicate the frequency range of normal ears and the heights would show the pressure ranges for auditory response at various frequencies. It should be noted that the scales of frequency and pressure are logarithmic; an advance of one space horizontally doubles the frequency, and an advance of one space vertically multiplies the pressure ten-fold.

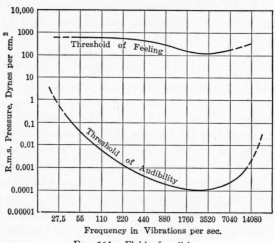

FIG. 364. Field of audition

345. Intensity Levels. — The sensation of loudness experienced by the ear is not related in a simple way to the intensity of sound incident upon it. In consequence, scales of measurement for loudness are based upon *intensity levels* rather than sensation levels. It is customary to express the intensity level α in terms of the sound intensity I, as follows:

$$\alpha = C \log_{10} \frac{I}{I_0}$$

where C is a constant that depends upon the units used, and I_0 is some particular value of sound intensity that may be chosen as a standard of reference. When C is taken as unity, the intensity level α is expressed in terms of a unit called the *bel*, named after the late Professor Bell, the inventor of the telephone. In practice C is taken as 10 and the corresponding unit for α is called the *decibel* (db.) as explained in § 312; as its name implies, it is one-tenth as large as the bel.

The reference standard intensity, I_0 (producing the zero of intensity level α_0) is often taken as the sound intensity of a free plane wave of 1 microwatt per sq. cm., that is, a wave transmitting 10^{-6} joule (same as 10 ergs) of sound energy per second through a square centimeter of sectional area. Using this value for I_0 as datum, the intensity level of a sound having an intensity of I microwatts per sq. cm. will be expressed as

$$\alpha = 10 \log_{10} I \qquad (222)$$

This gives the intensity level in decibels above or below the datum. A better idea of what 1 db. means may be gained by letting $\alpha = 1$ and solving for I; the result is $I = 10^{0.1} = 1.26$, showing that a 26 per cent increase of intensity corresponds to a 1-db. rise in intensity level.

To illustrate the application of equation (222), consider the speech powers cited in § 343, namely 10 microwatts for average conversational speech, and ranging from 1000 to 0.1 microwatts for very loud and for very soft speech respectively. At a distance of one-half inch from the lips, the usual distance from a transmitter while telephoning, the area through which this power is radiated is about 10 sq. cm. At that zone the intensity of average speech is 10 microwatts $\div$ 10 sq. cm. = 1 microwatt/cm.^{2}, which value is taken above as the datum, partly for this reason. For a power of 1000 microwatts through this zone, the intensity is 100 microwatts/cm.^{2}, and the equation gives the intensity level of very loud speech as $+20$ db.; for very soft speech the level is -20 db., that is, 20 db. below the datum intensity level. Thus the average voice has an intensity range of 40 db. The gain of telephone repeaters is expressed in decibels by equation (202), and the output of mechanical and electrical sources of acoustic energy is also stated in terms of this unit.

The decibel scale agrees somewhat with loudness sensation, but it does not follow that a sound at the 60-db. intensity level is judged twice as loud as one at the 30-db. level; in fact, experiment shows wide variations for tones of different frequencies and intensities.

346. Some Measurements in Sound. — Systematic progress in sound control requires a knowledge of acoustic quantities based on actual test. Some of the experimental methods used are described in the following paragraphs.

Pitch. — The pitch of a tone is usually measured by comparison with a standard. The standard tone may be generated by a card held lightly against the rim of a rotating toothed disk, or produced by a siren [§ 333], its frequency in either case being computed readily for a particular speed of rotation. By regulating the speed, the pitch of the standard tone is made equal to that of the tone being measured. The ear can determine this equality directly if the two sources are sounded alternately, or by the elimination of beats if they are sounded together.

An optical method is used for making precise comparison of the pitches of two tuning forks, one being a standard. This method applies where the pitches are very nearly in simple proportion, for example, 3 : 1. The forks have polished prongs to serve as mirrors and are mounted in such a manner that one fork vibrates in a horizontal plane and the other in a vertical plane, the vibrations being maintained electrically. A narrow beam of light projected upon one fork is reflected to the other, from which it is reflected again and falls upon a screen. Thus, the spot of light is given two harmonic motions at right angles, and traces a figure on the screen the shape of which depends upon the frequency ratio of these vibrations. If the frequencies remain constant, the figure will appear stationary, otherwise progressive changes of phase cause it to pass through a succession of shapes, returning to the original shape when one fork has lost or gained one cycle with respect to the other. Suppose, for example, that the standard fork vibrates exactly 200 times a second and the other very nearly 600 times a second, and that the figure on the screen goes through a cycle of shapes in exactly 4 sec. Since the fork under test completes either 2399 or 2401 vibrations in the 4-sec. interval, its frequency is either 599.75 or 600.25 vibrations per sec. To determine which of these is correct, the test is repeated with a tiny bit of wax fastened to one prong of the fork; such an addition will lower its frequency.

Wave Shape. — Various devices have been used to show the shape of a sound wave; two of the more modern ones illustrate the mechanical and the electrical method of operation.

The *phonodeik*, devised by Professor D. C. Miller, is shown in Fig. 365; it consists of a horn *H* closed by a thin glass diaphragm *D* that is supported lightly in soft rubber bushings at its edge. Attached to the diaphragm is a slender fiber which passes around a tiny pulley *P* and is kept taut by spring tension. The pulley carries a small mirror *M*, which rotates slightly as the diaphragm moves back and forth. A narrow beam of light strikes the mirror and may be reflected upon a moving film in a special camera or projected upon a screen. The record, corrected for the disturbing effects of the horn and diaphragm, is an accurate representation of the sound wave.

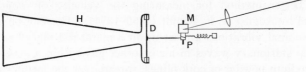

FIG. 365. The phonodeik

The *oscilloscope* is essentially a cathode-ray oscillograph [§ 286] actuated by a microphone. The sound waves striking the microphone are converted into equivalent electrical vibrations and these are rendered visible upon the fluorescent screen of the oscillograph.

Intensity and Loudness. — The classical method for measuring sound intensity is due to Lord Rayleigh (John W. Strutt, 1842–1919), English physicist, who found that a suspended disk tends to set itself at right angles to the to-and-fro motion of the particles in a sound wave. In using this device, the disk, supported by a torsion suspension, is placed where an antinode will be situated in a resonating tube, its plane making an angle of 45° with the axis of the tube. When a sound is established in the tube, a torque will act on the disk and deflect it, the torque being proportional to the intensity of the sound.

The loudness of a noise can be measured by the *audiometer*, a device designed primarily for the measurement of deafness. The audiometer produces tones of numerous frequencies, the intensities of which can be adjusted to various sensation levels. The sound is produced in a telephone receiver supported at a fixed distance from the ear, and its loudness is regulated until it is just masked by the noise being measured. The difference between this setting and a similar setting made in a quiet place is a measure of the loudness of the noise.

347. Measurement of Velocity of Sound. — The velocity of a sound wave in the atmosphere can be determined by observing the motion which produces a distant sound, and measuring the time interval which elapses before the sound reaches the ear as well as the distance between source and observer. Neglecting the time required for light to travel that distance, the velocity of sound can be computed directly, although the result is subject to considerable personal error. The distance to a lightning flash may be estimated in this way by counting seconds until its thunder is heard, allowing five seconds to the mile.

A better method for measuring the velocity of sound was devised by August A. E. Kundt (1839–1894), a German physicist. Longitudinal vibrations are set up in a metal rod placed so as to develop stationary waves in air or other gas within a glass tube. Lycopodium powder or cork filings, spread over the interior of the tube, permit the location of the nodes and antinodes to be determined. The arrangement is shown in Fig. 366, wherein A repre-

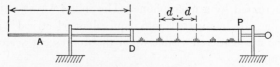

FIG. 366.   Kundt's tube for measuring velocity of sound

sents the rod clamped at its center to one end of the tube, and P represents a plunger at the other end. The rod is set into longitudinal vibration by stroking with rosined chamois and the plunger is moved until the powder shows distinct differences in appearance along the tube. At the nodal points the powder will be lumped together, and at the antinodes it will assume sharply defined ridges across the tube. A node will form at P and there will be an approximate node at the disk D fastened to the end of the rod. The rod has a length l, and its pitch f is measured by comparison with a siren or equivalent means. When producing the lowest tone, the sound wave in the rod has a wave length $\lambda = 2l$, and a velocity $V = f\lambda = 2fl$, as explained in § 337. If the average distance measured between the various antinodes is d, the sound wave in the gas has a wave length $2d$ and a velocity $V = 2fd$.

348. Sound Recording and Reproduction. — Edison conceived the idea in 1877 that by speaking in front of a diaphragm which carried a projecting point at the back, he could produce indentations in a cylinder of tinfoil which was moved in contact with the point to record speech, and that upon returning the cylinder to its original position and moving it as before, the diaphragm could be set into vibration and reproduce the original sound. The success of this experiment led to the development of the *dic-*

tating machine which employs cylinders of hard wax, and of the *phonograph* which operates with records in the form of disks.

In the ordinary phonograph record, the groove, when magnified, appears as a wavy line and represents a composite wave that is usually the resultant of many individual waves superimposed upon one another. In electrical reproduction of a phonograph record, the motion of the tracing point causes an iron armature to move within a coil of wire. The resulting disturbance of the magnetic flux induces an e.m.f. in the coil and sets up an electric current which is amplified by electron tubes and operates a loud speaker.

The sound record of a talking motion picture usually consists of a narrow strip or "sound track" which runs along one edge of the film and is crossed by lines of varying intensity. In making the record, the sounds produced are received by a sensitive microphone and cause corresponding variations of the electric current in the microphone circuit. This current, suitably amplified, is caused to control a neon lamp, the intensity of which responds instantly to current changes. The light from the lamp is passed through a narrow transverse slit upon the moving film, and produces a series of lines of varying degrees of darkness in the finished film.

In reproduction from the film, a steady light shines through a similar slit upon the sound track, the transmitted beam varying continually in intensity. This beam strikes a photoelectric cell [§ 307] and causes proportional changes in the current through it. The varying current, properly amplified, operates a loud speaker and reproduces the original sound.

349. Sound Ranging. — Most persons can estimate with considerable accuracy the direction from which a particular sound comes, an ability called the binaural sense. The waves received by the two ears vary slightly in intensity and phase, and from early childhood these differences have come to be associated with particular directions. Improved accuracy may be obtained by use of an instrument which virtually increases the base line between the ears. This device consists of a pair of telephone transmitters mounted in positions corresponding to the ears on an imaginary head of large size. The transmitters are connected through separate circuits to corresponding receivers worn by the observer. The direction from which the sound comes can be located by turning the device until the source appears to be directly in front. The same result can also be attained by shifting the phase relation of the currents in the two circuits to balance the phase difference in the sound waves at the transmitters.

A sound locator for detecting the presence and determining the angular position of hostile aircraft under conditions of poor visibility is shown in Fig. 367. It consists of four horns, binaurally matched in pairs, to collect and amplify the sounds of airplane motors and propellers, together with an acoustic "corrector" which applies a correction for the continued motion of the plane while

Fig. 367.   Sound locator in operating position
(*Photograph by U. S. Army Signal Corps*)

the sound wave is reaching the point of observation. The vertical pair of horns is connected through a tube and head set to the ears of the "elevation operator," and the lateral pair to those of the "azimuth operator." When the operators keep the horns directed upon the source of sound, the mechanical motion of the horns actuates the corrector and this, through electrical control, keeps a searchlight trained upon the source, and provides the information needed for operating the fire-control system.

The procedure can be extended to give the location of a sounding source as well as its direction. To locate the position of an enemy gun, for example, three or more receiving stations are arranged at definitely known locations, and equipped with microphones that are connected with appropriate electrical apparatus

at a central receiving point.   This apparatus records accurately
the time intervals between the reception of the sound impulses at
the different stations.   From this information, the location of the
sounding source can be determined graphically, as illustrated with
the aid of Fig. 368.

The three microphone stations are located at A, B and C, and
it is supposed that the electrical record shows the impulse to reach

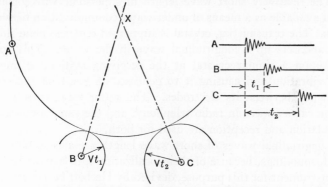

FIG. 368.   Method of locating an enemy gun and form of electrical record

B at an instant t_1 sec. after it arrives at A, and to reach C at an
instant t_2 sec. after it arrives at A.   At the moment the sound
impulse reaches A, it is still a distance Vt_1 from B, V being the
velocity of the wave, and is consequently at some point on the
arc of radius Vt_1 centered at B.   At the same instant the impulse
is distant Vt_2 from C, and has reached some point on the arc of
radius Vt_2 centered at C.   A circle passing through station A and
drawn tangent to the arcs around stations B and C shows the
position of the wave front at the instant considered.   The center
of the circle, X, gives the location of the source sought for.   The
mathematical procedure for locating this point is quite involved,
but graphical construction by trial can be carried out quickly.

350. Supersonic Vibrations. — The longitudinal vibrations of
sound have been investigated over a wide range of frequencies;
indeed, experiments have extended into the so-called *supersonic
region* beyond the upper limit of hearing.   Such vibrations may
be produced by a quartz crystal mounted between metal electrodes, making use of the piezoelectric effect described in § 315.
The crystal has a natural frequency determined by its elasticity
and density.   When an alternating e.m.f. of this same frequency

is impressed upon the electrodes, the crystal will be set into mechanical vibration, which it will communicate to the surrounding medium. Supersonic vibrations may also be produced by slight periodic changes in length of an iron or nickel rod that is magnetized by a high-frequency alternating current through a solenoid around the rod; the variation in length due to magnetization is called *magnestostriction.*

The relatively short wave length of supersonic waves makes them available as a means of under-water communication between ships. The transmitting crystal is supported outside of the ship's hull and sets up a longitudinal wave in the water. This wave acts upon a similar crystal at the receiving station, setting it into vibration and causing it to generate an e.m.f. of the same frequency between its electrodes. The water wave corresponds to the carrier wave in radio telephony, and the same methods of modulation and reception are used for both.

Longitudinal waves of short wave length are also suitable for depth-soundings, because of their localization into narrow beams. An instrument for this purpose, devised by Herbert G. Dorsey and called the *fathometer,* utilizes a vibration frequency of 17,500 cycles per sec., which is close to the supersonic region. The transmitting and receiving elements are one device, called a "transceiver," that alternately transmits a signal and receives the echo, making about twenty depth measurements per second, this device contains nickel tubes with a steel diaphragm pressed against them. By magnetostriction, an outgoing signal sets the diaphragm into vibration for an instant to launch the compressional waves downward from the ship, and the echo returning from the ocean bottom actuates the diaphragm and thereby lengthens and shortens the magnetic tubes, producing an e.m.f. in a coil surrounding them.

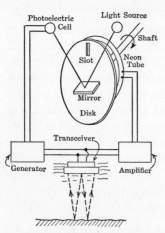

FIG. 369. Echo-method of determining depths in water

Fig. 369 shows the method utilized in the fathometer for measuring the time interval between the initiation of a signal and the return of its echo. A shaft, driven at constant speed, carries a mirror to reflect a beam of light from a small lamp upon a photoelectric cell once each revolution. The shaft also carries a disk which hides from view a ring-shaped neon tube mounted concentrically behind it in a fixed position. The illumination of this tube may be observed, however, through a narrow radial slot in the disk. Each time the cell is actuated a signal is sent out from the transceiver, at which time the slot is at the top or "zero" position. After reflection, the received echo is amplified to cause the neon tube to flash momentarily. In the meantime the slot has advanced to a new angular position and the observer sees the flashing of the tube only at that position; this enables him to determine the angular displacement of the disk while the signal travels down and back, and to obtain the depth of the water from a circular scale around the rim of the disk.

In a test with this device the disk was rotated at 20.5 rev. per sec. and was found to turn through an angle of 90° while the signal traveled to the ocean bottom and back. Find the depth of the water, taking the velocity of the supersonic waves in sea-water as 1500 meters per sec. Letting d represent the depth in fathoms, the distance traveled by the wave was $2\,d \times 6 = 12\,d$ ft., or $12\,d \times 30.48 \div 100 = 3.66\,d$ meters. The elapsed time was $\dfrac{90}{360} \times \dfrac{1}{20.5}$ sec. $= \dfrac{1}{82}$ sec. Therefore, $3.66\,d = 1500 \times \dfrac{1}{82}$ and $d = 1500 \div (82 \times 3.66) = 5.00$ fathoms.

Biological and chemical effects are produced in many substances by exposure to strong beams of supersonic radiation; for example, particles of colloidal material in liquids are shattered and form extremely fine emulsions.

The passage of supersonic waves through a liquid sets up planes of condensation and rarefaction which are so close together that the medium acts like a diffraction grating [§ 417], causing a beam of light perpendicular to the direction of wave propagation to be spread into spectra of several orders. This phenomenon has been used in the measurement of the moduli of elasticity of liquids and solids.

*351. Acoustics of the Auditorium. — The suitability of an auditorium for the purposes of speaking or the presentation of music depends primarily upon two factors, reverberation and interference. *Reverberation* is responsible for the slowness with which sounds die away, and may be controlled by selecting wall materials and coverings which will absorb sound energy to the desired extent. *Interference* causes variations in intensity from point to point; excessive interference may be avoided by a proper choice of the dimensions and shape of the room.

Reverberation is caused by echoes repeated in rapid succession. It may be explained by considering the effect of sustaining a tone within a room from which no acoustic energy escapes. When the source is set into vibration, the sound waves emitted travel to the walls and other surfaces, and are then reflected back and forth from one surface after another. If none of the acoustic energy were absorbed, the resulting sound intensity would increase indefinitely. Absorption does take place at the surfaces, however, and as a result, the intensity will reach a steady value when the rate of energy absorption equals the rate of emission. After this condition has been attained and the vibrating source is stopped, the sound does not cease instantly but dies away slowly as the acoustic energy within the room is absorbed. The intensity I at an instant t sec. after stopping a sound is given in terms of the maximum intensity I_0 by the equation:

$$I = I_0 \, \epsilon^{-kt}$$

ϵ being the base of natural logarithms and k being taken as a constant for a particular room (see § 376).

The time in which a sound diminishes until it can no longer be heard is called the *reverberation time*. Professor Wallace C. Sabine (1868–1919), an American pioneer in acoustics, regarded the reverberation time as the interval during which the intensity diminishes to one millionth of its initial value. A sound produced in a small room diminishes very rapidly because the reflections and absorptions at the walls are repeated at short intervals. In an auditorium, however, the reverberation time may be quite long, making it necessary for a speaker to talk very slowly to prevent confusion between the syllable being spoken and the echoes of the preceding one. On the other hand, the sound should not die away too quickly, for the room will be judged as "too dead." Values of 1.0 sec. for a small auditorium and of 1.8 to 2.0 sec. for a large one may be considered within the acceptable range. Taking Sabine's criterion, the reverberation time t is found from the equation for decaying intensity,

$$\frac{I}{I_0} = 10^{-6} = \epsilon^{-kt}$$

whence, by taking logarithms,

$$t = \frac{1}{k} \log_\epsilon \frac{I_0}{I} = \frac{2.303}{k} \log_{10} \frac{I_0}{I} = \frac{2.303}{k} \log_{10} 10^6 = \frac{2.303 \times 6}{k}$$

Since the persistence of sound is due to incomplete absorption at successive reflections, the reverberation time t will be longer in a large room than in a small one, consequently the interval between reflections will depend upon the volume. For a similar reason this time will vary inversely with the velocity of sound. Furthermore, it is influenced by the character of the surfaces in the room, being reduced if their *absorbing power* is large. Representing the volume of the room in cubic feet by B, the velocity of sound in feet per second by $V = 1100$, and the absorbing power of the room in effective square feet by a, these effects may be incorporated in the foregoing equation by taking $c\dfrac{B}{Va} = \dfrac{1}{k}$. Theory and experiment show that the constant c has the value 4 for the units employed; consequently, the reverberation time becomes

$$t = \frac{4 \times 2.303 \times 6}{1100} \times \frac{B}{a}$$

or
$$t = 0.05\,\frac{B}{a} \tag{223}$$

The absorbing power of the room, including furnishings and audience, is found by adding a number of terms for the various surfaces, each term consisting of the area s multiplied by an appropriate absorption coefficient β, thus

$$a = \beta_1 s_1 + \beta_2 s_2 + \beta_3 s_3 + \cdots$$

although a more exact appraisal of the absorbing power of a room must take account of the manner in which its various absorbing surfaces are distributed.

Absorption coefficients have been measured for many materials, and are expressed as fractions of the "absorption" at an open window of equal area. A felt surface is a good absorber because it contains many tiny channels in which the air vibrations are damped out and their energy converted into heat; its coefficient $\beta = 0.70$ indicates that 1 sq. ft. of felt is equivalent to 0.70 sq. ft. of open window space in quenching reverberation. On the other hand, glass and metals are poor absorbers. Absorption coefficients vary somewhat with the frequency of the sound and upon the condition of the surface. Some values suggestive of the order of magnitude appear in the accompanying table.

Absorption Coefficients

Open window	1.00
Brick wall.	0.03
Carpet, felt lined.	0.40
Draperies, cotton. . . . . : . . .	0.50
Excelsior tile.	0.80
Felt.	0.70
Glass.	0.025
Linoleum.	0.03
Plaster, smooth.	0.03
Wood paneling.	0.08

Absorbing Power (British units)

Auditorium chairs, wood, each.	0.3
Audience, each person	4.0

As an example of sound absorption, compute the reverberation time in an auditorium measuring $60 \times 90 \times 20$ ft., the absorbing materials consisting of 9500 sq. ft. of plaster, 7000 sq. ft. of wood, and 400 sq. ft. of glass, if the room has 800 seats and an audience of 500 persons. The absorbing power, based on the foregoing coefficients, is:

$$
\begin{array}{llll}
\text{Plaster:} & 9500 \times 0.03 & = & 285 \\
\text{Wood:} & 7000 \times 0.08 & = & 560 \\
\text{Glass:} & 400 \times 0.025 & = & 10 \\
\text{Seats:} & 800 \times 0.3 & = & 240 \\
\text{Audience:} & 500 \times (4.0 - 0.3) & = & 1850 \\
\end{array}
$$

Absorbing power   2945 effective sq. ft.;

whence, by equation (223), the reverberation time is

$$
t = 0.05 \frac{60 \times 90 \times 20}{2945} = 1.83 \text{ sec.}
$$

This value appears rather high for an auditorium of this size, and could be reduced by the use of more highly absorbing materials.

The second factor involved in the acoustics of an auditorium is that of interference produced by reflection of the sound waves from the walls and ceiling. As a result, the waves tend to reenforce one another at certain regions and to destroy one another at other regions. Tests by Sabine showed regions within an auditorium where the intensity of sound was greater than at the source, separated by zones of almost complete annulment. In particular, large curved surfaces tend to focus the sound at particular regions. If such a surface is to be used in the architectural design of a room, it should be so shaped that the point of concentration will lie outside the room, thus avoiding the effects observed in so-called "whispering galleries."

The reflection of sound waves in an auditorium is strikingly shown by a method perfected by Professor Arthur L. Foley. The sound disturbance is produced by an electric spark at a chosen point within a model of the auditorium, and spreads outward as a single wave pulse. The advancing compression is illuminated for an instant by a second spark after any desired time interval, and casts a shadow on a photographic plate, showing the position

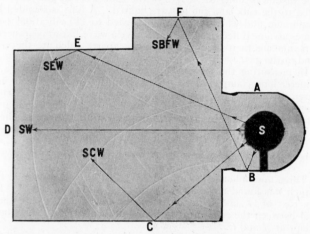

Fig. 370. Momentary positions of a sound wave and its reflections

then occupied by the wave front. The sound photograph shown in Fig. 370 was obtained in this manner, the outline A to F representing a horizontal section of a theatre. In the figure, SW is a sound wave, generated by the electric spark at S, that has not yet arrived at the rear wall D; SCW is one portion of SW that has been reflected from the wall C; and $SBFW$ is the portion of the original wave reflected from the wall B and then from the wall F. Every wave in the figure can be traced to the reflection from one or more of the walls of the model.

PROBLEMS

1. Calculate the intensity levels for a number of sound intensity values between 1 and 10 microwatts per sq. cm., and plot a curve showing these levels in decibels as ordinates against intensities as abscissas.

2. The intensity of a sound wave is 10 microwatts per sq. cm. To what value should this be increased in order to produce a 5-db. rise in intensity level?

3. What change in intensity level would be produced at a transmitter in telephoning if the lips were moved from a position $\frac{1}{2}$ in. away from the transmitter to a position 1 in. away from it?

4. The pitch of a tone is measured by sounding it simultaneously with a siren, the disk of which has 50 holes. When the siren is driven at 540 rev. per min., 3.2 beats are heard per sec., and when it is driven at the next higher speed afforded by the driving motor, namely 546 rev. per min., 1.8 beats are heard per sec. Determine the pitch of the tone under measurement.

5. A method for determining the velocity of sound in illuminating gas, devised by Rubens, utilizes a long metal tube that is closed at one end and fitted with a diaphragm at the other. A row of tiny holes drilled at equal distances along the length of the tube serve as gas jets. Gas is admitted to the tube and the jets are lighted. A tone is sounded before the diaphragm and when its pitch is adjusted to 440 vibrations per sec. the flames assume different heights and have a wave-like appearance. The nodal points are then found to be 56 cm. apart; calculate the velocity of sound in the gas.

6. In measuring the velocity of sound by Kundt's method, an iron rod 1 meter long clamped at the center produces the same pitch as that of a siren driven at 1488 rev. per min., the siren disk having 100 holes. The powder heaps within the tube are 6.9 cm. apart. Compute the velocity of sound in the iron rod and also that in the gas within the tube.

7. Two observers, A and B, listen to the sound from a distant source. To A the sound comes from a direction 35° east of north. To B, who is stationed 500 ft. east of A, the sound comes from a direction 12° east of north. Where is the source with respect to observer A?

8. Three microphone stations, A, B and C, receive the sound from a gun which was found to be 5.4 mi. north and 1.3 mi. east of A. If B is 3.0 mi. east of A, and C is 1.9 mi. southeast of B, compute the time interval between the receipt of the sound at A and B, and that between its receipt at A and C.

*9. Find the reverberation time of the auditorium described in the numerical problem of § 351 when there is no audience.

*10. A broadcasting studio measuring $70 \times 40 \times 25$ ft. has a reverberation time of 0.90 sec. when empty. What will the reverberation time be when an audience of 250 persons is present?

*11. An auditorium has a floor area of 45×30 ft. and is 15 ft. high. It has a linoleum floor and a plaster ceiling. The walls have a wood wainscot $3\frac{1}{2}$ ft. high, above which the windows have an area of 120 sq. ft. and the remaining surface is covered with acoustic material having an absorption coefficient of 0.60. Compute the reverberation time for the empty room.

*12. It is desired to reduce the reverberation time of the auditorium described in the numerical problem of § 351 by covering part of the plaster wall with cotton draperies. How many square feet should be covered in this manner in order to reduce this time to 1.0 sec. with an audience of 500 persons?

13. It is desired to photograph a single-pulse wave spreading outward in air from a sound disturbance, using a flash having a duration of 3 microseconds. How far does the wave advance during this flash?

LIGHT

CHAPTER XXXIII

SOURCES AND VELOCITY OF LIGHT

352. Some Properties of Light. — Light is radiant energy which is capable of affecting the eye to produce vision. Its exact nature, as in the case of gravitation and electricity, is not fully understood, but much has been learned about the way it is produced and propagated. The character of light and the associated problems of atomic structure will be considered in subsequent chapters. For present purposes it will suffice to state that light energy, like other forms of radiation [§ 190], is apparently emitted in tiny quantities called quanta, and transmitted by electromagnetic waves having the various properties described in Chapter XXX.

Our everyday experiences with the behavior of light have to do largely with reflection and refraction; we see our images by reflection in mirrors or in other highly polished surfaces, and we observe the bending of light by refraction where it passes from one medium into another. The latter is usually accompanied by the splitting up of white light into the component colors of the spectrum, an effect called dispersion. Three other effects of interest can be observed with simple facilities. On looking at a distant light source through a piece of silk, the patch of light appears to be made up of a group of small spots; this effect, called diffraction, is due to the slight bending of light in going through the small spaces between the fibres of silk. The colors observed in soap or oil films are due to the interference of waves of light that are reflected from both faces of the films. Passing light through a crystal like tourmaline, or a film like polaroid, gives it a one-sidedness called polarization; this change in character is evidenced by the quenching action produced with another specimen placed crosswise to the first. These and other effects of light are considered in the chapters that follow; the present chapter deals with light sources, the illumination produced by them, and the velocity of light.

583

353. Rays and Waves. — It is generally stated that light travels in straight lines within a uniform medium. This statement is true to a close degree of approximation, as can be shown in many ways. For example, the shape of the shadow which an object casts when illuminated by a distant source is determined by the shape of the object. The straight-line transmission of light is made use of by practically everyone in sighting along edges and surfaces to verify their straightness or flatness.

The direction or path of propagation may be represented by a straight line, called a *ray*. This method of representation will be used frequently in the study of light; thus, the radiation from a point source is often represented by rays diverging from this spot. When such divergent rays enter the eye [§ 402] they are rendered converging by its lens system and are brought to a focus upon the retina; the image there formed stimulates the nerve endings of the retina and the resulting sensation is that of "seeing" the spot from which the rays appear to diverge.

Many of the effects of light can be explained in simple form upon the hypothesis that light travels in straight lines. The fact that light has certain wave properties often provides a more satisfactory explanation of these effects, and in some phenomena like diffraction and polarization, the wave theory alone can be relied upon. In the following chapters either rays or waves will be used, whichever will provide the more simple and straightforward analysis for the particular phenomenon involved.

354. Sources of Light. — The production of light is attributed physically to actions taking place within the atoms of the glowing source. When an atom in its normal state is excited by collision with another atom or by other means, the energy it receives causes the electrons to assume higher energy levels. The subsequent falling of electrons to lower energy levels is accompanied by loss of energy through radiation, and this radiation, striking the eye, produces the sensation of light provided its frequency is within the range of the visible spectrum.

Our great natural source of light is the sun. Its radiation is described in § 189, and curves are given in Fig. 202 which show that most of the energy falls outside the field of vision. In a sense, the moon is also a natural source of light, but strictly speaking, it is merely a reflector of sunlight. Artificial sources of light, in the order of their development through the centuries, include the torch, the oil lamp, the candle, the gas lamp, the carbon arc lamp, the incandescent electric lamp, and luminous gas tubes.

The carbon arc is now used principally for picture projectors and searchlights. Ordinarily it consists of a pair of carbon rods connected in series with a resistance across direct-current supply mains. The arc is started by bringing the carbons into contact and then separating them. As the carbons burn away during operation, they must be fed toward each other manually or automatically to keep the gap between them fairly constant. Most of the light comes from a crater that is formed in the tip of the positive carbon; its temperature is about 3600° K. Arc lamps can also be operated on alternating-current circuits; when so connected both carbons of a lamp become equally bright and the result is not as satisfactory for projection purposes.

Incandescent Lamps. — The incandescent lamp consists essentially of a conducting filament enclosed within a glass bulb and heated so intensely by the electric current that it emits light. The original lamp of this type, brought out by Edison in 1880, used a filament of carbonized bamboo, mounted within an evacuated bulb to prevent oxidation. From this starting point, continued research has brought about numerous improvements, resulting in the tungsten-filament lamp of the present day. These lamps are commonly used for the illumination of streets and highways as well as for all sorts of interiors, and generally operate across 110-volt mains.

About 1910, when it became possible to draw tungsten into small wires, lamp filaments were made of this metal and operated in a vacuum. The early tungsten lamp was more efficient than those previously used because it could be operated at a higher temperature and still have the same life. Its principal drawback was a gradual blackening of the bulb due to deposition upon it of tungsten evaporated from the hot filament. Subsequent improvement brought about the gas-filled tungsten lamp, in which the bulb is filled with an inert gas, such as nitrogen, under a pressure of, say, an atmosphere. The presence of the gas retards the evaporation of the filament, as desired, but produces an undesirable cooling of the filament through convection currents. To offset the latter effect, the filament is arranged in the form of a closely wound helix; in fact, some modern projection lamps have doubly-coiled filaments. This concentration of the filament into a small zone produces a light of great brilliancy.

Luminous-tube Lighting. — Long tubes containing gas at low pressures are widely used for display lighting, neon being used to produce an orange-red light, argon and mercury for blue light and helium for pinkish-white light. These units are usually operated from 110-volt alternating-current mains through step-up transformers. When the circuit is closed an initial potential difference up to 15,000 volts is impressed upon the tube and the gas becomes ionized at the electrodes, the ionization almost instantly extending throughout the tube by collision of electrons and ions with the atoms of the gas. The conduction of electricity through the tube by these carriers is accompanied by the recombining of free electrons with positive ions, causing the electrons to assume lower energy levels and to radiate energy. The energy changes in any gas occur in definite steps and consequently the light emitted has a definite spectral composition and appears as a glow of characteristic color. Typical neon tube units have tubes 9 to 15 mm. in diameter, operating at gas pressures of 10 to 24 mm. of Hg., and taking currents of 15 to 50 milliamperes.

The mercury-vapor lamp, used for industrial lighting and for photographic purposes, has an inclined glass tube containing mercury vapor at low pressure. The negative terminal is a pool of mercury at the lower end of the tube, and the positive terminal at the other end is made of iron. The lamp has a high resistance when not in operation and may be started by tilting the tube so as to connect the terminals by a thin stream of mercury. When the tube is tilted back again this stream breaks, forming an arc which vaporizes the mercury, and the vapor glows with its characteristic blue-green color. Commercial lamps include auxiliary devices for starting automatically, and operate across 110-volt direct-current supply mains. Mercury-vapor lamps are also designed for use on alternating-current circuits.

355. Candle Power of a Light Source. — The luminous intensity of a source of light is expressed in terms of a source selected as a standard; for many years the flame of a spermaceti candle burning at the rate of 120 grains per hour has been used for this purpose. This so-called international candle is taken as having an intensity of 1 candle power when viewed in a horizontal plane. The candle is inconvenient to use, and as a temporary measure the international unit has been maintained by carefully calibrated incandescent lamps deposited in national laboratories.

A new primary standard, developed by the National Bureau of Standards at Washington, has been adopted by action of the International Committee on Weights and Measures, and was scheduled to become effective in 1940 but the change cannot be made so soon. It consists of a glowing enclosure operated at the temperature of solidifying platinum, the brightness of this standard being taken as exactly 60 candles per square centimeter. The arrangement is represented in cross-section by Fig. 371. The platinum, contained in a crucible of fused thorium oxide surrounded by heat insulation, is placed in an alternating magnetic field and melted by the currents thereby induced in it; this method of heating is used because of its violent stirring action. A sight

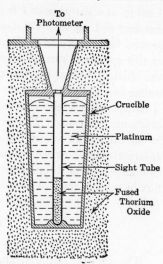

FIG. 371. Primary standard of luminous intensity

tube, also of fused thorium oxide and containing some of this material in a finely ground state, extends into the molten metal and serves as a black-body radiator [§ 189]. The brightness within this tube is taken as 60 cp. per sq. cm., when the metal, in cooling slowly, reaches its solidifying temperature. The new *candle* is therefore one-sixtieth of the luminous intensity of one square centimeter of a hollow enclosure at the temperature of solidifying platinum. The new candle is somewhat smaller than the international candle.

A 1-cp. source will produce a certain illumination of a surface near it. Any other source substituted for this one and which produces the same illumination is also rated 1 cp.; if it produces twice as much illumination it is rated 2 cp., and so on. Such measurements depend upon the response of the eye, and are influenced considerably by the color of the source.

The rate at which a source emits light energy, evaluated in terms of its visual effect, is spoken of as light flux, and is expressed in lumens. One *lumen* is the amount of light flux radiating from a uniform 1-cp. source throughout a solid angle of such size as to surround a unit area at a unit distance from the source. Such a 1-cp. source would radiate 1 lumen normally upon a surface of 1 sq. ft. at a distance of 1 ft., or upon a surface of 1 sq. meter at a distance of 1 meter. By imagining a spherical shell of 1-ft. radius around this source as center, it will be clear that each square foot of this spherical surface receives 1 lumen; since the total area of the shell is 4π sq. ft., the total light flux emitted by the 1-cp. source is 4π lumens.

Most light sources have different luminous intensities along different directions. The average of the candle powers measured in all directions about the source as origin is called the *mean spherical candle power*. Since a source having a mean spherical candle power of 1 cp. emits 4π lumens of light flux, the total flux in lumens emitted by a source of mean spherical candle power I_0 is

$$F = 4\pi I_0 \qquad (224)$$

The inputs, outputs, and efficiencies of some modern incandescent lamps of the tungsten gas-filled type for 110–120 volts are listed in the following table:

Efficiencies of Tungsten Lamps

Input, watts	Output, lumens	Efficiency, lumens per watt
15	140	9.3
25	260	10.4
40	465	11.6
60	835	13.9
75	1100	14.7
100	1580	15.8
150	2610	17.4
200	3640	18.2
300	5910	19.7
500	10050	20.1
750	14550	19.4
1000	20700	20.7

356. Illumination of a Surface. — *The illumination of a surface is defined as the amount of light flux it receives per unit area,* and may be expressed in lumens per square foot or lumens per square meter. The illumination will be uniform when the flux distribution is uniform and when all portions of the illuminated surface are equally distant from the source. Under these conditions, for a surface of area A which receives a total light flux F, the illumination is

$$E = \frac{F}{A} \qquad (225)$$

The illumination produced by a light source upon a given surface is determined by the intensity of the source and its distance from the surface, provided the rays of light strike the surface normally. Upon increasing the intensity I of the source, a proportional increase will occur in the light flux falling upon the surface. Upon increasing the distance from the source, the illumination of the surface will be reduced; its value will be found to vary inversely with the square of the distance. This agrees with the behavior of radiation in general, as expressed by the Inverse Square Law [§ 189]. Considering both of these factors, it is seen that the illumination $E \propto I/r^2$, or $E = k\,I/r^2$, where r is the distance from source to surface, and k is a proportionality factor. Illumination is frequently expressed in foot-candles; *one foot-candle is the illumination of a surface 1 ft. away from a uniform 1-cp. source.* Using this unit for illumination, the factor k in the preceding expression becomes unity, and the expression may be written

$$E = \frac{I}{r^2} \qquad (226)$$

giving the illumination produced by a source of I cp. upon a surface at a distance of r ft. The numerical value of illumination is the same whether expressed in foot-candles or in lumens per square foot.

For example, a surface that is everywhere 8 ft. away from a 256-cp. lamp has an illumination of $E = I/r^2 = 256 \div (8)^2 = 4.0$ ft-candles. To compute the illumination of this surface in lumens per square foot, consider the total light flux issuing from the lamp to be distributed uniformly over a sphere of 8-ft. radius. The total flux is $4\pi \times 256$ lumens, and the spherical surface has an area of $4\pi(8)^2$ sq. ft.; consequently the illumination becomes $E = F/A = (4\pi \times 256) \div (4\pi \times 64) = 4.0$ lumens per sq. ft., as before.

The following table lists a few values of illumination which illuminating engineers regard as minimum figures for the purposes designated. The present trend is toward considerably higher values; some twice as high have been used in recent designs.

Illumination Values

Class of service	Foot-candles
Boxing rings	50
Class rooms and laboratories	8
Corridors and stairways	3
Drafting rooms	15
Flood lighting	4
Hospital operating rooms	75
Library reading rooms	8
Manufacturing plants	3–10
Offices and waiting rooms	5
Retail stores	8
Show windows	30
Tennis courts	15
Theatre and church auditoriums	2

In calculating the illumination by equation (226), it is supposed that all parts of the surface are at the same distance r from the source. This expression is, therefore, true only for a spherical surface with the source at the center, as shown in part I of Fig. 372. It can also be used without appreciable error for a flat surface that is small compared with the distance to the source, provided the light flux is approximately perpendicular to the surface, as shown in part II of the figure. In brief, the equation $E = I/r^2$ applies to normal illumination.

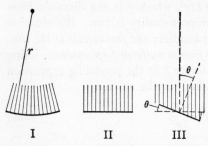

I   II   III

FIG. 372. Illumination of various surfaces

Suppose that a flat surface which would receive an amount of light flux F under normal illumination is inclined so that its normal makes an angle θ with the light rays, as indicated in part III of the figure. The light flux intercepted by the surface will be reduced from F to $F \cos \theta$, and the illumination will be lowered in the same proportion. A source of candle power I at a distance r ft. will produce upon such an inclined surface an illumination

$$E = \frac{I \cos \theta}{r^2} \qquad (227)$$

provided the surface is small in comparison with the distance to the source.

357. Measurement of Candle Power. — The eye is not capable of comparing the candle powers of two lamps by viewing them directly, but can determine quite accurately whether two surfaces side by side are equally illuminated. This is the operating principle of the *photometer*. In this device, two lamps are placed a suitable distance apart with a screen between them, each side of the screen being illuminated normally by one of the sources. The screen is moved laterally until the illumination is observed to be the same on both sides, and the distances from it to the lamps are measured. Applying equation (226),

$$\frac{I_1}{r_1{}^2} = \frac{I_2}{r_2{}^2} \tag{228}$$

where I_1 and I_2 are the candle powers of the sources, and r_1 and r_2 are their respective distances from the screen. From this equation, either candle power can be computed if the other is known.

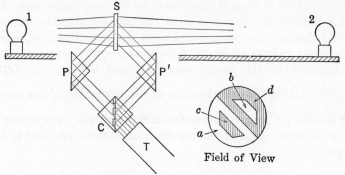

Fig. 373. Diagram of Lummer-Brodhun photometer

In the Bunsen "grease-spot" photometer, the screen consists of a small sheet of paper with a waxed spot near the center, and is provided with a pair of mirrors so that an observer may see both sides at the same time. The Lummer-Brodhun photometer has an improved optical system for accomplishing this purpose. Its elements, shown in Fig. 373, comprise a gypsum screen S, an observing telescope T, reflecting prisms P and P', and a compound glass cube C. The latter element consists of two prisms cemented together, one having a design etched in its principal face to give the field of view the appearance shown. The paths of light along which both sides of the screen can be observed in the telescope are also indicated in the figure. From the side illuminated by source **1**, the rays pass to P and are reflected to C [§ 374], the light passing through to the telescope without obstruction except where the cube is etched. From the other side, illuminated by source 2, the rays pass to P' and are reflected to C, where the light is reflected at the etched portions into the telescope. The field of view is thus illuminated at a and b by lamp 1 and at c and d by lamp 2. When the screen is so placed as to be equally illuminated by the sources, the pattern disappears and the field appears uniform throughout. This arrangement, whereby one portion of the field, illuminated by one source, is completely surrounded by another portion illuminated by the other source, makes it easy for the eye to judge equality of illumination, and permits the candle powers of the light sources to be compared with precision.

An elementary procedure for determining the candle power of a lamp by comparison with the primary black-body standard [§ 355] employs a photometer to compare the illumination on two sides of a screen. One of these is illuminated by the lamp under test. The other receives the radiation from the primary standard after it passes through an aperture of known size placed near it, a lens being used to form an image of the source upon the screen. The illumination of this image may be found by equation (226), $E = \dfrac{I}{r^2}$, taking I as the product of the brightness of the source (60 candles per square centimeter) and the area of the aperture in square centimeters, and r as the distance from the aperture to the screen.

To illustrate such a comparison numerically, suppose that equal illumination is produced when the lamp under test and the aperture of the primary standard are respectively 125 cm. and 340 cm. away from the screen, the aperture having a diameter of 1.7 cm. Expressing the illumination values in lumens per square centimeter, that due to the lamp under test of candle power x is $x/(125)^2$, and that due to the primary standard is $60 \times \pi(1.7 \div 2)^2/(340)^2$. Equating these values, the candle power to be determined is $x = 18.4$ cp.

Difficulties are encountered when it is attempted to compare the candle powers of two lamps that have different colors, since the eye cannot judge accurately the equality of illumination of two surfaces unless their colors match. In measuring incandescent lamps, it is sometimes possible to match their colors by altering the potential difference on the calibrated standard lamp, as the color is noticeably yellower when this is reduced. Lamps of different colors can be compared by means of a so-called *flicker photometer* which enables the observer to view one side of the screen and then the other alternately in rapid succession. Upon increasing the frequency of alternation, a value will be found for which the flicker due to color difference disappears, the colors of the two sources appearing to blend into a single resultant hue. If the frequency is not too high, however, the flicker due to illumination difference remains. The photometer screen is then moved until this flicker also disappears, whereupon the candle powers of the lamps can be compared in the usual way. A rotating prism, or other optical arrangement, is employed to bring the two sides of the screen alternately into the field of view.

The photoelectric cell may also be employed to compare the candle powers of two lamps, even though these sources have different colors. Cells are now available which, when used with suitable filters, have the same sensitivity characteristics as the normal eye [§ 402]. The cell is exposed to each lamp in turn and the corresponding currents are observed by a microammeter. Since the current is proportional to the illumination at the cell, as explained in § 307, the candle power of one lamp can be expressed definitely in terms of the other regarded as a standard.

358. Measurement of Illumination. — Since the object of artificial lighting is to produce adequate illumination, it is essential to have convenient means for measuring this quantity. One instrument for this purpose is the *illuminometer;* it is virtually a portable photometer for comparing the illumination of the surface under measurement with that produced by a small incandescent lamp of known candle power. The lamp is mounted within a light-tight enclosure and can be moved until it produces the same intensity of illumination as that existing upon the surface. Its value is then known to be $E = I/r^2$, I being the candle power of the standard lamp, and r its distance from the surface. A scale may be provided on the instrument to give the result in foot-candles, since each position of the standard lamp corresponds to a particular value of illumination.

A recent development in such measurements is the *photovoltaic cell*, which generates an e.m.f. under exposure to light. A plate of copper covered with a semi-transparent layer of copper oxide is exposed at the point where the illumination value is desired. Electrons pass to the copper electrode and the cell develops an e.m.f.

which is proportional to the illumination. The current is indicated on a microammeter, the scale of which usually is calibrated directly in foot-candles.   No external source of e.m.f. is necessary.   The "Photronic" cell shown with indicating instrument in Fig. 374 is of this general type.

FIG. 374.   Foot-candle meter.   (*Courtesy of Weston Electrical Instrument Corp.*)

359. Measurement of Light Flux. — Candle-power measurements of light sources are now usually conducted to give the average illumination in all directions around a lamp rather than the value in only one direction as afforded by the photometers mentioned in § 357.   Such measurements are made by placing the lamp under test within a large sphere, called a *sphere photometer*, and observing the illumination which it produces at the inner surface.   The walls of the photometer chamber are painted dull white in order to scatter the light in all directions.   While direct illumination of the surface by the light source may have different values at various points, the illumination produced by reflection is uniform over the surface and is proportional to the flux emitted by the source.   This illumination is measured at a small translucent window in the spherical shell that is shielded against direct radiation from the source, the readings being made with an illuminometer, a photoelectric cell, or a photovoltaic cell.

Calling the light fluxes emitted by two lamps F_1 and F_2, and the values of illumination that they produce E_1 and E_2 respectively, it follows that

$$\frac{E_1}{E_2} = \frac{F_1}{F_2}$$

and therefore, by equation (224), the ratio of the mean spherical candle powers I_{01} and I_{02} of these lamps becomes

$$\frac{I_{01}}{I_{02}} = \frac{E_1}{E_2}$$

showing that the mean spherical candle power of a lamp is proportional to the illumination which it produces on the window of the instrument.

*360. Illumination of a Room. — For correct interior lighting a sufficient amount of light should be provided to give the desired value of illumination, and the lighting units should be so designed and placed as to make it reasonably uniform, without glare.

Three methods of lighting are in common use, the so-called direct, indirect, and semi-indirect methods. With direct lighting, the lamps project light directly upon the desired working surfaces. With indirect lighting, the lamps are concealed entirely, and the illumination is produced by reflection from the walls and ceiling of the room. With semi-indirect lighting, the illumination is produced in part by light reflected from the walls and ceiling, and in part by direct transmission, usually through translucent glassware. In all of these methods, a large amount of light is absorbed by the walls and ceiling, particularly if these are dark colored, making it necessary to generate more light at the lamps than is

Coefficients of Light Utilization

Type of lighting unit	Color of both walls and ceiling	Floor area, sq. ft.			
		200	400	800	1600 and over
Direct	Light	0.30	0.34	0.38	0.41
	Dark	0.28	0.32	0.36	0.39
Semi-indirect	Light	0.16	0.20	0.23	0.26
	Dark	0.095	0.12	0.14	0.16
Indirect	Light	0.12	0.15	0.18	0.20
	Dark	0.045	0.065	0.080	0.090

received at the plane of utilization. This is particularly true for small rooms, where these surfaces are relatively large in comparison with the surface to be illuminated.

The usual method of determining the size of lamps to be installed is as follows: First, calculate the number of lumens which must reach the working plane in order to produce the desired illumination value. Next, apply a *coefficient of utilization* suitable for the installation, in order to obtain the number of lumens that must be generated in the lamps. Finally, knowing the efficiencies of the lamps, determine the size of lamp to be used. The coefficient of utilization gives the proportion of the light produced by the lamps which reaches the plane of work; its value varies with the type of lighting unit, the color of walls and ceiling, and the size of the room. Such coefficients have been measured under a wide variety of conditions, and some values suggestive of their order of magnitude are given in the accompanying table. The values listed are based on average conditions of cleanliness of the lighting units, and are appropriate for a 12-ft. ceiling height.

The procedure will be illustrated by calculating the size of lamps needed to give an illumination of 7 ft-candles in a room measuring 20 × 40 ft. with light-colored walls and ceiling. Fig. 375 shows the room divided into eight sections, with a lighting unit at the center of each; this arrangement would afford reasonable uniformity of illumination. The desired illumination is equivalent to 7 lumens per sq. ft., and since the area to be illuminated is 20 × 40 = 800 sq. ft., it follows that 7 × 800 = 5600 lumens must reach the working plane. The coefficient of utilization for the conditions of the room is found from the table to be 0.23 for semi-indirect lighting units; this means that 5600 ÷ 0.23 = 24,400 lumens must be generated in the lamps.

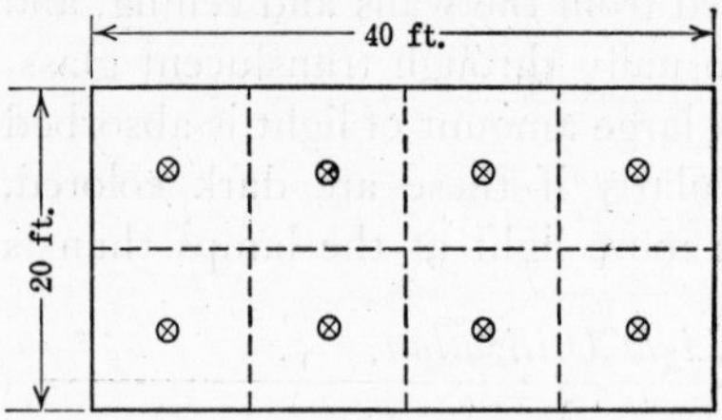

FIG. 375. Design of room lighting

Therefore, each lamp must furnish 24,400 ÷ 8 = 3050 lumens. Reference to the table of lamp efficiencies in § 355 indicates that one 200-watt lamp should be used in each lighting unit.

361. Velocity of Light. — The velocity of light is so extremely great that early attempts to measure it were entirely unsuccessful. It is recorded that Galileo conducted an experiment in which two men, stationed some distance apart, flashed signals to each other with lanterns, a new signal being sent out at the instant one was received. It was hoped that after sending a number of such signals, the velocity of light could be found by dividing the total distance the light traveled by the total elapsed time. It is easy to recognize now that appreciable time intervals are bound to elapse between the receipt of a signal and the sending of a new one, and that the method must fail on this account.

The first successful measurement of the velocity of light was made by the Danish astronomer, Ole Roemer (1644–1710), from observations on the revolution of one of the moons of the planet Jupiter. This method is illustrated in Fig. 376, which represents Jupiter and the earth in their orbits about the sun. Roemer found that the time interval between two eclipses of the satellite (about 40 hr.) was the same when measured with the earth at A and at C, but that the interval was lengthened when the earth was at B and shortened when at D. These variations he judged correctly were not due to irregular motion of the satellite, but were caused by the

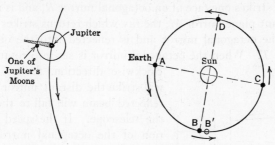

Fig. 376. Velocity of light by Roemer's method

fact that it takes time for light to travel. Thus, if the earth were at B at the beginning of a measurement, it would move away to some position B' during the 40-hr. interval between eclipses, and the light would have to travel the additional distance BB' to mark the conclusion of the test, thus increasing the elapsed time.

From measurements made with the earth at A, Roemer predicted the time at which the moon in question would emerge from behind Jupiter for a particular transit when the earth had moved to C on the supposition that the velocity of light is infinite, but he found that this took place many minutes later than predicted. He considered the difference between the observed and calculated times to represent the time required by the light to traverse the diameter of the earth's orbit. From more recent measurements the time difference is approximately 1000 sec. and the diameter of the earth's orbit is 186,000,000 mi., thus giving 186,000 mi. per sec. as the velocity of light.

362. The Rotating Mirror Method. — A terrestrial method for measuring the velocity of light was devised by the French physicist, Jean B. L. Foucault (1819–1868). He directed a narrow beam of light upon a plane mirror rotating at high speed, and the reflected beam flashed around accordingly. A distant mirror received a momentary flash of light and reflected it back to the rotating mirror, where it was reflected again. During the time interval in which the light beam traveled the measurable distance to the stationary mirror and back, the rotating mirror turned through some definite angle, and from observations of these quantities the velocity of light was computed.

The method just described was improved by the American physicist, Albert A. Michelson (1852–1931). The essential parts of the apparatus are indicated in Fig. 377. Light from a brilliant source X strikes one face of an octagonal mirror R, and is reflected to a distant plane mirror M; the ray which returns strikes another face of the octagonal mirror and is reflected into the observer's telescope T. When the octagonal mirror is set into rotation in a clockwise direction, flashes of light will strike the distant mirror and the reflected beam will fall to the left of the telescope. If the speed of rotation of the octagonal mirror is increased, a value will be reached such that in the time required for the light to travel to the mirror M and back again, mirror face 2 will advance to the position shown at 3. Under this condition the light will be reflected into the telescope again for observation.

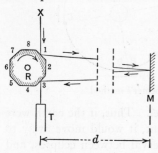

FIG. 377.   Velocity of light by Michelson's method

Letting n represent the speed of the mirror in revolutions per second, the time required to turn through one-eighth of a revolution is $1/(8n)$ sec. In this time the light travels to mirror M and back, a distance $2d$; consequently the velocity of light becomes

$$V = 2\,d \div \frac{1}{8\,n} = 16\,n\,d$$

In Michelson's experiment, the revolving mirror was located at the observatory on Mt. Wilson, California, and the stationary mirror was at Mt. San Antonio, the distance between them (about 22 mi.) being measured by the U. S. Coast and Geodetic Survey. The speed of the revolving mirror was determined by comparison with an electrically operated tuning fork, the fork in turn being calibrated against a free pendulum, which finally was compared with a standard astronomical clock. The velocity of light so determined becomes 299,776 ± 1 km. per sec. when reduced to a vacuum. Tests in an evacuated tube 1 mi. long gave results agreeing substantially with this value. In practice, the velocity is taken as 3×10^{10} cm. per sec. or 186,000 mi. per sec. The symbol c is generally used to represent the velocity of light in centimeters per second.

The velocity of light in the atmosphere is so nearly the same as in a vacuum that the latter values apply without appreciable error. In other media, the velocity is less than in a vacuum, and moreover, is different for different wave lengths, blue light traveling slower than red light.

So great is this velocity that light emitted by the sun reaches the earth in only 8.3 min., whereas an express train driven at 100 mi. per hr. would require over 100 years to travel the same distance. Even with this great velocity, the light from the stars takes years to reach the earth; for the nearest of them, α in the Centauri group, the time is about $3\frac{1}{2}$ years. The Great Nebula in Andromeda is more than 800,000 light-years distant.

PROBLEMS

1. A photographer's flash lamp has a maximum intensity of 4,500,000 cp. How much light flux does the lamp radiate when it has this intensity?

2. Compute the mean spherical candle power of a 100-watt tungsten lamp, assuming its output to be 1580 lumens.

3. The luminous intensity of the direct-current low-intensity electric arc directly in front of the positive crater is given empirically by the equation cp. $= 164\ I^{1.16}$, where I is the current in amperes. When operated at 33 amp. with 55 volts across the carbon electrodes, determine the candle power of an arc in the direction stated, and also the candle power produced per watt of electric power expended in the arc.

4. A white flaming arc taking 40 amp. at 37.5 volts has an efficiency of 79 lumens per watt. Compute the luminous output of this lamp.

5. Calculate the illumination on a desk top produced by a lamp 5 ft. directly above it, the luminous intensity of the source being 60 cp. in a downward direction, (a) when the desk top is horizontal, and (b) when it is inclined 20° with the horizontal.

6. An exhibition floor is illuminated by three 500-watt tungsten lamps located 15 ft. above it. The lamps are spaced 12 ft. apart in a straight line. Compute the illumination on the floor at a point directly beneath the center lamp.

7. A work bench is illuminated by two 300-watt lamps, each having an output of 5910 lumens. The lamps are 7 ft. above the bench and are spaced 16 ft. apart. Calculate the illumination in foot-candles on the bench (a) at a point directly beneath one of the lamps, and (b) at a point half way between them.

8. At what angular elevation will the sun produce half as much illumination on a horizontal surface as that which it produces when overhead?

9. Two lamps having candle powers of 27 and 42 respectively are spaced 150 cm. apart. At what point between them will they produce equal illumination?

10. A 30.0-cp. standard lamp and a lamp under test, located at opposite ends of a photometer bench 200 cm. long, are found to produce equal illumination on a screen placed between them when the screen is 87.5 cm. from the standard lamp. Compute the candle power of the lamp under test.

11. A simple form of photometer is shown in the diagram. The sources S_1 and S_2 illuminate the vertical wall W, upon which an object R casts shadows at regions a and b. These regions are found to be equally illu-

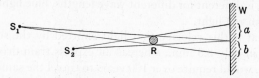

minated for $S_1 = 27.4$ cp. when the object is 1.0 ft. from the wall and the sources S_1 and S_2 are respectively 4.0 ft. and 2.8 ft. from the object. Calculate the candle power of source S_2.

*12. Determine the number and size of lamps to be used for illuminating a library reading room that measures 30×48 ft. and has light walls and ceiling. Semi-indirect lighting units having one lamp each are to be used.

13. In designing the apparatus for measuring the velocity of light by the revolving-mirror method, what speed of rotation must be provided for a 12-sided mirror, if the distant stationary mirror is 35.0 km. away?

14. The velocity of light has been measured by means of a toothed wheel revolving at high speed. Assume such a wheel to have 480 teeth that are just as wide as the spaces between them. A beam of light perpendicular to the wheel passes between two teeth and falls normally upon a stationary mirror 500 meters away. Compute the minimum speed of rotation which will cause a tooth to intercept the reflected beam.

15. (a) If rain is falling vertically with a speed of 6 meters per sec. and if a person is carrying an open tube along level ground at a speed of 1 meter per sec., at what angle should he incline the tube in order that a rain-drop entering at the top will follow the axis of the tube and emerge at the lower end? (b) If a star is directly above a telescope and if the telescope has a velocity of 18.5 mi. per sec. at right angles to this direction because of the earth's orbital motion, at what angle should the telescope be inclined in order that the star may be seen through it?

16. In a series of tests made by Michelson light was reflected back and forth in an evacuated tube about 1 mi. long, and its velocity was measured by the revolving-mirror method. In a typical test, the corrected light path measured 12.8112234 km. and the equivalent speed of the 32-sided mirror was 731.2187 rev. per sec. Compute the velocity of light from these data.

CHAPTER XXXIV

REFLECTION AND REFRACTION

REFLECTION

363. Regular and Diffuse Reflection. — The behavior of a spherical wave front upon striking a plane surface has been considered in Chapter XXX, wherein Huygens' construction was used to determine the location of the reflected wave front. Applying this procedure to the reflection of light, consider a source of luminous flux at S in Fig. 378, located in front of the plane mirror M. At some particular instant the wave front originating at S would have advanced to position WW had it not been for the reflecting surface. When points A and B on the wave front have reached

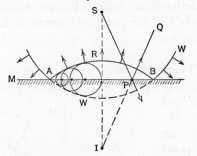

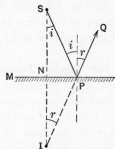

FIG. 378. Reflection of spherical wave at plane surface

FIG. 379. Reflection shown by ray

the positions shown, each intermediate point has reached the reflecting surface and returned to some position along the arc of a secondary wavelet, several of which are represented by the circles in the figure. A curve that meets these arcs shows the position of the reflected wave front R; the reflected wave appears to have come from I, and this point is said to be the *image* of S. By symmetry, the image I is located on a line through S normal to the mirror surface, and is as far back of the mirror as the object is in front of it. Thus a ray of light SP upon striking the mirror is redirected along PQ as though it had come from the image I.

601

These rays, together with the normal connecting source S and image I, are transferred to Fig. 379 for clearness. Since the object and image are equally distant from the mirror, $SN = NI$, and the triangles SNP and INP are similar, the side NP being common. It follows that angle i at S and angle r at I are equal, and these in turn are equal to the angles similarly marked at P. Thus the angle of incidence i between the incident ray and the normal is equal to the angle of reflection r between the reflected ray and the normal, as stated in the law of reflection.

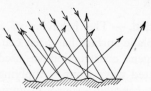

FIG. 380. Surface irregularities magnified to show diffuse reflection

Reflection of light from a smooth surface, like that of a mirror, takes place along a definite direction determined by the direction of the incident ray, and is called *regular* or *specular*. Reflection from a rough or mat surface, like that of plaster or blotting paper, occurs in a great many directions for any one direction of the incident beam, as indicated in Fig. 380, and is said to be *diffuse* or *scattered*. It is by diffuse reflection that non-luminous objects become visible. The law of reflection is evidently true for each tiny element of the reflecting surface in diffuse reflection.

364. Images Formed by Plane Mirrors. — The image of a point object formed by reflection in a plane mirror is known to be located the same distance behind the reflecting surface that the object is in front of it. For an extended object, each object point is similarly located and the complete image may be constructed readily. Fig. 381 shows an object O and its image I formed by reflection in the mirror M. Rays are also drawn for the extreme object points, extending to an eye at E. It will be observed that the

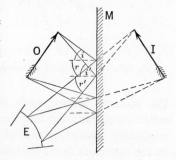

FIG. 381. Reflection in plane mirror

angles of incidence, as at i and i', are equal respectively to the angles of reflection, as at r and r'. The rays from each point enter the eye as a diverging pencil, and the image is at the point where the prolongations of these rays intersect.

Two plane mirrors which are inclined to each other yield multiple images of an object placed between them. These images can be found by the method just explained.

365. Rotation of Reflected Ray. — The rotation of a plane mirror upon which a ray of light falls causes the reflected ray to rotate also, the rotation of the reflected ray being *twice* that of the mirror. This fact is used in amplifying the deflections of galvanometers and other sensitive instruments, and is mentioned in § 96. To prove this relation, consider an incident ray of light from a light source S to fall upon a plane mirror M, Fig. 382, at an angle i with the normal N; it is reflected along Y at an equal angle r. Upon rotating the mirror through an angle β to M', the normal undergoes an equal rotation to N'; the angle of incidence increases to $i' = i + \beta$, and the angle of reflection r' increases equally, the reflected ray being rotated to the position shown at Y'. The reflected ray thus rotates through an angle $YOY' = r' - N'OY = r' - (r - \beta)$. But $r' = i'$ and $r = i$, hence the rotation of the reflected ray may be expressed as

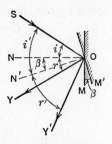

Fig. 382.   Effect of rotating mirror

$$i' - (i - \beta) = (i + \beta) - (i - \beta) = 2\beta$$

which is twice the rotation of the mirror.

In navigation it is necessary to measure the angle between the sun and the horizon which is subtended at the observer's position on board ship, in order to determine the latitude of that position. This is accomplished by the *sextant*, a telescopic instrument which is held in the hand while the observer brings images of the sun and horizon into coincidence in the field of view of a small telescope. The sextant consists essentially of two mirrors called the index glass M and the horizon glass m, Fig. 383, supported perpendicularly to the plane of the sextant on a metal framework which also carries the telescope and a scale. Mirror m is fixed in position and is clear over half its surface so that the observer at E can see the horizon beyond B directly, that is, without reflection at mirror m. Mirror M is carried by an arm which is pivoted at P and fitted with a vernier V at its other end to enable the position of the index glass to be read accurately on scale S. When the two mirrors are parallel, the observer will also see the horizon via the

path $AMmE$, and this image will blend with the direct one obtained
along BE; the vernier for this position of mirror M will read zero.
In viewing the sun at an angle θ degrees above the horizon, the
arm carrying the mirror will have to be turned through an angle
$\theta/2$ so that the rays from the sun coming along the line CM will
be reflected along the line Mm, and again reflected into the telescope by the silvered portion of the horizon glass m. The image

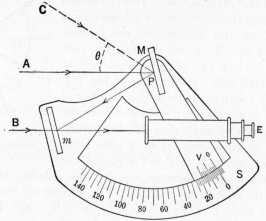

FIG. 383.   Design of a sextant

of the sun then matches the image of the horizon, and the altitude of the sun will be indicated by twice the angle through which
the vernier arm is turned.   By marking each half-degree division
on scale S as one degree, the angular elevation of the sun can be
read directly.

366. Spherical Mirrors. — Curved mirrors are used to deviate
a beam of light and at the same time to render it more or less

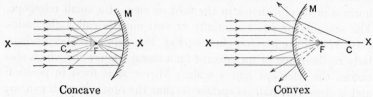

Concave   Convex

FIG. 384.   Reflection from spherical mirrors

converging than before incidence upon the mirror.   Spherical mirrors are classified as *concave* and *convex*, depending on whether
the reflecting surface is on the inside or outside of the spherical
shell.

Fig. 384 shows a concave and a convex mirror *M,M* with a parallel beam of light incident upon each. The center of the spherical surface is called the *center of curvature* of the mirror, and is designated by *C*. A line connecting the middle point of the mirror surface and the center of curvature is called the *principal axis* of the mirror; it is designated by *XX*.

Most spherical mirrors used for optical purposes are comparatively flat, that is, the size of the mirror surface is small in comparison with the radius of the surface; such mirrors are said to have a small *aperture*. With such a mirror, a bundle of rays parallel to the principal axis will pass through a common point *F* after reflection if the mirror is concave, or will diverge as though they originated from a common point *F* if the mirror is convex. The point *F* is the *principal focus* of the mirror, and its distance from the mirror is the *focal length*. The concentration of parallel rays from the sun at the focus of a concave mirror can be shown experi-

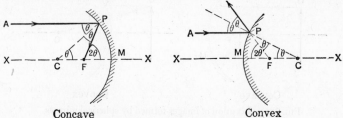

Concave   Convex

FIG. 385.   Location of focus of spherical mirror

mentally by melting a bit of wax or scorching a piece of paper placed at that point.

The principal focus of a spherical mirror is located on the principal axis half way between the center of curvature and the mirror surface. This relation can be proved by reference to the diagrams in Fig. 385. In each of these, an incident ray *AP*, parallel to the axis *XX*, strikes the mirror *M* at *P* and is reflected along the line *PF*. Let θ be the angle of incidence between the ray *AP* and the normal *PC*; then the angle made by the normal at *C* is also equal to θ, since *AP* and *XX* are parallel. The angle of reflection at *P* is equal to the angle of incidence θ; therefore, the angle between the reflected ray and the axis at *F* is 2θ, being the exterior angle of the triangle *CPF*. For mirrors of slight curvature, the angles θ are small, and *PM* may be considered perpendicular to the axis *XX*. Hence,

$$PM = CM \tan \theta = FM \tan 2\theta$$

and placing the angles equal to their tangents, $CM \times \theta = FM \times 2\theta$, or

$$CM = 2\ FM$$

showing that the focus F is half way between the center of curvature C and the middle of the mirror surface M.

367. Images Formed by Spherical Mirrors. — The images produced by spherical mirrors may be larger or smaller than the object, and may be either real or virtual. An image is called *real* if the rays after reflection actually pass through it, and *virtual* if they only appear to do so. Both types present the same appearance to the eye, but a real image can be caught upon a screen, whereas a virtual image cannot.

A graphical method of image location, using rays of light, is indicated in Fig. 386 for a concave and a convex mirror of small

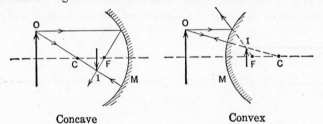

Concave   Convex

FIG. 386.   Location of images formed by spherical mirrors

aperture. In either case two rays are drawn from an object point O to the mirror M; one ray parallel to the axis passes through the principal focus F after reflection if the mirror is concave, or its prolongation does so if the mirror is convex; the other ray through the center of curvature C strikes the mirror normally and is reflected back upon itself. The intersection of these rays (or their prolongations) after reflection is the corresponding image point I. Any other point of the image may be found in the same way. The figure shows the entire objects and images sketched in position by symmetry. The image formed by the concave mirror is real, inverted, and reduced, and that formed by the convex mirror is virtual, erect, and reduced. Concave mirrors may produce images which are real or virtual, erect or inverted, magnified or reduced, depending upon the position of the object. Convex mirrors always produce virtual, erect and reduced images. Although two rays are sufficient to locate the image of a point, it must not be inferred that only two are effective in forming the image. All other rays from the point which strike the mirror contribute to the image as well; consequently the larger the mirror the brighter the image will be.

The image of an object can be located analytically by means of the equation

$$\frac{1}{p} + \frac{1}{q} = \frac{2}{r} = \frac{1}{f} \qquad (229)$$

in which p is the distance from the object to the mirror, q is the distance from the image to the mirror, r is the radius of the mirror, and f is its focal length. The equation can be made to apply to both concave and convex mirrors by considering distances back of the mirror to be negative; thus, r and f have *negative* values for a *convex* mirror. A negative value for q signifies that the image is behind the mirror and is, therefore, virtual.

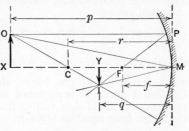

To derive this equation, consider the concave mirror shown in Fig. 387, but regard it as considerably flatter than depicted. The object and image are located respectively at O

Fig. 387.   Distances involved in the mirror equation

and I as in the previous figure, and the same two rays are shown joining their head-ends, one through P and F, and the other through C. Also another ray is shown between these points; it extends from O to M and is reflected by the mirror along MI, the incident and reflected rays making equal angles with the axis XM. Using these rays, two pairs of similar triangles are formed. From one pair, OXC and IYC, it follows that

$$\frac{OX}{IY} = \frac{XC}{CY} = \frac{p - r}{r - q}$$

and from the other, OXM and IYM,

$$\frac{OX}{IY} = \frac{p}{q}$$

Combining, $\dfrac{p}{q} = \dfrac{p - r}{r - q}$, or $q r + p r = 2 p q$. Dividing through by $p q r$ yields

$$\frac{1}{p} + \frac{1}{q} = \frac{2}{r}$$

and the focal distance $f = r/2$, as before. The relation between the object distance p, the image distance q, and the radius r can be shown to apply to any spherical mirror, whether concave or convex, provided it has a small aperture.

The sizes of object and image can be compared by reference to the similar triangles OXM and IYM. The size of the image IY is to the size of the object OX as the image distance q is to the object distance p, neglecting signs. Thus, for any spherical mirror

$$\text{Magnification} = \frac{IY}{OX} = \frac{q}{p} \tag{230}$$

To illustrate, an object is placed 12 cm. in front of a convex spherical mirror of 15 cm. radius. Locate and describe the image, and find its size if the object is 3.0 cm. high. Transposing equation (229) and substituting numerical values,

$$\frac{1}{q} = \frac{2}{r} - \frac{1}{p} = \frac{2}{-15} - \frac{1}{12} = -\frac{13}{60}$$

and therefore $q = -\dfrac{60}{13} = -4.6$ cm. Consequently, a virtual image will be produced 4.6 cm. behind the mirror. The second diagram in Fig. 386 if drawn to scale would serve as a graphical solution of this problem, and would show further that the image is erect. The height of the image, from equation (230), is

$$\frac{4.6}{12} \times 3.0 = 1.15 \text{ cm.}$$

368. Spherical Aberration. — The foregoing treatment of spherical mirrors applies to those of small aperture, the incident light rays being only slightly inclined to the principal axis. When such is not the case, the images formed are confused and imperfect. For example, rays issuing from a point source on the axis do not come to a focus at a common point because the rays reflected from the outer parts of the mirror cross the axis nearer to the mirror than those reflected from the central portion. This imperfection is called *spherical aberration*, and is illustrated in Fig. 388, where the symbols C, F and M have the same meaning as before. The image of the source P formed by this hemispher-

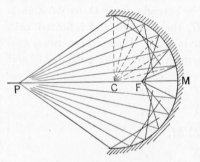

FIG. 388. Spherical aberration

ical mirror is drawn out along a surface generated by the intersecting reflected rays; a cross-section of this surface is a line called the *caustic* of the reflecting surface. This peculiarity can be observed on the surface of milk in a glass when illuminated obliquely by a distant source, the glass acting as the reflector and the milk as a screen.

It is possible, of course, to design a reflecting surface of such shape that rays from a definite object point will be brought to a common focus. For an object point at infinity, the mirror would be a paraboloid. This form of mirror is often used with searchlights and automobile headlights. The lamp is placed at the focus and the light which is directed toward the mirror is reflected in a parallel beam.

REFRACTION

369. Refractive Index. — The phenomenon of refraction is described in § 330, where it is shown that a plane wave undergoes an abrupt change of direction upon passing obliquely into another medium wherein it travels with different velocity. This result can be represented more simply by rays of light than by progressive positions of the wave front. Suppose the light to pass from medium 1, where its velocity is V_1, into medium 2, where its velocity is V_2. *The ray will be deviated toward the normal when the velocity is reduced*, that is, when $V_2 < V_1$; and *it will be deviated away from the normal when the velocity is increased*, that is, when $V_2 > V_1$. In Fig. 389, i is the angle of incidence and r is the angle of refraction, both with respect to the normal N. In this case $V_1 > V_2$ and therefore $i > r$. Some of the incident light will be reflected at the surface of separation, but the reflected ray is omitted in the figure for clearness.

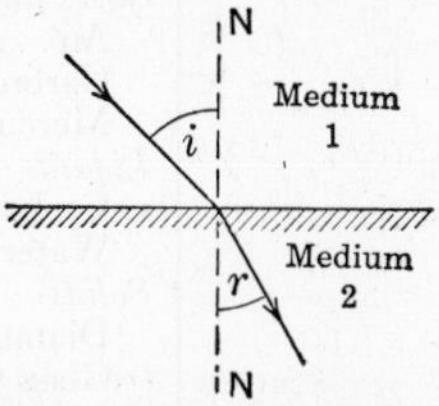

Fig. 389. Refraction shown by ray

The ratio of the light velocities V_1/V_2 in two contacting substances is a constant for those media, and is called the *refractive index* of the second medium relative to the first; it is represented by the symbol μ_{12}, the order of the subscripts indicating the direction of light travel. Combining this concept with equation (211), the law of refraction may be expressed mathematically as follows:

$$\frac{\sin i}{\sin r} = \frac{V_1}{V_2} = \mu_{12} \tag{231}$$

The (absolute) refractive index of a substance is its index with respect to a vacuum; this has practically the same value as the index against air. Thus, if the velocity of light is V_s in a particular substance, V_o in a vacuum, and V_a in air, the index of the substance is

$$\mu = \frac{V_o}{V_s} = \text{approximately } \frac{V_a}{V_s}$$

The refractive index of a substance can be measured very simply by passing a narrow beam of light into it in the manner suggested in Fig. 389, observing the angles of incidence and refraction, and applying equation (231). The refractive index of a substance varies somewhat with the wave length of light [§ 324]; the following list gives a few representative values as measured with yellow light of wave length approximately 0.00006 cm. It is natural that glass, being a synthetic product, should vary considerably in refractive index, depending upon the ingredients used; the table indicates the range of values to be expected. Methods are available for measuring the index of refraction of all kinds of substances very precisely.

Indices of Refraction

Gases and Vapors	
Air...........................	1.0002918
Carbon dioxide...............	1.0004498
Mercury vapor................	1.000933
Liquids	
Carbon disulfide..............	1.6276
Water........................	1.3330
Solids	
Diamond.....................	2.417
Glass (crown)................	1.48 to 1.61
" (flint)..................	1.53 to 1.96
Ice..........................	1.31
Rock salt....................	1.5443

To emphasize the physical meaning of the refractive index, consider a particular value. For ice $\mu = 1.31$, and this means that the velocity of light in vacuum (or air) is 1.31 as great as in ice; also that it will take the same time for light to travel through 1 cm. of ice as it takes to travel through 1.31 cm. of air. Thus, μ *indicates numerically the equivalent air distance of 1 cm. of a substance.*

370. Refraction in Parallel-sided Plates. — A ray of light in passing through one or more parallel-sided slabs and emerging into the original medium is displaced laterally but is not deviated. This result is shown in Fig. 390, where a, w and g represent any three different media such as air, water, and glass.

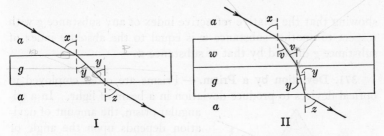

FIG. 390. Light passing through parallel-sided slabs

Consider, first, a single slab as in part I of the figure, and call the angles of incidence, refraction and emergence x, y and z respectively. Applying the law of refraction to each surface of the glass,

$$\frac{V_a}{V_g} = \frac{\sin x}{\sin y} = \mu_{ag} \quad \text{and} \quad \frac{V_g}{V_a} = \frac{\sin y}{\sin z} = \mu_{ga}$$

Multiplying these equations member by member shows that, since the product of the first members is unity,

$$\frac{\sin x}{\sin y} \times \frac{\sin y}{\sin z} = 1$$

whence angles x and z are equal, making the incident and emergent rays parallel. It appears further that

$$\mu_{ag} = \frac{1}{\mu_{ga}} \tag{232}$$

showing, for example, that the refractive index of glass with respect to air is the reciprocal of the index of air with respect to glass.

Applying the same procedure to the arrangement shown in part II of the figure, it can be shown that the angle of incidence x and the angle of emergence z are equal, and also that

$$\frac{V_a}{V_w} \times \frac{V_w}{V_g} \times \frac{V_g}{V_a} = 1$$

It follows herefrom that

$$\mu_{aw} \times \mu_{wg} \times \mu_{ga} = 1$$

whence

$$\mu_{wg} = \frac{1}{\mu_{aw} \times \mu_{ga}} = \frac{\mu_{ag}}{\mu_{aw}} \qquad (233)$$

showing that the relative refractive index of any substance g with respect to another substance w is equal to the absolute index of substance g divided by that of substance w.

371. Deviation by a Prism.

— Prisms are often employed in optical devices to produce deviation in a beam of light. In a tri-

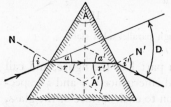

FIG. 391. Ray passing through prism

angular prism, the amount of deviation depends upon the angle of the prism, upon its refractive index, and also upon the angle of incidence. It can be shown, either by experiment or by calculation, that for such a prism the deviation has a *minimum* value when the ray passes *symmetrically* through it as shown in Fig. 391.

To prove this relation analytically, consider a beam of light to strike one face of the prism at an angle i with the normal N, and to be refracted at an angle r with this normal. It will then go through the prism and emerge from the second face making angles of incidence r' and refraction i', with the normal N'. From geometric considerations the angle A of the prism is equal to the angle A' between the two normals, and since the latter angle is the exterior angle of a triangle of which r and r' are the opposite interior angles, it follows that $A = r + r'$. The angle of deviation between the incident and emergent rays is the sum of the deviations produced at the two faces individually, or

$$D = a + a' = i - r + i' - r' = i + i' - A$$

Taking μ as the index of refraction of the prism relative to air, and applying the law of refraction, it follows that $\sin i = \mu \sin r$ and $\sin i' = \mu \sin r'$, making the deviation

$$D = \sin^{-1}(\mu \sin r) + \sin^{-1}[\mu \sin (A - r)] - A$$

In order to find the relation between the angles r and r' which will make the deviation a minimum, differentiate the foregoing expression with respect to r; then equate the result to zero and solve. Thus,

$$\frac{dD}{dr} = \frac{\mu \cos r}{\sqrt{1 - \mu^2 \sin^2 r}} - \frac{\mu \cos (A - r)}{\sqrt{1 - \mu^2 \sin^2 (A - r)}} = 0$$

whence

$$\frac{\cos^2 r}{\cos^2 r'} = \frac{1 - \mu^2 \sin^2 r}{1 - \mu^2 \sin^2 r'}$$

and it follows that $r = r'$. Consequently the minimum deviation of the beam in passing through the prism occurs when the angles r and r' are equal, whereby angles a and a' are also equal. Then the angle of minimum deviation will be

$$D_m = a + a' = 2a = 2(i - r)$$

The index of refraction μ of the material constituting the prism can be expressed in terms of the prism angle A, and the angle of minimum deviation D_m. This will be done by expressing the angles of incidence and refraction in terms of these quantities, and applying equation (231). From the foregoing, the angle of refraction is $r = \dfrac{A}{2}$, and the angle of incidence is $i = \dfrac{D_m}{2} + r = \dfrac{D_m + A}{2}$. Applying the law of refraction, there results

$$\mu = \frac{\sin i}{\sin r} = \frac{\sin \frac{1}{2} (D_m + A)}{\sin \frac{1}{2} A} \tag{234}$$

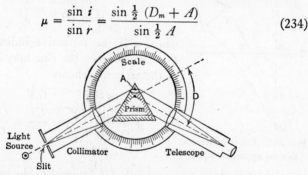

Fig. 392. Deviation of light measured on a spectrometer

An accurate determination of the refractive index of a substance can be made if measurements of A and D_m are taken on a prism of that substance. For liquids, a hollow glass prism is used to hold the liquid; the faces of the prism, being parallel-sided slabs, produce no deviation and thus do not influence the result. The measurements are made with a spectrometer, the essential parts of which are shown in Fig. 392. The test is conducted most simply with light of a single wave length, corresponding to a particular color of the spectrum.   The light enters the instrument through a narrow slit, is formed into a parallel beam by a lens, and falls upon the prism.   Here it undergoes refraction and upon emergence is received by a suitably placed telescope, in which the observer sees an image of the slit.   The prism and telescope are turned by trial until the angle of deviation D is observed to be a minimum; the value of this angle may be read from the circular scale.   The angle A is usually measured optically by reflecting light from one face of the prism, as from a plane mirror, and then rotating the prism until the second prism face occupies the same position; the angle A is found by subtracting the angle of rotation from 180°.

372. Apparent Depth of a Submerged Object. — Refraction

causes an object which is immersed in a medium of higher refractive index than air to appear nearer the surface than it actually is.   Suppose O, Fig. 393, to represent a stone in water a distance GO below the surface S, with light rays extending to the eye as shown.   Considering the ray OXY, the angle of incidence is equal to GOX and the angle of refraction is equal to GIX, therefore

$$\frac{\sin GOX}{\sin GIX} = \frac{1}{\mu}$$

where μ is the refractive index of water. For small angles the sine may be equated to the tangent, whence

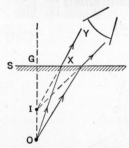

Fig. 393.   Effect of refraction on apparent depth

$$\mu = \frac{\tan GIX}{\tan GOX} = \frac{\dfrac{GX}{GI}}{\dfrac{GX}{GO}} = \frac{GO}{GI}$$

showing that the apparent depth, GI, is equal to the actual depth, GO, divided by the refractive index of the medium, when viewed from above.   A small part of the incident light along OX is reflected at the surface S, but this effect is omitted in the figure.

373. Atmospheric Refraction. — Probably most persons have

noticed the apparent quivering of an object when observed across the top of a hot radiator.   Heating the air lowers its refractive index, and the mixing of the warm air with the colder air in the process of convection produces an irregular bending of the transmitted light rays.

Light from outer space encounters air of increasing density and increasing refractive index as it approaches the earth. Consequently, a beam of light slanting downward through the atmosphere is bent more and more toward the vertical as it advances. For this reason, the stars are not seen in their true positions unless directly overhead. The same phenomenon also explains the fact

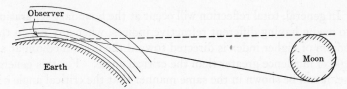

FIG. 394. Illustrating atmospheric refraction

that the entire disk of the sun or moon may be seen for a short time when it is geometrically below the horizon where it would not be visible at all except for atmospheric refraction. This effect is pictured in Fig. 394.

374. Total Reflection. — A ray of light in a medium of high refractive index and directed toward one of lower index, passes into the second medium with refraction, provided the angle of incidence is not too large. If the ray is inclined more and more, however, a position will be reached in which it *does not pass into the second medium*, but is *totally reflected* at the surface of separation.

Suppose a source O, located in water of refractive index μ, to emit light rays in various directions, a few of which are indicated in Fig. 395. The light emitted along OA is mostly refracted into the air along AP in such direction that $\dfrac{\sin i}{\sin r} = \dfrac{1}{\mu}$, but a small part is reflected along AW. Similarly, the light emitted along OB is partly refracted along BQ and partly reflected along BX.

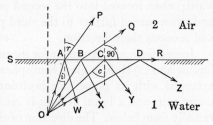

FIG. 395. Illustrating total reflection

The ray OC strikes the surface S at such an incident angle c that the refracted ray CR grazes the surface, the angle of refraction being 90°; the reflected part travels to Y. Any ray such as OD for which the angle of incidence is greater than c, does not emerge into the air but is totally reflected along some line DZ.

The angle c is called the *critical angle* of incidence; it is the angle of incidence in the more highly refractive medium for which the angle of refraction in the other medium is 90°; its value is evidently given by

$$\sin c = \frac{1}{\mu} \qquad (235)$$

In general, total reflection will occur at the boundary separating two media having different refractive indices, when any ray in the medium of higher index is directed toward the other medium at an angle of incidence greater than the critical angle. For this general case, it can be shown in the same manner that the critical angle c is given by the relation

$$\sin c = \frac{\mu_2}{\mu_1} \qquad (236)$$

when $\mu_2 < \mu_1$.

The principle of total reflection is frequently used in optical instruments. Fig. 396 shows three positions of a prism, having

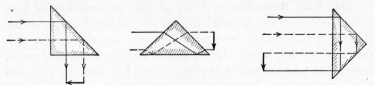

FIG. 396.   Total-reflecting prisms

two 45° angles, in the path of the light rays forming an image. In the first position, the prism acts like a plane mirror tilted downward; when rotated into the second position it inverts the image; and when turned further to the third position it displaces the rays and reverses their direction.

In one form of instrument for measuring the refractive index of liquids and crystals, a glass hemisphere of high refractive index is arranged with its plane face horizontal to receive the specimen under test, and a beam of light is caused to enter the hemisphere radially from below. The direction of the entering beam is adjusted so that when it impinges upon the specimen it will undergo total reflection. The reflected beam will emerge radially and is received by a telescope that can be moved along a scale for reading its position. In testing a liquid, a few drops of it are placed upon the hemisphere and the telescope is moved to the position which indicates the critical angle of total reflection. In testing a crystal, a few drops of a liquid of higher refractive index (like monobromnaphthalene) are placed between the hemisphere and the lower face of the crystal to provide optical contact and the same procedure is followed; the film of liquid has parallel faces and so does not introduce an error in the result.

A test is conducted with such an instrument to determine the refractive index of "lucite," a transparent plastic material. Using sodium light, for which the glass hemisphere has an index of 1.9180, the critical telescope position is 51° 50′ away from the vertical. Upon analysis it will be clear that the reading is unaffected by the presence of the contact liquid and that the refractive index of the lucite specimen is $1.9180 \times \sin 51° 50′ = 1.5080$. With the specimen removed but the liquid remaining in place the telescope position reads 59° 54′. From this value, the refractive index of the contact liquid mentioned is found to be $1.9180 \times \sin 59° 54′ = 1.6594$.

*375. The Refractometer. — A number of instruments called *refractometers* have been designed for the rapid and precise measurement of refractive index. One of these, due to Pulfrich, is illustrated diagrammatically in Fig. 397. It consists of a right-angle prism P upon which the specimen X is placed, a lens L for converging a beam of monochromatic light along the interface,

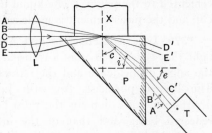

FIG. 397. Diagram of a refractometer

and a telescope T which can be moved around a graduated quadrant to show the direction of the emergent rays. The prism has a known refractive index, which is higher than that of any material to be tested. Rays such as A and B will be refracted to positions $A′$ and $B′$ respectively in the telescope, giving a band of light which is terminated sharply by the limiting ray $CC′$ that makes grazing incidence. Rays such as D and E will be totally reflected along $D′$ and $E′$ and will not enter the telescope, which is set on the boundary of the refracted beam.

The refractive index μ_X of the test specimen can be found in terms of the angle of emergence e and the refractive index μ_P of the prism. Applying the law of refraction, and noting that the critical angle c is complementary to the angle of incidence i on the vertical face,

$$\mu_P = \frac{\sin e}{\sin i} = \frac{\sin e}{\sin (90° - c)} = \frac{\sin e}{\cos c}$$

from which

$$\cos c = \frac{\sin e}{\mu_P}$$

Also for grazing incidence, by equation (236),

$$\sin c = \frac{\mu_X}{\mu_P}$$

But since $\cos^2 c + \sin^2 c = 1$, it follows that

$$\frac{\sin^2 e}{\mu_P{}^2} + \frac{\mu_X{}^2}{\mu_P{}^2} = 1$$

from which the index of refraction of the specimen becomes

$$\mu_X = \sqrt{\mu_P{}^2 - \sin^2 e} \qquad (237)$$

For measuring the refractive index of liquids, a short glass tube is cemented to the prism. The liquid under test is poured into this cup and the measurement is made as for a solid.

*376. Loss in Reflection and Absorption. — The amount of light that is reflected from a transparent substance depends upon the angle of incidence and the refractive index of the substance. The French physicist, Augustin J. Fresnel (1788–1827), first derived an expression for the ratio between the intensity of the reflected beam and that of the incident beam. For natural (unpolarized) light perpendicularly incident within a medium of refractive index μ_1, upon a transparent substance of refractive index μ_2, the ratio of intensity I of the reflected light beam to the intensity I_o of the incident beam is given by

$$\frac{I}{I_o} = \left(\frac{\mu_2 - \mu_1}{\mu_2 + \mu_1}\right)^2 \qquad (238)$$

For light reflected in air against glass of refractive index 1.5, the ratio of intensities is $(0.5/2.5)^2 = 0.04$, showing that 4 per cent of the incident light intensity is reflected as a result of perpendicular incidence upon an air-glass boundary.

The amount of absorption of light in its passage through a transparent substance depends upon the nature of the absorbing medium and upon its thickness. Regarding the total thickness as made up of a number of equally thin layers, each one will absorb the same fraction of the light incident upon it. Thus, if 1000 lumens impinge upon the first layer and if each absorbs 1/10 of the light which reaches it, the amount incident upon the second layer will be 900 lumens, upon the third layer 810 lumens, and so on. For light of a given color, it has been established by experiment that an infinitesimally thin layer cuts down the intensity by an amount which, expressed as a fraction of its value, is directly proportional to the thickness of the layer. Taking I as the intensity at a particular layer of infinitesimal thickness dt and $-dI$ as the change of intensity in this layer, the foregoing statements can be expressed mathematically in the form

$$-\frac{dI}{I} = k\, dt$$

where k is a constant of the material called its absorption coefficient. Integrating this expression gives the intensity of a light-beam after passing through a thickness t of a medium having an absorption coefficient k in terms of the intensity I_0 of the incident beam by the equation:

$$I = I_0 \epsilon^{-kt} \tag{239}$$

ϵ being the base of natural logarithms.

PROBLEMS

1. A man desires to purchase a plane mirror so that he can mount it vertically to see his full height. How small a mirror will serve this purpose for a person 5.75 ft. tall?

2. Locate the images of a point source of light placed between two plane mirrors which are inclined at 90° to each other, and show graphically the paths of the rays by which the images may be seen.

3. A ray of light impinges upon a plane mirror carried by a galvanometer coil and is reflected upon a straight scale parallel to the undeflected mirror and 50 cm. from it. If the coil swings through an angle of 10°, how far will the spot of light on the scale move from its undeflected position?

4. An object is located 20 in. in front of a concave spherical mirror having a radius of 8 in. Locate the image analytically and graphically and describe it fully. If the object is 4 in. high, what is the height of the image?

5. An object 5 cm. high is placed 60 cm. in front of a concave spherical mirror of 20-cm. radius. Locate the image both analytically and graphically. Describe the image and determine its size.

6. Compute the focal length of a concave spherical mirror which yields an image $\frac{1}{8}$ as large as an object 1 meter away from the mirror.

7. What magnification will be produced by a concave spherical mirror of 12-cm. radius if the object to be magnified is placed 10 cm. in front of it?

8. Given a concave spherical mirror of 15-cm. focal length. An object is placed successively at the following distances from the mirror: ∞, 60 cm., 30 cm., 20 cm., 15 cm., 10 cm., and 0 cm. Locate the corresponding images by the analytical method.

9. Compute the focal length of a convex spherical mirror which yields an image $\frac{1}{5}$ as large as an object 1 meter away from the mirror.

10. An object is located 2 ft. in front of a polished metal ball 1 ft. in diameter. Locate the image both analytically and graphically. Describe the image, and determine its size if the object is 4 in. high.

11. A ray of light impinges upon the surface of water at an angle of incidence of 45°. Compute the directions of the reflected and refracted rays.

12. A ray of light slanting downward 30° from the horizontal passes through a layer of water and enters ice having an absolute index of refraction of 1.31. Find the direction of the ray in the ice, and also the relative refractive index of the ice with respect to water.

13. A specimen of glass has a refractive index of 1.50. Compute the index of this glass relative to water, and also the index of water relative to the glass.

14. A ray of light passes obliquely through a parallel-sided glass plate of thickness t, the angles of incidence and refraction at the surface where the light enters the glass being denoted by i and r respectively. Show that the lateral displacement of the ray is given by $\dfrac{t \sin (i - r)}{\cos r}$.

15. Find the refractive index of the amber plate described in Problem 19 of Chapter XXX.

16. Determine the angle of minimum deviation produced by a glass prism of 45° angle, if the glass has an index of refraction of 1.62 for the light used in conducting the test.

17. A hollow prism of 60° angle, made with parallel-sided glass plates, is filled with carbon disulfide. Compute the angle of minimum deviation when yellow light is passed through this prism.

18. A horizontal ray of light strikes the center of one of the vertical faces of an equilateral triangular prism, the angle of incidence being 30°. Determine the changes in direction of the ray at the prism faces, and construct a diagram showing the path of the transmitted ray. Take the refractive index as 1.5.

19. A flint glass prism of 60° angle is found upon test to produce a minimum deviation of 52° 40' for yellow light. Determine the index of refraction of the glass for this light.

20. What is the largest angle that a prism of refractive index 1.60 can have, and still make it possible for light undergoing minimum deviation to enter and emerge from the prism?

21. A pole dips into water at an angle of 15° with the surface. If the portion immersed is 4 ft. long, find the apparent depth of the immersed end, as seen from directly above.

22. A pebble 2 ft. below the surface of still water when viewed obliquely from a point 3 ft. above the surface appears in a direction 30° downward from the horizontal. From this point of observation, along what direction should a rifle be aimed in order to point directly at the pebble?

23. Compute the minimum refractive index for a substance in order that a ray of light within it which strikes its surface at an angle of 45° may be totally reflected.

*24. A ray of light from glowing sodium vapor is passed upward through the flat bottom of a flint glass cup containing methylene iodide. For this light, the refractive index of the glass is 1.920 and that of the liquid is 1.738. At what critical angle of incidence in the glass will the refracted ray gaze the interface of the two media?

CHAPTER XXXV

DISPERSION, SPECTRA AND COLOR

377. Dispersion. — White light, such as that produced by the glowing carbons of an arc lamp, is in reality composed of many colors blended together. When a narrow slit is illuminated by such white light and the issuing beam is refracted through a prism, the colors are spread out into a brilliant array, merging insensibly into one another and forming a *spectrum*. Although there are hundreds of distinct hues in the spectrum, they may be grouped broadly into six principal colors. These are red, orange, yellow,

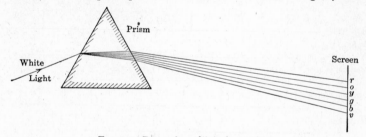

FIG. 398. Dispersion of light by a prism

green, blue, and violet, in the order of increasing deviation, and are indicated by their initial letters in Fig. 398. Color is determined by the frequency of vibration and the associated length of the light wave, the wave length being greatest for red and least for violet. Passing the light through a second prism, identical with the first and arranged to produce deviation in the same direction, will yield a spectrum of double length. If the second prism is opposed to the first, the colors will be recombined into white light. The spreading out of a light beam into its component colors is known as *dispersion*.

It has been observed that the deviation produced by a prism is greater for the shorter wave lengths of white light. No definite relation exists between wave length and deviation, however, and prisms of different substances spread out the component colors of the spectrum to somewhat different extents. If two such prisms are arranged one above the other in such a manner that their spectra match exactly at two colors, say at the extremes of the red and violet portions, it will be found that the intermediate colors do not register point by point. A few substances exhibit what is known as *anomalous* dispersion; prisms of such substances do not disperse white light in the regular color sequence. Thus, fuchsine deviates red and orange light more than blue and violet, and absorbs the middle portion of the spectrum.

The spectrum extends at both ends into regions which are invisible to the eye, the *infra-red* being beyond the red end, and the *ultra-violet* being beyond the violet end of the visible spectrum.

378. Emission Spectra. — The spectrum produced by a glowing object is termed an *emission* spectrum. Its appearance depends primarily upon the composition and state of the luminous object.

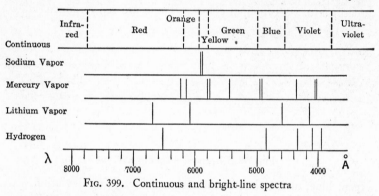

FIG. 399. Continuous and bright-line spectra

Incandescent solids, liquids, and gases under high pressure produce continuous spectra extending from color to color without interruption. Such a spectrum is represented at the top of Fig. 399. Since the colors blend imperceptibly into one another, the boundaries between them, marked by dotted lines in the figure, are only approximate.

Luminous gases and vapors under moderate or low pressure yield spectra consisting of definitely placed bright lines. Each is an image of the slit through which the radiation is received. Every gas emits radiation of particular wave lengths, and each spectrum is characteristic of the radiating substance. Sodium vapor yields two bright lines in the yellow part of the spectrum; they are so close together that unless the slit is very narrow they appear as one line. Mercury vapor yields several bright lines, the most conspicuous being in the green and blue regions. Fig. 399 shows the bright-line spectra of several elements over the range of the visible spectrum; for many of them, other lines may be found in the ultra-violet and infra-red regions. The continuous spectrum is an uninterrupted series of images of the illuminated slit.

The number of lines in a bright-line spectrum depends not only upon the nature of the source, but also upon the amount of energy with which its atoms are excited to produce glowing. Atoms may be excited by imparting energy to them, usually by supplying heat energy in a flame or by supplying electrical energy in an arc or spark, or in a discharge tube [§ 196]. The excitation produced by heating a substance in a Bunsen or in a hotter flame is not as intense as by heating it in an electric arc, and more lines will appear in its spectrum when excited in the latter manner. When the excitation is produced by a disruptive discharge or spark, formed between electrodes made of the material under investigation, the potential needed is much higher than in the case of the electric arc. As a result the excitation is increased, and the spark spectrum will contain more lines than the arc spectrum. Intense excitation of gases at low pressure may be obtained within a discharge tube energized by an induction coil or electrostatic generator.

379. Absorption Spectra. — When the light from a glowing solid or other source yielding a continuous spectrum is passed through an absorbing medium before being dispersed, the spectrum is usually crossed by dark spaces which show that radiations of particular wave lengths have been absorbed. If the absorbing material is solid or liquid, these dark spaces appear as broad, structureless bands. If it is gaseous, they consist of dark lines which occupy the same positions as the bright lines in the corresponding bright-line spectrum.

The production of a dark-line spectrum is illustrated by a well-known experiment showing the reversal of the sodium lines. An arc lamp is arranged to project an intense beam of light upon a prism, the beam being directed through a cloud of glowing sodium vapor produced by heating common salt in a Bunsen flame. A narrow slit is provided near the prism in the light path. In conducting the experiment, the glowing sodium vapor is first used alone; the resulting spectrum consists of the two bright yellow lines characteristic of sodium. Upon starting the arc lamp and shining its rays through the sodium vapor, a continuous spectrum is formed, having two dark lines at exactly the positions previously occupied by the bright lines. This reversal of the lines is explained by supposing that the sodium vapor, which emits these particular lines when excited, responds to the corresponding frequencies of vibration, and absorbs the energy of these particular vibrations from the beam proceeding from the arc. This vapor considered as a source has low luminosity as compared with the arc because of its relative coolness, and hence the spectral lines which it produces are dark in comparison with the rest of the spectrum.

The absorption spectrum of a gas may also take the form of fluted bands, which under sufficient dispersion are found to consist of closely spaced dark lines arranged in an orderly manner. *Band spectra* are emitted only by molecules, and may be contrasted with *line spectra*, since these are emitted only by single or uncombined atoms. From the study of band spectra much has been learned about the structure of molecules and the forces acting within them. Bands occasionally appear in bright-line or emission spectra, but less commonly than in absorption spectra, because the intense excitation used in producing emission spectra is likely to break up the molecules into their component parts.

The solar spectrum appears continuous from a casual inspection; a more critical examination, however, shows that it is crossed

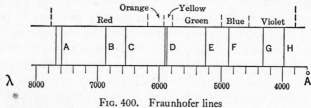

FIG. 400.   Fraunhofer lines

by numerous dark lines. No doubt the radiation from the sun comprises all wave lengths throughout the visible range, but in passing through the sun's atmosphere, certain ones are absorbed; thus the spectrum observed is in reality an absorption spectrum of that atmosphere. The dark lines indicate which gases are present around the sun and also reveal its own composition. The first careful study of these absorption lines was made by the German optician and physicist, Joseph von Fraunhofer (1787–1826), who assigned letters to several of the more conspicuous ones. Their locations are indicated in Fig. 400. These lines are located in

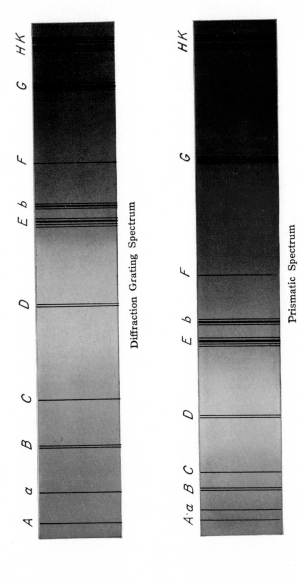

Diffraction Grating Spectrum

Prismatic Spectrum

definite color zones, and are frequently specified when reference is made to particular hues.

In a quantitative study of the spectrum, it becomes necessary to refer to each particular part of it with definiteness. This is done by specifying any hue by the vibration rate f of the light source, or its corresponding wave length λ, the relation between these quantities being given by equation (203), namely

$$c = f\lambda$$

where c is the velocity of light. The wave lengths may be designated in centimeters, but are more commonly expressed in terms of the *Ångström unit*, named in honor of the Swedish physicist, Anders J. Ångström (1814–1874). One Ångström unit $(\text{Å}) = 10^{-8}$ cm. For example, the green line of the mercury spectrum has a wave length $\lambda = 0.00005461$ cm. or 5461 Å. The wave lengths are indicated in the latter manner in Figs. 399 and 400.

It is known that lights of different color travel with different speeds in a transparent medium, a fact which explains why a beam of light comprising many colors is dispersed in passing through a prism. This is illustrated in Fig. 398, where the angles of refraction are different for the several colors, although the angle of incidence is the same for all. In consequence, the refractive index of the medium has a definite value for each color. The accompanying table lists the indices of refraction of a few common materials for light of particular wave lengths corresponding to the C, D, and F Fraunhofer lines. The index for the D line is often used as a reference value because this line is near the middle of the spectrum.

Variation of Refractive Index with Color of Light

	Index of refraction		
	C line (red) 6563 Å	D line (yellow) 5893 Å	F line (blue) 4861 Å
Carbon disulfide (20° C.)....	1.6182	1.6276	1.6523
Crown glass, sample........	1.5145	1.5172	1.5240
Flint glass, sample..........	1.6221	1.6270	1.6391
Water (20° C.).............	1.3312	1.3330	1.3372

380. Dispersion by a Prism. — The amount of dispersion is expressed quantitatively by the angular separation of particular colors of the spectrum. Thus the angle ψ (psi) in Fig. 401 indicates numerically the dispersion of white light produced by a prism from the red to the violet region. This angle is clearly the difference between the deviations of the violet and red components of the incident light beam. Calling these deviations D_v and D_r respectively, the dispersion becomes

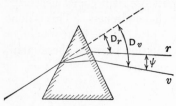

FIG. 401. Deviation and dispersion, with angles exaggerated for clearness

$$\psi = D_v - D_r$$

The deviation produced by a prism is definitely related to the angle of the prism by equation (234), which gives the refractive index as

$$\mu = \frac{\sin \frac{1}{2}(D_m + A)}{\sin \frac{1}{2} A}$$

where A is the prism angle and D_m is the angle of minimum deviation of the ray through the prism. When the prism angle is small, the sines of the angles may be placed equal to the angles, whence, neglecting the difference between the deviation D and the minimum deviation D_m,

$$\mu = \frac{\frac{1}{2}(D + A)}{\frac{1}{2}A}$$

from which the deviation is

$$D = A(\mu - 1) \qquad (240)$$

From this expression it is seen that for a prism of small angle, the deviation is directly proportional to the angle of the prism and to the amount by which the refractive index exceeds unity. This equation can be used for prism angles up to $A = 30°$ without exceeding about 5 per cent error in the deviation.

The dispersion between any two colors may be found for a small-angle prism by using the foregoing equation to compute the respective deviation values. The dispersion between violet and red is

$$\psi = D_v - D_r = A(\mu_v - 1) - A(\mu_r - 1) = A(\mu_v - \mu_r) \quad (241)$$

A prism which produces a large dispersion for a given median deviation is said to have a large *dispersive power*. The dispersive power of a prism is defined as the ratio of the dispersion which it

produces to the deviation of the median ray of the spectrum.
Taking the dispersion between violet and red, and considering
yellow as the middle color of the spectrum, the dispersive power
of a substance is

$$\delta = \frac{A\,(\mu_v - \mu_r)}{A\,(\mu_y - 1)} = \frac{\mu_v - \mu_r}{\mu_y - 1} \qquad (242)$$

When more definite values of deviation, dispersion, or dispersive power are needed, these quantities may be calculated with
reference to particular Fraunhofer lines in the desired regions of
the spectrum. For example, the dispersive power of crown glass,
listed in the table of § 379 over the region from blue to red (F line
to C line), is

$$\delta = \frac{1.5240 - 1.5145}{1.5172 - 1.0000} = \frac{0.0095}{0.5172} = 0.0183.$$

Deviation of light without dispersion can be produced by the
use of two prisms placed so as to deviate the light in opposite directions; the prism materials must have different dispersive powers
and the prism angles must be so proportioned that the dispersion
due to one will annul that due to the other.

For example, the dispersion produced by a 12° crown-glass prism
between the C and F spectral lines is 12° (1.5240 − 1.5145) = 0.114°,
using equation (241) and the refractive indices mentioned. To annul this
dispersion with a flint-glass prism, it must have an angle of 0.114/(1.6391–
1.6221) = 6.7°. The deviation produced by the prism combination, computed for the D line, is 12° (1.5172 − 1) − 6.7° (1.6270 − 1) = 2.005°.

381. Spectrum Analysis. — The detailed study of emission and
absorption spectra is termed spectrum analysis or spectroscopy,
and is of great importance. Perhaps the best-known application
is the identification of the elements present in a sample of unknown
composition by the recognition of their characteristic spectra.
Spectra reveal not only what elements are present but whether
the atoms are parts of molecules or exist by themselves, and in addition furnish evidence as to the conditions of ionization, temperature, and pressure under which they exist.

Analysis of the light from the sun and stars reveals the presence
of the same elements as occur upon the earth; helium derives its
name from having been first discovered in the atmosphere of the
sun. In the spectra of certain stars, the expected lines appear, but
are displaced slightly from their normal positions. This displacement indicates an apparent change in frequency, as explained by

Doppler's Principle [§ 340], and reveals the fact that there is relative motion between the star under examination and the earth. A shift toward the red end of the spectrum, for example, means an apparent increase in wave length or lowering of frequency, and shows that the star and earth are receding from each other. It is from measurements of this kind that the motion of the solar system mentioned in § 25 was computed.

382. Types of Spectroscopes. — Many kinds of instruments are used for the examination of spectra; it will suffice to describe briefly one type for each of the ultra-violet, visible, and infra-red ranges.

A spectrograph for the ultra-violet region is arranged as in Fig. 402. It consists of an equilateral prism of quartz mounted

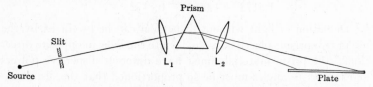

FIG. 402.   Diagram of a quartz spectrograph

between two quartz lenses L_1 and L_2, together with an adjustable slit and a photographic plate holder. Light coming through the narrow slit is made parallel by a collimating lens L_1, and after dispersion by the prism is brought to a focus upon the sensitized

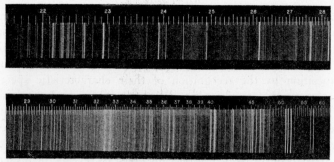

FIG. 403.   Spectral lines of copper arc in ultra-violet and visible regions

plate by a camera lens L_2 (see Chapter XXXVI). The plate is inclined considerably to the dispersed beam in order to accommodate the different focal lengths of the lens for radiations of wave lengths from 2000 to 10,000 Å. The exposure time is suited to the intensity of the source and to the width of the slit. Provision is often made for photographing a scale calibrated in wave lengths next to the spectrum, so that the wave lengths of its individual lines can be read off directly. A spectrogram of a copper arc showing the lines down to 2150 Å appears in Fig. 403.

A spectroscope for the visible region is illustrated in Fig. 404. It consists of a glass prism mounted on a table which can be rotated over a small angular range, two glass lenses L_1 and L_2 which serve

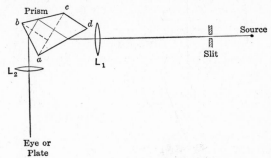

FIG. 404.   Plan of the constant deviation spectroscope

the same purposes as in Fig. 402, a slit of adjustable width, and either a telescope for visual observation of the spectrum or a camera for making a photographic record of it. The prism has the following angles: $a = 90°$, $b = 75°$, $c = 135°$ and $d = 60°$. Its action can be explained by drawing the line ac and dropping a perpendicular to this line from b; this divides the prism into two 30-60-90° prisms and one 45-45-90° prism, the latter serving as a mirror by total reflection. A little study will show that the deviation between the incident and emergent beams is a right angle, and that for all positions of the prism the center of the emergent beam will have minimum deviation. A calibrated scale is fitted to the prism table for reading directly the wave length of the spectral line that appears at the center of the field of view.

Fig. 405 illustrates a constant deviation spectrometer for the infra-red region. It consists of a rock salt prism and a mirror M mounted on a table so that the two can be rotated as a unit, a concave spherical mirror C_1 for forming the incident radiation into a parallel beam, another concave mirror C_2 for focusing the emerging radiation upon the receiving slit, and a thermopile behind the slit in which the radiation sets up an electric current that is measured with a galvanometer. The prism table is moved by a drum carrying a scale, so that the wave length of the radiation falling upon the thermopile can be read directly. The range of a typical instrument of this type is from 3800 to 170,000 Å. A study of the distribution and intensity of the radiation emitted by a black body over this range of wave lengths led to the quantum theory [§ 191].

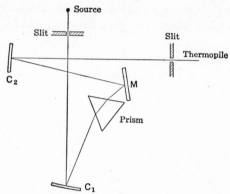

Fig. 405.   Scheme of an infra-red spectrometer

383. Spectral Series. — The definiteness of the spectral lines of the elements has long been regarded as the key to an understanding of atomic structure. Much experimental evidence on spectra has been accumulated and correlated with the quantum theory, as a result of which it is now known that the atom has definite energy levels, and that it assumes a higher energy level upon absorbing energy and assumes a lower one upon emitting energy through radiation.

Johann J. Balmer (1825–1898), a Swiss physicist, found that the spectral lines of hydrogen formed a *series* that could be expressed by the equation

$$\lambda = 3646 \, \frac{N^2}{N^2 - 4}$$

where λ is the wave length of the lines in Ångström units and N is an integer having values greater than 2. For the four most prominent lines in the visible portion of the spectrum, the wave lengths are 6563, 4861, 4340 and 4102 Å. The foregoing equation gives these values when N is taken successively as 3, 4, 5 and 6. For progressively shorter wave lengths, the values of N become larger and larger, the limiting value being for a wave length of 3646 Å in the ultra-violet region.

Other spectral series for hydrogen have been found beyond the visible region of the spectrum.   Professor Theodore Lyman, an American physicist, discovered a simple equation for the lines in the extreme ultra-violet, and Friedrich Paschen, a German scientist and spectroscopist, originated a similar equation for a series of lines in the infra-red region.   More recently two other series extending farther into the infra-red zone have been established. Lines of the various series are usually expressed in terms of the number of waves per centimeter, the so-called *wave number*, rather than the wave length, and when so expressed can be merged into the single equation

$$\nu = 109{,}737 \left[\frac{1}{M^2} - \frac{1}{N^2} \right] \tag{243}$$

where ν is the wave number or the reciprocal of the wave length in centimeters, and M and N are integers having the following values:

Lyman series $M = 1$ $N = 2, 3, 4, \ldots$
Balmer series $M = 2$ $N = 3, 4, 5, \ldots$
Paschen series $M = 3$ $N = 4, 5, 6, \ldots$

Applying these integers, the limiting wave numbers of hydrogen will be 5,334 and 12,193 for the Paschen series, 15,241 and 27,434 for the Balmer series, and 82,303 and 109,737 for the Lyman series. Expressions similar in character to equation (243) have been developed for many other elements.

The mathematical relationship between the wave numbers of spectral lines, as expressed by equation (243) for hydrogen, was explained on a physical basis by Professor Bohr in 1913.   Applying the planetary picture of the atom, comprising a positively charged nucleus with external electrons revolving about it in shells or orbits, he postulated that an electron could occupy any one of a definite number of orbits or *stationary states* without radiating, each of these representing a definite energy level.   For the hydrogen atom, with its single planetary electron, the normal state corresponds to the electron residing in its innermost orbit.   When this atom receives energy, the revolving electron moves to a larger orbit in opposition to the attractive force of the nucleus.   When the atom loses energy by radiation, the electron falls to definite inner orbits, and the amount of energy radiated is given by

$$E_h - E_l = hf \tag{244}$$

where E_h represents the higher energy level of an outer orbit, E_l represents the lower energy level of the inner orbit, h is Planck's constant [§ 190], and f is the frequency of the radiation given off. Each spectral line produced by an excited atom, therefore, corresponds to a definite change of energy as the electron falls from some outer orbit to a particular inner orbit. The spectral lines of any series are produced by the electrons of excited atoms falling back to a common inner orbit.

The relation between the wave number ν, the wave length λ (cm.) and the frequency f of the radiation is indicated by equation (203) as

$$\nu = \frac{1}{\lambda} = \frac{f}{c}$$

where c is the velocity of light in centimeters per second. Combining with equation (244), the wave number becomes

$$\nu = \frac{1}{h\,c}(E_h - E_l)$$

which has the same form as equation (243). Comparing corresponding terms, it appears that the energy levels of the hydrogen atom are given by

$$E_h = 109,737\,\frac{h\,c}{M^2} \quad \text{and} \quad E_l = 109,737\,\frac{h\,c}{N^2}$$

Using the numerical values of $h = 6.63 \times 10^{-27}$ erg-sec. and $c = 3.00 \times 10^{10}$ cm. per sec., it follows that the entire numerator for either expression becomes a constant having the value 21.8×10^{-12} ergs. Calling this value A, the energy levels can be expressed by

$$E = \frac{A}{k^2}$$

where k represents successive integers that have the values of M and N previously tabulated for the three spectral series.

Fig. 406 represents the energy levels of the hydrogen atom by horizontal lines for values of k up to 6. If such an atom changes its energy from level 3 to level 2, it will radiate energy amounting to $E = \dfrac{A}{2^2} - \dfrac{A}{3^2} = 21.8 \times 10^{-12}\,(\tfrac{1}{4} - \tfrac{1}{9}) = 3.03 \times 10^{-12}$ ergs, and produce only the spectral line having the wave number $109,737 \times (\frac{1}{4} - \frac{1}{9}) = 15,241$ waves per cm.; it is represented by the heavy vertical line in the figure. This wave number gives close agreement with the wave length of the red line, $\lambda = 6563$ Å, found by experiment. The vertical lines connecting levels $A/2^2$, $A/3^2 \ldots$ $A/6^2 \ldots$ with level $A/1^2$ represent the spectral lines of the Lyman series; lines connecting $A/3^2$, $A/4^2 \ldots A/6^2 \ldots$ with $A/2^2$ represent the spectral lines of the Balmer series; and similarly for the Paschen series.

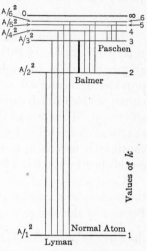

*384. Resonance and Ionization Potentials.—The emission of the line of lowest wave number in a spectral series involves the least energy. As more energy becomes available from the source of excitation, additional lines will appear; thus, the number of lines of a series that are present in the spectrum of an element is a measure of its energy of excitation. All the lines of a series will be present when the energy is just great enough to cause an electron to leave the atom, an action which constitutes ionization. These energy values may be expressed in ergs,

FIG. 406. Energy levels of the hydrogen atom

as in the preceding section, but are more commonly stated in electron-volts [§ 262]. Since 1 electron-volt is 1.60×10^{-12} erg, the expression for the energy levels becomes

$$E = \frac{13.60}{k^2}$$

The energy required to excite the first line of a spectral series, expressed in electron-volts, is called the *resonance potential* for that series. The energy required to excite all the lines of the series is called its *ionization potential*, for it corresponds to the complete removal of an electron from an atomic system. Resonance and ionization potentials may be determined experimentally with gaseous discharge tubes and such measurements confirm the atomic energy levels computed theoretically. Values of these potentials for a few atoms are given in the following table:

Resonance and Ionization Potentials

	Electron-volts to produce first spectral line	Electron-volts to cause ionization
Helium.....................	19.74	24.47
Hydrogen (Lyman series).........	10.20	13.60
Mercury.....................	4.67	10.38
Potassium....................	1.58	4.32
Sodium.....................	2.09	5.12

*385. **Quantum Relations.** — The application of the quantum theory of radiation [§ 191] to the planetary conception of the atom affords not only an explanation of spectral radiation, but also provides a theoretical verification of the numerical constant of equation (243) which expresses the wave numbers of the hydrogen spectrum. The form of this equation for spectral series is due to the Swedish scientist, Johannes R. Rydberg (1854–1919), and the constant is named after him; its value of 109,737 cm.$^{-1}$ will be established by the following analysis.

Consider the single electron of a hydrogen atom to revolve about the nucleus in a circular path of radius r with angular velocity ω. Because of the charge $-e$ on the electron and $+e$ on the nucleus, the force of attraction between them [§ 200] will be $\dfrac{-e \times e}{r^2}$, and will constitute the centripetal force $\omega^2 r m$ acting upon the revolving electron of mass m [§ 47]. Under the action of this force, the electron will revolve in a definite orbit of radius r such that

$$\frac{e^2}{r^2} = \omega^2 r m \qquad (245)$$

The energy of the electron is made up of potential energy amounting to $\dfrac{-e^2}{r}$ [§ 202], and of kinetic energy amounting to $\frac{1}{2} I \omega^2$ $= \frac{1}{2} m r^2 \omega^2$ [§ 72], where $I = m r^2$ is the moment of inertia of the electron about the nucleus. Thus, the total energy of the electron is

$$E = -\frac{e^2}{r} + \tfrac{1}{2} m r^2 \omega^2 = -\frac{e^2}{2r} \qquad (246)$$

by using equation (245).

The two foregoing equations could be satisfied by any value of the radius r and, if no other limitation were imposed, the electron could have any conceivable energy value. Under this supposition, the spectrum of hydrogen would comprise all frequencies in accordance with equation (244); but this conclusion is contrary to fact. In order to secure agreement with experiments on the hydrogen spectrum, Bohr introduced the idea of energy levels described in § 383 and assumed that the *angular momentum of the electron* in its orbit would have to be an exact multiple of $h/2\pi$, where h is Planck's constant. Accordingly, the angular momentum $I\omega$ [§ 103] must equal some integer times $h/2\pi$. Since $I = m r^2$, this restriction means that the electron can have only particular orbits such that the radius r will satisfy the relation

$$m r^2 \omega = k \frac{h}{2\pi} \qquad (247)$$

where the integer k is called the *quantum number*. Applying the quantizing condition, equation (247), to the relation stated in equation (245), the radius of the orbit will have definite and separated values given by

$$r = \frac{k^2 h^2}{4\pi^2 m e^2}$$

The energy of the electron rotating in the orbit of radius r, as given by this equation, is found by substitution in equation (246) to be

$$E = - \frac{2 \pi^2 m e^4}{k^2 h^2}$$

and is spoken of as the energy of the atom in the k'th stationary state. The energy radiated by the atom in passing from the N'th to the M'th stationary state is, therefore

$$E_h - E_l = \frac{2 \pi^2 m e^4}{h^2} \left[\frac{1}{M^2} - \frac{1}{N^2} \right]$$

Merging this result with equation (244), and remembering that the frequency f is equal to the wave number ν times the velocity of light c, the wave number of the spectral line emitted in this energy transfer will be

$$\nu = \frac{2 \pi^2 m e^4}{h^3 c} \left[\frac{1}{M^2} - \frac{1}{N^2} \right] \qquad (248)$$

Applying the numerical values: $m = 9.11 \times 10^{-28}$ gm., $e = 4.80 \times 10^{-10}$ e.s.u. of charge, $h = 6.63 \times 10^{-27}$ erg-sec., and $c = 3.00 \times 10^{10}$ cm. per sec., it will be found that the coefficient of the bracketed expression agrees with the Rydberg constant $R =$ 109,737 cm. $^{-1}$ that was found empirically.

The correlation of atomic energy levels that has been shown to exist with the production of the spectral lines of hydrogen also extends to elements having several electrons and producing complicated spectra.

386. Colors of Luminous Objects. — The color of a luminous object depends upon the frequencies of the radiation proceeding from it. Nevertheless, the same color sensation may arise in a variety of ways, and the composition of the radiated beam cannot be determined by its appearance but only by an analysis of its spectrum. Thus, if all the colors of a continuous spectrum are caused to overlap to form a single patch of light, the resulting beam is white, but it is also found that by combining only the yellow and blue portions of the spectrum, a white light is produced which the eye cannot distinguish from the other. There are several pairs of colors which yield white light when mixed; they are called *complementary* colors. Yellow and blue are complementary, as are also red and green. Again, the light from a sodium vapor lamp appears much like that of illuminating gas, but the former has primarily the yellow spectral lines while the latter has the continuous spectrum of carbon. Furthermore, by combining red, green, and blue-violet, the so-called *primary colors*, in suitable proportions, any color in the spectrum can be produced.

Certain substances, such as the sulfides of calcium and barium, when exposed to light, continue to glow after removal of the source; a phenomenon called *phosphorescence*. Petroleum, heavy mineral oils, and numerous other substances, behave similarly, except that the glowing persists only a fraction of a second; this phenomenon is known as *fluorescence*. In general, the light emitted by a phosphorescent or fluorescent object is of longer wave length than that to which it was exposed. A card coated with platinocyanide of barium when exposed to x-rays gives off longer wave lengths in the visible region of the spectrum, and serves as a screen against which the shadows cast by x-rays may be seen. In all such cases, the incident light or other electromagnetic wave excites the atoms of the substance, and the longer wave length of the emitted light is attributed to the return of the displaced electrons to their original energy levels in two or more stages rather than in a single transition.

Fluorescence is utilized in a new type of electric lamp, the fluorescent material being applied in a thin layer on the inner walls of a glass tube containing argon gas and mercury vapor. An electric discharge through the gas is initiated by the use of hot electrodes, and is rich in ultra-violet radiation. This energizes the fluorescent layer, which, in turn, becomes a brilliant source of visible light, the color depending upon the kind of fluorescent material used. In starting such a lamp a current is first established in a small coil of tungsten wire at each end of the tube, but after a moment the connection is automatically broken between the two coils and they then serve as electrodes for the gaseous discharge. The lamp with its auxiliary equipment operates from 110-volt alternating-current supply mains. Its temperature is low and its efficiency is high, a 15-watt tube producing about 450 lumens.

387. Selective Absorption. — The light incident upon a non-luminous object may be partly *reflected* and partly *absorbed*, and the remainder will be *transmitted*. The color of the object depends upon the composition of the incident light and the extent to which the various component colors are reflected, absorbed, and transmitted.

A sheet of ordinary glass held in front of a source of white light appears colorless by light transmitted through it, because it transmits practically all of the light falling upon it. On the other hand, a sheet of red glass absorbs most of the colors except red and orange, and since practically only these colors are transmitted, the glass appears reddish. The property of absorbing certain colors and transmitting others is called *selective absorption*.

Ordinary uncolored glass transmits the entire range of wave lengths of the visible spectrum, but is comparatively opaque to most ultra-violet and infra-red radiation, and thus exhibits selective absorption outside of the visible range. In a greenhouse, the glass transmits energy over the entire visible range to the plants within, where it is largely converted into heat and chemical energy. The radiation from the interior is principally in the infra-red region (so-called radiant heat), and since but little of this is transmitted outward by the glass, the interior of the enclosure remains warm.

The light given out by the ordinary incandescent electric lamp is redder than sunlight, that is, its spectrum is relatively more intense toward the red than toward the violet end as compared with that of sunlight. The so-called *daylight lamp* has an envelope of blue glass which, by selective absorption, removes some of the radiation from the red end of the spectrum, and the transmitted light, although somewhat dimmed, conforms more closely to sunlight in the relative proportions of the component colors.

The principles of selective absorption have recently been applied in the development of a lamp for destroying bacteria. This source of radiation, called a "Sterilamp," consists of a long closed tube containing inert gas and mercury vapor, and having coated electrodes at its ends. An electric discharge is maintained within the tube and produces radiation mostly in the ultra-violet region. The tube is made of special glass which absorbs the radiations not desired, and transmits over 80 per cent of the total radiation in the region of 2537 Å, which has been found effective in destroying micro-organisms. The lamp is used in sterlizing food and food containers and also articles subject to mold or fungus growths. A 20-in. tube operating at 375 volts takes approximately 12 watts, and the temperature is but a few degrees above that of the surroundings.

388. Color by Reflected Light. — Opaque bodies are seen by light diffusely reflected from them. Suppose an object to be examined in white light containing all wave lengths throughout the range of the visible spectrum. If the object reflects no light, it appears black; if it reflects all of the light incident upon it, it appears white; and if it reflects only part of the light, but reflects all wave lengths in equal proportions, it appears gray.

Most objects which appear colored when viewed by reflected light do so because of selective absorption. Reflection is not strictly a surface phenomenon, as the light seems to penetrate a short distance beneath the surface before reflection. A board painted blue reflects blue light and some of the neighboring colors, green and violet, the other colors being quenched by selective absorption. Similarly, a board painted yellow reflects yellow light, together with some of the neighboring colors, orange and green, the other colors being absorbed in like manner. If blue and yellow paints are mixed, the only color reflected by both will be green, for the blue paint will absorb the yellow and orange and the yellow paint will absorb the blue and violet. This result is quite different from that produced by mixing yellow and blue lights, as described in § 386.

An object has its true color when examined by light which contains all the wave lengths of the visible spectrum. If certain colors are absent from the incident light, the apparent color of the object may be quite different from its true color. Thus, dark blue cloth appears nearly black when examined under an incandescent electric lamp because of the deficiency of blue in the incident light. The light from the mercury vapor lamp contains no red radiations; a red object appears black under such a lamp. Mercury vapor lamps are sometimes used in combination with neon lamps, the red light from the glowing neon offsetting the deficiency of red color in the glowing mercury vapor.

A few instances occur in which bodies exhibit a *surface color* which is apparently due to *selective reflection*. The luster of metallic surfaces is attributed to this cause. Gold exhibits a yellow surface color, but this is not because the other colors are absorbed; in fact, the surface color itself is the one that is absorbed most strongly. This can be shown by passing white light through a thin sheet of gold, when it will be found that the transmitted light is bluish green, the yellow having been absorbed.

The rainbow is caused by the dispersion of sunlight in the interior of raindrops. The light that falls upon a drop is refracted at its surface, reflected within it, and refracted again upon emergence. Much of the light is scattered in various directions, but the rays near the path of minimum deviation from a series of drops merge into a fairly intense beam along the directions shown in Fig. 407. The dispersion resolves the incident white light into the spectral colors, the angle between the incident and emergent rays being about 40° for violet and 42° for red. An eye at *E* receives light of different colors from a multitude of

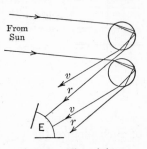

FIG. 407. The rainbow

drops, the red color appearing uppermost. Drops similarly located with respect to sun and observer but not in the plane of the page produce a corresponding effect, the collective action yielding the familiar rainbow. A secondary rainbow is sometimes formed outside of the first; it is produced by two reflections of the rays within the drops.

The light from the sky is due to the scattering of sunlight by the molecules of air, as well as by dust and other impurities contained in the atmosphere, as the sun's rays pass through it. It has been established that the intensity of scattered radiation varies directly as the fourth power of the frequency of the incident light, and for this reason the short waves, corresponding to the blue and violet colors, are scattered more than the longer waves of red light; this accounts for the prevailing blue color of the sky. Without the atmosphere, the sky would appear black. The light coming directly from the sun when it is near the horizon is predominantly red, because the blue portion has been scattered to a large extent from the direct beam in traversing long paths through the atmosphere.

*389. Color Photography. — The art of color photography depends upon the fact that any color occurring in nature can be matched by merging the primary colors in appropriate amounts. Latent images are formed on a light-sensitive emulsion separately for the red, the green and the blue portions of the subject being photographed, each showing the variations in the intensity of the light of that particular color emitted or reflected by the subject. Positives or negatives of the images, dyed the appropriate colors, can be combined in proper register to form a natural color photo-

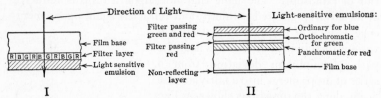

FIG. 408.   Sectional views of color photographic films:
I Dufay, II Kodachrome

graph. A simple way of doing this would be to dye the positive of each picture the respective primary color and then to throw pictures of the three positives from separate projectors upon a screen. This procedure is somewhat unwieldy, and the following methods are more commonly used in photography.

One method employs color filters between the film base and the emulsion, and the light entering the camera passes through the filters before reaching the emulsion, as shown sectionally in part I of Fig. 408. The filter layer is composed entirely of red, green, and blue specks indicated by R, G, and B, which are so small (about 1,000,000 per sq. in.) that they cannot be resolved by the unaided eye. Upon exposure there is formed behind the specks of each color a latent image of the object photographed. Development consists of treating the film so as to produce more or less opaque deposits in the emulsion behind those red specks which received little or no red light during exposure, and also opaque deposits behind those green and blue specks which were in red parts of the subject since these specks did not pass any red light. When the finished film is viewed by transmitted light, only that portion of it will appear red which received red light from the subject. Similarly, green and blue specks will appear in their proper places and in such numbers and of such transparency as to reproduce the original colors. This method is utilized by Dufay color film.

Another method separates the colors by using photographic materials that are sensitive to different parts of the spectrum, and arranging them in three separate layers. A cross-section of the film is illustrated in part II of the figure. The upper emulsion (ordinary type) is affected by blue and violet light, the next (orthochromatic type) by blue and green, and the lowest one (panchromatic type) by all colors. Between the first and second emulsions is a filter which transmits green and red but no blue, and between the second and third is a substance which is transparent only to red light. When the film is exposed in the camera three separate latent images are produced, one in the top layer formed by the blue light from the subject, one in the intermediate layer by the green, and one in the bottom layer by the red light.

By rather complex processing operations the filters are bleached out and the film is made to yield three negatives (the image being least transparent where most light reached the film), each in a color complementary to the color of the light by which the original latent image was produced. Thus, the top layer is converted into a transparent material which does not transmit blue light at places corresponding to regions where blue was missing from the subject. It will appear as a yellow negative because green, yellow, and red light add up to yellow. Similar changes are effected in the other two emulsions; the second subtracts green from those parts where it was absent in the subject, and the third subtracts red in the same way. When white light passes through a part on the film that corresponds to a blue portion of the subject, it passes through the top emulsion with practically no absorption, it has green removed from it in the second, and red in the third; thus the emergent light through that part of the film will be blue. If the original exposure was correct the absorption of each of the layers will be proportional to the intensity of the incident light of the appropriate color, and the resulting transparency will be in the original colors. The Kodachrome process uses this method.

To produce a picture upon paper instead of a transparency, three separate negatives must be made, one by the light of each of the primary colors. Images from these are dyed in complementary colors, the red-filter negative image being dyed blue-green, the green being dyed magenta (that is, bluish-red), and the blue-violet being dyed yellow; these are then transferred in register to a sheet of white paper. The picture is observed by light transmitted through the dyes to the paper, and reflected by it back through the dyes.

PROBLEMS

1. White light is passed symmetrically through a carbon-disulfide prism of 60° angle. Compute the deviation for the D spectral line and the angular dispersion between the C and F lines.

2. Compute the angles of incidence for rays of red and violet light that pass independently through a 50° prism with minimum deviation. Take the respective refractive indices of the prism as 1.56 and 1.58 for these colors.

3. What must be the angle of a carbon-disulfide prism in order that it may produce the same deviation for the D spectral line as a water prism of 10° angle?

4. If a ray of sodium light is to be bent through an angle of 5.0 degrees by a prism of crown glass, what angle should the prism have if the ray is to make equal angles with the prism faces? Use the refractive index listed in the table of § 379.

5. A 60° triangular prism made of glass plates is filled with ethyl cinnamate, a liquid of high dispersive power. The indices of refraction of this substance for the first three hydrogen lines are:

1.55216 for light of wave length 6563 Å
1.58043 for light of wave length 4861 Å
1.60053 for light of wave length 4340 Å

(*a*) What are the angular dispersions between these spectral lines? (*b*) Determine the dispersive power of this liquid with respect to the intermediate spectral line.

6. Calculate the dispersive power of flint glass over the region between the C and F spectral lines. Use refractive indices tabulated in § 379.

7. It is desired to combine a crown-glass prism with a 15° flint-glass prism so that the dispersion of one will annul that of the other over the region between the C and F spectral lines. Compute the angle of the crown-glass prism and also the deviation produced by the prism combination. Use refractive indices tabulated in § 379.

8. It is desired to combine a flint-glass prism with a 10° crown-glass prism in such a manner as to annul the dispersion between the C and F

Fraunhofer lines.   Using the refractive indices tabulated in § 379, what angle should the flint-glass prism have?

9. The wave length of the green line in the iron spectrum is 5270 A. Compute the corresponding frequency and wave number.

10. Calculate the wave numbers of the first five lines of each of the three spectral series of hydrogen.

*11. To what velocity must an electron be accelerated in order that it may acquire 1 electron-volt of energy?

*12. Construct an energy-level diagram for atomic hydrogen using electron-volts as ordinates, placing 0 volt at the top and the ionization potential of 13.60 volts at the bottom, and showing the next four levels above the latter.

CHAPTER XXXVI

LENSES

390. Types of Lenses. — A transparent material shaped to converge or diverge a beam of light transmitted through it is called a lens. It is usually a circular disk of glass that varies in thickness from the center to the rim, one or both surfaces being spherical. If a glass lens is thicker at the center than at the rim, it converges a parallel beam of light and is called a *converging* or *positive lens*. If it is thinner at the center than at the rim, it diverges such a beam and is called a *diverging* or *negative lens*.

The development of a lens from a prism can be shown graphically with the aid of equation (240), which shows that the angle

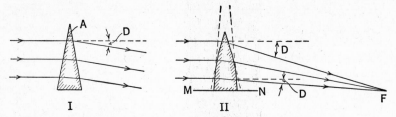

Fig. 409.   Development of a lens from a prism

of light deviation produced by a prism of angle A is equal to $A(\mu - 1)$ if the prism angle is small. Consider a parallel beam of monochromatic light to fall upon the prism as shown in part I of Fig. 409. The three rays depicted will be parallel upon emergence, each being deviated by the same angle D from the initial direction. To converge the beam at some point F requires that the upper ray be deviated more and the lower one less than the center one, as shown in part II of the figure. Since the refractive index μ of the prism is the same for all of the rays, the only way to change D is to make a corresponding change in A. Thus, the prism angle should be larger for the upper ray and smaller for the lower ray, as indicated. To bring all possible rays of the incident beam to the same point of convergence, the angle of the prism should change continuously from point to point; that is, at least one face should be curved. The prism may now be regarded as a semi-section of a lens by which the cylindrical beam of parallel light is brought to convergence at F on the principal axis MN of the lens.

Fig. 410 shows six shapes of converging and diverging lenses. The first is called double-convex, the next plano-convex, the third concavo-convex, and the others are named similarly. The center

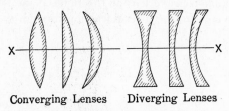

Converging Lenses   Diverging Lenses

Fig. 410.   Positive and negative lenses

line XX for any lens is called its *principal axis*; it is a line that passes through the centers of curvature of the lens surfaces.

391. Focal Length and Conjugate Distances. — The point of convergence or of divergence of an incident parallel beam of light rays, parallel to the principal axis, after passing through a lens is called the *principal focus* of the lens. In Fig. 411 the two upper diagrams show such parallel rays of light refracted in passing through a double-convex and a double-concave lens. The rays converge to point F in the first lens and diverge from point F in the second; the distance from the principal focus F to the lens in either case is called the *focal length* of the lens, the symbol for which is f. Should parallel light be incident upon these lenses from the right, instead of from the left as shown, the focal points would be on the other side of the lenses at the same distances f from them.

In the simpler theory of lenses the thickness of a lens is assumed to be negligibly small in comparison with its focal length, and this assumption will apply to this and to the sections that follow up to § 400. With *thin lenses*, therefore, distances may be measured to either lens surface. In diagrams, it is customary to show the lenses with appreciable thickness in order to reveal their shapes more clearly, particularly to indicate whether they are converging or diverging. In drawing lines to represent rays of light in such diagrams, the procedure is to deviate the lines at the transverse center line which actually shows the position of the ideally thin lens, instead of showing the refraction that occurs at each surface. The upper diagrams of Fig. 411 indicate this procedure.

The lower diagrams of this figure show the same results using wave fronts instead of rays of light. Plane waves normal to the principal axis are incident upon a double-convex lens at the left, and, because the retardation is greater at the center than near the edge of the lens, the waves converge upon the principal focus at F. With the double-concave lens at the right, plane incident waves appear to diverge from F after refraction through the lens.

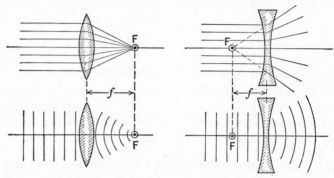

FIG. 411.   Foci of converging and diverging lenses

Fig. 411 represents the behavior of all six types of lenses; the left-hand figures typify converging lenses, and the right-hand figures typify diverging lenses.

When a point source of light is situated at some place along the principal axis of a lens, an image of it will be produced by the lens at some other point on the axis. Calling the object distance p and the image distance q as measured from the lens, the relation between these distances will be demonstrated in the following sections to be

$$\frac{1}{p} + \frac{1}{q} = \frac{1}{f} \qquad \bullet \quad (249)$$

where f is the focal length of the lens. Fig. 412 shows a spherical wave issuing from the point source at P, falling on the lens of focal length f, and converging to form an image at Q. The distances p and q are called *conjugate distances* of the lens. For every value of the object distance p there is a particular value of the image distance q. If q becomes negative, then Q will be a virtual image and will be located on the same side of the lens as P. If p is ∞,

q will be equal to f. Since the equation is symmetrical in p and q, it follows that object and image may be interchanged; that is, if the object is located at Q, the image would be located at P.

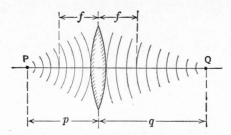

FIG. 412. Conjugate distances of a lens

392. Relation between Focal Length and Radii of Curvature. — Before applying equation (249) to lenses of particular shapes, it will be expressed in terms of the physical constants of the lens itself. It is easier to obtain this result by using wave fronts rather than rays of light, but it will be necessary first to establish a geometrical relation between the length of a chord, the radius of the associated arc, and the maximum radial distance from chord to arc. The latter distance is called the *sagitta* of the arc, and is shown as s in Fig. 413. Herein the radius OM of length r is intersected by the chord from L perpendicular to OM. Taking the chord to have a length $2y$, it follows that $r^2 = y^2 + (r - s)^2$, or $y^2 = 2rs - s^2$. For chords that are short in comparison with the radius, s^2 will be negligibly small with respect to $2rs$, and consequently the length of the sagitta becomes

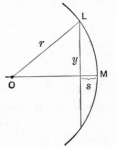

FIG. 413. Sagitta of an arc

$$s = \frac{y^2}{2r} \tag{250}$$

This is the desired relation between the radius and semi-chord of an arc and its sagitta.

In order to derive the relation between the conjugate distances of a lens and its radii of curvature, a diverging spherical wave front will be considered to fall upon a thin converging lens and to be brought to convergence after refraction. By setting up a relationship between the sagittas of the incident and emergent wave fronts and of the two surfaces of the lens, and applying equation (250), the desired expression can be found.

Consider light to issue from a source at P in Fig. 414 on the principal axis PQ of the converging lens, which produces an image of the source at Q. The lens has surfaces of radii r_1 and r_2, as shown, and the distance from its axis to its edge E is represented as y. Incident and emergent wave fronts, W_1 and W_2, are shown just touching the lens surfaces at M and N, and the extreme rays

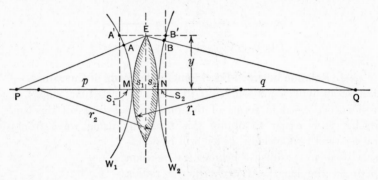

FIG. 414. Determining relation between conjugate distances and surface curvature of a lens

PE and EQ are drawn to the edge of the lens, intersecting these wave fronts at A and B respectively.

The wave advances from any point on the wave front W_1 to the corresponding point on W_2 in the same time. Consequently, at the edge of the lens the distance AEB (entirely in air) is traversed in the same time that is required at the center to traverse MN (entirely in the lens of refractive index μ). From the meaning of refractive index, it follows that

$$AE + EB = \mu(MN)$$

By supposing the extreme rays to make small angles with the principal axis, points A' and B' on the wave fronts at a distance y from the axis can be substituted for A and B without appreciable error. With this substitution, the lens surfaces and the wave fronts can be represented by arcs having the same semi-chord y. The sagittas of these arcs are marked in the figure as s_1 and s_2 for the lens surfaces and S_1 and S_2 for the wave fronts. Rewriting the foregoing equation with these modifications, $A'E + EB' = \mu(MN)$, the equality of light path is given by

$$S_1 + s_1 + s_2 + S_2 = \mu(s_1 + s_2)$$

whence

$$S_1 + S_2 = (\mu - 1)(s_1 + s_2)$$

Each of the sagittas may be expressed in terms of the semi-chord and radius in accordance with equation (250), giving

$$\frac{y^2}{2p} + \frac{y^2}{2q} = (\mu - 1)\left(\frac{y^2}{2r_1} + \frac{y^2}{2r_2}\right)$$

where $p = PM$ is the object distance, $q = NQ$ is the image distance, and r_1 and r_2 are the radii of the left and right lens surfaces as shown in the figure. Finally, dividing through by $y^2/2$, the relation between the conjugate distances becomes

$$\frac{1}{p} + \frac{1}{q} = (\mu - 1)\left(\frac{1}{r_1} + \frac{1}{r_2}\right) \tag{251}$$

When the object distance is infinitely great, the image will be at the focus; therefore, taking $p = \infty$ and $q = f$, equation (251) becomes

$$\frac{1}{f} = (\mu - 1)\left(\frac{1}{r_1} + \frac{1}{r_2}\right) \tag{252}$$

Equations (251) and (252) are the fundamental equations for lenses and apply to all forms of thin lenses, but for correctness the distances p, q and f should be such that the rays to the rim of the lens will subtend small angles at both object and image.

Opticians express the power of spectacle lenses in terms of a unit called the *diopter*. A lens having a power of 1 diopter has a focal length of 1 meter. The power of a lens is the reciprocal of its focal length f measured in meters; thus, the power in diopters becomes $D = 1/f$. Consequently, the shorter the focal length of a lens the greater will be its power.

393. Image Constructions. — It is frequently desired to verify the solution of a lens problem by constructing graphically the image which the lens produces of a given object. Such construction requires a knowledge of the focal length of the lens, and this may be procured by applying equation (252) if the radii of the lens and its refractive index are known. The procedure is illustrated in Fig. 415, wherein a number of rays are shown extending from the head-end of the arrow as object O to various points on the lens and thereafter refracted to a common point which forms the image of that object point. The same kind of picture applies to every other point of the object, and the net result will be the image I. Thus, every portion of the lens contributes its share to the production of each part of the image. A fragment of a broken lens, with portions of its refracting surfaces in good condition, will

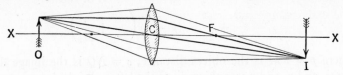

FIG. 415.   Rays from object to image

produce a clear image, but it will not be as bright as the image that could be produced from the same object with the entire lens, if unbroken.

Only two rays are necessary to locate a point of an image, and it is natural to choose the two that can be drawn most conveniently. These are shown in heavier lines than the others in Fig. 415. One is drawn from the head-end of the object parallel to the principal axis XX as far as the lens, and thereafter through the principal focus F, as in § 391. The other is drawn from the same point of the object straight through the center of C of the lens; it is unde-viated because planes tangent to the lens surfaces where this ray meets them are parallel and the lens merely acts as a parallel-sided slab of glass. The intersection of these lines (or their prolonga-tions backward) locates the image of the head-end of the object.

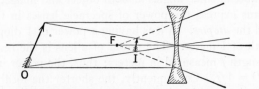

FIG. 416.   Image construction for diverging lens

The procedure is the same whatever is the shape of the lens and the location of the object. For converging lenses the focal point on the side of the lens opposite the object is used, while for diverging lenses the focal point on the same side is used. If the construction is carried out for both ends of a straight object, the entire image can be definitely located with four rays. Fig. 416

illustrates the image construction for an object inclined to the axis of a diverging lens. The horizontal rays from the object O appear after refraction to come from F, but they do not actually do so; in consequence the image I is virtual.

394. Application of Lens Formula. — The relation between the conjugate distances, the focal length, and the surface curvatures of a lens, as expressed by equations (249), (251) and (252), applies to all types of thin lenses, provided correct signs are chosen for the various quantities involved. The combined equation and the rules governing the choice of signs are as follows:

$$\frac{1}{p} + \frac{1}{q} = \frac{1}{f} = (\mu - 1)\left(\frac{1}{r_1} + \frac{1}{r_2}\right)$$

Focal length (f) is taken *positive* for *converging* lenses and *negative* for *diverging* lenses. Radius (r_1 or r_2) is taken *positive* for *convex* surfaces and *negative* for *concave* surfaces. Object distance (p) or image distance (q) is *positive* when object or image is *real*, and is *negative* when object or image is *virtual*. The significance of a virtual object is mentioned in § 396.

The following examples illustrate the application of these rules in locating the image I of an object O formed by a lens having its foci at F, F as shown in Fig. 417.

I. A double-convex lens of crown glass has radii of 11.6 and 9.45 cm., and a refractive index of 1.52. Calculate the focal length and determine where images will be located when the object is first 40 cm. and then 8 cm. from the lens. Taking $r_1 = 11.6$ cm., $r_2 = 9.45$ cm., and $\mu - 1 = 0.52$, it follows that

$$\frac{1}{f} = 0.52\left(\frac{1}{11.6} + \frac{1}{9.45}\right) = 0.100;$$

whence $f = 10.0$ cm. For an object distance $p = 40$ cm., $\frac{1}{40} + \frac{1}{q} = \frac{1}{10}$, and the image distance will be $q = 13.3$ cm. Similarly, when $p = 8.0$ cm., the value of q will be -40.0 cm. The first of the images is real, and the second is virtual. The graphical constructions are shown to scale at the top and center of Fig. 417; only two rays are drawn from the upper end of the object to avoid confusion.

II. A plano-concave lens of flint glass has a radius of 9.45 cm. and a refractive index of 1.63. Determine its focal length, and the location of the image of an object placed 40 cm. from it. Taking $r_1 = -9.45$ cm., $r_2 = \infty$, and $\mu - 1 = 0.63$, it follows that $f = -9.45/0.63 = -15.0$ cm. Further, for an object distance $p = 40$ cm., $\frac{1}{q} = \frac{1}{-15} - \frac{1}{40}$ and, therefore, the image distance will be $q = -10.9$ cm. The construction of this virtual image appears at the bottom in Fig. 417.

In both illustrations, computation will show that the same results are obtained if the lens is turned to present its other face to the object; this is true for all thin lenses. The diagrams indicate whether the images are erect or inverted.

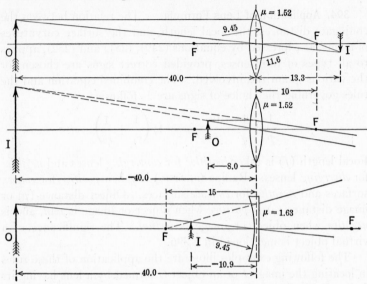

FIG. 417. Image constructions for verifying numerical illustrations

395. Magnification. — The image produced by a lens may be made any size desired if there is freedom of choice in the object and image distances. The diagrams of Fig. 417 indicate that when the object is nearer the lens than its image, the image will

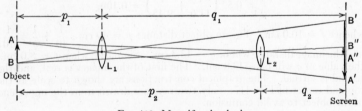

FIG. 418. Magnification by lens

be larger than the object, and vice versa. The magnification produced by the lens is the ratio of image size to object size. When these sizes are equal, the magnification is unity.

Fig. 418 shows two locations of a lens between object and screen. In position L_1, the lens produces an image $A'B'$ that is larger than the object AB, while in position L_2, the lens produces a reduced image $A''B''$. To gain clarity, only the rays through the lens centers are shown in the figure. The two triangles formed by the object and its image at the center of the lens in either position are similar, consequently the ratio of image size to object size is the same as the ratio of image distance to object distance. Thus, the magnifications for the two lens positions become

$$M_1 = \frac{A'B'}{AB} = \frac{q_1}{p_1} \quad \text{or} \quad M_2 = \frac{A''B''}{AB} = \frac{q_2}{p_2} \tag{253}$$

396. Lens Combinations. — Often the image formed by one lens serves as the object for another. The computation or construction for the location and size of the final image is carried out for the first lens and then for the second, as described previously. If the rays from the first lens to the image are intercepted by the second lens, that image then serves as a *virtual object* for the second lens; in the calculation for the final image the object distance for the second lens is regarded as negative.

To illustrate, consider an object placed 15 cm. in front of a converging lens having a focal length of 10 cm., and suppose that the rays to the image are intercepted by a second converging lens having a focal length of 8 cm. located 14 cm. from the first lens. Fig. 419 shows the image constructions

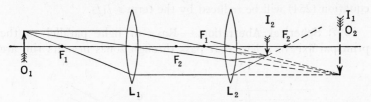

FIG. 419.   Construction of image formed by two lenses

to scale. An image I_1 is formed of object O_1 by lens L_1; the foci being located at points F_1. Taking the focal distance $f_1 = 10$ cm., and the object distance $p_1 = 15$ cm., an application of equation (249) shows that the image distance $q_1 = 30$ cm. The image serves as a virtual object O_2 for lens L_2, which has its foci located at points F_2. Taking the object distance $p_2 = -(30 - 14) = -16$ cm., and $f_2 = 8$ cm., a second application of the lens equation yields $\frac{1}{8} = \frac{1}{-16} + \frac{1}{q_2}$; from which the image is found to be located at a distance $q_2 = 16/3 = 5.3$ cm. to the right of lens L_2. The construction lines for the graphical determination of the image I_2 are shown in the figure only for the head-end of the object. It will be observed that the ray from that point through the nearer principal focus F_1, is parallel to the principal axis between the lenses, and will converge upon F_2 after passing through the second lens.

When two lenses are in contact, they may be regarded as a single lens of appropriate focal length. Let f_1 and f_2 be the focal lengths of the component thin lenses, and let the object distance be p as before. The first image will be located at a distance q_1 from the lenses, so that $\dfrac{1}{p} + \dfrac{1}{q_1} = \dfrac{1}{f_1}$. This image will serve as a virtual object for the other lens at a distance $- q_1$ from it, and the final image will be located at a distance q from the lenses, so that $\dfrac{1}{-q_1} + \dfrac{1}{q} = \dfrac{1}{f_2}$. Adding these equations, and taking $\dfrac{1}{p} + \dfrac{1}{q} = \dfrac{1}{f}$ for the equivalent single lens, it follows that

$$\frac{1}{f} = \frac{1}{f_1} + \frac{1}{f_2} \tag{254}$$

where f is the focal length of the equivalent lens formed of two lenses that have focal lengths of f_1 and f_2 and are placed close together. Expressed in diopters, this equation becomes quite simple, for the power of the combination is equal to the sum of the powers of the component lenses. Thus, combining a converging lens of $+5$ diopters with a diverging one of -2 diopters, results in a converging lens having a power of $+3$ diopters. When the lenses are separated by a distance s, the right-hand member of equation (254) will be reduced by the term s/f_1f_2.

397. Spherical Aberration. — Rays of light parallel to the principal axis of a lens that pass through zones near its rim are

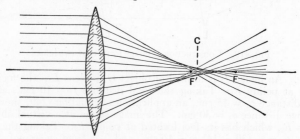

Fig. 420. Refraction of a wide pencil of rays by a lens

not brought to a focus at exactly the same point where rays meet that pass through the center of the lens. This imperfection, called *spherical aberration*, is not due to inaccuracies in the spherical surfaces of the lens. The effect with a converging lens is exaggerated in Fig. 420. The parallel rays from a distant source intersect at various points along the principal axis from F to F'. If a screen is placed at these points a blurred image of the source will be obtained, and a position can be found for the screen where the least blurring will occur. The figure shows this position to be at C, for the rays there constitute a *circle of least confusion*. The amount of spherical aberration produced by a lens is usually measured by the axial distance FF' between the intersections of the central and marginal rays.

In the design of lenses, spherical aberration can be reduced by a proper choice of radii for the surfaces. The minimum will be attained when, for a given ray, the deviation is the same at both refracting surfaces. It can be shown that a lens of refractive index μ will have minimum aberration for parallel incident light when the surface radii are in the proportion:

$$\frac{r_1}{r_2} = \frac{\mu + 4 - 2\mu^2}{\mu + 2\mu^2} \tag{255}$$

In a good photographic lens this aberration is less than $\frac{1}{2}$ per cent of its focal length. A plano-convex lens when used with the light incident upon the curved face gives relatively little spherical aberration.

398. Chromatic Aberration. — So far in this chapter, no mention has been made of the influence of the color of light upon the

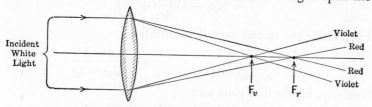

FIG. 421. Lens foci for two colors

action of a lens. Since the refractive index is greater for the violet end of the spectrum than for the red end, it follows from equation (252), namely

$$\frac{1}{f} = (\mu - 1)\left(\frac{1}{r_1} + \frac{1}{r_2}\right)$$

that the focal length of a lens will be less for violet light than for red. Fig. 421 shows a beam of white light incident upon a converging lens; every pencil of the beam will be dispersed like the two shown, and the collective effect will be the convergence of the several colors along individual points on the principal axis from the focus of violet light at F_v to the focus of red light at F_r. The color distribution can be observed by moving a screen along the axis; at F_v a concentric color pattern will be observed with violet at the center, and at F_r red will be at the center. This dispersive effect produced by a lens is called *chromatic aberration*.

In designing lenses to avoid dispersion, it is necessary to combine two (or more) lenses so that the dispersion produced by each will be annulled by the other. Such a combination, called an *achromatic lens*, employs lenses when in contact that are made of substances having different dispersive powers. The principle employed in the design of an achromatic doublet will be explained for a converging component lens of crown glass and a diverging component of flint glass.

The foregoing equation can be applied to either lens using light of any color. Choosing violet and red as the extreme colors for which the doublet is to be achromatized, and yellow as the central color of the spectrum for specifying the focal length of either lens, the reciprocals of the focal lengths of the crown-glass lens will be

$$\frac{1}{f_{vC}} = (\mu_{vC} - 1)\left(\frac{1}{r_1} + \frac{1}{r_2}\right), \qquad \frac{1}{f_{rC}} = (\mu_{rC} - 1)\left(\frac{1}{r_1} + \frac{1}{r_2}\right)$$

and

$$\frac{1}{f_C} = (\mu_{yC} - 1)\left(\frac{1}{r_1} + \frac{1}{r_2}\right)$$

Eliminating the second parenthesis herefrom,

$$\frac{1}{f_{vC}} = \frac{\mu_{vC} - 1}{f_C(\mu_{yC} - 1)} \qquad \frac{1}{f_{rC}} = \frac{\mu_{rC} - 1}{f_C(\mu_{yC} - 1)}$$

Similarly, for the flint-glass lens

$$\frac{1}{f_{vF}} = \frac{\mu_{vF} - 1}{f_F(\mu_{yF} - 1)} \qquad \frac{1}{f_{rF}} = \frac{\mu_{rF} - 1}{f_F(\mu_{yF} - 1)}$$

Putting the two lenses together, the focal length of the doublet can be ascertained by applying equation (254) for each color. For violet, the focal length is f_v such that

$$\frac{1}{f_v} = \frac{1}{f_{vC}} + \frac{1}{f_{vF}}$$

For red, the focal length is f_r such that

$$\frac{1}{f_r} = \frac{1}{f_{rC}} + \frac{1}{f_{rF}}$$

To achromatize over this color range, the focal lengths f_v and f_r of the doublet should be equal; consequently

$$\frac{1}{f_{vC}} + \frac{1}{f_{vF}} = \frac{1}{f_{rC}} + \frac{1}{f_{rF}}$$

Substituting the foregoing values of these fractions, there results

$$\frac{\mu_{vF} - \mu_{rF}}{f_F(\mu_{yF} - 1)} = \frac{\mu_{rC} - \mu_{vC}}{f_C(\mu_{yC} - 1)}$$

which reduces to

$$\frac{\delta_F}{f_F} = -\frac{\delta_C}{f_C} \tag{256}$$

where δ_F and δ_C are the dispersive powers of flint and crown glass respectively [§ 380]. This is the condition for achromatism.

Equations (254) and (256) enable one to specify the focal lengths of the component lenses of an achromatic doublet that shall have a particular focal length, provided the dispersive powers of the lens substances are known.

For example, taking the dispersive powers of crown and flint glass as 0.018 and 0.027 respectively, an achromatic lens formed of these materials must have component focal lengths such that

$$\frac{f_F}{f_C} = -\frac{0.027}{0.018} = -1.50$$

This is the relation that holds for the two lenses mentioned in § 394; consequently these could be combined to form an achromatic lens. The focal length of the combination when the two components of focal lengths 10 cm. and −15 cm. are in contact is given by $\frac{1}{f} = \frac{1}{10} + \frac{1}{-15}$, from which $f = 30$ cm.

It is possible to make an achromatic lens of two components that have the same dispersive power. This is done by using lenses of the same kind of glass and placing them coaxially a distance apart equal to one-half the sum of their focal lengths. The Huygens eyepiece, Fig. 422, illustrates this construction. It consists of two plano-convex lenses, one having a focal length about three times that of the other, with both plane faces directed toward the eye. The lens nearer the eye, called the *eye lens*, has the shorter focal length, and the other, called the *field lens*, is twice that distance from the eye lens. At the field lens the violet light

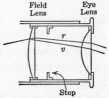

FIG. 422. Section of a Huygens eyepiece

is deviated more than the red, as shown by the rays marked *v* and *r* in the figure, but the eye lens receives the first of these rays at a point nearer the center and for this reason deviates it less than the other. With lenses of correct proportions and spacing the total deviation can be made the same for both colors, rendering the eyepiece achromatic.

*399. Astigmatism. — In addition to spherical and chromatic aberration, there are several other defects of a spherical lens which cause indistinctness in the image. An important one of these is called *astigmatism*; rays of light that pass through the lens obliquely from an object point remote from the principal axis do not converge upon a common image point.

Fig. 423 shows side and top views in part I of several rays from the upper end of a long slender object *O* in their passage through a

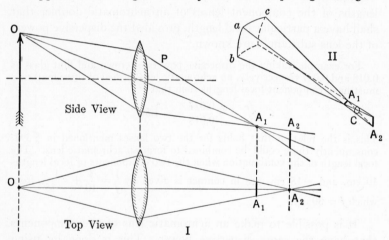

FIG. 423.   Astigmatic focal lines

converging lens. Viewed from the side, the rays converge upon A_1, and viewed from the top, they converge upon A_2. This shows that the emergent wave front possesses different curvatures in the two planes of view, the curvature in the vertical plane (side view) being the greater. Part II of the figure gives a perspective view of a pencil of the beam around ray *P*. It shows that the rays in vertical planes like *ab* intersect at points along a line at A_1, while those in horizontal planes like *ac* intersect along a line at A_2. These lines, at right angles to each other in part I, are called *focal lines*. If a screen is placed at either focal line, an elongated patch of light will be observed, but somewhere between the two focal lines, as at C, a roughly circular patch of light will be observed. This is the nearest approach to a point image that the astigmatic beam yields. Rays of light that are incident obliquely upon a spherical mirror produce the same effect upon reflection.

The amount of astigmatism of a lens or mirror for any object point is indicated by the distance between its focal lines as measured along the middle ray from that point. Astigmatism can be corrected by the use of two lenses with appropriate separation.

*400. Thick Lenses. — The lenses considered thus far were assumed so thin that no appreciable error would be introduced in calculations for focal lengths or conjugate distances by making

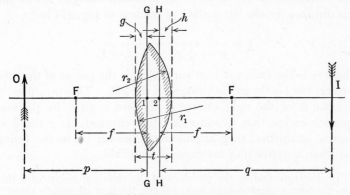

FIG. 424. Principal points and planes of a thick lens

measurements to either lens surface. Lenses that have thicknesses comparable with their focal lengths may also be computed by the usual equations if, instead of measuring distances to the lens surfaces, the distances are measured to two definite points that can be located easily. For the usual case where the rays enter a lens from some medium and reenter that medium upon emergence, these points are called the *principal points* of the lens. They are shown at 1 and 2 in Fig. 424, located within a double convex lens of thickness t; and lines G and H drawn through these points perpendicular to the principal axis represent the *principal planes*.

The figure shows that object and image distances, p and q, are measured respectively from O and I to the nearer principal point. The focal distance f, measured from either point to the principal focus F, is called the *equivalent focal length* of the lens. When p, q and f are measured in this way, equation (249), namely $\frac{1}{p} + \frac{1}{q} = \frac{1}{f}$, applies also to thick lenses. Equation (252) can be modified so that the equivalent focal length of a thick lens may be computed from its dimensions. For this purpose the equation proves to be

$$\frac{1}{f} = (\mu - 1) \left(\frac{1}{r_1} + \frac{1}{r_2} - \frac{(\mu - 1)\,t}{\mu\,r_1\,r_2} \right) \tag{257}$$

which reduces to the simpler form when $t = 0$.

The distance of a principal point from its associated lens surface depends upon the thickness of the lens, its refractive index, and both radii of curvature. An extended analysis shows that this distance for the left surface of the lens of Fig. 424 is

$$g = \frac{r_1\,t}{\mu\,(r_1 + r_2) - t\,(\mu - 1)}$$

where r_1 is the radius of that surface, r_2 is the radius of the other surface, and t is the axial thickness of the lens. The corresponding distance h for the right surface of the lens is given by the same equation except that r_1 and r_2 are interchanged. If g and h are positive quantities, they are measured inward (as in the figure), and when negative they are measured outward.

To illustrate finding the positions of the principal points of a thick lens, consider a plano-convex lens, 1.0 cm. thick at its middle point, to have a radius of 10 cm. and a refractive index of 1.5. The foregoing equation gives the following distances for $r_1 = \infty$ and $r_2 = 10$:

$$g = \frac{t}{\mu + \mu\,\dfrac{r_2}{r_1} - \dfrac{t}{r_1}(\mu - 1)} = \frac{1.0}{1.5} = 0.67 \text{ and } h = \frac{t}{\mu + \infty - \dfrac{t}{10}(\mu - 1)} = 0$$

Consequently, one principal point is on the curved surface, and the other is 0.67 cm. from the plane surface toward the other. The same will be true for a diverging lens of the same thickness, radii, and refractive index.

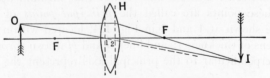

FIG. 425. Construction of rays for thick lens

The procedure in constructing graphically the image produced by a thick lens is illustrated in Fig. 425. A ray from the head-end of object O is drawn toward the first principal point, 1, and upon emergence appears to proceed in a parallel direction from the other principal point, 2. The other ray is drawn parallel to the principal axis as far as the second principal plane, H, where it is shown refracted to pass through the focus F. The intersection of these rays at I locates the head-end of the image. This construction assumes the same medium on both sides of the lens.

PROBLEMS

1. A converging lens is placed at a distance of 3.2 ft. from an illuminated lamp with the lens axis directed toward that lamp. An image of the lamp is produced on a screen at a distance of 8.5 ft. from the lens. What is the focal length of the lens?

2. A lamp is supported 117 in. from a wall. A reading glass held between them is moved until it produces a sharp image of the lamp on the wall, its axis being directed toward the lamp. If the reading glass is then 13. in. from the wall, determine its focal length.

3. A glass disk 200 in. in diameter is ground to form a spherical telescope mirror of 55.0-ft. focal length. Calculate the radial distance from the middle of the concave surface to the plane through the rim of the mirror.

4. A converging lens made of quartz has one convex and one concave surface. Compute the focal length of such a lens that has radii of 24 and 40 cm. Take the refractive index of quartz as 1.543.

5. Calculate the focal length of a plano-concave lens that has a radius of 15 cm. and is made of glass having a refractive index of 1.580 for a particular color of light.

6. A reading glass constructed with convex spherical surfaces each of 26-cm. radius is found to have a focal length of 25 cm. Determine the refractive index of the glass of which it is made.

7. Using a diverging lens having a focal length of 8.5 cm., locate the image of an object placed 5.4 cm. from the lens. Also draw the rays that will locate the image graphically.

8. A spectacle lens having a power of +2.5 diopters is held 1 meter from a light source. At what distance from the lens will it produce an image of that source? Show the graphical construction of the image.

9. An object is placed 20 mm. in front of a thin lens of 16-mm. focal length. Locate the image analytically and graphically and describe it fully. Compute also the magnification.

10. An object is placed 28 in. in front of a double-convex lens having radii of 12 in. and 15 in. The refractive index of the lens material is 1.62. Determine the location of the image and the magnification.

11. A thin plano-convex lens is made of glass having a refractive index of 1.72; its curved surface has a radius of 18.0 cm. Where should an object be placed with respect to this lens to yield a magnification of 5 diameters?

12. A plano-convex lens has a focal length of 25.0 cm. In verifying this value, an image of a remote object is obtained, and is assumed to be at the principal focus. How far from the lens must the object be located in order to attain an accuracy of 2 per cent?

13. (*a*) Construct the image of an object placed 25 in. in front of a converging lens having a focal length of 10 in. (*b*) Place a similar lens of 3-in. focal length coaxial with the first one and 12 in. behind it. Construct the final image.

14. A telephoto lens is formed of two thin lenses placed 16 cm. apart; the front lens has a focal length of $+20$ cm. and the rear lens has a focal length of -5 cm. What is the focal length of the combination?

15. A telephoto objective is formed of two thin lenses 2 cm. apart; the front lens has a focal length of $+3.33$ cm. and the rear lens has a focal length of -2.00 cm. A parallel beam of light impinges on the front lens; how far back of the rear lens will it be brought to a focus?

16. A converging lens is to be ground for a focal length of 6 in. and for minimum spherical aberration. If the index of refraction is 1.530, what should be the radii of the lens?

17. A converging crown glass lens is to be combined with a diverging flint glass lens in contact with it to form an achromatic combination having a focal length of $+10.0$ cm. Compute the focal lengths of the crown and flint glass components, using as their dispersive powers 0.0162 and 0.0276 respectively.

18. Assuming the contacting faces of the two lenses of Problem 17 to be plane, calculate the radii of the outer faces of the achromatic lens. Take 1.509 and 1.620 as the refractive indices for yellow light of crown and flint glass respectively.

*19. Regard the lens of Problem 10 as a thick lens which has an axial thickness of 1.5 in. Compute its focal length.

*20. Locate the principal points of the lens of Problem 4, assuming the lens to be 1 cm. thick at its middle point.

CHAPTER XXXVII

OPTICAL INSTRUMENTS

401. Optical Aids to Vision. — When objects are viewed at such close range that the eye, even if exerting its greatest effort, cannot focus sharp images of them upon its retina, or when the objects are so remote that their details are indistinguishable, instruments may be used to magnify the objects so that the eye may view them with maximum comfort and sufficient resolution of detail. Such instruments employ mirrors or lenses of appropriate design and location, and have a variety of forms. They include magnifying glasses and microscopes, astronomical and terrestrial telescopes, transits and levels for surveying, and binocular field and opera glasses, as well as low-power telescopes for such instruments as photometers, sextants, refractometers and spectroscopes, already described. The essential elements of some magnifying instruments and their magnifying powers will be considered in this chapter, while the factors governing their resolving power will be deferred to the next.

402. The Eye. — The human organ of vision consists of the eyeball cushioned in a bony socket, a muscular system for moving it, and lachyrmal glands and ducts for moistening its anterior portion. The eyeball comprises a lens system for producing images of objects under observation, a *retina* for the reception of the images and their conversion into nervous impulses, and the *optic nerve* for transmitting these impulses to the brain to produce the sensation of vision.

The eyeball has two coatings outside of the retina, as illustrated in part I of Fig. 426. The outermost is the white fibrous envelope which, because of its toughness, is called the *sclerotic* coat. Its front portion, transparent and more curved than the "white of the eye," is called the *cornea* because of its horny texture. The inner layer or *choroid* is composed of numerous blood vessels which nourish the eye and pigment cells that shield the retina from stray light. This dark coat extends forward to the colored *iris* diaphragm which, by involuntary muscular control, regulates the amount of light admitted through its circular aperture or *pupil.*

Within the eye is the *crystalline lens* comprising flexible layers of different refractive indices. The chamber in front of the lens contains the *aqueous humor*, which is a weak solution of sodium

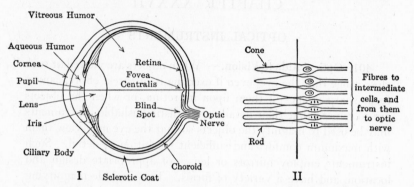

FIG. 426. Horizontal section of right eyeball and section of retinal surface

chloride, and the chamber in back of it contains a gelatinous substance called the *vitreous humor.* The approximate dimensions and refractive indices of the optical parts of the normal eye are as follows:

Constants of the Eye

	Radius in mm.		Thickness along axis in mm.	Index of refraction
	Front	Back		
Cornea.....................	7.8	7.3	0.5	1.351
Lens, for near objects.........	6.0	5.5	4.0	average
" " distant "	10.0	6.0	3.6	1.437
Aqueous humor, for near objects			3.2	1.337
" " " distant "			3.6	
Vitreous humor..............		12.0	15.9	1.337

The ability of the eye, not possessed by any other optical instrument, to focus automatically upon objects at different distances from it, is called *accommodation.* This result is accomplished by changing the shape of the lens, chiefly the curvature of its front surface, through the action of the muscles of the *ciliary body.* It is believed that in accommodating for a near object these muscles contract and relax the ligaments around the rim of the lens, thereby allowing the lens to thicken by its own elasticity. With increasing age the faculty of accommodation diminishes. When the eye is focused for parallel rays, that is, upon remotely distant objects, it is said to be unaccommodated.

The end organs of sight on the retina are microscopic elements called *rods* and *cones*, shown greatly enlarged in part II of Fig. 426. At the central point of the retina, the *fovea centralis*, only cones are present, and this is the place of acutest vision. In proceeding outward from this point the proportion of cones to rods decreases and in the peripheral portions there may be but 1 cone to 10 rods; these portions are sensitive in observing motion. No sensation of vision is produced by light which falls upon that part of the retina, known as the *blind spot*, where the optic nerve extends through the eyeball.

Experiment shows that the eye is most sensitive to light in the blue-green region having a wave length about 5560 Å. Calling the response at that wave length 100 per cent, the response for the same luminous energy at various wave lengths will be substantially as indicated in Fig. 427. Because the eye is so selective, luminous flux is evaluated in terms of the visual effect [§ 355] rather than by energy content. The quickness of perception upon exposure to light and the persistence of vision for a time after its removal are important properties of the eye; the operation of

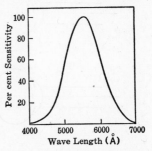

Fig. 427. Relative sensitivity of eye at average illumination

the flicker photometer and motion pictures depends upon these factors. It is well known that the projection of 16 or more images per second in motion pictures produces a continuous impression, each "frame" of the film being held stationary while being projected.

403. Some Defects of Vision and their Correction. — In considering the passage of light through the cornea, aqueous humor, lens, and vitreous humor to the retina of the eye, the greatest deviation occurs at the front surface of the cornea because this interface separates the two media of the lens system that have the greatest difference of refractive index. In the diagrams of Fig. 428, which show beams of light entering the pupils of typical eyes, all the refraction is regarded as occurring at this surface for simplicity.

Diagram I represents an eye which, when entirely relaxed, forms an image of a remotely distant object point upon the retina; it is called an *emmetropic eye*. Nearer object points can be focused upon the retina by making the lens system more converging through accommodation.

Diagram II represents a *myoptic eye* that is entirely relaxed; the parallel rays from a remotely distant object point focus in front of the retina, usually because the eyeball is too long. Such an eye cannot focus a distant object without a correcting glass and can

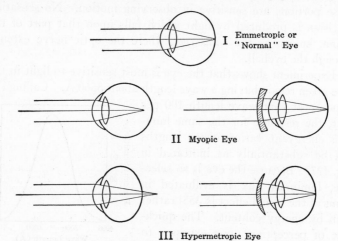

I Emmetropic or "Normal" Eye

II Myopic Eye

III Hypermetropic Eye

FIG. 428. Correction of myopia and hypermetropia by spectacle lenses

see only near objects distinctly. The vision is said to be near-sighted, and a diverging lens is needed to diminish the refracting power of the eye, as shown at the right. The opposite effect is shown in diagram III for the *hypermetropic eye;* a converging spectacle lens is needed to improve vision.

If the lens system of the eye is more converging in one plane than in another, an object point will be imaged along two focal lines as with an astigmatic pencil of light through a lens [§ 399]. This defect of vision is called astigmatism and is generally due to unequal curvature of the front surface of the cornea. It is corrected by cylindrical lenses so arranged that the convergence produced by eye and spectacle lens together is the same in all planes.

404. The Camera. — A picture of an object can be produced on a photographic plate or film merely by interposing a screen

having a tiny aperture. Rays of light from each object point
proceed through the aperture in straight lines to a corresponding
point on the plate, as illustrated in part I of Fig. 429. This
arrangement is termed the *pinhole camera*. If the aperture is
made larger to let more light fall upon the plate, a diverging pencil
will proceed from each object point and produce a patch of light
upon the plate; these patches will overlap and yield a blurred pic-

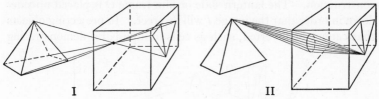

I   II

FIG. 429.   Action of the photographic camera

ture. Thus, brightness of the picture is attained at the expense of
definition.

By placing a lens in the aperture, all the rays from each object
point through the lens will be brought to a focus upon a corresponding image point, as shown in part II of the figure.   The usual photographic camera makes use of this arrangement, and includes
facilities for varying the distance between lens and plate to permit
focusing objects at different distances, and for regulating the
aperture of the lens by stops.

The brightness of the image upon the plate will depend upon
the aperture of the lens or objective, that is,
upon the diameter of the stop in the diaphragm
placed at the lens.   This diameter is expressed as
a fraction of the focal length of the objective; thus
a lens set at $f/8$ is stopped down to a diameter
one-eighth of its focal length.   If the stop is
changed to $f/4$, the aperture will be doubled and
four times as much light will reach the plate;   the

FIG. 430.   Anastig-
mat lens

corresponding exposure time will be one-fourth the previous value.

There are several types of objectives for cameras which are so
well corrected for spherical and chromatic aberration, astigmatism
and other deflects that they give splendid definition and may be
used for such exacting service as photo-engraving.   Most so-called
anastigmat lenses are of this type; Fig. 430 shows a section of the
well-known Tessar objective formed of four lenses, the two inner
ones having lower indices of refraction than the others.

405. Projection Apparatus. — A *projéctor* for lantern slides or motion picture films consists optically of a *condensing lens* for illuminating the glass slide or film, and a *projection lens* for forming an enlarged image of that object upon the screen.   A typical arrangement is illustrated in Fig. 431, wherein the condenser C consists of two plano-convex lenses, and the projection lens P consists of two lenses also although shown as one for simplicity of ray construction.   The lantern slide or film frame O is placed up-side-down in order that the image I will be erect.   In projecting objects that cannot be inverted, such as cells of liquids for demonstrating

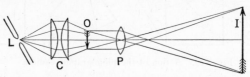

FIG. 431.   Optical system of a projector

capillarity and electrolysis, it is customary to use an erecting prism just beyond the projecting lens.   The magnification I/O is the ratio of image distance to object distance, and depends upon the focal length of the projection lens.   The source of illumination L may be an incandescent lamp with its filament concentrated in a small flat zone, or an arc lamp operated manually or automatically.

A motion-picture projector is tipped downward at an angle of 20° with the horizontal and throws a picture upon a vertical screen distant 100 ft. horizontally from its projection lens, which has a focal length of 4.5 in.   To test the distortion due to the projection angle, a slide marked with a circle $\frac{1}{2}$ in. in diameter is substituted for the film.   Find the dimensions of the image on the screen.

The focal length of the projection lens is $f = 4.5/12 = 0.375$ ft. and the distance from the lens to the center of the screen is $q = 100/\cos 20° = 106.4$ ft.   Using equation (249), $\dfrac{1}{p} + \dfrac{1}{q} = \dfrac{1}{f}$, the distance from the slide to the lens is found to be $p = 0.376$ ft., showing that the slide is almost at the principal focus of the lens.   The magnification, by equation (253), is $q/p = 106.4/0.376 = 283$, and if the picture were thrown perpendicularly on the screen its diameter would be $283 \times \frac{1}{2} = 141.5$ in. or 11.79 ft.   A rough sketch will suffice to show that because of the projection angle the vertical dimension of the image is increased to approximately $11.79/\cos 20° = 12.55$ ft.   Hence the screen image is elongated vertically, its height being greater than its width by about $12.55 - 11.79 = 0.76$ ft. or 9 in.   Further distortion will occur if the picture is not viewed directly from the front; its amount for various points of observation can be calculated similarly.

406. The Magnifying Glass. — The extreme rays from an object form an angle at the eye which is called the *visual angle* of

that object. This angle determines the *apparent size* of the object. In the top part of Fig. 432, α is the visual angle subtended by the object O at the distance d, and also by the inverted retinal image I. An object twice as long and located twice as far away would have the same visual angle and produce the same retinal image, consequently it would have the same apparent size. By bringing the object nearer to the eye its visual angle and apparent size increases, but a limit is reached by the accommodation of the eye. This limiting distance for the normal eye at middle age is about 10 in. or 25 cm., and is spoken of as the *distance of distinct vision.*

The visual angle of an object can be increased by bringing the object near the eye and interposing a converging lens to yield a virtual image of the object where it can be accommodated easily. In the figure, the object O

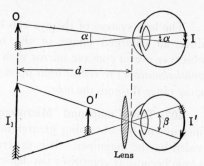

FIG. 432. Increasing visual angle with magnifier

at the distance of distinct vision d is moved to position O', thereby increasing the visual angle from α to β. Assuming the lens to produce an image I_1 of O' at the initial distance d, the magnification afforded by the lens will be the ratio of the apparent sizes of the object in the two positions, that is

$$M = \frac{I'}{I} = \frac{\beta}{\alpha} = \frac{I_1/d}{O/d} = \frac{I_1}{O} \tag{258}$$

The converging lens thus acts as a *simple magnifier*, having a magnification that is expressible either as the ratio of image size I_1 to object size O, or as the ratio of the angles β and α that these sizes subtend at the eye.

The magnification of the magnifying glass can be expressed in terms of its focal length by applying the procedure of §§ 393 and 395. Assume the object O to be located at a distance p from a converging lens of focal length f. With p numerically less than f, a virtual image I_1 will be formed on the same side of the lens at a distance q from it such that

$$\frac{1}{p} = \frac{1}{f} + \frac{1}{q}$$

Consequently the magnification will be

$$M = \frac{I_1}{O} = \frac{q}{p} = q\left(\frac{1}{f} + \frac{1}{q}\right) = \frac{q}{f} + 1$$

For the eye accommodated to the distance of distinct vision, the lens of focal length f cm. will have a magnification of

$$M = \frac{25}{f} + 1 \tag{259}$$

The lens system of the eye can be used as a magnifier to produce an enlarged image of the retina for examination. The observer uses a concave mirror with a hole at its center (called an *ophthalmoscope*) to reflect light upon the retina and then views it at close range through the hole.

407. The Compound Microscope. — The *microscope* is an instrument for obtaining greater magnification than can be provided by the magnifier. It is generally called a compound microscope because it comprises two lenses or lens systems; the first or *objective* forms a real enlarged image of the object under observation, and the second or *eyepiece* forms an enlarged virtual image

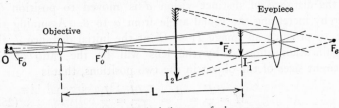

FIG. 433. Optical diagram of microscope

of this image just as in the simple magnifier. Fig. 433 illustrates in convenient proportions the construction of images formed by the microscope.

The object O is just outside the principal focus F_o of the objective, and the image I_1 produced by this lens is located at a distance L, called the *optical tube length*, from the lens. The magnification of the objective is very nearly

$$M_o = \frac{L}{F}$$

where F is the focal length of the objective. The image I_1 falls between the eyepiece and its principal focus F_e and, with the second image I_2 at the distance of distinct vision, the magnification produced by this lens of focal length f cm. is

$$M_e = \frac{I_2}{I_1} = \frac{25}{f} + 1$$

by equation (259). The construction of image I_2 shown in the figure follows the procedure of § 393, but is omitted in Fig. 432 to gain clarity. The total magnification of the microscope is the product of M_o and M_e, or

$$M = \frac{L}{F}\left(\frac{25}{f} + 1\right) \tag{260}$$

Microscope objectives are corrected for spherical and chromatic aberration over the entire aperture; Fig. 434 shows a section of a typical objective having six lenses.

Microscopes are used chiefly in biological, chemical and metallographic investigations. Fig. 435 gives microscopic views of two metal surfaces under a magnification of 100 diameters; at the left is structural steel with 0.25 per cent carbon showing the dark pearlite areas and light ferrite grains, and at the right is a light-weight lithium-

Fig. 434. Typical objective lens system

magnesium alloy showing light and dark colored constituents which are solid solutions containing two different percentages of lithium.

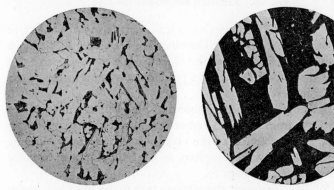

FIG. 435. Photomicrographs of metals
(*Courtesy of Professor Otto H. Henry*)

To secure maximum illumination in high-power microscopes their objectives are designed to use a liquid, such as cedar oil, that has about the same refractive index as glass, between the object and the lowest lens of the objective. This lens is hemispherical like that shown in Fig. 434, but the one above it has its lower surface concave instead of plane. An objective of this type, called an *oil-immersion* objective, permits rays over a wide angle to be collected by the lower lens and to be refracted for normal incidence upon the one above.

High-power microscopes enable an observer to discern objects down to about 0.0005 mm. in size; smaller particles (to about 0.000005 mm.) can be observed by scattered light against a dark background, the particles being illuminated by rays that are too oblique to enter the objective. When so used the instrument is called an *ultra microscope*. Minute organisms, colloidal particles, and Brownian movements [§ 114] can be rendered visible in this way; the method is also used in the Millikan oil-drop experiment [§ 204].

408. Astronomical Telescopes. — The apparent size of a distant object can be magnified by a *refracting telescope*, an instru-

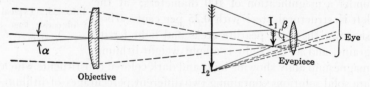

Fig. 436.   Refracting astronomical telescope

ment which consists of two lenses or lens systems, one the objective and the other the eyepiece. The objective has a long focal length and produces a real image of the object, while the eyepiece has a relatively short focal length and produces a virtual image of the first one for inspection.

The optical arrangement is shown in Fig. 436; the dotted lines represent rays from the head-end of the distant object converging upon image I_1 by action of the objective. These rays continue and are deviated by the eyepiece, so that they appear to come from the head-end of image I_2.

The full lines represent the extreme rays from object and image through the lens centers; they will aid in evaluating the magnifying power of the telescope. Without the telescope, the distant object would produce an image on the retina subtended by the visual angle α, and with the telescope the larger retinal image will be subtended by the angle β. Consequently the magnification is $M = \beta/\alpha$. Since image I_1 is located at the principal focus of the objective of focal length F, and since this image is practically at the principal focus of the eyepiece of focal length f, it follows that $\alpha = I_1/F$, and $\beta = I_1/f$; consequently the magnifying power of the telescope is

$$M = \frac{F}{f} \tag{261}$$

The objective of an astronomical telescope is a carefully corrected achromatic lens; the eyepiece is usually a compound one like the Huygens eyepiece.

The eyepiece of the familiar *opera glass* is a diverging lens; it is placed to intercept the rays to the image that would be formed by the objective, thereby producing an erect virtual image of the object for observation. This construction has the advantage of providing a relatively short tube length for a given magnifying power; however, cross-hairs cannot be used with such an instrument. Short tube length is secured in the *prismatic field glass* by the use of two total-reflecting prisms (as shown at the right in Fig. 396), which double back the rays twice between the objective and the converging eyepiece and yield an erect image.

The *reflecting telescope* has a large mirror for collecting light, and uses lens systems as eyepieces. Fig. 437 shows such a telescope of the Newtonian type, in which a small plane mirror on the axis, at 45° to it (or a prism), shifts the real image formed by the concave mirror from position I_1 to position I_2 for the eyepiece to enlarge. In the Cassegrainian type also widely used, the rays from the objective are doubled back by a convex hyperbolic mirror on the telescope axis and pass through a central hole in the principal mirror to the eyepiece.

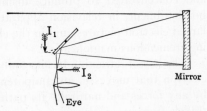

FIG. 437. Reflecting astronomical telescope

Refracting telescopes are in use that have objectives up to 40 in. in diameter; some reflecting telescopes are much larger. The 100-in. telescope at Mount Wilson Observatory in California has a mirror of 42.3 ft. focal length. The largest is a 200-in. mirror at Mount Palomar Observatory, also in California. This mirror was cast of a special Pyrex glass having a coefficient of linear expansion of only 0.00000245 per Centigrade degree. It will gather four times as much light as the 100-in. instrument and provide greater resolution of detail; it is expected to penetrate hundreds of millions of light-years into space.

When a telescope is used for making photographic records, the eyepiece is removed and the sensitized plates are located at the place where the images are formed by the objective. The optical arrangement is then the same as in the camera except that the focal length is much greater.

*409. The Electron Microscope.

—An entirely new approach to the problem of high magnification has been made recently by applying the deflecting action of electric and magnetic fields upon charged particles. The experiments of H. Busch in 1926, using cathode rays in fields that were symmetrical axially, showed that such fields could focus a beam of electrons very much as a lens focuses a beam of light. For this reason such symmetrical fields are spoken of as electrostatic and magnetic *electron lenses*, and the subject itself, dealing with the study of such lenses and their application, is termed *electron optics*. Its principles have been utilized in an apparatus styled the electric gun, wherein ions are accelerated and concentrated to produce disintegration of atoms by ionic bombardment, in television apparatus for the production of enlarged electron pictures, and in the electron microscope for obtaining tremendous magnification.

The law of refraction has its counterpart in electron optics. An electron that moves in an equipotential region is not acted upon by any forces and naturally its path will be straight, but when it travels from one such region to another between which there is a sudden difference of potential, the path will change abruptly.

Consider an electron beam to travel as shown in part I of Fig. 438 from a region of constant potential V_1 to another of value V_2. Assuming the latter region more highly positive than the first, an electron will change its direction toward the normal NN in crossing the potential step, because the component of its velocity along the normal will be increased while the component along the separating plane will be unchanged. Taking the electron velocities in regions 1 and 2 respectively as v_1 and v_2 and calling their unchanged velocity component v_x, it follows that $\sin i = \dfrac{v_x}{v_1}$ and $\sin r = \dfrac{v_x}{v_2}$, where i and r are the angles of incidence and refraction respectively of the electron beam at the plane separating the two equipotential regions. Herefrom

$$\frac{\sin i}{\sin r} = \frac{v_2}{v_1}$$

Now, let e represent the charge of an electron and m its mass; then the work done on the electron in crossing the boundary will be

$$e(V_2 - V_1) = \tfrac{1}{2}m\,v_2^2 - \tfrac{1}{2}m\,v_1^2$$

Assuming the work done upon the electron in bringing it initially into the zone of potential V_1 to be $eV_1 = \tfrac{1}{2}m\,v_1^2$, it follows that $eV_2 = \tfrac{1}{2}m\,v_2^2$. Consequently by division $V_1/V_2 = v_1^2/v_2^2$, and merging with the earlier result

$$\frac{v_2}{v_1} = \sqrt{\frac{V_2}{V_1}} = \frac{\sin i}{\sin r}$$

showing that the ratio of electron velocities in the two regions is proportional to the square root of the potential ratio and to the inverse ratio of sines of the angles the electron beam makes with the normal to the plane separating the potential regions.

While the abrupt bending of an electron beam as described is analogous to the refraction of light on entering a medium of greater

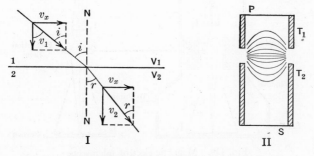

Fig. 438.   Electronic refraction and electrostatic electron lens

refractive index, in practically all arrangements applying electron optics the potential zones change gradually and consequently the electron paths shift gently from zone to zone. Thus, part II of Fig. 438 shows a simple arrangement, consisting of two cylindrical tubes T_1 and T_2 charged to different potentials, which is equivalent optically to a converging lens and serves as an electron microscope of low power. The curved lines are sections of symmetrical equipotential surfaces which spread into the tubes, the potential gradient being greatest at the midplane of the gap where these surfaces are closest together. To explain the action, suppose a light image to be projected from above onto the semi-transparent photoelectric surface P, causing it to release electrons from each spot in proportion to the intensity of light incident upon it. The beam of electrons from each spot diverges and reaches the electro-static lens between the tubes; this converges the beam upon a particular spot on the fluorescent screen S at the lower end. In this way an inverted image may be produced on the screen in a manner analogous to the formation of an image on a photographic film

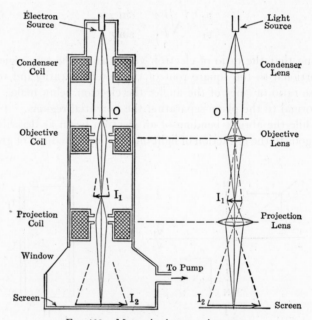

FIG. 439. Magnetic electron microscope

with a camera lens. The magnification can be made quite large and the focusing more precise by placing near the electron emitting surface several anode rings that are charged to appropriate potentials.

Magnetic lenses are more powerful than those of the electro-static type just described, but their action is more difficult to visual-ize. An electron slanting into a uniform magnetic field has two component motions: the one parallel to the field remains unchanged in direction, while the other crosswise of the field becomes circular, as in the cyclotron [§ 263]. The combination of these motions causes the electron stream to move along a helical path in such a manner that electrons issuing from a particular object point meet at a corresponding point on a plane to form the image. An elec-tron microscope using magnetic lenses is illustrated in Fig. 439, together with its optical equivalent; the object on a transparent film is shown at O, an intermediate image at I_1, and the final image at I_2. Such an instrument has possibilities of magnifications upwards of 20,000 diameters. The resolving power [§ 416] of any optical instrument is limited by the wave length of light, and since the equivalent wave length of an electron [§ 430] is very short, resolution of detail by the electron microscope is much superior to the optical microscope.

PROBLEMS

1. A cam which is known to be revolving at a speed between 7000 and 8000 rev. per min. is observed while illuminated by light flashes occurring 120 times per sec. If the cam appears to be turning backward at 18 rev. per min., find its actual speed of rotation.

2. Draw to scale, say 5 times full size, the optical surfaces of the eye. Show the conditions for the eye accommodated for near objects above the axis and those for the unaccommodated eye below.

3. A certain near-sighted person cannot see distinctly beyond 40 cm. from the eye. Apply equations (249) and (254) to determine the focal length and power in diopters of spectacle lenses to enable the person to see objects at great distances.

4. A certain far-sighted person cannot see objects distinctly closer than 45 cm. to the eye. Find the power of spectacle lenses which will enable this person to see objects 25 cm. away.

5. If a person needs spectacles having a power of $+2$ diopters in order to see an object distinctly which is 25 cm. from his eyes, what is the short-est distance at which he could see it distinctly without spectacles?

6. If a near-sighted person needs spectacles having a power of -2 diopters in order to see an object distinctly which is 25 cm. from his eyes, what is the greatest distance at which he could see it distinctly without spectacles?

7. A lens for the correction of an astigmatic far-sighted eye has a con-cave surface having a radius of 15 cm., and a convex surface having radii of 8.5 and 9.2 cm. in mutually perpendicular directions. Taking 1.56 as the refractive index of the lens material, determine the separation of the focal lines and the astigmatic correction in diopters.

8. A dime ($\frac{11}{16}$ in. diameter) held at a distance of $6\frac{1}{3}$ ft. from the eye has the same apparent size as the full moon. What visual angle is subtended by the moon?

9. It is desired to obtain a 4-in. photograph of a 3-ft. object with a newspaper camera having a lens of 9.5-in. focal length. What spacing should be provided (a) between the lens and the plate, and (b) between the lens and the object?

10. A camera objective having a focal length of 6 in. is adjusted to produce a sharp image for an object at infinite distance. How far and in what direction must the lens be moved to focus an object 10 ft. from the lens?

11. What are the relative speeds of a photographic objective when its stop openings are $f/16$ and $f/5.6$?

12. The objective lens of a camera when set to focus objects 8 ft. away is located $4\frac{2}{3}$ in. from the film. A so-called portrait attachment consists of a lens to be placed next to the objective. What should the focal length of this attachment be in order that objects placed 3 ft. away from the lens may be focused upon the film?

13. Compute the focal length of a projection lens which will throw a picture 8 ft. wide upon a screen 28.4 ft. away from a lantern slide having an aperture 3 in. wide.

14. A motion-picture projector, using a film with a picture width of 24 mm., throws a picture 24 ft. wide on a screen 144 ft. away from the projection lens. What is the focal length of this lens?

15. A reading glass produces an image 5 in. from it when the corresponding object is 45 in. away from the lens on the other side. What is the magnification of this lens when used as a simple magnifier?

16. A microscope has a 4-mm. objective and a 25-mm. eyepiece, these ratings being their focal lengths. Calculate the magnification of the instrument for an optical tube length of 160 mm.

17. Calculate the magnification produced by a compound microscope having an objective of 3.0-mm. focal length and an optical tube length of 250 mm., when used with an eyepiece having a magnifying power of 12 diameters.

18. The largest refracting telescope, that at the Yerkes Observatory in Wisconsin, has a diameter of 40 in. and a focal length of 65 ft. Compute its magnification when used with an eyepiece of 1-in. focal length.

19. A telescope tube for a spectroscope is 28.4 cm. long and is fitted with a thin lens at each end. Its magnifying power is 20. Determine the focal lengths of objective and eyepiece by applying equation (261).

20. In taking a photograph with a telescope the eyepiece is removed and a photographic plate is inserted in the plane of the image formed by the objective. How large a photograph of the moon would be obtained with a telescope having an objective of 40-in. focal length? The diameter of the moon is 2163 mi. and its distance from the earth may be taken as 240,000 mi.

CHAPTER XXXVIII

INTERFERENCE AND DIFFRACTION

410. Interference of Light. — The wave character of light leads to some important considerations involving interference effects. The superposition of two light waves upon arriving simultaneously at a given point will produce a total illumination that depends upon their wave lengths, amplitudes, and phases. With monochromatic light, waves of equal amplitude will reenforce each other if they arrive in phase and will annul each other if they arrive in opposite phase. When they annul and produce zero illumination at certain points there will be other points where the

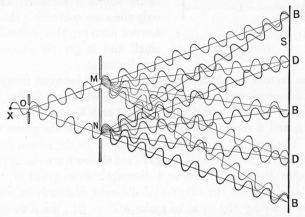

FIG. 440. Reenforcement and annulment of light waves

illumination is increased, since the total energy of the waves remains unchanged. With white light, in which many colors are blended, the annulment of one color at a particular point still leaves illumination by the other colors.

Interference of light was originally demonstrated and explained by the English physicist, Thomas Young (1773–1829), using an arrangement as shown in Fig. 440. Monochromatic light from a lamp X is directed upon a small opening O in the first shield; this serves as a point source for illuminating two pinholes M and N in the second shield. From these apertures waves spread out in all directions, a few of which are indicated in the plane of the apertures. Waves leaving M and N in phase agreement and proceeding to the screen S reenforce each other and produce brightness at certain places BBB, and annul each other and produce darkness at other places DD. *Reenforcement occurs where the two waves arrive at the screen in phase agreement*, both waves having traveled the same distance or either having traveled one or more complete wave lengths farther than the other. *Annulment occurs where the two waves arrive at the screen in phase opposition*, one

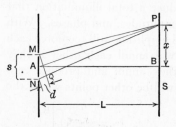

wave having traveled an odd number of half-wave lengths farther than the other. There results on the screen an interference pattern of lines, called *fringes*, which are alternately bright and dark. The figure shows a sectional view of only the zone containing the interference pattern; this region is very small and is greatly exaggerated for clearness.

FIG. 441. Interference produced by two slits

The factors which determine the spacing between fringes will be investigated with the aid of Fig. 441, which represents a sectional view of two parallel-sided slits M and N separated by a distance s, and a screen S which is distant L from the plane of the slits. The line AB is drawn perpendicular to the screen from A, midway between the slits; and rays are shown from the apertures to a point P on the screen at a distance x from point B. Light waves issuing from the slits travel different distances in reaching P. By drawing MQ so as to make $MP = QP$, the difference in path may be expressed as $d = NQ$. A line connecting points P and A will be perpendicular to MQ, and hence the angles NMQ and PAB will be equal. Since these angles are small, the sine of one may be equated to the tangent of the other, giving the simple relation

$$\frac{d}{s} = \frac{x}{L} \tag{262}$$

Representing the wave length of the light by λ, the condition for reenforcement or annulment at P may be expressed as $d = \dfrac{n\,\lambda}{2}$, reenforcement occurring when $n = 0, 2, 4, \cdots$ and annulment occurring when $n = 1, 3, 5 \cdots$ Using this value for d in equation (262) and rearranging, there results

$$x = \frac{n \lambda L}{2 s} \tag{263}$$

showing that the spacing of the fringes varies directly as the wave length λ and the screen distance L, and varies inversely as the distance s between the slits.

That the distance between fringes is very small will be evident from considering green light from a mercury vapor lamp ($\lambda = 0.00005461$ cm.) to be directed upon two slits 0.1 cm. apart. On a screen 100 cm. away the first dark line from B will be found at a distance of $x = \dfrac{5461 \times 10^{-8} \times 100}{2 \times 0.1} = 0.0273$ cm., the first bright line at 0.0546 cm., the second dark line at 0.0819 cm., and so on.

When white light instead of monochromatic light is used as a source, each color produces its own interference fringes, those for red light being spaced about twice as far apart as those for violet light, and the resulting pattern is due to the combined effect of all colors. Such brilliantly colored designs may also be observed by looking at a distant white-light source through a piece of silk or a fine-mesh screen, the meshes acting as closely spaced sources.

In order to show the interference effects described, the phase relation of the waves must remain unchanged where they emerge from the slits, and *this requires that the slits receive light from the same point of the source.* Several methods have been devised for accomplishing this result conveniently. In one of these, the pair of apertures is replaced by a thin prism having an angle of almost 180° and known as a *biprism.* Such a prism, shown at P in Fig. 442, refracts the light from a narrow slit A so that it appears to come from two virtual sources M and N. The screen S is illuminated by source M over the region RQ and by source N over the region UV. The interference fringes occur near B, at the center of the overlapping region UQ; these are usually observed with a low-power telescope. They are more distinct than with Young's arrangement because of the greater intensity of the sources M and N.

The photograph at the right shows the interference fringes produced by parallel white light through a biprism. The broader shadings at top and bottom are diffraction bands [§ 414].

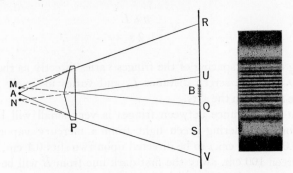

FIG. 442.   Fringes produced with a biprism

411. Thin Films. — Colors are frequently observed in films such as soap bubbles, thin layers of oil on water, and coatings of oxide on heated metal. Such films are usually observed by reflection, and the colors are due to interference of light waves reflected at the front and back surfaces. Fig. 443 represents a

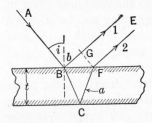

FIG. 443.   Interference at thin film

film of refractive index μ, illuminated by a beam of monochromatic light impinging upon the surface in the direction A. An eye at E receives light reflected partly at B and partly at C. By drawing a line FG perpendicular to these reflected rays, it is seen that the second ray travels farther than the first by an amount $2a - b$, where a represents the distance BC or CF and b represents the distance BG. The distance $2a$ within the film is equivalent to an air distance of $2 \mu a$, and hence the retardation of ray 2 with respect to ray 1 is $2 \mu a - b$. The distances in this expression depend upon the thickness of the film t and the angle of light incidence i, and it can be shown that the relative retardation is equal to $2 t \sqrt{\mu^2 - \sin^2 i}$, which for normal incidence becomes $2 \mu t$.

It might be expected that as the film thickness t approaches zero, the two rays would come into phase and reenforce each other, since their optical paths would then approach equality. It is found by experiments with soap bubbles, however, that a black spot appears where the film becomes so thin that it is about to rupture, showing that destructive interference of light rather than reenforcement occurs when the film has negligible thickness. The light wave is reflected at the front and back surfaces, one reflection taking place within a medium of low refractive index at the boundary of a medium of high index, and the other reflection taking place within a medium of high index at the boundary of one of low index. Under these circumstances, there is always a *phase displacement of a half-wave length* between the two reflected waves due to reflection, in addition to whatever phase displacement may exist because of the difference in the paths of the two rays.

In Fig. 443, the retardation of ray 2 with respect to ray 1 amounts to $2\mu t$ because of path difference, assuming normal incidence, and the phase displacement due to reflection is equivalent to a further retardation of a half-wave length or $\lambda/2$. Consequently, the total retardation of ray 2 with respect to ray 1 is

$$\text{Retardation} = 2\mu t + \frac{\lambda}{2}$$

When the retardation is an odd number of half-wave lengths, there will be destructive interference and darkness; when it is zero or an even number of half-wave lengths, there will be a maximum reenforcement and brightness.

Under illumination by white light, the thinnest film to show interference color by reflection is that for which $t = \dfrac{\lambda}{2\mu}$ for violet light; this film will have a residual reddish color. When a film is thick, it will not appear colored, because so many wave lengths will satisfy the conditions for reenforcement, namely that $t = \dfrac{\lambda}{4\mu}, \dfrac{3\lambda}{4\mu}, \dfrac{5\lambda}{4\mu} \cdots$, that the reenforced waves upon merging will produce the effect of white light.

An interesting experiment on the interference produced by films utilizes a plano-convex lens of large radius and an optically flat plate placed together to form a wedge-shaped film of air between them. If illuminated by monochromatic light, an interference pattern will be observed by reflected light which consists of a series of bright and dark rings concentric around the point of contact. This phenomenon was first described by Newton and the rings are called by his name. The effect is due to the interference of light reflected from both surfaces of the air film between the convex and plane surfaces.

As an illustrative problem, show that the bright rings in this interference pattern have radii which are proportional to the square roots of the successive odd integers. At the point of contact O of the two surfaces, Fig. 444, there will be interference because the air film there has zero thickness and the light waves reflected from its upper and lower boundaries differ in phase by $\lambda/2$, as explained. Reflection which occurs where the film has a thickness $t = \lambda/4$ will result in reenforcement because at these points the light reflected at the lower boundary will be retarded with respect to the other by an amount $\lambda/2 + \lambda/2$ or λ. Reenforcement will also occur when $t = 3\lambda/4, 5\lambda/4 \cdots$, or in general $(2n - 1)\lambda/4$, n being an integer. Using construction lines as in the figure, the right triangles OAB and ACB are similar, whence $AB:OB = BC:AB$. Letting R represent the radius of the lens and r the radius of a bright ring of the interference pattern, it follows that $r:t = (2R - t):r$. Since t is negligibly small compared with $2R$, the radius of the bright ring becomes $r = \sqrt{2Rt} = \sqrt{2R(2n-1)\,\lambda/4}$, or $r \propto \sqrt{2n-1}$, where the quantity under the radical represents any odd number.

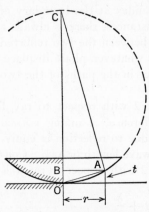

FIG. 444. Newton's rings

The interference patterns due to thin films under monochromatic light are used to detect slight surface irregularities in lenses, optical plates, and mirrors.

*412. Non-reflecting Glass. — Recent experimentation for treating glass surfaces to minimize reflection makes use of transparent films that adhere to the glass. The films are designed of such materials and thickness that the light reflected from the film will annul the light reflected from the glass. The two reflected waves should have *equal amplitudes and opposite phase to produce light interference*.

The requirements for meeting the first condition can be determined from equation (238), which gives the intensity of a reflected beam from a boundary surface between two transparent media of indices μ_1 and μ_2, assuming perpendicular incidence and reflection. Remembering that the intensity of a light wave is proportional to the square of its amplitude, the ratio of the amplitude of the reflected wave to that of the incident wave will become

$$\frac{A}{A_o} = \frac{\mu_2 - \mu_1}{\mu_2 + \mu_1}$$

Taking μ_f and μ_g as the refractive indices of film and glass respectively, the reflected rays shown in Fig. 445 will be equal when

$$\frac{\mu_f - 1}{\mu_f + 1} = \frac{\mu_g - \mu_f}{\mu_g + \mu_f}$$

or $$\mu_f = \sqrt{\mu_g} \qquad (264)$$

This indicates that the films to be placed on ordinary glass (of index 1.5 to 1.6) should have very low indices of refraction.

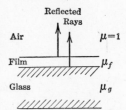

The condition for interference of the two reflected rays, assuming monochromatic incident light of a definite wave length, means that the equivalent air thickness of the film should be an odd number of quarter-wave lengths, as explained in the previous section. For the minimum thickness t and for a wave length λ, it follows that

$$\mu_f t = \frac{\lambda}{4}$$

Fig. 445. Annuling reflection of light from glass surface

Ordinary window glass ($\mu_g = 1.52$) can be rendered non-reflecting for yellow light ($\lambda = 0.0000589$ cm.) by placing upon it a film of refractive index $\sqrt{1.52} = 1.23$ and having a thickness $0.0000589/(4 \times 1.23) = 0.000012$ cm. Such thin films can be produced by evaporation, and the index of refraction of the film substance can be lowered to the desired value by decreasing its density through control of the evaporation conditions. Films of the metallic fluorides, such as magnesium fluoride, have been found to stick firmly to the glass and to possess mechanical strength. Glass plates with such films on both sides show very little reflection of white light and they transmit well over 98 per cent of the incident beam. Multilayer films have also been experimented with; they allow a wider choice of film materials and methods of application. The use of non-reflecting glass for store windows would remove most of the glare which prevents observers from seeing objects on display.

413. The Interferometer. — The *interferometer* makes use of interference in measuring the wave length of light in terms of a standard of length, or in measuring an unknown length in terms of known wave lengths of light. The essential parts of the instrument devised by Michelson are arranged as in Fig. 446; they com-

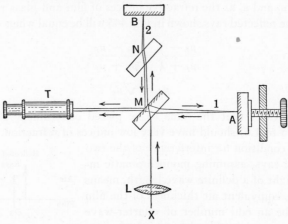

FIG. 446. Plan of interferometer

prise two plane mirrors *A* and *B*, a glass plate *M*, of which the upper surface is very lightly silvered, and a telescope *T*. One of the mirrors (*A* in the figure) is mounted on a fine pitch screw, and the silvered plate is set at 45° to the axes *BX* and *AT*.

Monochromatic light from the source *X* is formed into a parallel beam by a lens *L* and projected upon the plate *M* where it divides into two beams, 1 and 2; these advance to the mirrors *A* and *B* respectively and return to *M* and thence to the telescope. Ray 1 passes through the half-silvered plate *M* three times, while ray 2 passes through it only once; a second plate *N* is introduced to equalize the two paths. If the waves after recombination at *M* are in phase, the field of the telescope appears bright, and if they are in opposition, the field appears dark.

Suppose that light of wave length λ is directed upon the half-silvered plate and that the distances to mirrors *A* and *B* are such as to cause the field of the telescope to be dark. If the movable mirror is now advanced slowly, a movement of $\lambda/4$ causes a change of path of $\lambda/2$ and the field will appear bright; a further movement of $\lambda/4$ will make it dark again, and so on. If this mirror is provided with an accurate scale for measuring the distance through

which it is moved, the wave length of the incident light can be
determined directly from the number of light annulments. Thus,
if n successive interferences are observed while the mirror is moved
a distance l, the wave length is found to be

$$\lambda = \frac{2l}{n} \qquad (265)$$

On the other hand, if λ is known, short distances can be measured
in terms of this wave length.

Usually the mirrors are not exactly at right angles to each other,
as implied in the foregoing description, but depart slightly from
this condition. With this adjustment, the field of the telescope
will be crossed by dark interference fringes, separated by bright
reenforcement fringes, and the movement of mirror A can be
observed by counting the fringes as they sweep past the cross hair
of the telescope.

The interferometer can be used to measure extremely small
distances, for example, the expansion of crystals under slight temperature changes. Michelson also used this instrument by a
doubling process to measure the length of the standard meter in
terms of the wave length of the red line in the cadmium spectrum;
this measurement fixes for all time the length of the standard
in terms of an unvarying unit. The diameters of a few of the
larger stars have been determined by interference methods applied
to a telescope.

414. Diffraction. — Although it is commonly said that light
travels in straight lines, careful observation shows that it bends
slightly around the edges of an obstruction. The spreading of a
beam of light into the region behind an obstacle is known as *diffraction*. Because of diffraction, a parallel beam of monochromatic light passing through a slit toward a screen will ordinarily
produce a bright band somewhat wider than the slit, and this
band will be bordered at the edges by a few narrower bands which
are alternately dark and bright. This effect can be explained with
the aid of Fig. 447, which shows a single slit MN of width s located
a distance L from a screen S. The line AB is drawn perpendicular
to the screen from the middle of the slit, and P represents any
point on the screen distant x from the point B. The line MQ is
drawn at right angles to a line connecting A and P to show the
difference in path length of the extreme rays NP and MP; this
difference is marked d.

If the path difference of the rays from the slit edges is one wave length of light ($d = \lambda$), P will be a point of darkness rather than brightness. This can be proved by imagining the slit to be composed of a series of much narrower slits extending uniformly from M to N, and observing that each of these elementary slits in the upper part MA of the actual slit will annul the effect of a similarly located element in the lower part AN, since such a pair of elementary slits differ in their distance to P by $\lambda/2$. Consequently the light issuing from the entire upper half of the slit annuls that

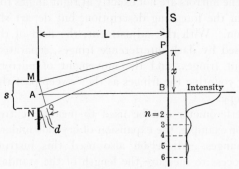

FIG. 447. Diffraction of light by a slit

issuing from the entire lower half. For a point further along the screen from B for which the path difference is $d = 3\lambda/2$, the slit may be regarded as composed of three sections, two of which will annul each other as just explained, while the remaining section will produce reduced illumination. If $d = 2\lambda$, P will be dark; if $d = 5\lambda/2$, that point will be illuminated by $\frac{1}{5}$ of the slit, and so on. In general, for annulment or reenforcement, the path difference for the extreme rays of the slit will be $d = \dfrac{n\lambda}{2}$; interference occurring for even values of n and partial reenforcement for the odd values. The locations of the fringes on the screen above and below B are found as in equation (263) to be given by

$$x = \frac{n\lambda L}{2s} \tag{266}$$

annulment occurring when $n = 2, 4, 6 \cdots$ and reenforcement occurring when $n = 3, 5, 7 \cdots$ The diffraction pattern consists of a central band, illuminated by the entire slit and having a width $2x = 2\left(\dfrac{2\lambda L}{2s}\right) = \dfrac{2\lambda L}{s}$, bordered on each side by narrower

bands, alternately dark and bright, which become less distinct as
the distance from the center is increased. The relative intensities
at different points are indicated by the curve in the lower part of the
figure. It will be observed that the narrower the slit used, the
wider will be the spacing of the bands forming the diffraction pattern. If, however, the width of the slit is reduced to the same
order of magnitude as the wave length of light, it will be apparent
from the foregoing construction that no points of annulment will
appear on the screen and there will result merely a spreading of
light over its surface by diffraction. In Young's experiment, for
example, in addition to the interference effects described in § 410,
some light will reach all parts of the screen through both slits by
diffraction.

The diffraction pattern produced by a circular hole consists of
a round patch of light, surrounded by a few rings which are alternately dark and bright. This result may be thought of as a
development of that just described. Upon dividing the circle into
imaginary strips of equal width it will be apparent that the outermost strips produce little effect because of their small area.
Disregarding these outer strips, a circular hole may be considered
as equivalent to a slit of reduced width; consequently its diffraction
pattern will have a proportionately wider spacing. Mathematical
analysis shows that the diffraction bands produced by a round hole
of diameter s are spaced 1.22 times as far apart as those for a
parallel-sided slit of width s.

*415. Diffraction by a Lens. — It has been shown that parallel
light passing through a circular hole produces a spot of light somewhat larger than would be indicated by the rectilinear propagation
of light. For the same reason, parallel light passing through a
lens will produce at the focal plane a small disk of light rather
than an ideal point of light such as indicated by the geometrical
lens constructions of Chapter XXXVI. It should be observed
that this result is not due to any imperfection of the lens but is a
consequence of the nature of light itself. The smallness of the
disk image determines the ability of the lens to register detail in
the object under observation.

Fig. 448 represents a lens of diameter D converging a plane
incident wave of wave length λ upon the principal focus F at a
distance AF away; this is the focal length f. By diffraction,
the light passing through the lens will spread beyond the region

bordered by *MF* and *NF*. By analogy with the diffraction at a
slit, annulment may be expected at a point such as *G*, the location
of which is determined by rotating the figure *MNF* to the position
MQG, making $NQ = \lambda$. The distance *FG* will then represent the

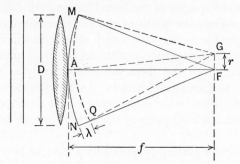

FIG. 448.   Diffraction diagram for lens

radius *r* of the disk image of an infinitely distant (point) source.
The angle between the curves *MN* and *MQ* may be taken as equal
to that between their radii, and hence, as a close approximation

$$\frac{\lambda}{D} = \frac{r}{f}$$

Applying the correction for the circular shape of the lens, the radius
of the disk increases in the ratio 1.22 to 1. Consequently the disk
image has a diameter

$$d = \frac{2.44 f \lambda}{D} \qquad (267)$$

and subtends at the lens an angle *d/f*.

The diffraction pattern produced by a lens of an object point
consists of the central bright disk surrounded by alternate dark
and bright rings. The registration of minute detail implies a
small diffraction pattern, and hence requires the lens to be of large
size as compared with its focal length. Aside from the lens constants, the smallness of the disk image involves the wave length λ
and is thus limited by the wave character of light.

*416. Resolving Power. — The ability of a lens to reveal detail
in an image is spoken of as its *resolving power*. If two object
points subtend too small an angle at the lens, their image disks will
merge and they cannot be resolved. Resolving power is measured
by the *smallest angle* between two object points at which these

points can be recognized as separate. Users of optical instruments find that they can distinguish two points as separate when their disk images do not overlap by more than the radius of one of the disks. This limit is pictured in Fig. 449, greatly magnified. The angular separation of the object points is clearly the same as that between the disk images and, at the limit of resolution, is one-half

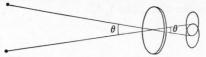

FIG. 449. Overlapping disk images formed by lens

of the angle subtended by a single disk image at the lens. From the preceding section, this limiting angle of resolution of a lens becomes

$$\theta = \frac{d}{2f} = \frac{1.22\,\lambda}{D} \qquad (268)$$

The objective lens of the Yerkes telescope has a diameter of about 102 cm., and hence its limiting angle, taking 0.00006 cm. as an average value for the wave length of light, becomes $\frac{1.22 \times 0.00006}{102} = 7.2 \times 10^{-7}$ radians or about $\frac{1}{8}$ second of arc. With this lens two dimes placed side by side could be distinguished as separate objects at a distance of about 14 miles.

Two objects 1 in. apart can be resolved by the eye at a distance of about 100 yd., from which the limiting angle of resolution of the eye is found to be about 1 minute of arc. Rays entering the eye with this angular separation fall upon adjacent cones at the central part of the retina.

417. The Diffraction Grating. — The principles of interference and diffraction are applied to the measurement of wave length in the *diffraction grating*. As constructed for use with transmitted light, the grating is essentially a transparent plate upon which there are a large number of opaque lines, usually several thousand to the centimeter, all parallel and evenly spaced. A parallel beam of monochromatic light incident upon the grating sets up secondary wavelets at the slits between the lines, in accordance with Huygens' Principle [§ 328]. In Fig. 450, part I shows the positions of these wavelets after advancing λ, 2λ, 3λ, ⋯ beyond the grating, λ being the wave length of the incident light. Lines drawn tangent to these wavelets connect only points which are in phase agreement, and consequently represent wave fronts which advance in the directions of the arrows. One of these, joining wavelets which have advanced equal distances, continues along 0 without change of direction. Other wave fronts, joining wavelets from adjacent slits, one wavelet having advanced one wave length farther than the other, are deflected through rather large angles θ and travel along the directions 1, 1.

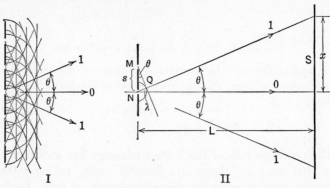

FIG. 450. Diffracted wave fronts

Part II of the figure is a plan view showing two of the grating slits, M and N, separated by a distance s, and a screen S at a distance L from the grating, toward which the waves advance along the directions indicated. The wave length λ is the radius of the wavelet at N and can be evaluated by noting that the angle between the wave front MQ and the grating is also equal to θ, whence

$$\lambda = s \sin \theta = s \frac{x}{\sqrt{L^2 + x^2}} \tag{269}$$

The experimental arrangement of the diffraction grating is represented in Fig. 451. A narrow slit A, illuminated by monochromatic light from the source X, serves as a source, and is placed at the principal focus of the converging lens L_1, from which a beam of parallel light is directed normally upon the grating G. A second converging lens, L_2, receives the parallel bundles of rays after diffraction and forms images of the illuminated slit upon the screen S, as shown. The upper and lower ones are called the *first order* diffracted images. Images of higher order are formed by wave fronts which join wavelets from adjacent slits, one wavelet having advanced two or more wave lengths farther than the other. With a white light source each diffracted beam is dispersed into its component colors because of their different wave lengths, and continuous spectra are produced on each side at some distance from

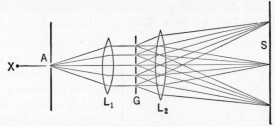

Fig. 451. Formation of images from grating with lens

the central white image. Each diffraction spectrum has the same color sequence as observed with a prism, but the order is reversed, the red color being deflected more than the violet because of its greater wave length.

Light from magnesium vapor passes through a narrow slit and falls normally upon a diffraction grating that has 5000 lines per cm. The spectrum of magnesium includes three green lines having wave lengths of 5167 Å, 5173 Å, and 5184 Å. Calculate the angular positions of the intermediate of these spectral lines for the various orders as observed on a spectrometer, and also determine the separation of the outer green lines in the second-order spectrum as observed on a straight scale parallel to the grating and distant 80 cm. from it.

Reckoning angular positions from the normal to the grating surface and taking the grating space as $1/5000 = 0.0002$ cm., $\sin \theta_1 = \lambda/s = 0.00005173 \times 5000 = 0.2587$ for the first-order spectrum, $\sin \theta_2 = 2\lambda/s = 0.5173$ for the second-order spectrum, and $\sin \theta_3 = 3\lambda/s = 0.7760$ for the third-order spectrum; there are no spectra of higher order under the conditions given because $n\lambda/s$ will be greater than unity for values of n larger than 3. The corresponding angles of diffraction are as follows: $\theta_1 = 15° 0'$, $\theta_2 = 31° 9'$, and $\theta_3 = 50° 54'$.

For the second-order spectrum, $\dfrac{2\lambda}{s} = \dfrac{x}{\sqrt{L^2 + x^2}}$; consequently the departure of the diffracted image from the central one will be $x = \dfrac{2L\lambda}{\sqrt{s^2 - 4\lambda^2}}$. Herefrom, the image position for wave length 0.00005167 cm. will be $\dfrac{2 \times 80 \text{ cm.} \times 0.00005167 \text{ cm.}}{\sqrt{(0.0002)^2 - (2 \times 0.00005167)^2} \text{ cm.}} = 48.28$ cm., and that for wave length 0.00005184 will be 48.50 cm.; thus, the separation of these two images in the second-order spectrum becomes 0.22 cm.

Many diffraction gratings operate by reflection rather than by transmission of light. The reflection grating is made by ruling lines with a diamond point on a polished surface, speculum metal (Cu 68%, Sn 32%) often being used for this purpose.

418. Diffraction of X-rays. — The extent to which a wave will spread by diffraction depends upon the wave length. Since light has short wave lengths, it is diffracted only slightly, and x-rays, which are still shorter waves, will exhibit even smaller diffraction effects. In 1912 the German physicist, Max von Laue, suggested that crystals might act as natural diffraction gratings for x-rays, because of the supposedly close and symmetrical spacing of their atoms. The experiment was successful and furnished the key to both the nature of x-rays and the structure of crystals.

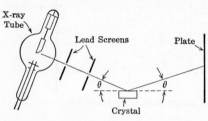

FIG. 452.   Method of investigating crystal structure

In Fig. 452, a narrow beam of x-rays is directed upon a crystal. Varying the direction of the beam discloses certain discrete values of the *glancing angle* θ for which a diffracted beam occurs. This beam makes an equal angle with the crystal, and is detected by an ionization chamber or a photographic plate. These results verify the wave-like character of x-rays and also the orderly arrangement of the atoms, the diffracted beam appearing only when the waves emerging from the various crystal planes reenforce one another.

The law covering crystal diffraction, announced by the British physicist, William L. Bragg, may be developed by the aid of Fig. 453, in which the small circles represent the atoms in a crystal, and the rays show an incident beam of x-rays from the source X meeting

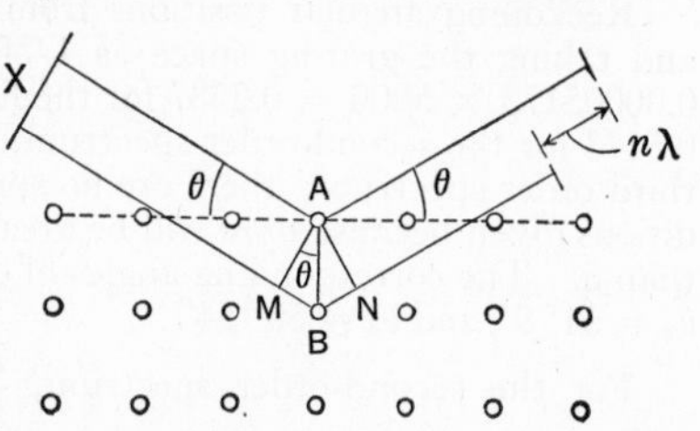

FIG. 453.   Diffraction of x-rays by crystal

the atomic planes at the small angle θ. Reflection at an equal angle occurs at innumerable planes, each reflected ray being retarded more than the one next above it by an amount $MB + BN = 2AB \sin \theta$. For reinforcement, the retardation must be an integral number of wave lengths, and hence

$$2d \sin \theta = n \lambda \qquad (270)$$

where d represents the spacing AB between the atomic planes, and n is an integer giving the order of the diffracted image. Using this relation, either the atomic spacing of the crystal or the wave length of the x-rays may be determined by simple experiment if the other of these quantities is known.

It has recently been found possible to produce x-ray spectra independently of crystals, by using a ruled diffraction grating of the reflection type and directing a narrow beam of x-rays upon it so that they almost graze the surface. The diffracted images are received upon a photographic plate and from this record the wave lengths can be determined accurately. Their order of magnitude is indicated by the value obtained for one of the copper lines, namely, $\lambda = 1.542$ Å.

When x-rays of this wave length are diffracted by a rock salt crystal, the smallest glancing angle for reinforcement ($n = 1$) is found by experiment to be 15.83°. The spacing between the crystal planes is given by Bragg's Law as

$$d = \frac{n\,\lambda}{2\sin\theta} = \frac{1.542 \times 10^{-8}}{2\sin 15.83°} = 2.83 \times 10^{-8} \text{ cm.}$$

An independent evaluation of this spacing can be made from the density of NaCl, 2.163 gm./cu. cm., and its molecular weight, 58.45. From Avogadro's number [§ 130], there are 6.02×10^{23} molecules in 58.45 gm. of NaCl; this gives 1.03×10^{22} molecules per gm. or $1.03 \times 10^{22} \times 2.163 = 2.23 \times 10^{22}$ molecules per cu. cm. Taking 2 atoms to the molecule, there will be 4.46×10^{22} atoms per cu. cm., and then supposing the crystal lattice to be a multitude of cubes with atoms at the corners, there will be

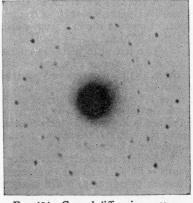

FIG. 454. Crystal diffraction pattern

$\sqrt[3]{4.46 \times 10^{22}} = 3.54 \times 10^7$

atoms in a row 1 cm. long. The spacing between atoms and also between rows is therefore $d = \dfrac{1}{3.54 \times 10^7} = 2.83 \times 10^{-8}$ cm. This result verifies the other value, and indicates that the method using x-rays is correct.

Fig. 454 shows the effect of directing a small bundle of x-rays upon a crystal and thence to a photographic plate. The x-rays encounter atomic planes inclined in various directions and forming a three-dimensional grating; the result is a symmetrical pattern which shows the orderly structure of the crystal. X-ray diffraction also reveals the changes in crystal structure produced by mechanical processes such as the hardening, annealing, rolling, and drawing of metals.

PROBLEMS

1. By passing sodium light (wave length = 5893 Å) through two pinholes 0.06 cm. apart, an interference pattern is formed upon a screen parallel to the plane of the pinholes and distant 50 cm. from them. Compute the distance along the screen from the center of the interference pattern to the second dark fringe.

2. (*a*) Monochromatic light of wave length 5461 Å passes through two narrow slits 1 mm. apart and forms an interference pattern on a screen parallel to the plane of the slits and 60 cm. distant from this plane. Calculate the distance measured along the screen between adjacent dark interference fringes. (*b*) Repeat the foregoing calculation if the screen is turned through an angle of 88° about the central bright fringe as an axis.

3. Determine the minimum thickness of a soap bubble which will cause annulment of violet light of wave length 4047 Å, when viewed by reflected light. Assume the index of refraction of the soap solution to be 1.40 as measured with this light.

4. A crack in ice is viewed by reflected white light and appears red where its thickness is such as to cause destructive interference for violet light. Compute the minimum width of such a crack, taking the wave length as 3970 A.

5. Two flat glass plates in contact at one end are separated at the other end by a fiber of unknown diameter. The wedge-shaped air film between the plates is viewed by reflected monochromatic light of wave length 0.00005461 cm., and is found to be crossed by 74 dark interference fringes. Calculate the diameter of the fiber.

6. An interferometer is illuminated with monochromatic light and its mirror is moved sufficiently to cause 1000 interference fringes to sweep across the field. If the mirror was moved 0.02305 cm., compute the wave length of the light used.

7. An interferometer illuminated by red light from calcium (wave length = 6438 Å) is used to measure the distance between two points. Compute this distance if 576 interference fringes sweep past a reference point in the field while the interferometer mirror is being moved from one of the points to the other.

8. A plane wave of monochromatic light of wave length 0.00005893 cm. passes through a slit 0.6 mm. wide and forms a diffraction pattern on a screen parallel to the slit and 1 meter away. Compute the distance along the screen between the two dark diffraction bands which border the central bright band.

9. A beam of monochromatic light of wave length 6708 Å is passed through a parallel-sided slit 0.070 cm. wide and produces a diffraction pattern on a screen which is parallel to the plane of the slit and 80 cm. distant therefrom. Determine the distance measured along the screen from the center of the pattern to the first dark diffraction band on either side.

10. If the slit referred to in Problem 8 is replaced by a circular hole, compute the diameter of the central round patch of light upon the screen, the diameter of the hole being (*a*) 0.6 mm., (*b*) 1.2 mm.

11. A distant arc lamp is photographed with a pinhole camera upon a plate 10 cm. away from the pinhole, which has a diameter of 0.5 mm. Considering the lamp as a point source and taking the wave length of light to be 0.00006 cm., compute the diameter of the disk image on the plate.

*12. Solve Problem 11 assuming the pinhole to be replaced by a lens 1 cm. in diameter.

*13. Compute the minimum separation of two points on the moon at a distance of 240,000 mi. which can be identified as separate points by the unaided eye, taking 1 minute of arc as the limiting angle of resolution of the eye.

*14. A beach is covered with pebbles about $\frac{1}{4}$ in. in diameter. At what limiting distance can these be recognized as separate objects by the eye?

*15. Compute the limiting angle of resolution of the lens mentioned in Problem 12. What is the maximum distance at which two objects 6 in. apart could be recognized as separate in a photograph taken with this lens?

*16. Two stars at a distance of 10 light-years from the earth are viewed through a telescope having a lens 20 in. in diameter. What is the minimum separation of these stars for which they would still be distinguishable as separate objects?

17. A narrow beam of light from glowing vapor is passed perpendicularly through a diffraction grating having 6000 lines per cm. and produces 3 lines upon a screen 80.0 cm. from the grating, each of the outside lines being 30.25 cm. from the central line. Compute the wave length of the light and identify the vapor emitting it.

18. A narrow beam of sunlight is passed through a diffraction grating having 20,000 lines per in. and forms a first-order spectrum on a screen 100 cm. from the grating and parallel to it. Compute the distance measured along the screen between the positions of the *C* and *F* Fraunhofer lines. See table in § 379.

19. A parallel beam of x-rays of wave length 0.71 Å is directed upon a rock salt crystal in the manner shown in Fig. 453. Compute the values of glancing angle necessary to produce the first-, second-, and third-order diffraction images.

CHAPTER XXXIX

POLARIZED LIGHT

419. Polarization of Light. — The wave character of light is demonstrated by the phenomena of interference and diffraction; the transverse wave nature of light is revealed by *polarization*. This phenomenon can be illustrated by a simple test using two thin plates of a mineral called *tourmaline*, the plates having been cut from the crystal in a particular manner. A beam of light is passed through one of these plates and, except for a slight tinting due to the color of the tourmaline, remains unchanged in appearance. It has, however, been profoundly altered, as a test with the second plate placed in the light path will show. When the plates are parallel the light passes through both, but when one is turned the amount of light transmitted becomes less, and when they are at right angles the light is almost entirely quenched, and the overlapping region appears dark.

A somewhat similar effect can be pictured for a mechanical wave by supposing transverse vibrations in all directions to be set up in a rope stretched horizontally. When the rope is unobstructed the waves will travel freely along its entire length, but if the test is repeated with the rope passed through a vertical slit, the horizontal components of the vibrations will be prevented from traveling beyond the slit and only the vertical components will be transmitted. A second slit will produce no further change if it is vertical also, but if it is turned to the horizontal all vibrations beyond will be quenched.

The significance of the test with the tourmaline plates will be considered by the aid of Fig. 455. Light is regarded as a wave in which the vibrations are transverse; that is, in planes at right angles to the line of propagation. For natural light, it is supposed that in these planes, the vibrations occur in all directions, a few of which are represented by the radial lines on the incident ray in the figure. Tourmaline transmits only vibrations or their components which are parallel to the crystal axis. Thus, in the light

698

transmitted by the first plate, *P*, the vibrations are restricted to a
single plane, as represented by the short dashes in the figure. This
light is said to be *plane polarized*. The second plate, *A*, when
crossed with the first as shown, extinguishes the light because the
vibrations incident upon it have no components along the direction
in which it is capable of transmitting. Plate *P* is used to polarize

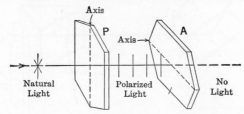

FIG. 455. Polarizing action of tourmaline

the light and is called the *polarizer*, and the plate *A* is used to
analyze the polarization and is called the *analyzer*.

It is believed that light waves, like radio waves, are due to
magnetic and electric fields which continually build up and collapse, and which are at right angles to each other. In specifying
the plane of vibration of a light wave, the plane of the electric
field is meant.

The term polarization implies a lack of symmetry around the
axis of propagation. The fact that a light wave can be polarized
is taken as evidence that the wave is transverse, as a longitudinal
wave appears to be inherently symmetrical with respect to its
direction of travel.

420. Polarization by Reflection. — It is found by experiment
that when natural light is reflected from the surface of a transparent substance it is partly polarized, the vibrations being parallel
to the reflecting surface. This action is indicated at *P* in Fig. 456,
which shows a beam of natural light incident upon an unsilvered
glass plate. The extent to which the reflected ray is polarized
depends upon the direction of the incident light. The angle of
incidence for which the polarization is a maximum is called the
polarizing angle, and is shown in the figure between the incident
ray and the normal *N*; its value for glass is about 57°. Even at
this angle, the amount of polarized light produced by a single
plate is relatively small, and a pile of six to eight plates is often used
to attain sufficient intensity by combining the reflected rays from
all the surfaces.

If the polarized ray from the transparent plate P is directed upon a similar plate A that can be turned conveniently, it will be found that when the reflecting surfaces are parallel, the polarized

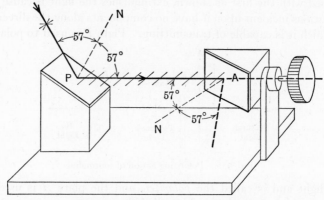

Fig. 456.   Light polarized by reflection

ray will be reflected from A as with natural light.   If, however, the second plate is rotated 90° about ray PA as an axis to the position shown, there will be no reflection.   This action explains why a transparent plate can be used to test the polarization of light.

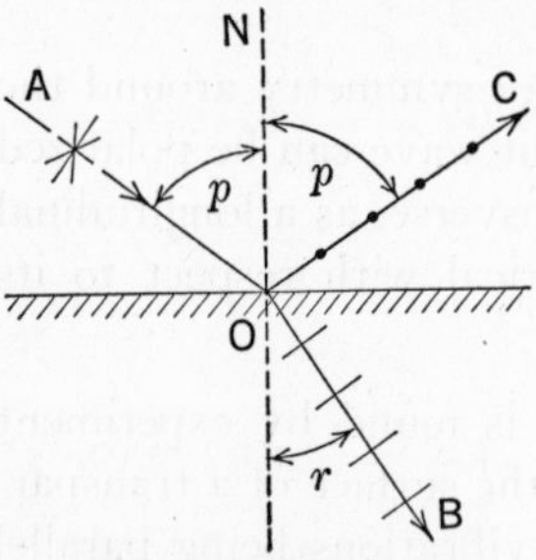

Fig. 457 shows a ray AO of natural light impinging upon the reflecting surface at the polarizing angle p.   The reflected ray OC makes an equal angle with the normal N and is partly polarized, its vibrations being parallel to the surface, as represented by the dots in the figure.   Most of the light is transmitted into the transparent medium along the direction OB, the angle of refraction being r.   The transmitted light is also polarized, being deficient in those vibrations found in the beam OC.

Fig. 457.   Polarization of reflected and refracted rays

The Scottish physicist, Sir David Brewster (1781–1868), discovered that when light impinges at the polarizing angle p upon a medium of refractive index μ, these quantities are related by the simple equation

$$\mu = \tan p \qquad (271)$$

From this expression, known as Brewster's Law, and from the law of refraction, it follows that $\dfrac{\sin p}{\sin r} = \mu = \dfrac{\sin p}{\cos p}$, whence $\sin r = \cos p$, or $r + p = 90°$. Consequently the angle COB is $90°$, showing that the reflected and refracted rays are at right angles for maximum polarization.

421. Double Refraction. — Many crystals possess the property of *double refraction*, a single incident beam being split into two beams within such a crystal. Calcite (Iceland spar, $CaCO_3$), quartz (SiO_2), and mica are doubly refracting substances.

Consider a crystal of calcite, as shown in section in Fig. 458, and a beam of natural light from X incident normally upon the end face. Ray O will pass through without deviation and is called

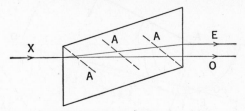

Fig. 458. Separation of rays in calcite

the *ordinary* ray because it obeys the law of refraction, while ray E will be deviated despite perpendicular incidence and is called the *extraordinary* ray. The emergent beams will be parallel.

The calcite crystal has six faces forming a rhombohedron, and the three face angles that meet at two opposite corners are $102°$. A line through one of these blunt corners which makes equal angles with the three faces meeting there, or any line parallel to it, is called the *optic axis* of the crystal. Lines A in the figure show the optic axis of calcite. A plane containing the optic axis and the normal to any face is called a *principal section*. The view of the calcite crystal in Fig. 458 is a principal section.

The direction of the rays within the crystal will depend upon the direction of the incident beam. The ordinary ray travels with constant velocity regardless of its direction, the refractive index of calcite for this ray having a constant value of 1.658, as measured for the D spectral line. The extraordinary ray travels with different speeds depending upon its direction. If it happens to advance along the optic axis, its velocity will be the same as that of the ordinary ray and the two rays will coincide. If it travels in any other direction its velocity is greater, having a maximum value along a direction at right angles to the optic axis. The refractive index of calcite for the extraordinary ray, as measured for the D spectral line, varies from 1.658 along the optic axis to 1.486 at right angles to that direction.

The wave front of the extraordinary beam within the crystal is ellipsoidal, and the minor axis of the ellipsoid lies along the optic axis, in which direction it coincides with the spherical wave front of the ordinary beam. These conditions are represented in Fig. 459, in which a plane wave front AB is shown impinging upon the

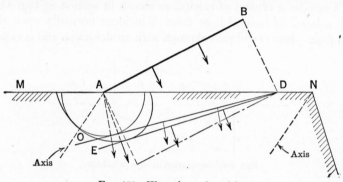

Fig. 459. Wave fronts in calcite

crystal surface MN. Using Huygens' construction as in Fig. 343, the wave fronts DO and DE for the ordinary and extraordinary beams are found. It is interesting to observe that for the extraordinary wave, the rays are not perpendicular to the wave front.

The crystals which exhibit double refraction belong to the hexagonal and tetragonal systems. For some of these, such as quartz, the velocity of the extraordinary ray, except along the optic axis, is less than that of the ordinary ray. For these crystals, the ellipse representing the extraordinary wave front has its major axis coincident with the radius of the circular wave front of the ordinary beam, and the extraordinary ray makes a smaller angle with the optic axis than the ordinary ray. Some crystals have two optic axes with characteristic angles between them; they are called biaxial crystals.

The ordinary and extraordinary rays in a doubly refracting crystal are found to be polarized.

422. Polarization by Double Refraction. — The polarization produced by a doubly refracting crystal is indicated in Fig. 460, which shows a principal section of a calcite crystal and includes views of the end faces. The vibrations of the incident natural light are resolved into components in the plane of the principal section and at right angles to this plane, and these components are transmitted by the extraordinary and the ordinary rays respectively.

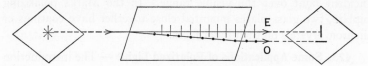

FIG. 460. Polarization by calcite crystal

Thus, the emergent beams E and O are polarized at right angles to each other.

The Nicol prism, named for its inventor and used extensively in optical devices utilizing polarized light, is a calcite crystal of the shape shown in Fig. 461. It is prepared by resurfacing the end faces of the crystal at an angle of 68°, sawing the crystal in two diagonally at right angles to these end planes, and cementing the two parts together with Canada balsam. The refractive index of the balsam, as measured for the D spectral line, is 1.53, and is

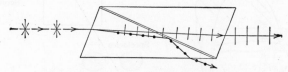

FIG. 461.   Principal section of Nicol prism

intermediate between the refractive indices of calcite for the ordinary and extraordinary rays. The incident ray of natural light is separated as usual into ordinary and extraordinary rays. The ordinary ray is totally reflected at the balsam layer and passes to one side where it is absorbed in suitable covering materials. The extraordinary ray emerges as plane polarized light, its vibrations being in the plane of the principal section.

Some doubly refracting materials absorb one transmitted ray more than the other, and if the thickness is sufficient one ray will be almost completely absorbed. Such a material is called a *dichroic* substance; the best known example is tourmaline, which transmits only the extraordinary ray and absorbs the other. Sulphate of iodo-quinine is utilized in the new polarizing materials and very thin layers absorb one light component effectively. In *polaroid* the dichroic crystals are distributed densely in a cellulose film mounted between glass plates or bonded between transparent flexible plastic sheets. The individual crystals are needle-shaped and have girth diameters less than a wave length of light. The average intensity of the transmitted beam is 37 per cent of the incident light over the visible range. In the Marks polarizing biplate, two glass plates mounted close together have coatings of dichroic crystals on their inner faces.

423. Some Applications of Polarized Light. — The introduction of polarizing substances that are relatively inexpensive, like polaroid, has made possible a number of interesting applications, a few of which will be considered briefly.

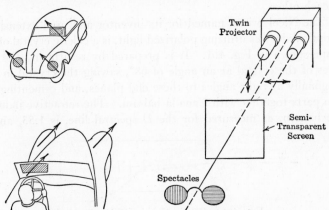

FIG. 462. Method of eliminating headlight glare

FIG. 463. Scheme for stereoscopic projection

The light that is reflected from matt surfaces over a range of angles contains considerable glare-light which exhibits polarization, the direction of vibration being parallel to the surface (like that of ray *OC* in Fig. 457). The glare of sunlight reflected from sidewalks and pavements can be reduced by the use of polaroid glasses arranged to transmit only vibrations in the vertical plane. The glare from paper observed in reading under desk lamps can be reduced by placing at the lamp opening a sheet of polaroid that is oriented to eliminate the horizontal vibrations.

Fig. 462 shows a method of eliminating the glare of automobile headlights that would require each car to be equipped with polarizing screens on headlamps and windshield. With the direction of polarization at 45° as indicated, the driver can see by the light of his own headlamps, but his windshield screen will reduce greatly the light from cars coming toward him.

Vision in three dimensions is based primarily upon the fact that both eyes give their impressions simultaneously, each eye viewing the scene from a slightly different angle than the other. To simulate this so-called stereoscopic effect upon a flat surface, giving "depth" to motion pictures, it can be arranged that the right eye will see the scene as pictured by a camera at the right, and the left eye will see it from the left. Fig. 463 shows schematically how this may be accomplished, utilizing a twin projector equipped with polarizing screens set at right angles to each other for forming images on a ground-glass surface, and providing each observer with polaroid spectacles so oriented as to give each eye the image intended for it. Such stereoscopic projection is also possible by reflection using surfaces of fine texture preferably coated with aluminum.

424. Optical Rotation. — Certain materials, notably quartz and solutions of sugar, have the property of *rotating the plane of polarization* in transmitting polarized light. This effect may be observed with a *polarimeter*, consisting of a polarizer and an analyzer, together with means for supporting the optically active substance in the light path between them.

Optical rotation is used in determining the percentage of sugar in solutions of unknown concentration. Polarimeters especially designed for testing sugar are known as *saccharimeters*, and are arranged to pass the polarized light through a tube filled with the solution under test. If the polarizer and analyzer are crossed initially, giving a dark field, it will be found upon introducing the sugar solution that the analyzer must be turned to a new position to restore darkness. The difference between these positions is the angle through which the plane of polarization has been rotated, or else differs from it by 180°. The rotation is found to be proportional to the length of the liquid column and to the strength of the solution, and depends also upon the wave length of light used. With sodium light, an aqueous solution of cane sugar in a tube 10 cm. long produces an optical rotation of 6.65° for a concentration of 0.1 gm. of sugar per cu. cm. With the same light, quartz causes a rotation of 21.72° per mm. of thickness.

Faraday discovered in 1845 that some materials of high refractive index, such as dense glass, rotate the plane of polarization of light when located in a strong magnetic field. This effect may be observed by placing the specimen between the poles of an electromagnet, the pole pieces being bored so that the polarized light may be passed in the same direction as the magnetic field.

425. Interference Effects. — In order to annul plane polarized light by interference, experiment shows that the interfering *waves must originate from a common point of the source and differ in phase by one half-wave length, and the vibrations must be in the same plane.* Interference is usually produced by inserting a thin plate of doubly refracting substance in the light path between a polarizer and an analyzer. In Fig. 464, the polarizer *P* and analyzer *A* are

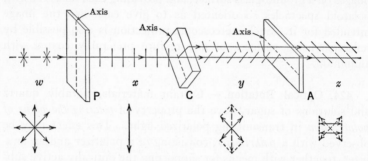

FIG. 464. Producing interference colors with crystals

represented as crossed plates, and the doubly refracting crystal *C* is shown between them with its optic axis inclined to the plate axes. White natural light (having transverse vibrations in all directions) entering at *w* is polarized by the polarizer, giving only vertical vibrations at *x*. These are resolved by the doubly refracting crystal into two components shown at *y*, the extraordinary ray having its vibrations in the plane of its optic axis and the ordinary ray having its vibrations at right angles to this plane. These rays are unequally retarded in traversing the crystal, principally because of the difference in refractive index, and the relative retardation will often be an odd number of half-wave lengths for some color in the incident light. The analyzer passes only the horizontal components of these vibrations, and at *z* the color referred to is annulled by interference and the residual colors are observed. The successive resolutions of the vibrations along the light path are represented in the lower part of the figure. The doubly refracting crystal *C* is supposed to be so thin that the waves beyond it will overlap almost completely, although shown widely separated in the figure for clearness. Thus, a colorless crystal when viewed by polarized light shows colors by interference, the colors varying with the thickness and refractive index of the specimen.

The arrangement described is useful in the examination of crystals and in the study of thin rock sections. When viewed with a microscope, they will usually appear colored irregularly and will reveal details and structural differences not readily observed by other means. Such examinations enable the microscopist to determine whether a crystal is uniaxial (like quartz) or biaxial (like mica), whether it is optically active, and the amount of clockwise or counter-clockwise rotation of its plane of polarization, and also to measure the numerical values of its refractive indices. Such information permits him to specify to which of the six crystal systems a sample belongs and to effect its identification.

A plate of singly refracting material when substituted for the doubly refracting crystal between polarizer and analyzer would produce no interference effects, since the incident ray would not be separated into two rays. Many singly refracting materials, such as glass or celluloid, become doubly refracting when mechanically strained. Consequently, such substances may be tested by polarized light and the presence of strains, not apparent when viewed in natural light, revealed by the appearance of interference fringes. Either white or monochromatic light may be used in such tests.

It was discovered by the Scottish physicist, John Kerr (1824–1907), that a transparent insulator such as glass or turpentine becomes doubly refracting when located in a strong electric field. A specimen of proper thickness placed in a beam of plane polarized light between a polarizer and an analyzer will cut off the light by interference when the field is established. With a rapidly alternating field the arrangement acts as a quick operating shutter, and this action has been used in measuring the velocity of light and for many other purposes.

*426. Elliptical and Circular Polarization. —It can be shown mathematically or graphically that two harmonic vibrations of equal frequency, taking place in perpendicular planes, will give elliptical motion as a resultant when they are combined. The ellipse may have various shapes depending upon the amplitudes and phase relation of the component vibrations. It will be circular if these components are equal and differ in phase by $\frac{1}{4}$ cycle. A typical illustration is the production of a rotating magnetic field in the induction motor [§ 296] by combining two harmonically varying fields at right angles.

When plane polarized light is passed through a thin doubly refracting plate, as at *C* in Fig. 464, the components traverse the plate with different velocities, and in general emerge displaced from each other in phase. The issuing light is said to be *elliptically polarized*; it becomes *circularly polarized* if the two components have equal amplitude and if the relative retardation is a quarter-wave length. A doubly refracting plate designed to produce circular polarization is called a *quarter-wave* plate, and must have proper thickness and appropriate refractive indices for the wave length of light to be used with it. With circularly polarized light, the field remains equally bright for all positions of the analyzer.

The Dutch physicist, Pieter Zeeman, discovered that if a light source is placed in an intense magnetic field, its spectral lines are broken into two or more components. In the simplest case, when viewed along the direction of the field, a line will be seen as two, the two beams being circularly polarized in opposite directions; and when viewed at right angles to the field three lines appear, the outside beams being plane polarized parallel to the field and the central one being plane polarized at right angles to the field. In many cases, the lines are resolved into four or six components. Such tests have led to important deductions concerning the structure of matter. They have also allowed the ratio of the electronic charge and mass to be evaluated, the results showing close agreement with those obtained by purely electrical methods [§ 262].

*427. Photo-elasticity. — The distribution of internal stresses in structural or machine parts may be observed by passing polarized

FIG. 465. Stresses in beam shown by polarized light

light through models made to scale from sheet celluloid or bakelite, which are subjected to external forces simulating those in the actual structures. The method will be illustrated by considering the forces within a loaded beam and the photo-elastic picture of a model of it constructed of sheet bakelite. Such a picture taken by monochromatic circularly polarized light is shown in Fig. 465; the beam supports two loads that are indicated by the shaded arrows.

Throughout the region between the loads the beam fibers are under tension and compression only (see § 100), and under these conditions the relative retardation of the ordinary and extraordinary rays transmitted is directly proportional to the fiber stress. The picture shows 3.5 interference fringes between the neutral axis or "zero-strain" region and the outside fibers, and the model was subjected to a maximum fiber stress of 1570 lb. per sq. in. Consequently for this bakelite sheet, each interference fringe corresponds to a stress of 1570 ÷ 3.5 = 450 lb. per sq. in. This value can be

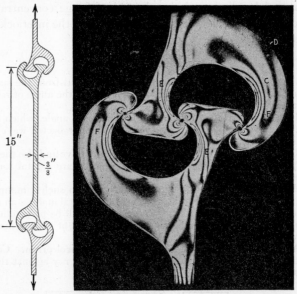

FIG. 466. Sheet piling and interlock

used beyond the region of uniform loading. Thus at points *A*, where the fringe nearest the neutral axis comes out to the edge of the model, the fiber stress is 450 lb. per sq. in., and at points *B*, where the next fringe meets the edge, the fiber stress is 2 × 450 = 900 lb. per sq. in.

Fig. 466 shows a section of steel sheet piling such as is driven into the ground to form a wall and permit deep excavation, together

with a photo-elastic picture of the interlock between adjacent
units. The model of the interlock was made from the same sheet
of bakelite referred to in the preceding paragraph, and consequently the same stress values apply to the interference fringes.
For example, a zero stress point appears at C, and the first fringe
meets the edge at D; this shows the fiber stress at D to be 450 lb.
per sq. in. The corresponding stresses in the actual structure are
determined from such values by taking account of the relative
sizes of the structure and model and the relative loads employed.
The three points of contact of the interlock exhibit high concentration of stress as indicated by the closeness of the fringes about
these points, but this result being due to direct pressure of contact
is not regarded as particularly objectionable. The narrow sections E and F are subjected to external forces which cause both
tension and bending, and the absence of fringe concentration at
these critical places is taken as indicating that the interlock is well
designed.

PROBLEMS

1. At what angle of incidence will light reflected from the surface of
water show maximum polarization? What will be the angle of refraction
of the transmitted ray?

2. Light impinges upon glass at the polarizing angle, which is 56.5°
for the sample used. What is the velocity of the reflected wave? of the
transmitted wave?

3. Compute the velocity of the ordinary light wave and also the highest
velocity of the extraordinary light wave in a calcite crystal for the D
spectral line of sodium.

4. A calcite crystal has its surfaces reground in such a manner that
when a ray of natural light impinges against the crystal making an angle of
incidence of 60°, the extraordinary refracted ray will be perpendicular to
the optic axis. Determine the angular separation of the ordinary and
extraordinary rays within the crystal.

5. A beam of sodium light is directed upon a Nicol prism. Compute
the critical angle for total reflection of the ordinary ray against the layer
of Canada balsam.

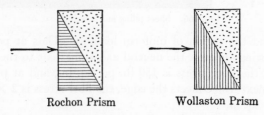

Rochon Prism　　　　　　　　Wollaston Prism

6. In the accompanying figure are shown the sectional views of the
Rochon and Wollaston prisms used to produce double images. Each

consists of two equal triangular prisms made of calcite and cemented together; the horizontal and vertical shading lines represent the direction of the optic axes, and the dots represent that axis to be at right angles to the page. A ray of light is shown impinging normally upon the left surface of each prism. Sketch the directions along which the incident ray will be doubly refracted at the interfaces of the prisms.

7. Ice has a refractive index of 1.309 for the ordinary ray and 1.313 for the extraordinary ray, when measured with sodium light. What minimum thickness of ice placed between a polarizer and an analyzer will cause annulment of this light?

8. A tube 20 cm. long filled with a solution containing 26 gm. of cane sugar per 100 cu. cm. of water is placed in the path of plane polarized sodium light. Through what angle will the plane of polarization be rotated?

9. A column of a particular sugar solution having a length of 20 cm. and a volume of 12.5 cu. cm. is found to rotate the plane of polarization of sodium light 5.42°. How much sugar does the solution contain?

*10. Compute the thickness that a quartz plate should have for use as a quarter-wave plate for sodium light. The refractive index of quartz measured with that light is 1.544 for the ordinary ray and 1.553 for the extraordinary ray.

CHAPTER XL

RADIATION AND ATOMIC STRUCTURE

428. X-ray Spectra. — The diffraction of x-rays by reflection from the various atomic planes of crystals [§ 418] has led to an accurate knowledge of the character of x-rays emitted by the elements, and this knowledge has been of great aid in determining the structure of atoms. The radiation from the target of an x-ray tube [§ 306], when investigated by reflection at all angles from a crystal, is found to consist of a continuous spectrum and a superposed bright-line spectrum extending over a range of wave lengths from about 10^{-6} to 10^{-9} cm.

The continuous spectrum differs in intensity over its range, increasing from very low values at the longer wave lengths to a maximum value and then falling sharply to zero at a particular shorter wave length. This short-wave limit depends upon the potential difference of the x-ray tube and is independent of the target material. These facts would indicate that the continuous x-ray spectrum is caused by the rapid retardation and consequent loss of kinetic energy of the cathode-ray electrons as they strike the atoms of the target. The maximum kinetic energy of such an electron is Ve ergs, where V is the peak value of the potential difference across the tube and e is the charge of the electron [§ 204. This will be the energy of the quantum that corresponds to the highest frequency f_m; it is given in § 306 as

$$Ve = hf_m$$

in which Planck's constant $h = 6.63 \times 10^{-27}$ erg-sec., and the electronic charge $e = 4.80 \times 10^{-10}$ e.s.u. Since 300 volts = 1 e.s.u. of potential difference, and the velocity of propagation is 3.00×10^{10} cm. per sec., it follows that the minimum wave length is

$$\lambda_{min} = \frac{3.00 \times 10^{10} \times 6.63 \times 10^{-27} \times 300}{4.80 \times 10^{-10} \, V} = \frac{12.43}{V} 10^{-5}$$

The wave length will be in centimeters when the potential difference on the tube is in volts. The wave length corresponding to the maximum intensity is about $\frac{3}{2} \lambda_{min}$.

712

Bright-line x-ray spectra are characteristic of the target materials, and the spectrum for any one element consists of several well-defined groups of lines. These groups are conventionally called the K, L, M, N ... series, but the lighter elements give only the first-mentioned ones. The spectra of all the elements are found to be similar, but the corresponding lines of any series occur at different wave lengths for the different elements. The English physicist, Henry G. J. Moseley (1887–1915), found that the wave length for a particular line depended upon the atomic number of the element and not upon its atomic weight. The relation between wave length λ, wave number ν, and atomic number Z, known as Moseley's Law, is given by

$$\frac{1}{\lambda} = \nu = C \, (Z - \sigma)^2 \qquad (272)$$

where C and σ are constants; the value of C depends on the particular line of the series while that of σ is the same for all lines of a series. The higher the atomic number of an element the shorter will be the wave length for the particular line under consideration. Fig. 467 shows the K-series lines for four metals of atomic

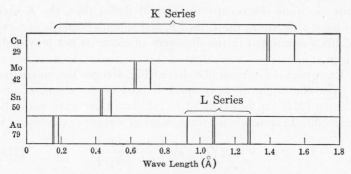

FIG. 467. X-ray spectra of copper, molybdenum, tin and gold

numbers 29, 42, 50 and 79, and the L-series lines only for the last metal because the others fall beyond the chart.

Analysis and experiment indicate that the emission of characteristic x-rays is due to the inner electrons of the atom. Using the planetary picture of the atom, the lines of the K series will be emitted when electrons from outer shells fall into the innermost ones to fill vacancies there, those of the L series are emitted when electrons fall similarly to the second shell, and so on. Accordingly, these shells are referred to as the K and L shells. Thus, when an impinging electron collides with an atom of the target and ejects one of its electrons of the K shell, the vacancy is filled by an electron from the L shell, or one from the M shell, and so on. As a result, a line of the K series will be emitted, the energy value depending on the source of the electron. If it comes from the L shell the line will have a greater wave length than if the transition occurred from the M shell, because the energy difference is greater between the M and K shells than that between the L and K shells. The vacancy in the other shell is made up similarly and spectral lines of other series will result. For the light atoms that have two shells of electrons only lines of the K series can be emitted.

The fact that x-ray spectra of the elements are *similar*, except as to their wave-length scales, indicates that the inner structure of all but the lighter atoms is the same. In contrast, optical spectra have different characteristics from element to element and show that the outer structure of atoms differ; their lines are produced by electrons falling from a number of outer normally unoccupied levels to inner ones. Studied together with the chemical properties of atoms, both types of spectra reveal how many electrons can occupy the several shells; thus, the K shell can have 2 electrons, the L shell 8, and so on. Analysis of x-ray spectra also resulted in the discovery of elements not previously known.

Energy level diagrams like that of Fig. 406 can be constructed to show the origin of x-ray spectral lines of the elements, and equation (243) can be extended to calculate their wave numbers. The modified expression for the number of waves per centimeter is

$$\bar{\nu} = R\,(Z - \sigma)^2 \left[\frac{1}{k_2{}^2} - \frac{1}{k_1{}^2} \right] \tag{273}$$

where R is the Rydberg constant, Z is the atomic number, k_1 and k_2 are the quantum numbers for the initial and final energy levels, and σ is a constant. For hydrogen $Z = 1$ and $\sigma = 0$, and the equation reduces to (243) for calculating the wave numbers in the infra-red, visible and ultra-violet regions. For molybdenum $Z = 42$, and for the K series in the x-ray spectrum $\sigma = 0.5$; the α line of this series is produced by an electron falling from shell L of quantum number $k_1 = 2$ to shell K of quantum number $k_2 = 1$. Taking $R = 109{,}737$, the wave number becomes $\nu = 14.1 \times 10^7$ waves per cm., and the wave length becomes $10^8/\nu = 0.71$ Å. It will be observed that equations (272) and (273) agree in form; the value of C in the former can be evaluated readily.

429. Corpuscular Nature of Light. — The effects of interference, diffraction, and polarization, described in the two foregoing chapters, give ample evidence of the *wave character* of light. On the other hand, the photoelectric effect shows that light is *corpuscular* in character. Regarding this effect, it has been stated [§ 307] that: (1) when radiation is incident upon certain substances electrons are emitted, and these are often called photoelectrons to indicate their origin; (2) the velocity of their emission is not influenced by the intensity of the radiation; (3) the velocity of the photoelectrons increases with the frequency of the incident radiation; (4) the frequency must reach a certain critical value depending on the substance before emission occurs at all; (5) the number of photoelectrons emitted per unit time varies with the intensity of radiation.

Since the photoelectron receives energy from the incident radiation in order to leave the substance, it is difficult to explain on the wave theory why the energy (and therefore the velocity) imparted to the photoelectron will not diminish when the radiation intensity is reduced, say by moving the source further from the substance. The difficulty is removed by assuming that the energy is distributed discontinuously over the radiation wave front in little packets called quanta which maintain their identity in traveling from the source. The quanta, often called *photons*, have different energy values depending upon the radiation frequency, the values being given by equation (128), $E = hf$. Consequently, the maximum energy of the expelled electrons is given by Einstein's equation as

$$\tfrac{1}{2} m v_m{}^2 = hf - w \tag{274}$$

where m is the mass of the photoelectron, 9.11×10^{-28} gm., h is Planck's constant in erg-seconds, f is the frequency in vibrations per second, and v_m is the velocity in centimeters per second.

The factor w, called the *work function*, represents the energy required to remove one of the least firmly bound electrons, and its value differs with different substances. Its presence in the equation explains why the radiation frequency must have a sufficiently high value before emission can occur, for the minimum frequency is w/h and the corresponding maximum wave length is $h\,c/w$, where c is the velocity of light. For potassium the wave length λ for emission must not exceed about 0.00007 cm.; consequently the work function becomes

$$w = hc/\lambda = 6.63 \times 10^{-27} \times 3.00 \times 10^{10} \div 7 \times 10^{-5} = 2.84 \times 10^{-12}$$

ergs. Since 1.60×10^{-12} ergs = 1 electron-volt [§ 262], this energy corresponds to 1.77 electron-volts. Thus, the energy necessary to remove an electron from potassium is equal to the work done on an electron in falling through a potential difference of 1.77 volts. Equation (274) has been verified experimentally from energy values of this magnitude up to a million electron-volts.

Thus, light is regarded as a swarm of photons, following each other with the speed c and differing in energy content hf in accordance with the frequency or wave length. This corpuscular theory of light receives further support by an effect discovered by Professor Arthur H. Compton, and now known by his name. He found that when a beam of homogeneous (monochromatic) x-rays of high energy impinged upon the lighter elements like carbon, and was scattered by the element, a part of the scattered radiation exhibited an *increase in wave length*, and this corresponds to a decrease in energy. This effect is explained on the quantum theory by stating that some x-ray photons collide with electrons and in doing so give up some of their energy to the electrons to set them in motion. As a result the photons will rebound with diminished energy. Each direction of recoil of a photon is correlated with a certain direction of recoil of the electron, the occurrence of recoil particles in the various directions being governed by laws of probability. The corresponding change in wave length of the scattered radiation is given by

$$\Delta\lambda = \frac{h}{m c} (1 - \cos \theta) \tag{275}$$

where, θ is the angle with respect to the straight forward direction, at which the scattered radiation is observed and m is the mass of the electron. The validity of this explanation confirms the belief that all radiation behaves as particles, at least under certain conditions; for example, in its interactions with free or lightly bound electrons.

The dual nature of light in acting both as waves and as particles presents a problem which has received the attention of physicists for some time; an account of the progress made is beyond the limits set for this book.

*430. **Electron Diffraction.** — A new concept of matter was introduced in 1923 by Louis V. de Broglie to the effect that particles of small mass, such as electrons, have a wave character like photons of light energy. By analogy with equation (275), these so-called "matter waves" would have a wave length of

$$\lambda = \frac{h}{m\,v} \qquad (276)$$

where m and v are the mass and velocity of the particle respectively. For example, an electron traveling at a speed of 10^6 cm. per sec. would have on this hypothesis a wave length of

$$\lambda = \frac{6.63 \times 10^{-27}}{9.11 \times 10^{-28} \times 10^6} = 7.28 \times 10^{-6} \text{ cm.} = 728 \text{ Å}$$

Experiments were conducted by Clinton J. Davisson and Lester H. Germer, physicists of the Bell Telephone Laboratories, to test this hypothesis. They reasoned that if electrons were waves, it should be possible to cause their diffraction with crystals, and in 1927 they succeeded in producing diffraction patterns by projecting electrons upon a nickel crystal. Fig. 468 shows a

FIG. 468.   Diffraction pattern produced by electrons
(*Courtesy of G. P. Thomson*)

diffraction pattern produced by cathode rays of about 30,000 electron-volts passing through gold leaf. Measurements of patterns like these show that Bragg's equation (270) will hold when the wave length satisfies equation (276). Thus, while tests with the cloud chamber show that electrons are undoubtedly particles, their diffraction shows that they act as light waves. Similarly, atoms and molecules possess a wave character.

It would seem, therefore, that all particles of matter have wave characteristics; the larger their masses, the shorter will be the wave lengths according to the de Broglie equation. The science of Mechanics must take this behavior into account in dealing with particles of electronic and atomic magnitudes, even though the wave effects, like diffraction, are still smaller than in optics. The extension of Mechanics to include such phenomena is called *Wave Mechanics*.

De Broglie's equation is consistent with the quantum condition introduced by Professor Bohr to fix the energy levels of the normal hydrogen atom [§ 385], namely that the angular momentum of the electron moving in its circular orbit of radius r must be an integral multiple of $h/2\pi$. For the electron to exhibit a wave character, the length of its path in any stable orbit should contain an integral number of wave lengths, just as is the case with vibrating strings [§ 336]. Consequently, the wave length λ should be some integer times $2\pi r$. Taking the integer as unity

$$\lambda = 2\pi r$$

and combining this result with the equation for the angular momentum of the electron, namely

$$m r^2 \omega = m r v = \frac{h}{2\pi}$$

equation (276) will follow directly.

*431. Relativity. — The fact that all motion is relative has been recognized for a long time. A person on a river steamer who looks out and sees only the water near the ship because of fog, cannot tell by observing the water moving past him whether the ship is under way or the tide is passing the ship at anchor, assuming that he is not assisted in this observation by other effects, such as ship vibration caused by its engine. Our own motion in walking along the street is reckoned with respect to the earth as fixed, no consideration being given to the facts that the earth rotates on its axis and travels around the sun. These and other illustrations [§ 25] show that motion in space is ambiguous; it has definite meaning only when expressed relative to something that may be regarded as fixed. Professor Einstein has extended this fundamental idea of relative motion and formulated what is known as the theory of relativity. Much experimental evidence has been accumulated in its support, and the consequences of the theory are of great theoretical importance.

The theory postulates that (1) the motion of a body traveling uniformly through space cannot be detected by observations on that body alone, and (2) the velocity of light in free space is independent of the relative motion of observer and light source. The analysis of these postulates and the many deductions from the theory are very interesting, but it will suffice here to summarize the consequences in so far as they fall within the scope of this chapter.

A surprising result of the theory of relativity is that it implies *an increase of inertia* (that is, of *mass*) *with velocity*. This variation in mass is insignificant except when the body has velocities approaching that of light. Representing the mass of a body at rest by m_0, its mass at velocity v will be

$$m = \frac{m_0}{\sqrt{1 - \dfrac{v^2}{c^2}}} \tag{277}$$

where c is the velocity of light. Thus, an electron having a mass of 9.11×10^{-28} gm. at rest will have a mass when moving with a velocity 0.9 that of light amounting to 20.9×10^{-28} gm.

The theory also indicates that *mass and energy can be transformed into each other*. The equivalence of mass and energy can be obtained by computing the work done on a body, of mass m_0 when at rest, in accelerating it to a velocity v, taking account of the fact that the mass increases to a value m in the transition. The result as obtained by integration shows that the energy increase is c^2 times the increase in mass, from which is concluded that any quantity of energy E is equivalent to a mass m if

$$E = m c^2 \tag{278}$$

This also means that if a mass m were annihilated in some way, an amount of energy E would be liberated that could be computed from the same equation. Since the velocity of light c is approximately 3.00×10^{10} cm. per sec., it follows that the energy equivalent of an electron is $9.11 \times 10^{-28} \times 9 \times 10^{20} = 8.20 \times 10^{-7}$ ergs, also to $8.20 \times 10^{-7} \div 1.60 \times 10^{-12} = 512,000$ electron-volts.

By way of illustration, it is interesting to speculate upon the amount of energy that might be made available in this way through the conversion of a mass as large as 1 gm. By equation (278), $E = 1$ gm. $\times (3.00 \times 10^{10}$ cm./sec.$)^2 = 9 \times 10^{20}$ ergs $= 9 \times 10^{13}$ joules (or watt-sec.) $= 2.5 \times 10^7$ kw-hr.; this is equal to the average energy supplied by the Edison affiliated companies in New York City in $1\frac{2}{3}$ days.

432. Radioactivity. — Within a year after the discovery of x-rays, the French scientist, Antoine Henri Becquerel (1852–

1908), found that uranium in various states of chemical combination emitted spontaneously an invisible radiation that was capable of affecting a photographic plate and producing ionization of the air. This property of uranium was found subsequently to be possessed by a number of the heavy elements, and the name *radioactivity* was applied to it. Remarkable discoveries in this field were made by Pierre Curie (1859–1906) and his wife Marie Sklodowska Curie (1867–1934), French physicists and professors at the Sorbonne in Paris; among them may be mentioned the isolation of the elements polonium and radium from pitchblende.

It was soon found that radioactive substances emit three kinds of rays that are widely different in character; they are called α, β and γ rays. They can be differentiated by their power of penetrating matter and of producing ionization.

Alpha rays are particles that carry positive charges, and have been identified as the nuclei of helium atoms. They have a mass 4 times that of the hydrogen atom and a charge equal to that of 2 electrons. Alpha particles have velocities of the order of 2×10^9 cm. per sec. As they move through air they produce ionization by knocking electrons out of its atoms, and naturally their speed is reduced by the successive collisions. In air at atmospheric pressure the α particles are slowed down in traveling 3 to 9 cm. to such an extent that they no longer can produce ionization. Their range is greatly reduced when they are passed through metal foil; for example, a thickness of 0.001 mm. of silver is equivalent to over 2 cm. of air. The alpha particle is believed to be a combination of two protons (that is, hydrogen nuclei) and two neutrons, which has not been broken apart by collision.

Beta rays are particles that carry negative charges, and are in reality high-speed electrons. They are ejected from radioactive substances with velocities varying from 0.3 to 0.99 that of light. They are much more penetrating than α particles, but measurement of their ranges in air is difficult because of their irregular paths. The mass of the α particle is much greater than that of the β particle and consequently, in colliding with electrons in the atoms of air, the α particle knocks them out of its way and continues along a fairly straight path, while the β particle is deviated from its path with each collision. The ratio e/m for β rays is not constant as it is for slow-speed electrons because the mass of the β ray is higher at speeds comparable with the velocity of light, as explained in the previous section.

Gamma rays are electromagnetic radiations of the same character as x-rays but extend to much higher frequencies. Crystal diffraction tests [§ 418] and measurements of velocities of ejected photoelectrons show that γ rays have wave lengths ranging from about 0.005 to 1 Å. They are much more penetrating than either α or β rays and can pass through thicknesses of many centimeters of lead.

In the present concept of atomic structure, with nearly all the mass of an atom concentrated in its nucleus, the radiation of an α particle by a radioactive element means that the nucleus of some atom has lost that particle. In consequence, the weight of that atom has been reduced and the charge of its nucleus has been decreased, thereby leaving an atom of lower atomic weight and number. Thus, the emission of α particles is evidence that radioactive elements are slowly but continually disintegrating. It is quite likely that the nucleus, after a disturbance such as the emission of an α particle, passes from one energy state to another and in the process emits a γ ray, in much the same way as bright-line visible and characteristic x-ray spectra are produced. The origin of β rays is more problematical. According to the present belief electrons are not regarded as forming a component part of the nuclear structure. Apparently a neutron in the nucleus becomes a proton and emits an electron in the same manner that an atom in an excited state emits a light quantum in assuming a lower energy state.

433. Ray Tracks and Ray Counters. — Two instruments of importance in the investigation of radioactive rays and other charged particles are the *cloud chamber* and the *ray counter*.

The cloud chamber devised by the British physicist C. T. R. Wilson utilizes the fact that when air saturated with water vapor is expanded suddenly, the cooling effect causes the formation of a cloud of tiny drops. These drops form upon dust or other particles and persist long enough, before they evaporate again, to allow a visual or photographic examination. In using the chamber for the study of charged particles, the air is first rendered dust-free, the particles are then admitted, and immediately thereafter the air is expanded. An α particle, for example, creates a large number of ions along its path, and in the cloud chamber produces a track of water drops that appears as a white line against a dark background.

Fig. 469 illustrates the tracks made by α particles in nitrogen. The forked track shows the rare occurrence when a nitrogen nucleus captured the alpha particle that struck it and emitted a proton (upper branch); the remaining part (lower branch) constitutes the oxygen isotope of atomic weight 17. Tracks are also made by β rays, but since the electron is so much lighter than the α particle, it produces fewer ions per unit length of path and its path is easily altered. Consequently, the drops forming a β ray

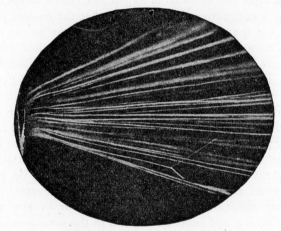

FIG. 469. Tracks of alpha rays
(*Courtesy of Professor W. D. Harkins*)

track are more widely separated than those forming an α ray track and frequently they do not lie on a straight line.

The ray counter, devised by the German physicists, H. Geiger and A. Müller, consists of a cylindrical chamber with insulating ends supporting a fine wire arranged axially. A difference of potential is maintained between wire and cylinder that is adjusted so that the counter is on the verge of discharging. When an α particle (or a proton or high-speed electron) enters the evacuated chamber, it produces a number of ions and the discharge is observed with an electrometer. The passage of the particles can be counted automatically with the aid of thermionic amplifiers and thyratron tubes [§§ 312 and 305] to operate counting mechanisms.

434. Radioactive Transformations. — Experimental study of the disintegration of the radioactive elements by the emission of α and β rays has resulted in a definite knowledge of their successive transformations, atomic numbers, atomic weights, and stability. These elements form three groups: the uranium-radium series, the thorium series, and the actinium series. The transformation of the first two series are illustrated graphically in Fig. 470 and the successive products are listed in the following table with corresponding numbers:

Radioactive Disintegration Products

No. in Fig. 470	Uranium-Radium Series		Thorium Series	
	Substance	Half-period	Substance	Half-period
1	Uranium I	45×10^8 yr.	Thorium	2×10^{10} yr.
2	" X_1	23.8 days	Mesothorium I	6.7 yr.
3	" X_2	1.15 min.	" II	6.2 hr.
4	" II	2×10^6 yr.	Radiothorium	1.90 yr.
5	Ionium	86×10^3 yr.	Thorium X	3.64 days
6	Radium	1580 yr.	" Emanation	55 sec.
7	" Emanation	3.8 days	" A	0.14 sec.
8	" A	3.05 min.	" B	10.6 hr.
9	" B	26.8 min.	" C	61 min.
10	" C	19.6 min.	" C'	10^{-11} sec.
11	" C'	10^{-6} sec.	Lead	
12	" D	16 yr.		
13	" E	4.9 days		
14	Polonium	136 days		
15	Lead			

Each inclined line in the figure signifies the emission of an α particle; such a change causes the atom to be transformed into another having an atomic weight lower by 4 and an atomic number lower by 2, than the values for the parent atom. Each horizontal line represents the emission of a β particle; such a change is equivalent to increasing the net positive charge on the nucleus, that is, raising the atomic number by 1, without changing the atomic weight. The end product in both cases is lead containing 82 electrons, that from the uranium series having an atomic weight of 206 and that from the thorium series 208. In addition to these isotopes of lead, another of atomic weight 207 has been found recently; theory shows that this can only come from the actinium series. The recent determination of the atomic weight of proactinium as 231 and the discovery of an isotope of uranium of atomic weight 235 prove the latter to be the parent element of the actinium series. The positions of all the members of that series are now fixed (see Problem 6). Elements that appear in the same vertical line in the figure are isotopes; thus thorium X is an isotope of radium.

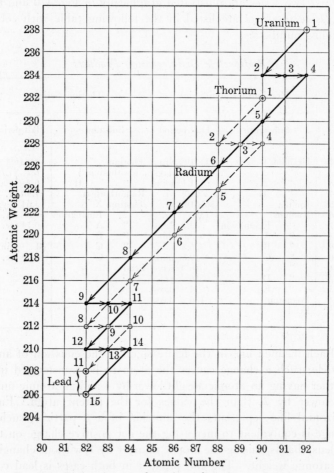

FIG. 470.   Radioactive transformations of uranium and thorium series

It is customary to express the stability of a radioactive element by its half-period, that is, the time for half of its atoms to be transformed to something else. Since the number of atoms that disintegrate per unit time is proportional to the number present, the equation of decay becomes

$$M = M_0 \epsilon^{-\delta t} \qquad (279)$$

where M_0 is the initial mass, M is the mass at time t, ϵ is the base of natural logarithms, and δ is the decay constant. The half-period is found herefrom by taking $M = M_0/2$ and solving for t. It is determined experimentally by counting the number of particles emitted with a ray counter.

Transmutation of one element into another, as occurs spontaneously in radioactivity, has also been provoked artificially in non-radioactive substances by bombardment with high-energy α particles, protons and deuterons, and high- and low-energy neutrons. The forked α-ray track shown in Fig. 469 indicates the transmutation of a nitrogen atom to an oxygen isotope.

435. The Mass Spectrograph. — The masses of atoms can be measured by passing positively charged ions of the substance through electric and magnetic fields to deflect them, very much as in the determination of e/m for electrons [§ 262]. Instruments for such measurements have been devised by Professors Francis W. Aston of Cambridge University and Arthur J. Dempster of the University of Chicago, and are called *mass spectrographs*.

Fig. 471 shows a diagram of the Aston instrument. Positive ions (called positive rays) enter from a discharge tube through slits S_1 and S_2 and pass through an electric field between plates P_1

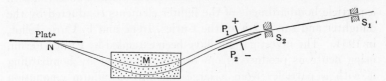

FIG. 471.   Arrangement of the Aston spectrograph

and P_2 and a magnetic field M at right angles to the page. The electric field deflects the rays downward and the magnetic field upward, in both cases the ions of higher speed being deflected less than the slower ones. The field intensities are adjusted so that, no matter what speeds the ions have, the rays will converge to a common focus N on the photographic plate. Ions having different masses or charges will, of course, be deflected differently, and only those having the same e/m ratio will arrive at a given point on the plate. Various lines will appear on the plate when the ions have various masses, and consequently the atomic weights of the isotopes of an element can be determined accurately. At present about 250 stable isotopes are known, the elements of even atomic number having the most isotopes. Tin is the most complex element and has 11 isotopes ranging from 112 to 124 in atomic weight.

436. Nuclear Structure. — Extensive studies of spectra, radioactivity and quantum relations, together with experiments using the electron gun [§ 409] to bombard elements with high-speed particles like protons, have thrown some light upon the structure of atomic nuclei. While much information is needed to attain a satisfying explanation, it is generally believed that the primary units for building the nucleus are the proton and the neutron, and that a very stable combination of these units is the α particle composed of two protons and two neutrons. On this view, a nitrogen nucleus, for example, would consist of 7 protons and 7 neutrons, giving an atomic weight of 14 and an atomic number of 7.

Bombardment of elements by neutrons is particularly fruitful in bringing about their transformation. It has been found that the neutron can enter the structure of even the heaviest nuclei rather freely and be captured by them. The resulting nucleus is often unstable and breaks up by ejecting electrons or positrons; since this behavior is analogous to radioactivity, the process is known as *artificial radioactivity*. This effect was first observed with α-particle bombardment of the lighter elements conducted by the daughter and son-in-law of the Curies, Irene and F. Curie Joliot, in 1934. The investigations have been extended by Enrico Fermi, using neutrons produced from beryllium powder by bombarding it with α particles from a large amount of radium emanation enclosed in the same tube. Cylinders made of the various elements to be transformed were placed around the tube containing the source of neutrons and then around a ray counter; in this way many new radioactive elements were produced from parent elements over a wide range of atomic number, and their half-periods were ascertained.

It has been found that greater efficiency in producing transmutation can be achieved through the use of slow neutrons, the slowing down being accomplished by passage through materials containing hydrogen, such as water and paraffin.

Gamma rays of high energy incident upon elements of large atomic weight are found to produce electrons and positrons in pairs. Apparently such a ray interacts with the intense electric field near an atomic nucleus and converts the wave radiation of

energy $E = hf$ into matter.   The energy equivalent of an electron
has been found to be 512,000 electron-volts [§ 431], and consequently a γ ray must have an energy exceeding 1 million electron-
volts to accomplish such a transformation.   The converse effect
will also occur, that is, a positron-electron pair annihilated in the
neighborhood of a nucleus will produce a γ-quantum of corresponding energy.

*437. Atomic Cleavage. — A new type of atomic disintegration
was discovered in 1938 by Professors Otto Hahn and Fritz Strass-
mann of Berlin, by the splitting of uranium into two particles of
about half the mass of the parent atom.   This was observed through
the production of barium by neutron bombardment of uranium.
Such a break-up of the uranium nucleus is accompanied by the
release of energy of the order of 2×10^8 electron-volts per disintegration.

Recent reports from these and other investigators show
further products of irradiated uranium to be isotopes of tellurium,
lanthanum, antimony and iodine.   The thorium nucleus has also
been split by neutron bombardment, and essentially the same
chemical elements were produced.   It seems that only fast
neutrons having high energy can split uranium of atomic weight
238 and also thorium, while slow neutrons of less energy are effective in splitting uranium of atomic weight 235.   These so-called
fission products of the uranium and thorium disintegrations have a
half-period that varies from seconds to several days.

438. Cosmic Rays. — The existence of a penetrating radiation
from sources outside the earth was shown about 1910 by Victor F.
Hess, and attention has been given since to a study of the character and possible origin of this so-called *cosmic radiation*.   At first
the rays were considered to be like the γ rays from radioactive substances, but to have a shorter wave length because of their greater
penetration, a penetration amounting to several feet of lead.   Now
most investigators believe them to be electrically charged particles.
Evidence of this corpuscular character is afforded by the observation that the intensity of the rays is less at the magnetic equator of
the earth than near the poles, because of the difference in their
deflection by the earth's field.   This reduction was found through
recent stratosphere flights to be more pronounced at the higher
altitudes.

Geiger counters [§ 433] are widely used in cosmic ray investigations, generally by employing a double or triple coincidence method to register the direction of the rays. In the double arrangement, for example, two counters are aligned and connected to electron tube circuits in a manner such that a current will be established only when ionization occurs simultaneously in both. In passing through matter the cosmic rays excite secondary rays of various kinds; the positron was discovered by Carl D. Anderson in the study of such rays.

Studies of cosmic rays with the cloud chamber [§ 433] have given rise to the belief that some of the particles have masses about 100 to 200 times that of an electron. The name *mesotron* has been used to designate such supposed particles. These relatively heavy particles have been considered in theories of nuclear structure to account for the great penetrating power of cosmic rays, and for the production of "showers" of such rays.

It appears that the cosmic rays originate far away, perhaps beyond our own galaxy, and approach the earth's atmosphere from all directions with approximate uniformity. A number of conjectures on the manner of producing these rays have been advanced. Some of the particles are believed to have energies of the order of 10^9 electron-volts, amounts vastly greater than those to be expected from atomic transformations. On the other hand, the aggregate energy received by cosmic rays is less than that received by starlight.

PROBLEMS

1. Compute the wave length of the $L\alpha$ line of the x-ray spectrum of gold which corresponds to an electron falling from shell M of quantum number 3 to shell L of quantum number 2. Take $Z = 79$ and $\sigma = 6$.

2. The photoelectric work function of a certain sodium surface is 2.10 electron-volts. What is the maximum velocity with which electrons will leave this surface when it is illuminated by light of wave length 4861 Å?

3. A beam of x-rays having a wave length of 1.54×10^{-8} cm. is scattered by the free electrons in a graphite block. If one of the x-ray photons is scattered through an angle of 180°, how much energy has the scattering electron received?

4. Calculate the change in wave length of the scattered radiation of x-rays when observed at angles of 60°, 90° and 120° from the incident beam.

*5. What is the percentage increase in mass of an α particle when its velocity increases from rest to 2×10^9 cm. per sec.?

6. The elements of the Actinium series are believed to have the following atomic weights and atomic numbers in the order in which the transformations occur: Actino-uranium 235, 92; Uranium Y 231, 90; Pro-

actinium 231, 91; Actinium 227, 89; Radio-actinium 227, 90; Actinium X 223, 88; Actinon 219, 86; Actinium A 215, 84; Actinium B 211, 82; Actinium C 211, 83; Actinium C' 211, 84; Lead 207, 82. Make a chart of these transformations as in Fig. 470, and indicate which changes involve the emission of α rays and which of β rays.

7. Determine the decay constant for radium emanation (also called niton and radon) from its half-period of 3.8 days.

8. A measurement of the decay constant for ionium by counting the number of α particles emitted yielded a value of 8.096×10^{-6} per year. Determine herefrom the half-period of this element.

9. How much energy in electron-volts would have to be supplied to a helium atom in order to disintegrate it into four hydrogen atoms? Assume the atomic weights of helium and hydrogen to be 4.0039 and 1.0081.

APPENDIX

TABLE I. — LOGARITHMS TO BASE 10

No.	0	1	2	3	4	5	6	7	8	9
10	00000	00432	00860	01284	01703	02119	02531	02938	03342	03743
11	04139	04532	04922	05308	05690	06070	06446	06819	07188	07555
12	07918	08279	08636	08991	09342	09691	10037	10380	10721	11059
13	11394	11727	12057	12385	12710	13033	13354	13672	13988	14301
14	14613	14922	15229	15533	15836	16137	16435	16732	17026	17319
15	17609	17898	18184	18469	18752	19033	19312	19590	19866	20140
16	20412	20683	20952	21219	21484	21748	22011	22272	22531	22789
17	23045	23300	23553	23805	24055	24304	24551	24797	25042	25285
18	25527	25768	26007	26245	26482	26717	26951	27184	27416	27646
19	27875	28103	28330	28556	28780	29003	29226	29447	29667	29885
20	30103	30320	30535	30730	30963	31175	31387	31597	31806	32015
21	32222	32428	32634	32838	33041	33244	33445	33646	33846	34044
22	34242	34439	34635	34830	35025	35218	35411	35603	35793	35984
23	36173	36361	36549	36736	36922	37107	37291	37475	37658	37840
24	38021	38202	38382	38561	38739	38916	39094	39270	39445	39620
25	39794	39967	40140	40312	40483	40654	40824	40993	41162	41330
26	41497	41664	41830	41996	42160	42325	42488	42651	42813	42975
27	43136	43297	43457	43616	43775	43933	44091	44248	44404	44560
28	44716	44871	45025	45179	45332	45484	45637	45788	45939	46090
29	46240	46389	46538	46687	46835	46982	47129	47276	47422	47567
30	47712	47857	48001	48144	48287	48430	48572	48714	48855	48996
31	49136	49276	49415	49554	49693	49831	49969	50106	50243	50379
32	50515	50651	50786	50920	51055	51188	51322	51455	51587	51720
33	51851	51983	52114	52244	52375	52504	52634	52763	52892	53020
34	53148	53275	53403	53529	53656	53782	53908	54033	54158	54283
35	54407	54531	54654	54777	54900	55023	55145	55267	55388	55509
36	55630	55751	55871	55991	56110	56229	56348	56467	56585	56703
37	56820	56937	57054	57171	57287	57403	57519	57634	57749	57864
38	57978	58092	58206	58320	58433	58546	58659	58771	58883	58995
39	59106	59218	59329	59439	59550	59660	59770	59879	59989	60097
40	60206	60314	60423	60531	60638	60746	60853	60959	61066	61172
41	61278	61384	61490	61595	61700	61805	61909	62014	62118	62221
42	62325	62428	62531	62634	62737	62839	62941	63043	63144	63246
43	63347	63448	63548	63649	63749	63849	63949	6 048	64147	64246
44	64345	64444	64542	64640	64738	64836	64933	65031	65128	65225
45	65321	65418	65514	65610	65706	65801	65896	65992	66087	66181
46	66276	66370	66464	66558	66652	66745	66839	66932	67025	67117
47	67210	67302	67394	67486	67578	67669	67761	67852	67943	68034
48	68124	68215	68305	68395	68485	68574	68664	68753	68842	68931
49	69020	69108	69197	69285	69373	69461	69548	69636	69723	69810
50	69897	69984	70070	70157	70243	70329	70415	70501	70586	70672

TABLE I. — LOGARITHMS TO BASE 10. — (*Continued*)

No.	0	1	2	3	4	5	6	7	8	9
51	70757	70842	70927	71012	71096	71181	71265	71349	71433	71517
52	71600	71684	71767	71850	71933	72016	72099	72181	72263	72346
53	72428	72509	72591	72673	72754	72835	72916	72997	73078	73159
54	73239	73320	73400	73480	73560	73640	73719	73799	73878	73957
55	74036	74115	74194	74273	74351	74429	74507	74586	74663	74741
56	74819	74896	74974	75051	75128	75205	75282	75358	75435	75511
57	75587	75664	75740	75815	75891	75967	76042	76118	76193	76268
58	76343	76418	76492	76567	76641	76716	76790	76864	76938	77012
59	77085	77159	77232	77305	77379	77452	77525	77597	77670	77743
60	77815	77887	77960	78032	78104	78176	78247	78319	78390	78462
61	78533	78604	78675	78746	78817	78888	78958	79029	79099	79169
62	79239	79309	79379	79449	79518	79588	79657	79727	79796	79865
63	79934	80003	80072	80140	80209	80277	80346	80414	80482	80550
64	80618	80686	80754	80821	80889	80956	81023	81090	81158	81224
65	81291	81358	81425	81491	81558	81624	81690	81757	81823	81889
66	81954	82020	82086	82151	82217	82282	82347	82413	82478	82543
67	82607	82672	82737	82802	82866	82930	82995	83059	83123	83187
68	83251	83315	83378	83442	83506	83569	83632	83696	83759	83822
69	83885	83948	84011	84073	84136	84198	84261	84323	84386	84448
70	84510	84572	84634	84696	84757	84819	84880	84942	85003	85065
71	85126	85187	85248	85309	85370	85431	85491	85552	85612	85673
72	85733	85794	85854	85914	85974	86034	86094	86153	86213	86273
73	86332	86392	86451	86510	86570	86629	86688	86747	86806	86864
74	86923	86982	87040	87099	87157	87216	87274	87332	87390	87448
75	87506	87564	87622	87679	87737	87795	87852	87910	87967	88024
76	88081	88138	88195	88252	88309	88366	88423	88480	88536	88593
77	88649	88705	88762	88818	88874	88930	88986	89042	89098	89154
78	89209	89265	89321	89376	89432	89487	89542	89597	89653	89708
79	89763	89818	89873	89927	89982	90037	90091	90146	90200	90255
80	90309	90363	90417	90472	90526	90580	90634	90687	90741	90795
81	90849	90902	90956	91009	91062	91116	91169	91222	91275	91328
82	91381	91434	91487	91540	91593	91645	91698	91751	91803	91855
83	91908	91960	92012	92065	92117	92169	92221	92273	92324	92376
84	92428	92480	92531	92583	92634	92686	92737	92789	92840	92891
85	92942	92993	93044	93095	93146	93197	93247	93298	93349	93399
86	93450	93500	93551	93601	93651	93702	93752	93802	93852	93902
87	93952	94002	94052	94101	94151	94201	94250	94300	94349	94399
88	94448	94498	94547	94596	94645	94694	94743	94792	94841	94890
89	94939	94988	95036	95085	95134	95182	95231	95279	95328	95376
90	95424	95472	95521	95569	95617	95665	95713	95761	95809	95856

TABLE I. — LOGARITHMS TO BASE 10. — *(Continued)*

No.	0	1	2	3	4	5	6	7	8	9
91	95904	95952	95999	96047	96095	96142	96190	96237	96284	96332
92	96379	96426	96473	96520	96567	96614	96661	96708	96755	96802
93	96848	96895	96942	96988	97035	97081	97128	97174	97220	97267
94	97313	97359	97405	97451	97497	97543	97589	97635	97681	97727
95	97772	97818	97864	97909	97955	98000	98046	98091	98137	98182
96	98227	98272	98318	98363	98408	98453	98498	98543	98588	98632
97	98677	98722	98767	98811	98856	98900	98945	98989	99034	99078
98	99123	99167	99211	99255	99300	99344	99388	99432	99476	99520
99	99564	99607	99651	99695	99739	99782	99826	99870	99913	99957

Characteristics of Logarithms:

$$\log 4030 = 3.6053 \qquad \log 0.403 = \overline{1}.6053$$
$$\log 403 = 2.6053 \qquad \log 0.0403 = \overline{2}.6053$$
$$\log 40.3 = 1.6053 \qquad \log 0.00403 = \overline{3}.6053$$
$$\log 4.03 = 0.6053 \qquad \log 0.000403 = \overline{4}.6053$$

$$\log_e x = 2.3026 \log_{10} x$$
$$\log (a^x) = x \log a$$

TABLE II.—GREEK ALPHABET

A,	α	. . . . *Alpha*	N,	ν	. . . . *Nu*
B,	β	. . . . *Beta*	Ξ,	ξ	. . . . *Xi*
Γ,	γ	. . . . *Gamma*	O,	o	. . . . *Omicron*
Δ,	δ	. . . . *Delta*	Π,	π	. . . . *Pi*
E,	ϵ	. . . . *Epsilon*	P,	ρ	. . . . *Rho*
Z,	ζ	. . . . *Zeta*	Σ,	σ	. . . . *Sigma*
H,	η	. . . . *Eta*	T,	τ	. . . . *Tau*
Θ,	θ	. . . . *Theta*	Υ,	υ	. . . . *Upsilon*
I,	ι	. . . . *Iota*	Φ,	ϕ	. . . . *Phi*
K,	κ	. . . . *Kappa*	X,	χ	. . . . *Chi*
Λ,	λ	. . . . *Lambda*	Ψ,	ψ	. . . . *Psi*
M,	μ	. . . . *Mu*	Ω,	ω	. . . . *Omega*

TABLE III.—TRIGONOMETRIC FUNCTIONS (*Natural*)

Angle	Sine	Cosine	Tangent	Angle	Sine	Cosine	Tangent
0°	0.000	1.000	0.000				
1°	.018	1.000	.018	46°	.719	.695	1.036
2°	.035	0.999	.035	47°	.731	.682	1.072
3°	.052	.999	.052	48°	.743	.669	1.111
4°	.070	.998	.070	49°	.755	.656	1.150
5°	.087	.996	.088	50°	.766	.643	1.192
6°	.105	.995	.105	51°	.777	.629	1.235
7°	.122	.993	.123	52°	.788	.616	1.280
8°	.139	.990	.141	53°	.799	.602	1.327
9°	.156	.988	.158	54°	.809	.588	1.376
10°	.174	.985	.176	55°	.819	.574	1.428
11°	.191	.982	.194	56°	.829	.559	1.483
12°	.208	.978	.213	57°	.839	.545	1.540
13°	.225	.974	.231	58°	.848	.530	1.600
14°	.242	.970	.249	59°	.857	.515	1.664
15°	.259	.966	.268	60°	.866	.500	1.732
16°	.276	.961	.287	61°	.875	.485	1.804
17°	.292	.956	.306	62°	.883	.470	1.881
18°	.309	.951	.325	63°	.891	.454	1.963
19°	.326	.946	.344	64°	.899	.438	2.050
20°	.342	.940	.364	65°	.906	.423	2.145
21°	.358	.934	.384	66°	.914	.407	2.246
22°	.375	.927	.404	67°	.921	.391	2.356
23°	.391	.921	.425	68°	.927	.375	2.475
24°	.407	.914	.445	69°	.934	.358	2.605
25°	.423	.906	.466	70°	.940	.342	2.747
26°	.438	.899	.488	71°	.946	.326	2.904
27°	.454	.891	.510	72°	.951	.309	3.078
28°	.470	.883	.532	73°	.956	.292	3.271
29°	.485	.875	.554	74°	.961	.276	3.487
30°	.500	.866	.577	75°	.966	.259	3.732
31°	.515	.857	.601	76°	.970	.242	4.011
32°	.530	.848	.625	77°	.974	.225	4.331
33°	.545	.839	.649	78°	.978	.208	4.705
34°	.559	.829	.675	79°	.982	.191	5.145
35°	.574	.819	.700	80°	.985	.174	5.671
36°	.588	.809	.727	81°	.988	.156	6.314
37°	.602	.799	.754	82°	.990	.139	7.115
38°	.616	.788	.781	83°	.993	.122	8.144
39°	.629	.777	.810	84°	.995	.105	9.514
40°	.643	.766	.839	85°	.996	.087	11.43
41°	.656	.755	.869	86°	.998	.070	14.30
42°	.669	.743	.900	87°	.999	.052	19.08
43°	.682	.731	.933	88°	.999	.035	28.64
44°	.695	.719	.966	89°	1.000	.018	57.29
45°	.707	.707	1.000	90°	1.000	.000	∞

Trigonometric Functions for Angles Larger than 90 Degrees

When the angle lies beyond the first quadrant, the accompanying table of trigonometric functions of any angle θ can be used by applying the following:

Second Quadrant............ $\begin{cases} \sin(90+\theta) = \cos\theta \\ \cos(90+\theta) = -\sin\theta \\ \tan(90+\theta) = -\cot\theta \end{cases}$

Third Quadrant............ $\begin{cases} \sin(180+\theta) = -\sin\theta \\ \cos(180+\theta) = -\cos\theta \\ \tan(180+\theta) = \tan\theta \end{cases}$

Fourth Quadrant............ $\begin{cases} \sin(270+\theta) = -\cos\theta \\ \cos(270+\theta) = \sin\theta \\ \tan(270+\theta) = -\cot\theta \end{cases}$

TABLE IV.—CONSTANTS AND CONVERSION FACTORS

$\pi = 3.1416$ $\qquad \epsilon = 2.7183 \qquad$ $\log_\epsilon 10 = 2.3026$

1 Ångström unit = Å = 10^{-8} cm.
1 micron = 0.001 mm.
1 centimeter = 0.39370 in.
1 inch = 2.5400 cm.
1 foot = 30.480 cm.
1 radian = 57.2958 degrees

1 sq. inch = 6.4516 sq. cm.
1 sq. foot = 929.03 sq. cm.
1 cu. inch = 16.387 cu. cm.
1 liter = 1000 cu. cm.
1 gallon = 3.785 liters
1 gallon = 231 cu. in.

1 gram = 15.432 grains
1 ounce = 28.350 gm.

1 pound = 453.59 gm.
1 kilogram = 2.2046 lb.

1 pound (wt.) = 445,000 dynes
1 atmosphere = 14.697 lb. per sq. in.
1 joule = 10,000,000 ergs
1 calorie = 4.186 joules

1 foot-pound = 1.3549 joules
1 B.t.u. = 252.00 cal.
1 B.t.u. = 778 ft-lb.
1 horsepower = 746 watts

1 coulomb = 3×10^9 e.s.u. of charge
1 volt = $\frac{1}{300}$ erg per e.s.u. of charge
1 farad = 9×10^{11} e.s.u. of capacitance

1 abampere = 10 amp.
1 abvolt = 10^{-8} volts
1 faraday = 96,500 coulombs

Charge of electron = 4.80×10^{-10} e.s.u.
Mass of electron (at rest) = 9.11×10^{-28} gm.
Avogadro's number = 6.02×10^{23}
Planck's constant = 6.63×10^{-27} erg-sec.
Mass of hydrogen atom = 1.661×10^{-24} gm.
Velocity of light = 299,776 km. per sec. in vacuum

TABLE V. — PERIODIC TABLE *

Periods	Group O	I A	I B	II A	II B	III A	III B	IV A	IV B	V A	V B	VI A	VI B	VII A	VII B	Group VIII
Type of Oxide	....	R₂O		RO		R₂O₃		RO₂		R₂O₅		R₂O₆(RO₃)		R₂O₇		RO₄
Type of Hydride	....	RH		RH₂		RH₃		RH₄		RH₃		RH₂		RH		.....
First short period	He *2*, 4.002	H *1*, 1.0078	Li *3*, 6.940		Be *4*, 9.02		B *5*, 10.82		C *6*, 12.00		N *7*, 14.008		O *8*, 16.00		F *9*, 19.00	
Second short period	Ne *10*, 20.183	Na *11*, 22.997		Mg *12*, 24.32		Al *13*, 26.97		Si *14*, 28.06		P *15*, 31.02		S *16*, 32.06		Cl *17*, 35.457		
First long period — Even Series	A *18*, 39.944	K *19*, 39.10		Ca *20*, 40.08		Sc *21*, 45.10		Ti *22*, 47.90		V *23*, 50.95		Cr *24*, 52.01		Mn *25*, 54.93		Fe *26* 55.84; Co *27* 58.94; Ni *28* 58.69
First long period — Odd Series			Cu *29*, 63.57		Zn *30*, 65.38		Ga *31*, 69.72		Ge *32*, 72.60		As *33*, 74.93		Se *34*, 79.2		Br *35*, 79.916	
Second long period — Even Series	Kr *36*, 82.9	Rb *37*, 85.44		Sr *38*, 87.63		Y *39*, 88.92		Zr *40*, 91.22		Cb *41*, 93.3		Mo *42*, 96.0		Ma *43*, ?		Ru *44* 101.7; Rh *45* 102.91; Pd *46* 106.7
Second long period — Odd Series			Ag *47*, 107.880		Cd *48*, 112.41		In *49*, 114.8		Sn *50*, 118.70		Sb *51*, 121.76		Te *52*, 127.5		I *53*, 126.932	
Third long period — Even Series	Xe *54*, 130.2	Cs *55*, 132.81		Ba *56*, 137.36		La *57*, 138.90		Ce *58*, 140.13								
Third long period — Odd Series						The Rare Earth Elements — Atomic Numbers 59–71										
Fourth long period — Even Series								Hf *72*, 178.6		Ta *73*, 181.4		W *74*, 184.0		Re *75*, 186.31		Os *76* 190.8; Ir *77* 193.1; Pt *78* 195.23
Fourth long period — Odd Series			Au *79*, 197.2		Hg *80*, 200.61		Tl *81*, 204.39		Pb *82*, 207.22		Bi *83*, 209.0		Po *84*		- *85*	
Fifth period	Rn *86*, 222	- *87*		Ra *88*, 225.97		Ac *89*, 227		Th *90*, 232.12		UX₂ *91*		U *92*, 238.14				

* The italic number at the right of the symbol is the Atomic Number of the element, and the number below is the Atomic Weight.

TABLE VI—PHYSICAL CONSTANTS

Tables of the physical characteristics of materials are scattered throughout the text where these properties are discussed, in order to give the reader a conception of the order of magnitudes involved. For ease of reference the locations of these tables are listed below:

ANSWERS TO PROBLEMS
HAVING ODD NUMBERS

MECHANICS

Chapter I

1. 6190 meters. **3.** 111.0 and 14.4 meters respectively. **5.** 745 ft.
7. 0.00716°. **9.** 1° 52′. **11.** 59.23 ft. **13.** 175 mi. from A; 195 mi. from
B. **15.** 3633 mi. **17.** 22.1 in. **19.** 240 cu. in.; 3.92 gal. **21.** 27,150 gal.
23. 167,600 gal. **25.** 2830 lb. **27.** Scales A and B: $2.25 \times 6.25 = 14.06$;
$14.06 \div 6.25 = 2.25$. Only one of each other pair follows: $CD\ 1.50 \times 2.50$
$= 3.75$; $AD\ (3.75)^2 = 14.06$; $BC\ (2.50)^2 = 6.25$; $CCI\ 1.00 \div 2.50 = 0.400$;
$CID\ 3.75 \times 4.00 = 15.0$; $DK\ (3.75)^3 = 52.7$.

Chapter II

1. 136.1 mi., 8° 27′ east of north. **3.** 11.53 mi., 47° 30′ north of east.
5. 6.56 km. north; 7.55 km. east. **7.** 30.1 ft., 10° 24′ west of south.
9. 25.0 and 43.3 lb. respectively. **11.** 2.94 lb. **13.** 185.8 lb. at angle of
59′ to right of 60-lb. force. **15.** 4.67 lb. **17.** 10.0 lb-ft.

Chapter III

1. 4.46 ft. per sec.; 3.05 mi. per hr. **3.** 66,600 mi. per hr.; 1036 mi.
per hr. **5.** 5.0 min. **7.** 121 sec. **9.** 17.5 ft. per sec. **11.** (a) 440 ft. per
min., (b) 210 rev. per min. **13.** 1800 ft. per sec. **15.** 120 ft. **17.** 45.1 ft.
per sec. **19.** 5.025 mi. per hr.; 5° 42′ west of north. **21.** 30.99 knots
westward; 31.69 knots eastward. **23.** 927 ft. per min. **25.** 11.5 mi.
per day.

Chapter IV

1. 4.40 ft. per sec. per sec.; 134 cm. per sec. per sec. **3.** −9.64 ft. per
sec. per sec. **5.** 154.4 ft. **7.** 50.0 mi. per hr. per sec. **9.** 1026 ft.
11. 3.16 sec.; 101.1 ft. per sec. **13.** Distance $= g(n - \frac{1}{2})$. **15.** 1.70 sec.
17. 100 ft. **19.** 27,060 ft. **21.** (a) 459.6 ft. horizontally from starting
point and 241.7 ft. up, (b) 156.6 ft. per sec., 12° 1′ above horizontal.
25. 2.09 radians per sec. per sec.

Chapter V

1. 2.56 ft. per sec. per sec. **3.** 28,000 poundals. **5.** 5.97×10^{24} kg.
7. (a) 898 cm. per sec. per sec., (b) 22.45 meters. **9.** 1125 kg. per sq. cm.
11. 146 lb. **13.** 2.13 ft. per sec. per sec. toward left. **15.** 1470 and
1180 lb. respectively. **17.** 4.69 ft. **19.** $P = m \left(g \sin \theta + \dfrac{2s}{t^2} \right)$. **21.** 163.3
cm. per sec. per sec. **23.** (a) 1800 lb., (b) 2750 lb. **25.** 0.25. **29.** (a)
1.84 sec., (b) 2.26 sec. **31.** 380 lb. **33.** 2.64 lb. **35.** 189 rev. per min.
37. 54,800 rev. per min. **39.** 71.8 rev. per min. **41.** 18° 35′. **43.** $[LT^{-1}]$;
$[L]$; $[L^2T^{-2}]$; $[MT^{-1}]$.

Chapter VI

1. 1.745 ft. per sec. per sec. **3.** $\frac{2}{3}g$. **5.** (a) 0.900 lb-ft.^{2}, (b) 3.15 lb-ft.^{2}
7. 33,598 lb-ft.^{2} **9.** 28.9 cm. **11.** 44.7 cm. **13.** 2.16 lb-ft. **15.** 4.62 radians per sec.

Chapter VII

1. (a) 48.0 lb., (b) 36.0 lb. **3.** 67.2 lb. in shorter wire; 60.7 lb. in other. **5.** 57.7 gm. **7.** 52.7 cm. **9.** 3.00 ft. from man. **11.** 2.35 lb. **13.** 72.4 in. in front of rear axle. **15.** 29.1 in. in front of rear axle. **17.** 4.85 tons at left; 3.15 tons at right. **21.** Tension 118 lb.; thrust 107 lb. at angle of 20° 35′ downward from horizontal. **23.** Tension 1480 lb.; thrust 1630 lb. at angle of 50° 7′ downward from horizontal. **25.** $A = 6825$ lb.; $B = 8175$ lb.; $C = 3000$ lb.

Chapter VIII

1. 2400 ft-lb. **3.** 900 ft-lb. **5.** 790 ft-lb. **7.** 840 ft. **9.** 15,100 ft-lb. **11.** 4.37 ft.; 515 × 10^6 ft-lb. **13.** 0.1245 hp. **15.** 70.0 hp. **17.** 47.3 lb-ft. **19.** 257 hp. **21.** (a) 7530 watts, (b) 18,850 watts, (c) 23,560 watts. **23.** 12,060 lb. **25.** 6.82 hp.

Chapter IX

1. 2.40 vibrations per sec.; 0.416 sec. **3.** (a) 3.14 ft. per sec.; 0 ft. per sec. per sec., (b) 0 ft. per sec.; 19.7 ft. per sec. per sec., (c) 2.72 ft. per sec.; 9.85 ft. per sec. per sec. **5.** 3.09 cm. above midposition; 488 cm. per sec. per sec. downward; 3660 dynes downward. **7.** 1480 lb. at ends of stroke. **9.** 1.44 vibrations per sec.; 25.6 cm. per sec.; 231.6 cm. per sec. per sec.; 139,000 dynes. **11.** (a) 99.4 cm., (b) 1.00 sec. **13.** 1.53 sec. **15.** 66.67 cm. **17.** 0.80 lb. each.

Chapter X

1. Yes; 0.0146 in. **3.** 0.00173; 38.2 kg. per sq. mm.; 22,100 kg. per sq. mm. **5.** 840 lb. **7.** 250,000 lb. per sq. in. **9.** 0.00144; 15,000 lb. per sq. in.; 10,420,000 lb. per sq. in. **11.** 476 kg. per sq. mm. **13.** 35.7 ft. **15.** 33,750 lb-ft. **17.** W lb., r ft., T sec., R ft., g ft. per sec. per sec., E lb. per sq. ft. **19.** 18.7 cm. per sec. **21.** 35,340 cm. per sec.

Chapter XI

1. 499 lb. per sq. ft.; 31,900 lb. **3.** 3745 lb. per sq. in. **5.** 93,600 lb.; 312,000 lb-ft. **7.** 124,800 lb.; 116,000 lb-ft. **9.** 1800 lb.; 36.0. **11.** Glass 2.61 gm. per cu. cm.; turpentine 0.875 gm. per cu. cm. **13.** 4.79 cm. **15.** 0.90; no effect. **17.** 0.422 cm. **19.** 102 × 10^9 lb-ft.^{2} **21.** 37.0 dynes per cm. **23.** 6.12 cm.

Chapter XII

1. 0.309 cu. ft. per sec. **3.** 8.18 min. **5.** 79.1 per cent. **11.** 93.2 cm. per sec. **13.** 10.9 poises.

Chapter XIII

1. 4.41 × 10^{-11} sec. **3.** 25,400 lb. **5.** 11.9 lb. per sq. in. **7.** 1.38 in. **9.** 0.505 and 15.21 lb. per sq. in. respectively. **11.** 38.8 lb. per sq. in. **13.** 168.7 ft. per sec. **15.** 0.099 gm. **17.** 30.1 cm. per sec. **19.** 0.152 joule; 5.62 × 10^{-14} ergs.

HEAT

Chapter XIV

1. −37.8°; 674.1° F. **3.** 120.2° F.; 167° F.; 194° F. **5.** 0.249 in. **7.** 247° C. **9.** 18,780 lb. **11.** 0.025 in. **13.** 59.2 cu. in. **15.** 10.42 cm. **17.** 152.2 cm.

Chapter XV

1. 32,500 cal. **3.** 48.4 cent. deg. **5.** 31.37 min. **7.** 14,000 cal. **9.** Water at 20.0° C. **11.** 220° C.; 56 per cent tin, 44 per cent lead. **13.** Temperature 0° C. with 3.47 lb. of ice formed. **15.** 76.3 gm. of ice and 23.7 gm. of water, all at 0° C. **17.** 388.2 B.t.u.

Chapter XVI

1. 41,580 cal. **3.** 5.0° C. **5.** 50.0° F. **7.** 0.120. **9.** 0.0913. **11.** 750.9 cal. **13.** Temperature 32° F. with 4.30 lb. of ice unmelted. **15.** 2.97 lb. **17.** 2350 lb. per hr. **19.** 0.976 cu. ft. per min.

Chapter XVII

1. 8.07 in. **3.** 8.52 in. **5.** 86.95 cu. cm. **7.** Gage pressure 679 lb. per sq. in. **9.** 15.6 liters. **11.** (a) 108.2 gm. per sq. cm., (b) 124.0 gm. per sq. cm. **13.** 48.2° C. **15.** 1.236 lb. **17.** 3.71 joules. **19.** 773.4 cu. cm.; Isothermal 387 and 258 cu. cm.; Adiabatic 473 and 351 cu. cm. **21.** 49 per cent. **23.** 0.00759 lb.; 14.3 B.t.u.

Chapter XVIII

1. 22.9 fahr. deg. **3.** 1723 times. **5.** 45.1 kw-hr. **7.** 71.2° C. **9.** 27.5 per cent. **11.** 16.0 hp. **13.** Indicated 22.6 hp.; rated 26.3 hp. **15.** (a) 0.589 lb. per hp-hr., (b) 21.6 per cent. **17.** 1212 lb-ft.; 652 hp.

Chapter XIX

1. 5570 B.t.u. per hr. **3.** 22.2 lb. per day. **5.** 0.000376 cal. per sec. per °C. per cm. **7.** 2.51 sec. **9.** 1.55. **11.** 251 cal. per sec. **13.** Stefan ratio 2.07; Newton ratio 1.87; 9.7 per cent less. **15.** 5.69 min. **17.** Curve points: 1000° K. 2.885×10^{-4} cm.; 2000° K. 1.443×10^{-4} cm.; 3000° K. 0.962×10^{-4} cm.; 4000° K. 0.721×10^{-4} cm.; 5000° K. 0.577×10^{-4} cm.

ELECTRICITY AND MAGNETISM

Chapter XX

1. 40.0 dynes. **3.** 80.0 dynes attraction. **5.** 12.5 dynes per e.s.u. downward. **7.** (a) 14.4 dynes per e.s.u. away from larger charge; +44.0 ergs per e.s.u., (b) 2.87 dynes per e.s.u. downward 48° 28′ from the horizontal, 18.1 ergs per e.s.u. **9.** 1.46 dynes per e.s.u. toward smaller charge; −18.67 ergs per e.s.u. **11.** 47.9 volts. **13.** 209.

Chapter XXI

1. 1742 dynes. **3.** 8.00 oersteds toward right. **5.** 17.78, 3.75 and 0.694 oersteds respectively. **7.** 0.4711 oersted at angle of 66° 58′ to horizontal. **9.** 7.20 oersteds. **11.** 4.42 oersteds at angle of 15° 40′ down from vertical toward S pole. **13.** 0.92 per sec.

Chapter XXII

1. 40.0 joules. 3. 5.38 cents. 5. $1.40. 7. (a) 19.83 ohms, (b) 120.8 volts. 9. 45.7 cent. deg. 11. 48.0 watts. 13. $43.80. 15. 10.570 ohm-C.M. per ft. 17. 0.00443 cm. 19. 0.462 ohm. 21. 88.7 mils. 23. 29.9 volts. 25. 0.0714 ohm. 27. 144 ohms. 29. (a) 267 ohms, (b) 0.146 amp.; 39.0 volts. 31. 0.140 amp. 33. 1-ohm: 2.40 amp., 2.40 volts; 2-ohm: 0.80 amp., 1.60 volts; 3-ohm: 0.53 amp.; 1.60 volts; each 4-ohm: 0.40 amp., 1.60 volts; 5-ohm: 1.60 amp., 8.00 volts; 6-ohm: 0.27 amp., 1.60 volts; 10-ohm: 0.80 amp., 8.00 volts. 35. 312.4 ohms. 37. −13.0° C.

Chapter XXIII

1. +0.232 amp. 3. 43.0 kg. 5. 3.12 × 10²¹ atoms. 7. 0.533 amp. 9. 20.12 gm. 11. 26 min. 23 sec. 13. 6.12 hr. 15. (a) 5.20 volts, (b) 6.80 volts. 17. 0.288 amp. 19. 11.0 amp. for cell of higher e.m.f. and 9.0 amp. for other. 21. 1.081 volts; 3.86 ohms.

Chapter XXIV

1. 0.942 oersted. 3. 0.236 amp. 5. 0.394 oersted. 7. 70.0 dynes directed 45° to horizontal plane and perpendicular to wire. 9. 28.3 divisions. 11. 0.01003 ohm. 13. 0.002503 ohm. 15. 0.01125 coulomb in either case. 17. 0.652 microcoulomb. 19. 0.177 oersted. 23. 19,570 gausses.

Chapter XXV

1. 2.50 millihenries. 3. 6.25 millihenries. 5. 6.00 and 1.80 volts respectively. 7. 4.15 amp. 9. 2720 maxwells. 11. (a) 0.00582 unit, (b) 0.0136 unit. 13. 2032 gausses. 15. 3.33 × 10⁻⁵ mf. 17. (a) 2.83 × 10⁻⁹ coulombs, (b) 0.566 erg, (c) 19.8 × 10⁻⁹ coulombs, (d) 4.53 ergs. 19. 5-mf.: 240 microcoulombs, 48.0 volts; 7-mf.: 336 microcoulombs, 48.0 volts; 8-mf.: 576 microcoulombs, 72.0 volts. 21. 87.3 microcoulombs.

Chapter XXVI

1. (a) 134.2 volts, (b) 109.6 volts. 3. 2036 volts. 5. 2010 ohms. 7. 11.0 ohms; 0.0292 henry. 9. 79.6 ohms; 0.0796 volt. 11. 663 ohms; 0.166 amp. 13. 14.5 or 6.58 millihenries. 15. Resistance: 0.120 amp.; coil: 0.117 amp.; condenser: 0.080 amp.; main: 0.168 amp. 17. 1.06 amp.; 58.0°. 19. 37.0 watts. 21. $4243.

Chapter XXVII

1. 115.2 volts. 3. 12,160 amp-turns. 5. 120. 7. (a) 117.6 volts, (b) 144 watts. 9. 3.98 × 10⁸ dyne-cm.; 6.70 hp. 11. (a) 0.60 amp., (b) 19.4 amp., (c) 116.9 volts, (d) 72.0 watts, (e) 60.2 watts. 13. (a) 30.0 amp., (b) 0.82 amp., (c) 30.82 amp. 15. 11.72 amp. 17. (a) 60 cycles per sec., (b) 20. 19. 28.8 amp. 21. 242 amp.

Chapter XXVIII

1. 55.6 millivolts; 57.9 microvolts per cent. deg. 3. 6.75 millivolts. 5. 43.4° C. 7. 0.00101 amp. per sq. cm. 9. 41.3 milliamp. 11. 8.9. 13. 1160 microamp. per volt. 15. 0.90 microamp.

ANSWERS TO PROBLEMS 743

Chapter XXIX

1. 536 mi. **3.** 27.6 milliamp. for one key closed; 64.9 milliamp. for both keys closed. **5.** (*a*) 109.6 milliamp., (*b*) 2.74 per cent. **7.** 24.8 db. **9.** 0.080 watt. **11.** 1145 kilocycles per sec. **13.** 0.00266 mf.

SOUND

Chapter XXX

1. 0.0050 sec.; 5.50 ft. **3.** 429 ft. per sec. **5.** 8.20 lb. **7.** 455 meters. **9.** 4785 ft. per sec. **11.** 1260 meters per sec. **13.** 0.258 sec. **15.** 66.0 ft. **17.** 3.83 ft. per sec. **19.** 196,000 km. per sec. **21.** $A = 254$, $B = 269$, and $C = 262$ vibrations per sec. **23.** 250 gm.

Chapter XXXI

1. 0.148 erg per sec. per sq. cm. **3.** First 211, second 476, and third 330 ergs per sec. per sq. cm. **5.** 42.9 vibrations per sec. **7.** 183 lb. **9.** 2087 and 6262 vibrations per sec. **11.** 920 vibrations per sec. **13.** 212 and 407 vibrations per sec. **15.** 39.9 beats per min. **17.** 307.6 vibrations per sec. **19.** 330, 371, 412, 440, 495, 550, 619 and 660 vibrations per sec.

Chapter XXXII

1. From 1 to 10 in steps of 1 microwatt per sq. cm. the levels are: 0, 3.01, 4.77, 6.02, 6.99, 7.78, 8.45, 9.03, 9.54 and 10 db. **3.** −6.02 db. **5.** 493 meters per sec. **7.** 1026 ft. north and 718 ft. east of *A*. **9.** 4.93 sec. **11.** 0.93 sec. **13.** 0.0396 in.

LIGHT

Chapter XXXIII

1. 56.6×10^6 lumens. **3.** 9470 cp.; 5.22 cp. per watt. **5.** (*a*) 2.40 ft-candles, (*b*) 2.26 ft-candles. **7.** (*a*) 10.22 ft-candles, (*b*) 5.48 ft-candles. **9.** 66.8 cm. from 27-cp. lamp. **11.** 15.8 cp. **13.** 357 rev. per sec. **15.** (*a*) 9° 28′ from vertical, (*b*) 20.5 sec. of arc from vertical.

Chapter XXXIV

1. 2.88 ft. **3.** 18.2 cm. **5.** 12.0 cm. in front of mirror, real, inverted, reduced; 1.00 cm. **7.** 1.5. **9.** −25.0 cm. **11.** Reflected 45° 0′; refracted 32° 2′. **13.** 1.125; 0.889. **15.** 1.532. **17.** 48° 56′. **19.** 1.665. **21.** 9.34 in. **23.** 1.414.

Chapter XXXV

1. Deviation 48° 56′; dispersion 3° 25′. **3.** 5° 19′. **5.** (*a*) Respectively 1° 42′ and 1° 12′, (*b*) 0.0833. **7.** Prism 26° 50′; deviation 4° 28′. **9.** 5.69×10^{14} vibrations per sec.; 18,980 waves per cm. **11.** 594 km. per sec.

Chapter XXXVI

1. 2.32 ft. **3.** 3.79 in. **5.** −25.9 cm. **7.** −3.30 cm. **9.** 80.0 cm. beyond lens, real, inverted, enlarged; 4.00 times. **11.** 30.0 cm. from lens. **13.** (*a*) Image is 16.7 in. beyond lens, (*b*) image is 1.83 in. beyond second lens. **15.** 3.97 cm. **17.** Crown +4.13 cm.; flint −7.03 cm. **19.** 11.0 in.

Chapter XXXVII

1. 7182 rev. per min. **3.** −40.0 cm.; −2.50 diopters. **5.** 50 cm. **7.** 7.5 cm.; 0.50 diopter. **9.** (a) 10.55 in., (b) 95.0 in. **11.** 1 to 8.16. **13.** 10.0 in. **15.** 3.2 diameters. **17.** 1000 diameters. **19.** Respectively 27.05 and 1.35 cm.

Chapter XXXVIII

1. 0.0737 cm. **3.** 0.00001445 cm. **5.** 0.00202 cm. **7.** 0.0185 cm. **9.** 0.0767 cm. **11.** 0.0293 cm. **13.** 69.8 mi. **15.** 0.2517 min. of arc; 6831 ft. **17.** 0.00005895; sodium. **19.** Respectively 7° 12', 14° 31' and 22° 6'.

Chapter XXXIX

1. Incidence 53° 7'; refraction 36° 53'. **3.** Ordinary 1.81×10^{10} cm. per sec.; extraordinary 2.02×10^{10} cm. per sec. **5.** 67° 20'. **7.** 0.0737 mm. **9.** 0.509 gm.

Chapter XL

1. 1.23 Å. **3.** 4.1×10^{-10} erg. **5.** 0.22 per cent. **7.** 0.183 per day. **9.** 2.64×10^{7} electron-volts.

Flux, dielectric, 342; light, 594; linkages, 439; magnetic, 418
Focal length of lens, 645, 660; of lens systems, 653; of mirror, 605; lines, astigmatic, 658
Focus of lens, 645; of mirror, 605
Foley, Arthur L., sound photographs, 581
Foot-candle, the, 589
Foot-pound, the, 129
Force, acceleration by, 65; **action of,** 63; between electric charges, 340; between magnetic poles, 353; centrifugal and centripetal, 83; definition of, 27; electromotive, 366; exerted by liquid, 189; in harmonic motion, 154; lines of, 360; magnetomotive, 446; moment of, 30; of friction, 78; on conductor in field, 419; resolution of, 28; resultant of parallel forces, 113; units of, 67, 71; vector addition of, 27
Forced vibrations, 555
Formation, heat of, 270
Foucault, Jean B. L., light velocity, 597
Fourier, Jean B. J., wave analysis, 548
Fraunhofer, Joseph von, **spectral** absorption lines, 624
Freezing point, 249
Frequency of alternating e.m.f., 458, 482; of circuit, natural, 466; of sounding bodies, 550-554; of vibration, 151, 524
Fresnel, Augustin J., absorption of light, 618
Friction, coefficient of, 79; energy to oppose, 135; kinds of, 77
Fringes, interference, 680
Fusion, effect of pressure on, 250; heat of, 250, 267; of mixtures, 252; process of, 249

Gages, pressure, 219; vacuum, 227
Galileo Galilei, experiments on falling bodies, 52; light velocity, 596
Galvanometer, types of, 421
Gamma rays, nature of, 721
Gas, behavior at constant volume, 274; constant, 279, 285; general law of, 278, 294; perfect, 218, 281; refrigerator, 312; thermometer, 277
Gases, density of, 221; diffusion of, 228; electric conduction in, 334;

expansion at constant temperature or pressure, 274; ionization of, 335, 348; kinetic theory of, 214; liquefaction of, 287, 313; pressure exerted by, 216; specific heats of, 283; spectra of, 622; thermal behavior of, 274; thermal capacity of, 283; velocity of sound in, 533; viscosity of, 225
Gauss, Karl F., flux density, 418
Gauss, the, 418
Gay-Lussac, Joseph L., free expansion, 281
Gears, mechanical advantage of, 146
Geiger-Müller ray counter, 721, 728
Generators, alternating-current, 481; direct-current, 473; e.m.f. of, 476; electrostatic, 339; shunt type, 478
Germer, Lester H., electron diffraction, 717
Gilbert, the, 447
Glass, non-reflecting, 684
Gram of force, 72; of mass, 13
Grating, diffraction, 691
Gravitation, law of universal, 69
Gravitational systems of units, 71, 86
Gravity, acceleration due to, 53; cell, 403; center of, 114; specific, 191
Great-circle distances, 10
Greek alphabet, 733
Gyration, radius of, 99
Gyroscope, action of, 103

Hahn, Otto, atomic cleavage, 727
Half-period, meaning of, 724
Hammond organ, 561
Harmonic analyzer, 549; motion, properties of, 150; tones, 550
Head, hydraulic, 207
Hearing, range of, 567
Heat, conduction of, 316, 318, 321; convection of, 317, 320; effects of, 231; from electric current, 370; mechanical equivalent of, 299; nature of, 231; of combustion, 269; of formation, 270; of fusion, 250, 267; of vaporization, 258, 267; radiation, 317, 322; specific, 263; transfer of, 316; transformation to work, 300; units of, 248
Helmholtz, Hermann L. F., tone quality, 547
Henry, Joseph, inductance coefficient, 436